Project WILD

K–12 Curriculum & Activity Guide

Principal Sponsors

Project WILD is administered by the Council for Environmental Education and is cosponsored by the Western Association of Fish and Wildlife Agencies.

Awards and Recognition

Project WILD, its sponsors, and many of its participants—including students and educators—have received a variety of awards and recognition. Project WILD was honored at the White House in 1991 as one of the first recipients of a Gold Medal for Education and Communications in the President's Environment and Conservation Challenge Award program. This award was bestowed "for excellence in developing innovative solutions to the nation's environmental challenges." Project WILD has also received the Conservation Education Award from The Wildlife Society. These materials have been endorsed by the National Council for Social Studies and are consistent with recommendations of the National Science Teachers Association.

Acknowledgements

The following organizations provided support for this third edition of the *Project WILD K–12 Curriculum and Activity Guide*:

U.S. Environmental Protection Agency

U.S. Fish and Wildlife Service

The views and conclusions contained in this document are those of the authors and should not be interpreted as representing the opinions or policies of the U.S. Government. Mention of trade names or commercial products does not constitute their endorsement by the U.S. Government.

Project WILD
5555 Morningside Drive, Suite 212
Houston, TX 77005
Phone: (713) 520-1936   Fax: (713) 520-8008
E-mail: info@projectwild.org
Web: www.projectwild.org

COUNCIL FOR ENVIRONMENTAL EDUCATION

5555 Morningside Dri
Houston, TX
Phone: (713) 520-1936
E-mail: info
Web: www

© Copyright 2001, 2000, 1992, 1985, and 1983 by the Council for Envir
All rights reserved.
Revised Edition. Printed in the U.S.A. on recycled paper us

Table of Contents

Project WILD Sponsors iv

Preface vi

Introduction viii

How to Use the Project WILD K–12
Curriculum and Activity Guides ix

Section One: Ecological Knowledge

Wildlife Populations (WP)
Color Crazy 2
Grasshopper Gravity 4
What's Wild? 7
Classroom Carrying Capacity 9
Interview a Spider 12
Habitat Rummy 14
Bearly Growing 19
How Many Bears Can Live in This Forest? 23
My Kingdom for a Shelter 28
Tracks! 30
Spider Web Geometry 34
Oh Deer! 36
Wild Words 41
We're in This Together 44
Carrying Capacity 46

Habitats, Ecosystems, and Niches (HN)
Graphananimal 49
Wildlife Is Everywhere! 51
Habitracks 53
What's That, Habitat? 56
Beautiful Basics 58
Everybody Needs a Home 59
Habitat Lap Sit 61
Who Fits Here? 64
Which Niche? 66
What Did Your Lunch Cost Wildlife? 68
Urban Nature Search 70
Rainfall and the Forest 73

Interdependence (ID)
Environmental Barometer 77
Habitrekking 79
Microtrek Treasure Hunt 82
Stormy Weather 85
Ants on a Twig 88
Good Buddies 91
What's for Dinner? 96
Seed Need 98
Owl Pellets 100
Eco-Enrichers 102
Energy Pipeline 105
Birds of Prey 111

Changes and Adaptations (CA)
Thicket Game 114
Seeing Is Believing! 116
What Bear Goes Where? 118
Surprise Terrarium 120
Quick-Frozen Critters 122
Polar Bears in Phoenix? 125
Adaptation Artistry 128
Muskox Maneuvers 130
I'm Thirsty 134
Forest in a Jar 137
Fire Ecologies 140

continued

© Council for Environmental Education 2001

Biodiversity (BD)
Move Over Rover 144
Planting Animals 152
Here Today, Gone Tomorrow 154
Time Lapse 158
Ecosystem Facelift 166
Bottleneck Genes 172

Section Two:
Social and Political Knowledge
Cultural Perspectives (CP)
First Impressions 178
And the Wolf Wore Shoes 180
Museum Search for Wildlife 182
Saturday Morning Wildlife Watching 184
Wildlife in National Symbols 186
Prairie Memoirs 188
Cartoons and Bumper Stickers 192
Power of a Song 194
For Your Eyes Only 197
Ethi-Reasoning 203
Wildlife on Coins and Stamps 208

Economic, Commercial, and Recreational Considerations (EC)
What You Wear Is What They Were 210
Does Wildlife Sell? 213
Pay to Play 216
Arctic Survival 234

Historical and Geographic Development (HG)
Make a Coat! 243
Lobster in Your Lunch Box 245
Let's Talk Turkey 248
Wildlife Bibliography 253
Changing Attitudes 255
Changing Societies 258

Political and Legislative Frameworks (PL)
History of Wildlife Management 267
Wild Bill's Fate 270
Know Your Legislation: What's in It for Wildlife? 272

Section Three:
Sustaining Fish and Wildlife Resources
Attitudes and Awareness (AA)
Learning to Look, Looking to See 278
Animal Charades 280
Animal Poetry 282
Drawing on Nature 285
The Hunter 287
Wildlife Issues: Community Attitude Survey 297

Human Impacts (HI)
Too Close for Comfort 300
Ethi-Thinking 303
No Water Off a Duck's Back 305
Migration Barriers 308
Shrinking Habitat 310
Smokey Bear Said What? 314
Noisy Neighbors 317
Flip the Switch for Wildlife 319
To Zone or Not to Zone 321
Hazardous Links, Possible Solutions 326

Issues and Trends (IT)
World Travelers 330
Rare Bird Eggs for Sale 335
Pro and Con: Consumptive and Nonconsumptive Uses of Wildlife 338
Riparian Zone 341
Changing the Land 345
Cabin Conflict 353
Back from the Brink 355
Philosophical Differences 364
Turkey Trouble 367

Wildlife Management (WM)
Career Critters 371
Wildwork 385
Checks and Balances 387
Deer Crossing 392
From Bison to Bread: The American Prairie 395
Bird Song Survey 406
A Picture Is Worth a Thousand Words ... 409

Wildlife Research...............................418	Guidelines for Interviewing People..................
Dropping in on Deer.............................420	Guidelines for Responsible Use of Animals
Deer Dilemma 426	in the Classroom...............................47

Responsible Action and Service (RA)

Playing Lightly on the Earth 432	Using Local Resources 478
Litter We Know.................................434	Hints for Using Simulated Field Trips 480
Planning for People and Wildlife 436	Using Simulations for Instructional Purposes....481
Improving Wildlife Habitat	A Guide to the Ecosystem Concept 482
in the Community..........................440	Taking Action.....................................487
Enviro-Ethics....................................443	Evaluating and Assessing Student Learning.......492
Can Do! 446	Skills Index..494
Sustainability: Then, Now, Later.......449	Topic Index.......................................498

Appendices

Conceptual Framework........................458	Expanded Topic Index 503
Early Childhood Extensions.................470	Metric Conversion Chart 513
Using the Outdoor Classroom 473	Glossary 514
Field Ethics 474	Agencies and Organizations 522
Observations and Inferences 475	Evaluation of Project WILD Materials.............526
	Acknowledgements 528
	Project WILD Supplementary Resources..........534
	Alphabetical Listing 536

© Council for Environmental Education 2001

iii

Project WILD Sponsors

Project WILD State Sponsoring Agencies and Organizations

Alabama Department of Conservation and Natural Resources

Alaska Department of Fish and Game

Arizona Game and Fish Department

Arkansas Game and Fish Commission

California Department of Fish and Game

Colorado Division of Wildlife

Connecticut Department of Environmental Protection

Delaware Department of Natural Resources and Environmental Control

District of Columbia Environmental Health Administration

Florida Fish and Wildlife Conservation Commission

Georgia Department of Natural Resources

Hawaii Department of Land and Natural Resources

Idaho Department of Fish and Game

Illinois Department of Natural Resources

Indiana Department of Natural Resources

Iowa Department of Natural Resources

Kansas Department of Wildlife and Parks

Kentucky Department of Fish and Wildlife Resources

Louisiana Department of Wildlife and Fisheries

Maine Department of Inland Fisheries and Wildlife

Maryland Department of Natural Resources

Massachusetts Division of Fisheries and Wildlife

Michigan State University Department of Agriculture and Natural Resources Educational and Communication Systems

Minnesota Department of Natural Resources

Mississippi Department of Wildlife, Fisheries, and Parks

Missouri Department of Conservation

Montana Department of Fish, Wildlife, and Parks

Nebraska Game and Parks Commission

Nevada Division of Wildlife

New Hampshire Fish and Game Department

New Jersey Division of Fish and Wildlife

New Mexico Department of Game and Fish

New York State Department of Environmental Conservation

North Carolina Wildlife Resources Commission

North Dakota Department of Game and Fish

Ohio Division of Wildlife

Oklahoma Conservation Commission

Oklahoma Department of Wildlife Conservation

Pennsylvania Fish and Boat Commission

Pennsylvania Game Commission

Puerto Rico Department of Natural and\ Environmental Resources

Rhode Island Division of Fish and Wildlife

South Carolina Department of Natural Resources

South Dakota Department of Game, Fish, and Parks

Tennessee Conservation League

Tennessee Wildlife Resources Agency

Texas Parks and Wildlife Department

Utah Division of Wildlife Resources

Vermont Department of Fish and Wildlife

Virginia Department of Game and Inland Fisheries

Virginia Division–Izaak Walton League of America

Washington Department of Fish and Wildlife

West Virginia Division of Natural Resources

Wisconsin Department of Natural Resources

Wyoming Game and Fish Department

International Organizational Sponsors

Canadian Wildlife Federation

Czech Junak, Czech Republic

Centre for Environment Education, Ahmedabad, India

National Centre for Educational Materials, Iceland

Parks and Recreation Foundation of Japan

Umea University, Sweden

Associate Sponsors

American Fisheries Society

Defenders of Wildlife

National Wildlife Federation

U.S. Environmental Protection Agency

U.S. Fish and Wildlife Service

Preface

Project WILD is an interdisciplinary conservation and environmental education program emphasizing wildlife. The goal of Project WILD is to assist students of any age in developing awareness, knowledge, skills, and commitment to result in informed decisions, responsible behavior, and constructive actions concerning wildlife and the environment.

Project WILD is based on the premise that young people and their educators have a vital interest in learning about the Earth as home for people and wildlife. For instructional purposes in Project WILD, wildlife is defined as any nondomesticated animal. Wildlife may be as small as a microscopic organism or as large as a great blue whale. Wildlife includes but is not limited to insects, spiders, birds, reptiles, fish, amphibians, and mammals.

Project WILD's primary audience is educators of kindergarten through high school students. This approach does not limit the usefulness of Project WILD to formal educational settings, however. Volunteers working with young people in pre-school and after-school programs; representatives of private conservation, industry, and other community groups providing programs for young people; and personnel involved in preparation of future teachers are all among those who effectively use the instructional resources of this program.

Since Project WILD was first introduced in 1983, more than 650,000 educators in the United States have participated in Project WILD workshops. Those educators, in turn, have provided instruction using Project WILD to more than 38 million youths.

Project WILD originated as a joint project of the Western Regional Environmental Education Council Inc. (WREEC) and the Western Association of Fish and Wildlife Agencies (WAFWA) in the 13 western states. WREEC was founded in 1970 in a unique and visionary effort to create a partnership between education and natural resource professionals. WAFWA comprises of directors of the public agencies responsible for management of wildlife in their respective states.

In 1996, WREEC officially changed its name to the Council for Environmental Education (CEE) to reflect its national network of state department of education and natural resource agency professionals. CEE's missions are to support environmental education through the management and development of environmental education programs, to publish and disseminate environmental education materials, and to facilitate the development and maintenance of partnerships for environmental education. Contributions, grants, and cooperative agreements also provide support for the work of Project WILD.

Project WILD's educational materials are provided to educators through practical, interactive workshops conducted by representatives of sponsoring state wildlife, natural resources, and educational agencies. The dedication and commitment of teachers, wildlife biologists, interested citizens, school administrators, and other ecological enthusiasts who volunteer hours of time and effort make Project WILD possible at the state and local levels.

The board and staff of the Council for Environmental Education; the Project WILD Program Committee; WAFWA members; and all associate, state, and international sponsors are dedicated to achieving the highest possible standards of professional quality, factual accuracy, and objectivity in all programs, activities, and materials bearing the Project WILD name. Project WILD's policies and guidelines commit to neutrality on controversial issues, recognizing that people need information from a variety of sources to make their own informed decisions. Project WILD programs, activities, and materials are not to be used to promote agency or organizational policies or political points of view.

For Additional Information

For additional information about participation in Project WILD as an associate or international sponsor, please contact the following:

Project WILD
Council for Environmental Education
5555 Morningside Drive, Suite 212
Houston, TX 77005
Phone: (713) 520-1936
E-mail: info@projectwild.org
Web: www.projectwild.org

Other programs cosponsored by CEE

Project Learning Tree (PLT)
1111 Nineteenth Street, NW, Suite 780
Washington, DC 20036
Phone: (202) 463-2462
Web: www.plt.org

Project WET (Water Education for Teachers)
201 Culbertson Hall
Montana State University
Bozeman, MT 59717
Phone: (406) 994-5392
Web: www.montana.edu/wwwwet

WET in the City
5555 Morningside Drive, Suite 212
Houston, TX 77005
Phone: (713) 520-1936
Web: www.wetcity.org

Council for Environmental Education Staff

Josetta Hawthorne
Executive Director

Suzy Sanders
Manager, Project WILD

Elisa Lewis
Manager, Education Programs

Heidi Massin
Project Assistant

Introduction

A concern for the land, its resources, and its continuing viability is basic to our survival and well-being—as individuals, as a nation, and as members of the world community. Two groups within society play important roles in shaping future environments: resource management professionals and educators. Educators have the responsibility for equipping learners with the skills and knowledge necessary to access and evaluate information upon which sound judgments can be made. Resource management professionals provide us with the information and technology necessary to achieve our goals.

Project WILD was created by the Western Regional Environmental Education Council (WREEC), which was founded in 1970 to bring together state-level resource management professionals and education administrators from 13 western states to work on environmental education programs of regional and, ultimately, national importance. Funding and support were provided by the Western Association of Fish and Wildlife Agencies (WAFWA).

Based on WREEC's successful Project Learning Tree model, the Project WILD conceptual outline was developed with input from educators, preservationists, conservationists, wildlife managers, business and industry representatives, and others. Learning activities in a variety of subject matter and skill areas were written by classroom teachers in regional writing workshops, and their work was tested extensively by other educators before being edited and assembled in final form. WREEC did not seek to produce a course of study, but aimed at developing a collection of good learning activities that could be used in many settings and content areas.

As with all good educational materials, Project WILD is concerned with providing information, as well as helping students to evaluate choices and to make reasonable decisions. In short, Project WILD's mission is to help students learn *how* to think, not *what* to think.

This revised edition of Project WILD adheres to those strict efforts for balance and objectivity, backed by sound educational practices and theory. It also represents the work of many within the fields of education and natural resource management from across the country. The materials are available to those who attend instructional workshops offered by certified leaders and supported by a network of sponsoring state, national, and international agencies.

We are pleased to bring this new and improved version of Project WILD to you in an easy-to-use format that organizes activities by thematic topic, subject matter, and grade level. If you have used Project WILD before, you will find much that is familiar, as well as some new activities designed to more effectively teach core concepts. If you are new to Project WILD, we hope that this curriculum guide will become a most valued educational resource.

Personally, I take great pride in being part of the Council for Environmental Education and the great Project WILD family that has done so much for literally hundreds of thousands of students over the years. For those who are just now joining us, a hearty and sincere welcome. Yes, working together we can make a difference!

Rudolph J. H. Schafer
Founder
Western Regional Environmental Education Council

Board Member
Council for Environmental Education

How to Use the Project WILD K–12 Curriculum and Activity Guides

Project WILD has been designed to be an instructional resource for educators who care about natural resources and the environment—beginning with the recognition that the Earth is home for both people and wildlife.

Supporting Academic Concepts Required in the Classroom

The activities found in Project WILD are intended for use in both classroom and nonformal settings. The instructional materials are designed to support state and national academic standards appropriate for grades K–12. The activities can easily be adapted to meet the learning requirements for academic disciplines ranging from science and environmental education to social studies, math, and language arts. Educators may choose one or numerous Project WILD activities to teach a concept or skill. The activities may be integrated into existing courses of study, or an entire set of activities may serve as the basis for a specific course.

Updates and Revisions

The *Project WILD* and *Project WILD Aquatic K–12 Curriculum and Activity Guides* have been updated in response to education reform. Both the conceptual framework and individual activities have been revised to help meet national education standards and assessment criteria. The background information found in the activities also has been revised (1) to provide current statistics and updated factual information and (2) to highlight successful conservation efforts.

Organization of Materials

The Project WILD curriculum has been organized into three sections: (1) Ecological Knowledge, (2) Social and Political Knowledge, and (3) Sustaining Fish and Wildlife Resources. Each of those sections is divided into topic areas that correspond directly to the conceptual framework found in the back of the guide. The activities within each topic are ordered by complexity, moving the student from basic conceptual understanding to application. Therefore, the educator may find the activities in the beginning of a topic area more applicable to elementary classrooms, while those at the end may be more suited for higher grade levels.

Section One: Ecological Knowledge

Activities found in this section are generally introductory lessons that focus on awareness. They are designed to establish a foundation for most of the activities that follow, to develop a basis of understanding for the characteristics of environments, and to comprehend how they function. There are five areas of study: (1) *wildlife populations*, addressing characteristics and population dynamics; (2) *habitats, ecosystems, and niches*, addressing distribution and importance of these concepts; (3) *interdependence*, addressing commonalties and interactions among living things; (4) *changes and adaptations*, addressing environmental changes and organism adaptations; and (5) *biodiversity*, addressing types of biodiversity, human influence, and the importance of habitat.

Section Two: Social and Political Knowledge

This section builds on awareness and moves the students toward understanding. Students examine the way human cultures, economics, and politics have affected people's attitudes toward natural resources. There are four areas of study: (1) *cultural perspectives*, addressing cultural development, expressions, and appreciation of wildlife and natural resources; (2) *economic*,

continued

© Council for Environmental Education 2001

commercial, and recreational considerations; (3) *historical and geographic development*, addressing the development of society and commerce as related to natural resources; and (4) *political and legislative frameworks*, both domestic and international.

Section Three: Sustaining Fish and Wildlife Resources

Activities found in this final section of the book are generally higher level lessons that take the students from understanding to action. The activities are designed to serve as a way for students to recognize, evaluate, and make responsible choices in their own lives regarding natural resources while reflecting on the knowledge and skills they have acquired in earlier activities. There are five areas of study: (1) *attitudes and awareness*, including human perspectives and values; (2) *human impacts*, both positive and negative; (3) *issues and trends* in global perspectives, land use, consumptive and nonconsumptive uses of wildlife, and wildlife populations; (4) *wildlife management*, addressing basic concepts related to management considerations and practices; and (5) *responsible action and service*, focusing on how students and others can take action on behalf of wildlife and the environment.

Organization of Each Activity

Each activity includes a statement of the instructional objective, a brief description of the instructional method used, a list of materials, educator background, step-by-step procedures, extensions or additions to the activity, and several evaluation ideas. Several activities also include variations or alternate procedures. In the small box at the bottom of the first page of the activity, educators will find a summary of the suggested appropriateness based on the grade level, duration, group size, and location (indoors or outdoors). It is important to note that the grade level reference is based on a correlation to national subject standards, not on the ability of students to perform the activity. Activities may be adjusted by educators for use with broader grade levels, as appropriate. Subject areas listed in the box indicate that the activity meets specific national learning standards for that discipline. This reference box also includes key terms relating to the activity, appendices to note, and a list of concepts taught from the conceptual framework found on page 458. The conceptual framework topic reference codes in the box are specific only to the topic area under which the activity falls. The first two letters of the code indicate the topic section.

Appendices

The appendices include a glossary of terms, a metric conversion chart, and a list of agencies and organizations that are referenced in one or more Project WILD activities. Other useful appendices include a brief guide to the concept of ecosystems, tips for using the outdoors as a classroom, a guide to keeping an aquarium in the classroom, guidelines for the study of live animals in the classroom, and tables that cross-reference skills and topics to the activities.

Also listed in the Appendices is the conceptual framework in outline form. The conceptual framework is part of an overall "learning framework," a matrix that organizes all the Project WILD concepts and major subject area learning standards for each activity. This matrix also cross-references all the Project WILD activities by topic, grade level, activity type, and assessment type. Both a summary of each activity and literature books appropriate for each activity are presented. The complete learning framework is available on the Project WILD website at **www.projectwild.org**.

NOTE: At the time of printing, all website addresses referenced in this guide were up-to-date. However, due to the dynamic nature of this media, these sites may no longer be functioning. Furthermore, views expressed on these sites do not necessarily reflect those of Project WILD or its sponsors, nor does Project WILD endorse the factual accuracy of the information presented.

Section One
Ecological Knowledge

Color Crazy

Objective
Students will recognize and generalize that wildlife exists in many colors.

Method
Students create colorful representations of wild animals.

Materials
Pictures of brightly colored animals such as fish found living around coral reefs, tropical birds, and insects; crayons; paint; chalk; construction paper; scissors; glue; OPTIONAL: other brightly colored materials like artificial feathers, tissue paper, acorn shells, uncooked pasta noodles

Background
Animals use coloring and markings as survival tools. For example, animals use color as protection and as a way to attract mates. The colors that humans see are not always the same colors that all animals see. An animal's bright colors may not be visible to its primary predators.

Grade Level: K–4

Subject Areas: Science, Language Arts, Expressive Arts, Environmental Education

Duration: one 45-minute session

Group Size: any

Setting: indoors

Conceptual Framework Topic Reference: WPIA2

Key Terms: color, wildlife, camouflage, mimicry

Appendices: Using Local Resources, Early Childhood

Camouflage, or the ability to blend with surroundings, can determine whether a prey species, like a rabbit, remains hidden from a predator or is easily identified, killed, and eaten. Predators such as leopards and trout have camouflaged bodies so that their prey will not see them. Some animals go through seasonal color changes to remain camouflaged. For example, ptarmigans are ground-dwelling birds that live in arctic and alpine regions of the Northern Hemisphere. In winter, ptarmigans are white and blend with the color of snow. In summer, they turn mottled brown and resemble the color of the alpine forest during that time of year.

Many animals are brightly colored. The eastern newt in its land-dwelling juvenile, or eft, stage is a bright red salamander. The red color warns predators that the newt's skin contains a compound that can be toxic or irritating to the predator. A predator that eats a newt learns to avoid newts in the future. Bright colors or other markings also may serve as a defense. Some animals use color to appear to be something that they are not. Polyphemus moths have giant eye spots that create the impression that the animal is larger than it really is. Color also plays a role in animal mating rituals. The brightly colored male scarlet tanager and peacock both use color to attract mates.

Wildlife exists in a wide range of colors that are linked to their survival.

Procedure
1. Open the discussion by asking students to name and describe real, brightly colored animals. Show students photographs of a variety of brightly colored animals. Discuss how the animals' colors and markings might help them survive.

2. Ask the students to use the brightly colored crayons, paint, chalk, construction paper, scissors, glue, and other materials to draw, paint, or construct a colorful creature. This creature could be a real wild animal. The students can make birds, reptiles, amphibians, insects, fish, and mammals—whatever real wild animal they would like. Have the students describe how the coloring on the animal would help it to survive.

3. Make a "Colorful Wildlife Gallery." Post the animal creations in the classroom, nature center, or other area in the building.

4. Develop a vocabulary list that is based on the students' descriptions of the animals.

5. Ask the students what they have learned about wild animals. Encourage the generalization that wild animals occur in a wide variety of colors and that animals' colors and markings help them survive. OPTIONAL: Bring in reference books on wildlife, and allow the students to find real animals similar to those they created.

Extensions

1. Make a "Museum of Color" by matching the students' invented animals with pictures of real animals. Find the primary colors of red, yellow, and blue. Look for "rainbow" animals that have three or more distinct colors on their bodies.

2. Make a "Colors from Nature" exhibit and include colors from plants, rocks, and soil, as well as wildlife.

3. Place the pictures of animals beside pictures of their natural surroundings. Look for animals that blend in and for those that stand out.

Aquatic Extensions

1. Make a colorful, wild, aquatic animal.

2. A coral reef is one of the most colorful places in the world. Find pictures of reef fish or other reef animals. A tropical fish tank in a pet store or aquarium would also show the diversity of colors found in coral reef animals. Pick a picture of a colorful animal that lives in a coral reef. Think of at least one way its color might help the animal survive in its environment. Using brightly colored crayons or other art materials, create a colorful reef animal. Then draw a picture of it in its habitat.

3. Research light extinction in water. Find out, for example, why bright red fish are camouflaged. Then design a fish based on the depth of its aquatic habitat. View the fish through appropriately colored cellophane or plastic to simulate the effect of its camouflage.

Evaluation

1. Identify a wild animal that is red or has red markings on its body. Identify two wild animals that are brown or have brown markings on their bodies. Identify one animal that is yellow or has yellow markings, one that is blue or has blue markings, and two that are green or have green markings on their bodies.

2. Create a model or picture of a colorful butterfly or moth and place it in the room. Explain how the colors will help it survive. Explain where in the room its chances for survival would probably be best.

Grasshopper Gravity

Objectives

Students will (1) describe the relationship between the structure and function of grasshoppers; (2) generalize that wildlife ranges from small to large organisms and exists in a variety of forms; and (3) recognize that people have influence on other animals, and with that influence comes the responsibility to act with compassion.

Method

Students observe, handle, and describe live grasshoppers or crickets.

Materials

Plastic containers to collect grasshoppers in, hand lens, live grasshopper or cricket for every two students, chalkboard

Grade Level: K–4

Subject Areas: Science, Language Arts, Environmental Education

Duration: one 45-minute session or longer if all questions on page 6 are used; the activity can also serve as basis for two-week unit of study

Group Size: any

Setting: outdoors and indoors

Conceptual Framework Topic Reference: WPIA2

Key Terms: wildlife, compound, antennae, appendage, estimate, habitat, responsibility

Appendices: Outdoors, Field Ethics, Animals in Schools, Early Childhood Classrooms

Background

"Grasshopper" is the common name for any of the winged insects with hind legs adapted for jumping. They include the longhorned grasshoppers, pygmy grasshoppers, and shorthorned grasshoppers, or locusts. They are distributed worldwide wherever vegetation grows.

Grasshoppers are 1 to 5 inches (3 to 13 centimeters) long when fully grown. They are closely related to crickets, and male grass-hoppers make chirping noises similar to those produced by crickets. Pygmy grasshoppers are the smallest grasshoppers. Longhorned grasshoppers have antennae that, when folded back, extend beyond the hind end of the body. Longhorned grasshoppers include the katydids, the meadow grasshoppers, and the so-called Mormon cricket (*Anabrus simplex*). Shorthorned grasshoppers, also known as true grasshoppers, are named for their relatively short antennae. A common species, the American grasshopper (*Schistocerca americana*), is about about 4 inches (10 centimeters) long when fully grown.

While participating in this activity, students develop important observation skills and an increased appreciation for grasshoppers.

Procedure

1. To collect grasshoppers, send a small group of students outside with plastic containers and a clear plastic sheet. Have two students place the sheet over the ground while two other students collect the grasshoppers that have been trapped under the plastic sheet.

NOTE: Caution the students not to harm the grasshoppers. When the class is through studying the grasshoppers, release them. Be prepared, however, for an accidental mishap in which a grasshopper doesn't survive. Deal with such accidents on a case-by-case basis, encouraging the students to be careful.

2. The questions from page 6 may be used in a design for a data chart or table for the students to use while observing the grasshoppers. (This list can be shortened and different questions can be used.) Educators may want to define some of the vocabulary before using the questions— like "antennae," and "appendage."

3. Finally, remind the students that a grasshopper is only one kind of animal. Animals are all sizes and shapes. Some are smaller than a grasshopper and some— like the whale—are much, much bigger.

4. Ask the students to take the grasshoppers outside and let them go. Some of the students may want to keep the grasshoppers as pets. Talk with the students about how difficult it is for a grasshopper to live very long in captivity. How much space does a grasshopper need to live? Can you supply that in captivity? Tell the students that by studying grasshoppers they have done what some scientists do. They have studied something very carefully to learn more about it. People have power over other animals in many circumstances. The students exercised power over the grasshoppers while they studied them. With that power comes important responsibility. In this case, the students exercised their power by making an effort to be careful in handling the grasshoppers and releasing them safely. Ask the students about other situations in which they feel a responsibility for their actions affecting animals. *Examples:* Taking care of pets, not leaving litter outside that can hurt wild animals.

Extensions

1. What contributions do grasshoppers make to ecological systems? What animals use grasshoppers as a food source?

2. Why do some farmers and gardeners consider grasshoppers a nuisance? Find out what actions, if any, can be taken to reduce crop damage from grasshoppers. Do the actions seem appropriate? Why or why not?

Aquatic Extensions

Do this activity with a water-related insect, if possible. Adjust the specific questions as needed to suit the insect's characteristics, still using these general categories: Interesting Features, Legs, Wings, Head, Mouth, Antennae, Motion, Noise, Colors, Habitat, Conclusions.

Evaluation

1. If you were a biologist studying wildlife, which of these could you study and call wildlife: tigers in India, deer in the forest, cows on a farm, foxes in Iowa, sparrows in the city, spiders in the forest, ants in a building, rats in a garbage dump, white mice in a laboratory cage? (probably all except the cows on a farm and the white mice in a laboratory cage)

2. Identify three wild animals that are smaller than a grasshopper.

3. Identify three wild animals that are larger than a grasshopper.

4. Identify three types of wildlife that have one of the same colors as your grasshoppers but aren't insects.

5. Show how grasshoppers protect themselves from predators in a simulation or kinesthetic activity format. Show how a grasshopper's body is adapted for survival.

6. Create several guidelines or rules that people should follow when studying wildlife. Explain why those rules are important. When, if ever, is it acceptable for people studying wildlife to damage or kill wildlife?

continued

Grasshopper Questions

Interesting Features
What are the features of a grasshopper?

Legs
How many legs does it have? Are they alike or different? Which legs are the jumping legs? Notice where the legs are attached to the grasshopper's body.

Wings
Look at the wings, if they are present. How many wings are there? Notice where they attach to the body.

Head
Look at the head. How many eyes do you see? Do they look like your eyes? Check carefully in front and below the large, compound eyes for three smaller, simpler eyes. Why do you think they have so many eyes? These eyes probably see light but may not be able to see shapes, sizes, and colors.

Mouth
Do you see a mouth? Does the grasshopper have lips? Try to feed the grasshopper a leaf to watch the mouth parts move. Hold the leaf up to the mouth just touching it. Do not try to put the leaf in the mouth, of the grasshopper. Try to describe the mouth parts and how they move.

Antennae
Where are the antennae? Are they each a long, string-like, single appendage, or are they made up of many parts? Can you count the parts? Do they all look alike in size, shape, and color? Why do you think a grasshopper needs the antennae? For what? Think about radio and television antennae.

Motion
We usually think that grasshoppers "hop." Do they also walk? How do they walk on the ground or floor? If possible, watch the grasshopper climb a small stick, weed stem, or blade of grass. Does it use all of its legs? Without hurting your grasshopper, place it on the ground and make it jump (if it is an adult with wings, it may fly instead). Follow it and make it hop or jump several times (at least five times). Does it hop the same distance each time? Measure or estimate the distance of each hop or flight. Does the grasshopper seem to get tired? What makes you think so?

Noise
Do grasshoppers make noises? If your grasshopper makes a noise, try to learn if it does it with its mouth or with some other part of its body.

Colors
Look at the whole grasshopper carefully. Is it the same color all over? Are the colors, shapes, and sizes the same on both sides? What is attractive about your grasshopper? Is it clean? Watch to see what the grasshopper does to clean or groom itself.

Habitat
Where does the grasshopper live? What does it eat? Do grasshoppers live in your neighborhood year-round? Suggest two reasons why grasshoppers might not be seen during the winter (such as freezing temperature, not enough food).

Conclusions
Did you think there were so many interesting things about grasshoppers? Do you think other insects might be as interesting? What other insects or small animals might be interesting to look at and learn more about?

What's Wild?

Objective
Students will (1) distinguish between wildlife and domesticated animals, and (2) recognize that wildlife occurs in a variety of forms.

Method
Students locate, classify, and construct collages made from pictures of wild and domesticated animals.

Materials
Magazine or newspaper pictures of a wide variety of animals, poster board or heavy construction paper, glue

Background
Differences between wild and domesticated animals are important. A basic definition of an animal is any living organism other than a plant. Wildlife is an animal that lives in a natural state, providing for its own food, shelter, and other needs in a suitable habitat. Wildlife also refers to animals that are not tamed or domesticated.

Wildlife may be microscopic or as large as a whale. Wildlife includes but is not limited to insects, spiders, birds, reptiles, fish, amphibians, and mammals, if nondomesticated. Domesticated animals are those that humans have kept in captivity and bred for special purposes. The process of domestication takes place over a long period of time and has involved genetic manipulation through selective breeding. All domesticated animals have their origins in wild ancestors. Livestock (such as cattle, sheep, and pigs) and pets (such as dogs and cats) are all examples of domesticated animals. Tame animals are "pets." Many domesticated animals are **not** tame.

Confusion can arise about animals that sometimes may be wild, sometimes may be tamed, and sometimes may be domesticated. If an animal or population of animals can live on its own, survive, and even reproduce, it is probably wild. Individual animals may be tamed—like some animals in zoos—while most of their numbers remain wild. A wild animal may appear to be tame but still should be considered wild unless it is both tamed and domesticated. Some animals that usually are considered domesticated—such as dogs, cats, horses, and goats—may become wild. The term "feral" refers to when once-domesticated animals become wild. For example, there are feral goats on California's Catalina Island, and feral horses roam in some areas of the western United States.

When it is difficult to distinguish whether an animal is wild or domesticated, encourage the students to think in terms of what is usually the case. Remember that wild animals basically take care of themselves as long as they have a suitable environment or habitat in which to live. Domesticated or tame animals basically depend

---

Grade Level: K–4

Subject Areas: Science, Language Arts, Expressive Arts, Environmental Education

Duration: one 60-minute session

Group Size: any

Setting: indoors

Conceptual Framework Topic Reference: WPIA, WPIA2, WPID

Key Terms: animal, wild, domesticated

Appendices: Early Childhood

---

continued

© Council for Environmental Education 2001

7

on people to feed and take care of them, and are typically used by people (for example, as a source of products and as pets). Whereas domesticated animals like cats and dogs are normally considered suitable pets, wild animals—even if tamed—are nearly always unsuitable, inappropriate, and frequently illegal pets.

The major purpose of this activity is for students to be able to distinguish between wild and domesticated animals.

Procedure

1. Ask students to bring in pictures of as many animals as they can find in magazines, in newspapers or on the Internet. For the purposes of this activity, reinforce with the students the concept that animals are any living things except plants.

2. Discuss with students the difference between wild and domesticated animals. Then either alone or in groups, have the students classify their collection of animal pictures into these categories. Discuss how not all domesticated animals are tame.

3. Once the students have classified the pictures, ask the students to use poster board or construction paper and glue to make two collages: one featuring wildlife and the other featuring domesticated animals. Design an art gallery using the students' work.

Extensions

1. Make a master list of the wildlife and domesticated animals from the pictures the students used in the collages. Use the words for spelling, and talk about the variety of animals found.

2. Make mobiles that show animals in their habitat—in the sea, on land, and in the air. Construct a large individual animal mobile for each student representing deserts, forests, prairies, mountains, seas, and the skies. Different colors of yarn can be used to hang the animals in the mobile according to the ecosystem in which they live (for example, blue yarn may connect all the animals that live in aquatic ecosystems).

3. Instead of collecting pictures, have students bring in a stuffed animal. After a discussion of wild versus domesticated animals, have each student determine the category for their animal. Then they can make a poster or picture depicting the animal's habitat.

Aquatic Extensions

1. Aquatic wildlife occurs in a variety of forms. Create a collage of aquatic animals, including as many different species as possible.

2. Create posters or collages of freshwater or marine habitats.

Evaluation

Which animals have been domesticated by humans: goldfish, horses, cows, ducks, boa constrictors, mosquitoes, bats, chickens, lions, eagles?

Classroom Carrying Capacity

Objectives

Students will (1) define carrying capacity, (2) give examples of factors that can influence the carrying capacity of an area, and (3) describe how exceeding the carrying capacity can affect the behavior of animals and humans.

Method

Students sit unusually close to each other and describe the results.

Materials

Chalkboard; any area with room to sit closely, in crowded conditions, and then move comfortably into a larger area

Background

Carrying capacity affects all living things, including humans. Carrying capacity may be seen as a type of dynamic equilibrium. It is typically expressed as the number of animals of a given type that can be supported in a given area.

Carrying capacity is also interpreted more broadly as the number of living things—plants and animals—that any area of land or water can support at any one time. It is the dynamic equilibrium expressed by the availability of habitat components (quantity and quality of food, water, shelter, and space plus the suitability of their arrangement) and the number of organisms that the habitat can support. Each area of land or water, and ultimately the planet, has a carrying capacity of plants and animals. The same area will have different carrying capacities for different life forms.

Carrying capacity for many species is in a constant state of change, both seasonally and annually. For example, terrestrial animals are typically most limited in the winter season when food supplies are reduced. Annual variations may result from factors such as natural disasters, changes in rainfall and temperature patterns, or human interventions. Factors affecting plant growth will affect animals because they are either directly (as herbivores or omnivores) or indirectly (as carnivores) dependent on plants.

Populations of living things tend to fluctuate naturally around some level. Carrying capacity is that level. A population may be below carrying capacity as in the spring following a hard winter, or temporarily above it. The latter situation inevitably results in a decline of the population caused by a variety of natural limiting factors (for example, mortality, disease, emigration, and lowered reproduction rate) and usually lasts for

---

Grade Level: K–4

Subject Areas: Science, Social Studies, Environmental Education

Duration: Grades K–2, one 20-minute session; Grades 3–4, one 45-minute session

Group Size: any (does require at least a small group)

Setting: indoors or outdoors (designed for classroom)

Conceptual Framework Topic Reference: WPIIA2a1, WPIIA2a2, WPIIA2a2c

Key Terms: carrying capacity, crowded

Appendices: Ecosystem, Early Childhood

---

continued

a short period. The carrying capacity of any area can be affected and adjusted by such natural factors as well as by human intervention.

A population will, therefore, tend to naturally fluctuate with carrying capacity, with or without human intervention. Humans may not always be willing to accept the consequences of natural events, however. Examples of intentional human intervention are reintroducing predators, feeding in winter, constructing nesting boxes, planting additional vegetation suitable for food, relocating animals, and hunting. Human intervention can reduce a population or prevent its expansion to meet an expected natural reduction in carrying capacity. Such an intervention may result in a higher survival rate.

Intentional intervention may be based on a particular management philosophy or practice. Management of an area of land or water in relation to its carrying capacity for certain species can be subject to question and controversy. Whether and/or how it is appropriate for humans to intervene in natural systems is sometimes a part of such questions and controversy. Management may be defined as intentional choice based on human goals and objectives. Such goals and objectives are open to question by other groups and individuals.

Procedure

1. Ask the students to sit close together in a group on the floor. They should be fairly tightly packed together. Tell them to pay attention as you give a short lesson in spelling, language, or math. Conduct the lesson for 5 to 10 minutes. Then ask the students to describe what happened during the lesson. Did they feel crowded? How did they act? Is this the way they usually act when they are sitting at their desks, not so close together? OPTIONAL: Try this a second time with the available "habitat" even smaller.

For Grades K–2

2. What if you were animals and you were this crowded? You might be domesticated animals like cats or dogs or pet rabbits—or you might be wild animals like deer or wolves. Would you be able to live? Is there enough room for you? What would you need in order to survive? (You would need food, water, shelter, and enough space in which to live, arranged according to your needs.) The number of plants and animals that an environment can support is called its "carrying capacity." If the classroom were the environment, were there too many, too few, or just the right number of people for the classroom carrying capacity when everyone sat together and crowded? (If the only area available was the small space with people crowded, there were probably too many people.) What are examples of things that can happen to affect how many plants and animals an environment can support ("carry")?

3. Ask the students to define carrying capacity and say why it is important. In which habitats is carrying capacity important?

For Grades 3–4

2. After the students have returned to their seats, develop a basic definition of carrying capacity. How was the "carrying capacity" of their classroom instructional area affected when they were sitting so crowded and close together? Some people may have felt uncomfortable when they were squeezed together. Others may not have been bothered at all. It is important to recognize that even within a species, there is a range of tolerance for physical closeness. This is true for humans as well as other animals. Ask the students how the behavior of a population of animals might change if the population suddenly exceeded the carrying capacity of a habitat, or if the size of a habitat was suddenly decreased.

3. Why might an animal population exceed the carrying capacity of a habitat? How might a habitat or its carrying capacity suddenly be decreased in size? What are some of the ways that the carrying capacity of a habitat might be increased? (The carrying capacity might be increased, for example, by providing for some of the basic survival needs of the animals, such as putting out nesting boxes, planting food crops, artificial feeding, and revegetation programs. Also natural causes such as increased rainfall or mild winters might result in increased habitat support.)

4. Introduce the students to the idea that there may be a set carrying capacity. In what ways, if any, are people, domesticated animals, and wildlife affecting the carrying capacity of the planet Earth? Are there positive effects? Negative effects?

5. Ask the students to summarize what they have learned by listing "Some Important Things to Remember About Carrying Capacity." Ask them to share their lists.

NOTE: When discussing the carrying capacity of the planet, emphasize the importance of learning about some difficult issues in order to be able to contribute to effective, constructive, and informed decisions.

Aquatic Extension

Carrying capacity doesn't just apply to land. Water only can "carry" so many plants and animals as well. Ask the students to give examples of how the concept of carrying capacity might apply to aquatic environments (for example, to a pond or a stream).

Evaluation

1. What is carrying capacity and how is it important?

2. Identify four things that influence carrying capacity.

3. Describe how exceeding the carrying capacity might affect the behavior of animals and humans.

4. Choose a wildlife species found in your area. Create a plan for a farm, city park, or school grounds that will increase the area's carrying capacity for the wildlife species you choose. Describe some of the possible effects on other wild species and the habitat as a result of your plan. Describe some possible affects on people.

Interview a Spider

Objective
Students will generalize that wildlife ranges in size and occurs in a variety of forms, colors, and adaptations.

Method
Students use interviewing, researching, and writing techniques to gather information about the natural history of a wildlife species.

Materials
Writing and research materials

Background
The diversity of wildlife species is immense. Although many people think of mammals and perhaps birds as wildlife, wildlife also includes fish, reptiles and amphibians, insects, spiders, and worms and other invertebrates.

Grade Level: 5–8

Subject Areas: Language Arts, Science, Environmental Education

Duration: three 30-minute sessions; some research and writing done by students

Group Size: any

Setting: indoors and outdoors

Conceptual Framework Topic Reference: WPIA2

Key Terms: interview, reporting, anthropomorphism

Appendices: Field Ethics, Using Local Resources, Early Childhood

---

NOTE: Students may have a tendency to project human characteristics to animals, especially because the "interview" format puts the "animals" in a human situation. Assist the students in avoiding anthropomorphism. Stress that they should try to see the world from the animal's perspective.

Procedure
RECOMMENDATION: To begin this activity, invite a local newspaper reporter to talk with the students. Ask him or her to describe what a reporter does, and to talk about interviewing and writing techniques used in journalism.

1. Have the students brainstorm a list of wildlife species. Check the list to make sure it includes many different types of wildlife. OPTIONAL: Make a list of native wildlife species available to the students to help them focus on animals they might not have readily classified as *wildlife*.

2. Instruct students to design a research, interview, and reporting format for their use as reporters. For example, try these:

Research
Each team of two students could:
- decide what animal to interview,
- develop a list of questions to ask, and
- use reference materials to find appropriate responses to the questions.

Each team could find out how the animal is classified, where it lives, what type of habitats it is found in, what it eats, etc.

Interview

Each team selects an animal to study. The team members will first need to gather information about the animal. They can do that by actually observing the animal, consulting resource materials, or both. During the interview, one student asks questions while the other student assumes the role of the animal and responds to the interviewer's questions. Instruct the students to then switch roles. Remind the students to convey the perspective of the interviewed animal without projecting inapplicable human attributes.

Reporting

Next, organize the information gathered through the process of researching and interviewing the animal. Using this information, have the students write a newspaper article about the animal.

3. Conclude this activity by discussing the diversity of wildlife. Ask each student to define wildlife—verbally or in writing—in a way that shows his or her understanding of the term, including that wildlife ranges from microscopic organisms to whales and exists in a variety of forms and colors.

Variation

To develop public speaking skills each team can conduct its interview in front of the other students.

Extension

With the newspaper articles complete,

- publish a wildlife newspaper for everyone to read and keep a copy, or
- read the articles aloud for everyone to hear, and
- then post the articles on the school's webpage.

Aquatic Extension

Just as on land, wildlife in aquatic habitats ranges from microscopic forms to forms weighing many tons. From plankton to pelicans, from water striders to great blue whales, from mollusks to manatees, from shrimp to salmon—the variety is incredible. Do "Interview a Spider" with the students choosing an aquatic animal to research, interview, and report about.

Evaluation

Choose three animals that were interviewed. Which of the following words can be used to describe each animal: invertebrate, vertebrate, predator, prey, herbivore, carnivore, insectivore, omnivore, mammal, bird, amphibian, reptile, insect, spider, fish, aquatic, terrestrial, colorful, dull, striped, spotted, runner, flyer, hopper, slider, gigantic, large, small, microscopic? What other words might describe each of the animals?

Habitat Rummy

Objectives

Students will (1) identify components of habitat as food, water, shelter and space in a suitable arrangement; and (2) apply knowledge of these components to habitat requirements of various species of animals.

Method

Students make cards and play a card game.

Materials

Writing paper and pencils, drawing paper, construction paper, scissors, glue, chalkboard (or copies of master cards for educators who want to eliminate the research phase)

Background

Humans and other animals—including pets, farm animals, and wildlife—have some of the same basic needs. Every animal needs a home. But a *home* is not just a house where people live. Home, for many animals, includes the out-of-doors. The scientific term for an animal's home is *habitat*. An animal's habitat includes food, water, shelter or cover, and space. Because animals need the food, water, shelter, and space to be available in a way that meets the animals' needs, we say that these things must be available in a suitable arrangement.

A house may be considered shelter for people. People build houses, apartments, trailers, houseboats, and other kinds of shelters in which to live. An animal's shelter might be underground, in a bush, in the bark of a tree, or in some rocks. Animals need a place to find food and water. They also need enough space in which to live and find the food, water, and shelter they need. *Home* for an animal is more like a *neighborhood* that has everything in it that is needed for survival.

Procedure

Preparation of Cards (Go to page 16 if using the master cards on pages 17 and 18.)

1. Assign students to groups of two or three. Ask each group to pick one animal it will research. Encourage a wide range of animals, including both wild and domesticated.

2. Ask the students in each group to use reference materials to research their animal. (If library references are a problem, students might be asked to choose from a list of animals for which educators have references.) Included in their findings should be a list of what each animal uses to meet its need for food, water, shelter, and space. They also should find out where the animal lives. For example, if students pick a lizard, they might determine that most lizards eat insects for food, use insects as a water source because of their high moisture content, rest in rock crevices or trees for shelter, and use a hillside

---

Grade Level: 5–8

Subject Areas: Science, Environmental Education

Duration: two 40-minute sessions

Group Size: groups of two to three students

Setting: indoors

Conceptual Framework Topic Reference: WPIC

Key Terms: habitat, survival needs, food, water, shelter, space, arrangement

Appendices: Using Local Resources

or sandy wash as a space in which to find food. The lizard might live in a desert environment. Note that some similar kinds of animals can live in a variety of habitats. The amount of technical details can depend on the age of the students.

3. Make a large master *Habitat Information Chart* that includes the major categories of information found by the students, as seen below.

4. Once this information is on the master chart make a smaller version by hand or by using a computer. Using a table format make six, equal-sized rectangles on each page, with each page including the habitat components needed for one animal. Once copied, these rectangles will serve as playing cards, or the students can glue the information to 3" × 5" note cards.

NOTE: Sample cards are included on pages 17 and 18 and can be used instead of preparing new ones.

5. Make a copy of each card set for every two to three students.

6. Distribute a complete set of the card sheets to every group of students along with heavy construction paper and glue. Students can glue card sheets onto the paper. Once cut, each set of five habitat cards per animal makes a *book*. For example, the card may be blank on one side with the species of animal and habitat components on the other side.

Habitat Information Chart

Animals

Habitat Components		Lizard	Osprey	Bear	Chipmunk
	Food	Insects	Fish	Insects, Fish, Berries, Birds, Eggs, Mammals	Seeds, Berries
	Water	Freshwater (as available)	Water (as available)	Rivers, Lakes, Streams	Freshwater (streams, ponds, dew)
	Shelter	Rock Crevices	Cliffs, Sand Dunes	Caves	Burrows
	Space	Hillsides	Ocean Coasts	Hills, Valleys	Hillsides
	Arrangement	Deserts	Coasts and Inland	Woodland	Meadow Woodlot

continued

To Play Habitat Rummy

1. The object of the game is for a player to acquire five cards from the one vertical column or a complete set of habitat components for each animal as listed on the master *Habitat Information Chart* on page 15. The game ends when all "books" or complete sets of habitat components have been made. The student having the most books is the winner. Every group of two to three students playing the game uses one complete set of habitat cards, and each group has a winner. The game is based on luck but the students become familiar with the habitat components for the species of animals in the game. For the students' information, it is helpful to post the *Habitat Information Chart* on page 15 on a chalkboard or easel.

2. The game begins as one student in each group deals five cards to each of the players in his or her group. After dealing is completed, the first player may discard an unwanted card and select another from the remaining deck, which is situated in the center of the circle of play. Play progresses around the circle with discarded cards being added to the leftover cards in the center (either face-up or face-down) and new cards being drawn until one player acquires a book—a complete set of five habitat components for an animal. (The master *Habitat Information Chart* on page 15 serves as a reference in this process.) When a player acquires a book, he or she yells HABITAT! This process continues until all habitats are complete and the student in each group with the most books or complete habitats is the winner. Winners could compete with other winners with class champion given the title of *Wildlife Biologist*.

3. Ask the students to summarize what they have learned.

Extensions

1. Showdown Challenge: Deal out all cards to players. Players showdown with the player to their left, starting at the dealer's left. Players challenge other players according to predator/prey relationships—with predators winning the challenge. The player with the most cards wins. Play for a specified time, using a time limit to end the game.

2. Food Chain Rummy: Play the game like rummy, but players receive a point for each component of every complete food chain. Cards may be added to either end of a food chain by any other player, acquiring points for every card added. The player with the highest score wins. Cards remaining in hand at the end of the game must be subtracted from the player's score.

3. Additional Cards (for older students): Instead of giving each group of two to three students a deck of cards with one complete habitat set for each animal, give them a deck with two or more habitat sets for each animal. Extra sets will encourage students not to just mechanically collect all the "lizard" cards, but to actually make certain that they are collecting each component of habitat.

Aquatic Extension

Make new cards for species that live in aquatic ecosystems.

Evaluation

1. Identify habitat needs (food, water, shelter, and space, in what arrangement) for any five wild animals.

2. Write a story that describes a day in the life of a wild animal as it meets its needs for survival. Identify and describe all the necessary components of habitat for that kind of animal.

Ecological Knowledge

Habitat Rummy

continued

Ecological Knowledge

Habitat Rummy

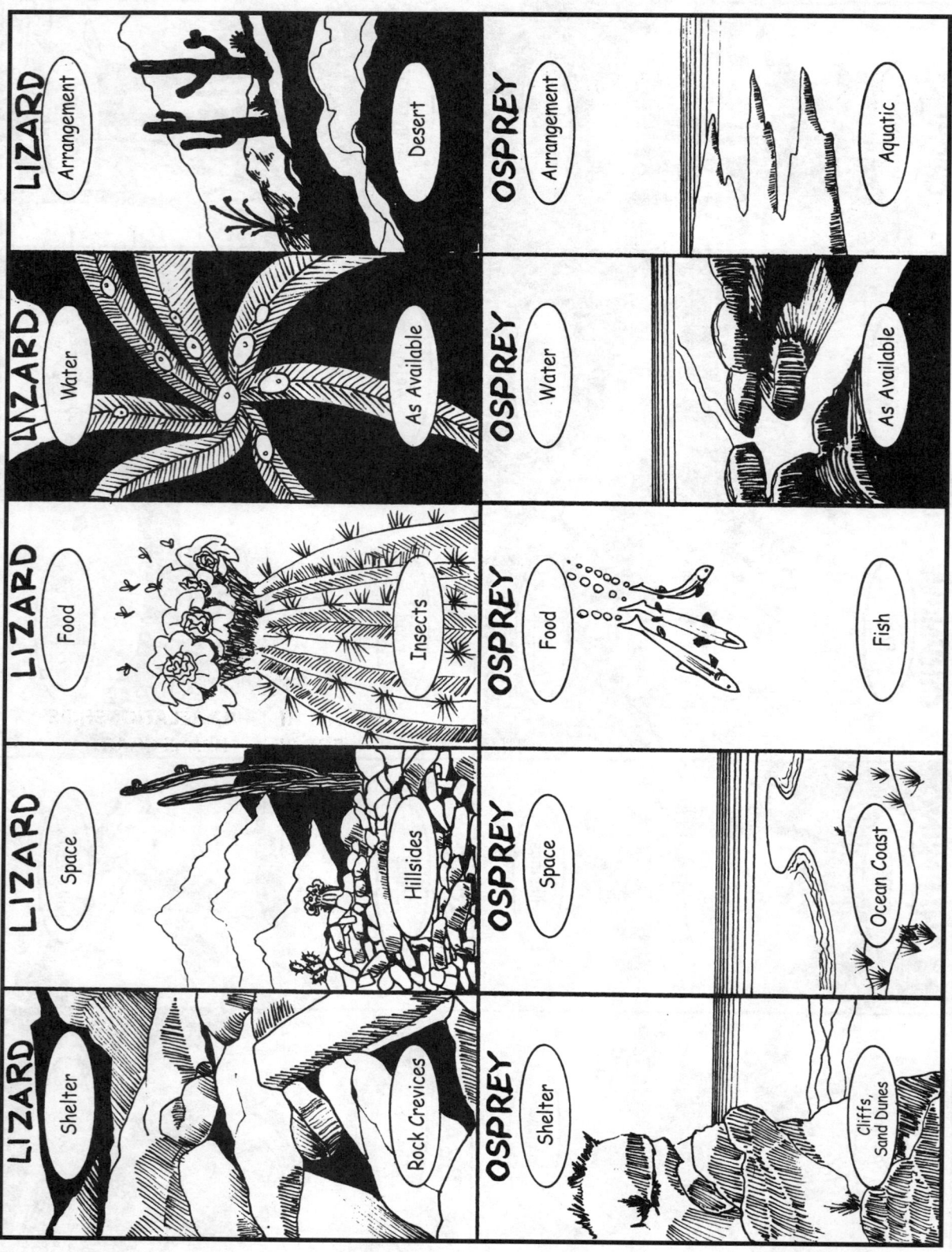

Bearly Growing

Objectives
Students will compare similarities and differences between the growth of black bears and humans.

Method
Students illustrate, compute, and graph differences between people and black bears at various stages of maturity.

Materials
Graph and drawing paper, copies of "Student Data Page," and "Compare Yourself to a Black Bear" chart (pages 21–22); OPTIONAL: yardsticks, 36-inch tape measure

Background
See "Black Bear Biology," page 21

Procedure
1. Begin a discussion with the students about black bears. Distribute "Student Data Page" and "Compare Yourself to a Black Bear" (pages 21 and 22). Have the students use the information on bear biology to help them complete the chart.

2. Ask students for their ideas about how long sows are pregnant, what bear cubs eat when they are born, how much they might weigh when they are a year old, how many cubs might be born at the same time, how much they weigh when they are full grown, and how long they live.

3. Following the discussion, post the Weight and Age Relationships for Black Bears Chart or provide it as a handout.

WEIGHT AND AGE RELATIONSHIPS FOR BLACK BEARS CHART

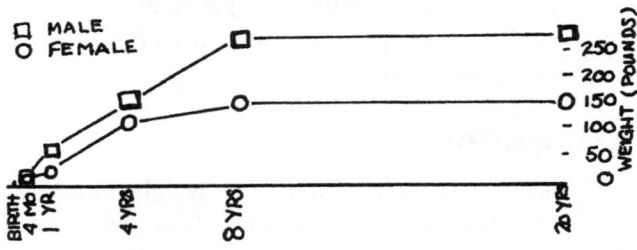

(Data are characteristic of black bears in the southwestern United States. There will be regional variations.)

4. Ask the students to plot their own weight at the same ages as the black bears shown on the chart. They will be required to estimate for years past their present age. Ask the students to graph both sets of data.

Grade Level: 5–8

Subject Areas: Mathematics, Science, Environmental Education

Duration: two 30-minute sessions

Group Size: any

Setting: indoors

Conceptual Framework Topic Reference: WPIB

Key Terms: similarities, differences, survival needs, omnivore

Appendices: Using Local Resources, Metric Conversion Chart, Early Childhood

continued

One student's comparative data might look like this:

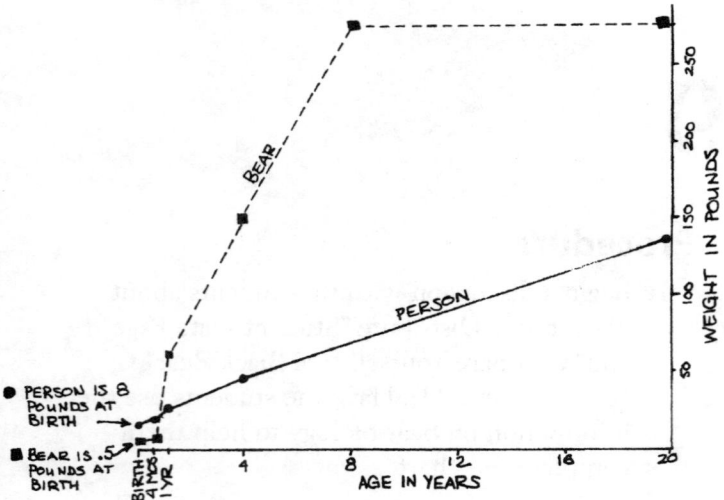

5. Ask the students to compute the following, and include their results with their graph and drawing:

   a. How much weight did the black bear gain at each interval—that is, from birth to 4 months, 4 months to 1 year, etc.?

   b. How much weight did you gain during the same intervals?

   c. How many times more weight did the bear gain during each period?

6. In discussion, ask the students to comment on the similarities and differences between bears and people.

Extensions

1. Researchers can estimate the weight of a bear by measuring the bear's girth (the distance around a bear's chest). Given the following data, students can measure the girth of a boy's chest and estimate how much he would weigh if he were a black bear.

   22 inch girth: 50 pounds
   30 inch girth: 100 pounds
   35 inch girth: 150 pounds
   39 inch girth: 200 pounds
   45 inch girth: 300 pounds
   52 inch girth: 400 pounds

Or have the students find a few boys to volunteer to weigh themselves and measure their chest girths. Graph or chart their weights and girths. Graph or chart the weights and girths of black bears. Weigh and measure the girth of older students, teachers, and family members. Graph or chart the results. Possible questions:

   a. Using the Weight and Age Relationship for Black Bears, how much does a 4-year-old bear weigh per inch of girth? A 10-year-old? A 20-year-old?

   b. How much do various age groups of children weigh per inch of girth of their chest?

   c. Are bears or children heavier per inch of chest girth? How about adults compared to bears?

2. Calculate how fast a given bear population, if unchecked by limiting factors, can increase over a specific period of time, assuming that a sow will have two cubs (one of each sex) in her fifth year of life; the total time frame is 10 years, from July 1 to June 30; and the initial bear population is one 5-year-old boar and two 6-year-old sows, one with two cubs. Graph or chart the results.

Aquatic Extension

Identify various species of aquatic wildlife. Find out the average life span of each organism, how much it weighs at birth, and how much it weighs at maturity.

Evaluation

1. Use the data in Table A to construct a graph that compares the growth of catfish from Lake Erie and the growth of catfish from the Ohio River.

   a. Which catfish grew the most between the ages of 4 and 5 years?

   b. How much larger is the Ohio catfish at 9 years of age than it is at 1 year of age?

Student Data Page

Part I: For use in completing chart on page 22

Black Bear Biology

The black bear (*Ursus americanus*) can be found in the United States, Canada, and Alaska. In the east, the black bear primarily inhabits forests and swamps. In the west, the black bear roams chiefly in mountainous areas. Black bears are primarily nocturnal but occasionally roam around during the mid-day.

A black bear's life span averages 20 to 25 years. Longevity and survival of the black bear depend upon the availability of a suitable habitat and its ability to avoid humans. An adult female bear is called a sow. An adult male bear is called a boar. A baby bear is called a cub. When a sow becomes sexually mature between 2 and 3 years old, she is capable of breeding and may have one to four cubs. Contrasted with human fetal development of about 9 months, the sow is pregnant for about 7 months.

The sow has her cub or cubs in the shelter or den where she spends the winter months. On average, a female black bear will have two cubs. The sow does not have a litter every year but every other year. At birth, a young cub weighs about 8 ounces—about the size of a guinea pig. Bear cubs stay in the den with their mother until they are able to move around very actively, usually until late April or early May.

Bears and humans are classified as mammals, which means that both are warm-blooded, nourish their young with milk, and are covered with varying amounts of hair. Bear cubs and humans survive solely on their mother's milk for the first few months of life. Cubs nurse while in the den and only for a short time after leaving the den in early spring. By the time berries ripen and grasses are plentiful, the cubs have learned to climb and can eat the available food sources. Soon the cubs will need to hunt and gather food for themselves without the help of the sow. At about 18 months of age, the cubs must go out searching for their own home range. The sow will allow the female cubs to stay within her home range. The male cubs, however, must find territory to claim as their own.

Black bears are omnivores, which means they eat both plant and animal material. In early spring, they tend to eat wetland plants, grasses, insects, and occasionally carrion (dead animal matter) or the protein-rich maggots found near the carrion. In late spring and early summer, bears feed on berries, grubs, and forbs (broad leafed plants). In late summer and early fall, bears feed mostly on nuts and acorns. In the fall season, bears must add much fat to their bodies in order to survive the winter months in their dens. Cub growth will vary throughout the country.

When black bear cubs reach one year of age, the female cubs weigh 30 to 50 pounds and the males weigh 50 to 70 pounds. A mature female bear weighs 150 to 185 pounds, and a male bear weighs about 275 pounds. (Sources: *Arkansas Black Bear: A Teacher's Guide for Kindergarten Through Sixth Grade*, Arkansas Game and Fish Commission; *WILD About Bear*, ID Dept of Fish and Game and; *A Field Guide to the Mammals*, Houghton Mifflin Co., 1980).

Part II: For use in completing the evaluation on page 20

Catfish in Lake Erie and the Ohio River

Table A

	\multicolumn{9}{c}{AGE IN YEARS}
	1	2	3	4	5	6	7	8	9
Lake Erie catfish	69	115	160	205	244	278	305	336	366
Ohio River catfish	56	101	161	227	285	340	386	433	482

(size in mm)

continued

Compare Yourself to a Black Bear

The average height of an adult male black bear standing upright:	**Your height:**
The weight of an adult male black bear:	**Your weight:**
The average weight of a 1-year-old male black bear:	**Your weight at 1 year of age:**
The average birth weight of a black bear cub:	**Your birth weight:**
The average number of cubs that a black bear has per litter:	**Average number of babies your mom had at one time:**
The length of time a cub stays with its mother:	**Number of years you probably will stay at home:**
The range of a black bear's life span:	**Average person's life span:**

How Many Bears Can Live in This Forest?

Objectives

Students will (1) define a limiting factor, and (2) describe how limiting factors affect animal populations.

Method

Students become "bears" to look for one or more components of habitat during this physically involved activity.

Materials

Five colors of construction paper (a couple of sheets each of red, yellow, green, blue, and orange) or an equal amount of light poster board or colored tokens; one black felt pen; envelopes (one per student); pencils; one blindfold; five sheets green construction paper (for extension)

Background

Black bears are the focus of this activity that illustrates the importance of suitable habitat for wildlife. The activity demonstrates the consequences for a population of bears if one or more habitat components is relatively scarce. When any element or factor in a habitat is inappropriate or exceeds the tolerance range for an animal or population, it directly affects the well-being of the animal(s) and may result in death or population reduction. This factor "limits" the animal or population. Limiting factors may include habitat components such as food, water, shelter, and appropriate space, as well as life history parameters such as disease, predation, and climatic conditions. Limiting factors also may be related to human activity such as development, pollution, and hunting. Populations tend to increase in size until limited by one or more of these factors.

Black bear habitat limits black bear populations, especially through the influences of shelter, food supply, and the social tolerances or territoriality of the animal. Shelter or cover is a prime factor. Black bears need cover—for feeding, hiding, bedding, traveling, raising cubs, and denning. With limits of space, adult bears will kill young bears or run them out of the area. These young bears must keep moving around either until they die or until they find an area vacated by the death of an adult.

When food supplies are reduced by factors such as climatic fluctuations, competition becomes more intense. Some adult bears might temporarily move to seldom-used areas of their home range, sometimes many miles away. They must live on what food is available in the area. These individuals may become thin and in poor

---

Grade Level: 5–8

Subject Areas: Science, Environmental Education, Mathematics

Duration: one 20- to 45-minute session or longer

Group Size: 10 to 45

Setting: outdoors

Conceptual Framework Topic Reference: WPIIA2b, WPIIA2b1, WPIIA2b2

Key Terms: limiting factors, habitat, shelter, cover

Appendices: Simulations, Ecosystem

---

continued

Number of Cards to Make

Paper Color	Label	Represents	10–15	16–20	21–25	26–30	31–35	36–40	41–45
			\multicolumn{7}{c	}{Number of Students in Group}
Orange	N-20	Nuts, 20 lbs.	2	3	3	4	5	6	7
Orange	N-10	Nuts, 10 lbs.	8	13	17	21	25	29	33
Blue	B-20	Berries, 20 lbs.	2	3	3	4	5	6	7
Blue	B-10	Berries, 10 lbs.	8	13	17	21	25	29	33
Yellow	I-12	Insects, 12 lbs.	2	3	3	4	5	6	7
Yellow	I-6	Insects, 6 lbs.	8	13	17	21	25	29	33
Red	M-8	Meat, 8 lbs	2	3	3	4	5	6	7
Red	M-4	Meat, 4 lbs.	8	13	17	21	25	29	33
Green	P-20	Plants, 20 lbs.	2	3	3	4	5	6	7
Green	P-10	Plants, 10 lbs.	8	13	17	21	25	29	33

condition for winter hibernation or, in the case of young bears, be forced from the area by more aggressive adults.

All possible conditions are not covered by the design of the activity. However, by this simple illustration it is possible for students to grasp quickly the essential nature of the concept of "limiting factors"—habitat components that affect the survival of an animal or restrict the numbers or range of an animal population.

Procedure

1. Make a set of 2" × 2" cards from the colored construction paper. Use the chart on this page to determine how many cards of each color to make and what to write on each one.

   As shown in the chart, the color of the card determines the type of food it represents:

   orange—nuts (acorns, pecans, walnuts, hickory nuts)

   blue—berries and fruit (blackberries, elderberries, raspberries, wild cherries)

   yellow—insects (grub worms, larvae, ants, termites)

   red—meat (mice, rodents, peccaries, beaver, muskrats, young deer)

   green—plants (leaves, grasses, herbs)

   The number on each card represents the number of pounds of food. For example, a card with the label M-4 represents 4 pounds of meat.

2. The following estimates of total pounds of food needed for one bear for 10 days are used for this activity:

Nuts	20 pounds	(25%)
Berries and fruit	20 pounds	(25%)
Insects	12 pounds	(15%)
Meat	8 pounds	(10%)
Plants	20 pounds	(25%)
	80 pounds	(100%)

   NOTE: These figures represent the food of a typical black bear in Arizona. The components of an actual bear's diet will vary between areas, seasons, and years. For example, a bear in the state of Alaska would likely eat more meat (fish) and fewer nuts than a bear in Arizona. One similarity among black bears everywhere is that the majority of their diet is normally made up of vegetable material.

   If the teacher follows the table when making the food cards, there should be less than 80 pounds of food per student, so there is actually not enough food in the area for all the "bears" to survive.

3. It is also possible to include water as a habitat component by making additional squares from light blue paper. To calculate how many water cards to make, multiply the number of students by 1.25 (round to the nearest whole number). For example, for a group of 20 students, make 20 × 1.25 = 25 water cards. Divide the water squares into five equal piles (or roughly equal), and mark each group with one of the following letters: R, L, ST, SP, and M. These letters represent all the places where a bear could find water: rivers, lakes, streams, springs, and marshes.

4. In a fairly large open area (e.g., 50' × 50'), scatter the colored pieces of paper.

5. Do not tell the students what the colors, initials, and numbers on the pieces of paper represent. Tell them only that the pieces of paper represent various kinds of bear food. Since bears are omnivores—they like a wide assortment of food—and the students should gather different colored squares to represent a variety of food.

6. Have the students write their names on an envelope, which will represent each student's "den site" and should be left on the ground (perhaps anchored with a rock) at the starting line on the perimeter of the field area.

7. Have the students line up on the starting line, leaving their envelopes between their feet on the ground. Give them the following instructions: "You are now black bears. All bears are not alike, just as you and I are not exactly alike. Among you is a young male bear who has not yet found his own territory. Last week he met up with a larger male bear in the big bear's territory and before he could get away, he was hurt. He has a broken leg. (Assign one student as the injured bear and tell him or her to "hunt" by hopping on one leg.) Another bear is a young female who investigated a porcupine too closely and was blinded by the quills. (Assign one student as the blind bear; he or she must hunt blindfolded.) The third special bear is a mother bear with two fairly small cubs. She must gather twice as much food as the other bears. (Assign one student as the mother bear.)

8. Students must walk into the "forest." Bears do not run down their food; they gather it. When students find a colored square, they should pick it up (one at a time) and return it to their "den" before picking up another colored square. (Bears would not actually return to their den to eat; they would eat food as they find it.)

9. When all the colored squares have been picked up, the food gathering is over. Have students pick up their den envelopes containing the food they gathered and return to class.

10. Explain what the colors and numbers represent. Each color is a kind of food and the numbers represent pounds of food eaten. Ask students to add up the total number of pounds of food they gathered—whether it is nuts, meat, insects, berries, or plant material. Have students write the total weight on the outside of their envelopes.

11. Using a chalkboard, list "blind," "injured," and "mother." Ask the blind bear how much food she acquired. Write the amount after the word "blind." Ask the injured bear and the mother bear how much they acquired and record the information. Ask the other students how much food they found and record each response on the chalkboard. Tell the students each bear needs 80 pounds to survive. Which bears survived? Is there enough to feed all the bears? How many pounds did the blind bear collect? Will she survive? What about the mother bear? Did she get twice the amount needed to survive? What will happen to her cubs? Will she feed her cubs first or herself? Why? What would happen to her if she fed the cubs? What if she ate first? If the cubs die, can she have more cubs in the future, and perhaps richer, years? (The mother bear will eat first and

continued

the cubs will get whatever, if any, is left. The mother must survive; she is the hope for a continued bear population. She can have more cubs in her life; only one needs to survive for the population to remain static.)

12. If the water squares are included, each student should have picked up at least one square representing a water source or that bear will not survive. Water can be a limiting factor and is an essential component of habitat.

13. Ask students to record how many pounds of each of the five categories of food they gathered. Next, ask each student to convert those numbers into percentages of the total poundage of food each gathered. Provide the students with the background information about black bears so that they can compare their percentages with the typical percentages eaten by black bears in Arizona. Ask students to guess how healthy their bears would be. How do the bears' requirements for a diet seem to compare with the needs of humans for a balanced and nutritious diet?

14. Ask the students to arrive at a class total for all the pounds of food they gathered as bears. Divide the total by the 80 pounds needed by an individual bear (approximately) in order to survive in a 10-day period. How many bears could the habitat support? Why then did only ____ bears survive when your class did this activity? Is that realistic? What percentage of the bears survived? What percentage would have survived had the food been evenly divided? In each case, what percentage would not survive?

15. Ask the students to determine the amount of food tokens that must be added to support all of the bears in this activity. If sufficient food were available for all of the bears, would the population likely increase the following year? Have the students support their answers. Other than food, what factors, natural or human-related, might also limit the growth of the bear population? How would each of these factors affect the bear population? Could the bear population increase indefinitely if unlimited food were available? Why or why not?

16. Drawing on their discussion, ask the students to try to define the term "limiting factor." Have them suggest examples of limiting factors, cultural and natural, that would be likely to actually influence the survival of other animals and their populations.

Extensions

1. Cut paper or poster board into 2" x 2" squares. Make five squares per student. For example, with a class of 30 students, you would make 150 squares. Divide all the squares into five equal piles and mark the cards in each pile with one of the following letters: B, T, D, H, and F. These represent B = bedding sites, T = travel ways, D = dens, H = hiding cover, and F = feeding sites. For this activity, these terms are defined as follows:

    bedding sites: Black bears are usually active in early morning and late evening, and bedded most of the rest of the day and night. Bedding sites are usually in areas of dense vegetation, steep topography, or large trees where the bears feel secure.

    travel ways: Bears require corridors of cover (made up of thick vegetation or steep topography) to enable them to travel between areas of food, water, and shelter within their home range.

    dens: Black bears use dens as shelter for hibernation from November to April in each year. Bears have been found denning in hollow logs, caves, holes dug into hillsides, under buildings on top of the ground, and even in culvert pipes. Bears often prepare and may use more than one den; they may change dens during the winter because of disturbance or a leaky den. Bears seldom re-use dens from year to year.

    hiding cover: Black bears evolved as animals that escape danger from predators and other bears by hiding in thick cover.

feeding sites: Bears often will use areas with less cover than hiding areas or bedding sites for feeding. Feeding sites are, however, often found close to thick hiding cover to allow the bear to quickly escape danger, if necessary.

NOTE: This information is based on actual research data from a study in Arizona. These components of shelter may vary slightly in different parts of North America.

2. In a fairly large open area (e.g., 50' × 50'), scatter the colored pieces of paper.

3. Have the students line up along one side of the area. Tell them that they are to become "bears" for this activity. Review the concept of habitat—that a bear would need shelter, food, water, and space in a suitable arrangement in order to survive. Do not tell the students what the letters on the squares of paper represent. Tell them only that the squares represent one element or component of bear habitat.

4. Direct the students to move as individual "bears" into the area. Each bear must pick up as many of the components of habitat as possible. Some competitive activity is acceptable as long as it is under control. Bears are territorial. Remember that if bears fight, which they seldom do, they can become injured and unable to successfully meet their needs for survival.

5. When the students have picked up all of the squares of paper in the area, have them return to the classroom or be seated in any comfortable area. Ask the students to separate their squares of paper into piles according to the letter on each. Using a chalkboard or large pad for a visual reference, ask the students to predict what the letters on the green cards represent—giving them the clue that each is an element of cover or shelter for a black bear. What kinds of shelter would a bear need? What do those initials represent? Record how many bears acquired at least one of each kind of shelter. How many got only four kinds? Three? Two? How many got only one kind of shelter? For this activity, only those bears with at least one of each kind of necessary shelter can survive through 1 year.

6. Shelter is a very important part of a bear's habitat. A bear needs shelter in which to search for food and water. Bears also need shelter for traveling through their home range as well as shelter for bedding, hiding, and denning. Ask students why a den is important. (The bear could live from April through October but would not have a secure place to hibernate and might not survive the winter.) Ask the students what would happen if a bear did not have travel ways? (Without travel ways, home ranges become fragmented and bears are not able to reach needed food, water, or other shelter. Without suitable habitat, bears move into marginal habitats and get into trouble with people.)

7. In this activity, how many bears survived? What was a limiting factor for this population of bears? (Shelter.) What other things could possibly become limiting factors? (Water and space—or territory—are two examples.) Could food be a limiting factor for bears? (Yes, however bears are omnivores and can use many sources of food.)

8. Ask the students to summarize what they have learned about the importance of suitable habitat for bears' survival. How are the bears' habitat needs similar to and different from the needs of other animals?

Evaluation

1. Define limiting factor.

    a. Describe some of the factors that may limit the survival of an animal.

    b. What might be the consequences to the individual animal and to its population if one of these limiting factors were no longer limiting?

My Kingdom for a Shelter

Objective
Students will identify and describe the materials and techniques used by at least one wild animal to construct its shelter.

Method
Students create a model of a shelter used by an animal.

Materials
Natural materials such as twigs, leaves, dirt, mud, moss, and bark. CAUTION: Do not harm animals or their habitats while gathering materials.

Background
This activity emphasizes one habitat need of animals—shelter. Animals must use materials in their habitat to create shelters. People, farm animals, pets, and wildlife need shelter.

Grade Level: 5–8

Subject Areas: Science, Environmental Education, Expressive Arts

Duration: minimum of two 45-minute sessions (recommended 45 minutes to introduce activity and begin research, additional research and model construction as independent study and homework, 45 minutes for reports and discussion)

Group Size: any

Setting: indoors, outdoors for observation

Conceptual Framework Topic Reference: WPIC

Key Terms: shelter, habitat, design

Appendices: Outdoors, Field Ethics

The major purpose of this activity is for students to recognize the importance of suitable shelter to wildlife.

NOTE: This activity can build on the objectives and themes following an introductory activity that teaches all of the components of habitat. For example, see the Project WILD activities "Beautiful Basics," "Everybody Needs a Home," "What's That, Habitat?," "Habitracks," "Habitat Rummy," "Ants on a Twig," "Habitat Lap Sit," and "Habitrekking."

Procedure

1. This activity can be done either individually or in small groups. Each student or group should choose a wild animal to research. During the research, students will need to identify the characteristics of the animal's shelter (nests, dens, caves) including what construction materials the animal uses. Identify what techniques the animal uses and the length of time it takes to build the shelter. Pay attention to scale and form. Some animals with architecturally interesting shelters are beavers, termites, muddaubers, caddis flies, spiders, cliff and barn swallows, chimney swifts, prairie dogs, Siamese fighting fish, underwater bubble spiders, and osprey.

2. Besides using reference materials, go outside to learn what animals use to construct their shelters; pay close attention to how the shelters are constructed. (If observing animal shelters, do not harm or destroy the shelter. It is recommended that educators do not conduct this activity during the animal's mating and reproducing seasons.)

3. Ask the students to collect representative materials from the environment that are similar or comparable to those the animals would use in constructing the shelters. Caution the students to be careful in collecting materials, again doing no harm to the animal or its habitat. Instruct them not to gather any feathers or bird nests.

4. Build models of each animal's shelter. If possible, build these to scale. If not, indicate the difference.

5. Display the completed shelters, asking the students to describe their shelter and identify the animal that uses it. Contrast how much time it took to replicate the shelters with how much time it would take the animal to build it. Contrast the techniques the students used during the activity with those the animals would have used. Compare similarities and differences in the shelters and kinds of habitats in which the animals live. Discuss consequences of habitat loss for each of the animals. Which animals are most vulnerable to loss of materials for creating shelter?

Extensions

1. Create a diorama, putting the shelter within a model of the habitat in which the animal lives.

2. Follow this activity with one about animal adaptation.

Aquatic Extension

1. Create models of shelters used by a variety of species of aquatic wildlife.

Evaluation

1. How would the students research the materials and techniques used by a yellow jacket wasp to construct its shelter?

2. Choose an animal and describe the materials and techniques it uses to build its shelter.

3. Write a poem that contrasts the characteristics of the shelter needed by at least two different kinds of animals.

Tracks!

Objective
Students will identify common animal tracks.

Method
Students make plaster casts of animal tracks.

Materials
Casting plaster, containers for mixing, spray shellac or plastic, petroleum jelly, milk cartons or plastic 2-liter soda bottles, cardboard, knives, sandpaper, black ink or paint; OPTIONAL: loops of wire

Background
Looking for evidence of wildlife is one method of determining what animal species live in a certain area. Signs of wildlife—such as burrows, nests, droppings (scat), or food litter—can be seen and identified but some of the easiest signs to interpret are animal tracks.

Animal tracks can be the basis for several types of investigations. The students can develop an animal species list by the tracks found in the region. Wildlife population estimates can be made by observing the number of tracks found during a specified length of time. Habitat requirements of certain species can be determined by finding their tracks in certain areas and not finding them in others.

Track hunting is an easily acquired skill. Find a spot of level ground with fairly soft, fine, textured soil. Smooth the soil over with your hand. After several days, return to the spot to see what animals have been there. The best places to look for animal life are near water or on well-worn trails. Larger animals will use the more open areas, while a small spot the size of your hand cleared under some bushes will reveal tracks of mice, shrews, and various reptiles.

Tracks can be preserved and collected by making plaster casts. This simple procedure will allow educators to collect tracks and add them to other evidence such as bones or scat that may have been previously collected.

NOTE: You may need a special permit from the state natural resources agency to possess animal parts.

Once the tracks have been observed or preserved, the animal that made them can be identified. For example, all mammals have basically the same foot structure but they use the parts of the foot in different ways. For instance, compare an animal's foot in relation to the human hand. Some animals walk on their hands like raccoons and bears. Others walk or run on their toes like cats and coyotes, while some animals walk on their toenails or hooves like deer and elk.

Grade Level: 5–8

Subject Areas: Science, Expressive Arts, Environmental Education

Duration: two 45-minute sessions or longer

Group Size: small groups of two to five

Setting: outdoors

Conceptual Framework Topic Reference: WPIA1

Key Terms: tracks, evidence

Appendices: Outdoors, Field Ethics,

If students look at a track, they can determine how that animal gets around. With this information, a student can also study what part of the foot the animal walks on, whether claws are present and how many steps are taken in a measured distance.

Procedure

1. Take a class or group on a field trip to an area where there will be a variety of tracks—a nearby lake, stream, or wildlife refuge area.

   NOTE: If a field trip is not possible, track prints may be purchased from science and nature stores or catalogs. The purchased track prints can then be imprinted into a box of sand or other loose soil type and filled with plaster.

2. Divide students into small groups to find tracks. Divide them into groups according to areas where they will look for tracks (e.g., one group under bushes, one group at a meadow's edge, one group near a pond's edge). Prepare the students to look carefully and responsibly.

3. Once a track is found, clean it of loose particles of soil, twigs, leaves, and other litter.

4. Spray the track with shellac or plastic sealant from a pressurized can to seal the track.

5. Form a two-inch wide strip of cardboard into a ring surrounding the track. Press the cardboard ring firmly into the ground to give support, leaving at least one inch above ground to mold for the plaster. One of the easiest ways to make the mold is to cut plastic two-liter soda bottles or paper milk cartons in half. Cut both the top and bottom from a tuna or cat food can or a plastic margarine tub to make simple round molds. Stapled strips of cardboard in the shape of a circle can also be used.

6. Mix about two cups of plaster in a container, adding water slowly until it is about as thick as heavy cream. Carefully pour the mixture into the mold until the plaster is almost to the top. Allow the plaster to harden at least 15 minutes before lifting it out of the track. If the soil is damp, the plaster may take longer to harden.

7. When the cast is hard, lift it out and remove the ring. Clean the cast by scraping it with a knife blade or toothbrush and washing. Please note that you may need to wait a few hours to ensure that the cast is sufficiently dry.

8. To make a reverse image of the track, apply a thin coating of petroleum jelly to the track and surface of the cast. Place the animal cast on a flat surface and surround the cast with a two-inch strip of cardboard as before. The original cast now becomes the mold.

9. Mix the plaster and pour it into the mold, making certain that the top surface of the casting is smooth and level with the mold. If you plan to use the casting as a wall plaque, place a loop of wire in back of the casting while the plaster is still soft. Allow two hours for the plaster to harden. Discuss different ways of recording animal tracks—photos, drawing, plaster, or so forth.

10. Carefully remove the mold when the plaster is dry. Separate the two layers, and wipe the excess petroleum jelly from the face of the cast and track. Scrape any rough places with a knife blade, or use fine sandpaper to smooth the surface. Wash the completed cast with water.

11. When the cast is thoroughly dry, paint the inside of the track with India ink or black poster paint. Label each cast with the name of the track and the student's name. A coat of clear shellac or clear plastic may be applied to protect and preserve the casting.

continued

Extensions

1. In a sandy area, have the students move their bodies in different ways such as walking, running, and jumping. Compare the differences between sets of tracks made by the same student doing each movement. Evaluate how speed, directional changes, and other variations in travel alter the tracks.

2. Write a wildlife story through the use of appropriate tracks. As a variation, make up a "track story" and have others guess what happened in the story.

Aquatic Extension

Display all the tracks according to the habitats where the tracks were found. How many of the tracks, if any, were found near water? If any were found near water, identify the kind of aquatic environments near which the tracks were found (e.g., pond, stream, lake, marsh, beach).

Evaluation

1. Have the students group the tracks and discuss how characteristics indicate the life style and size of the animal. Students could summarize verbally or in writing their discussion of the tracks and could make predictions for other animals in the same group and in different groups.

2. What is the advantage of using plaster casts versus photography to study and preserve animal tracks?

3. What are the advantages and disadvantages of the plaster medium?

4. Draw and label tracks of animals common to your area.

5. How would the knowledge about animal tracks and tracking help the following people? Consider a biologist studying lions, a wildlife photographer interested in elk, and a shepherd with a flock of sheep. What kinds of things would they need to know about animal tracks to do their jobs?

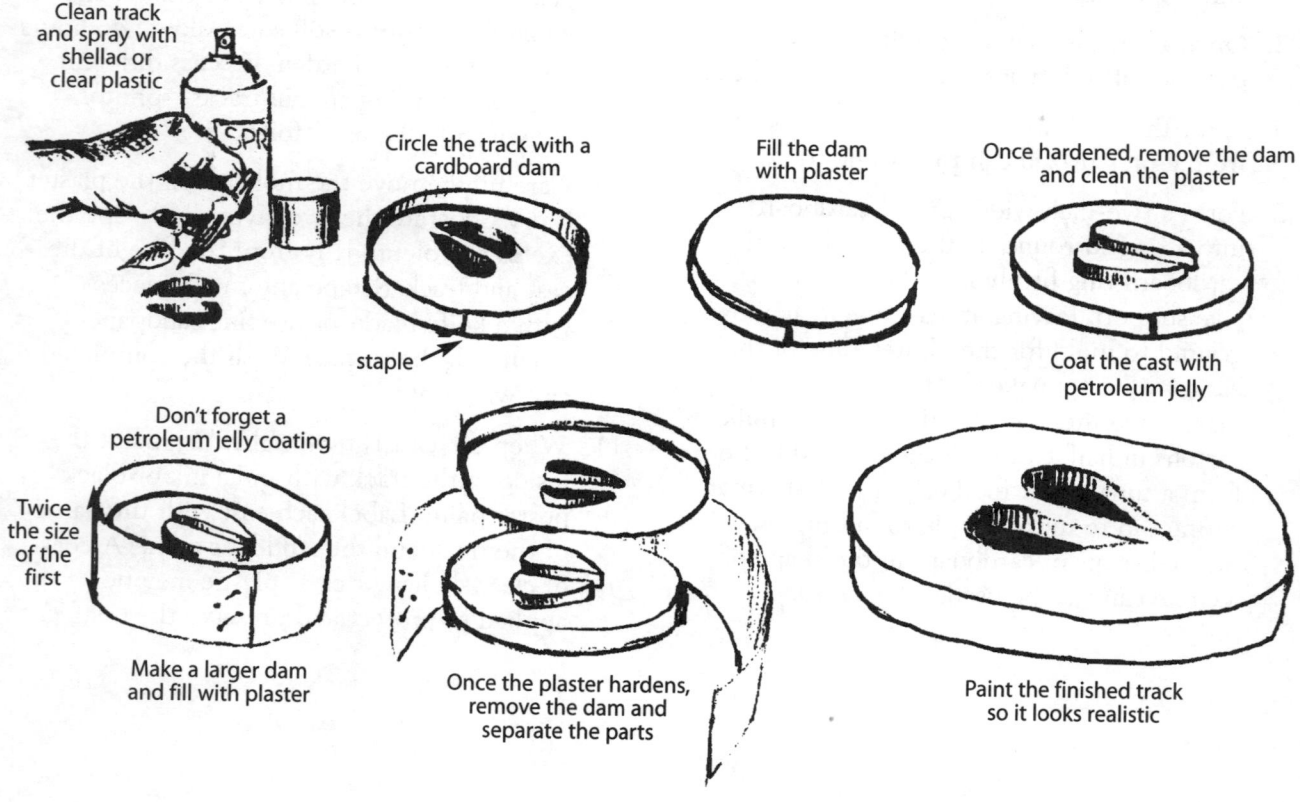

Whitetail Deer

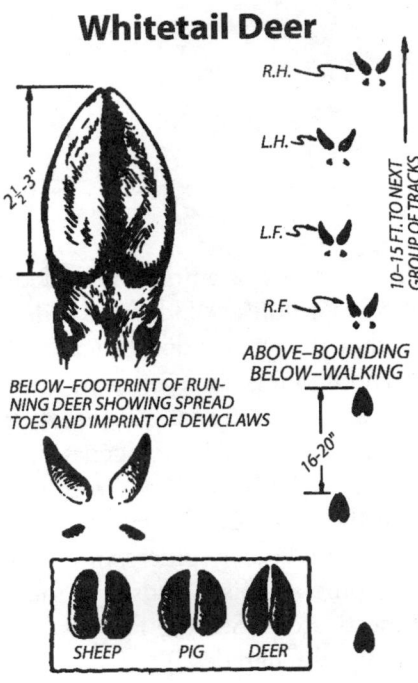

Gray Squirrel

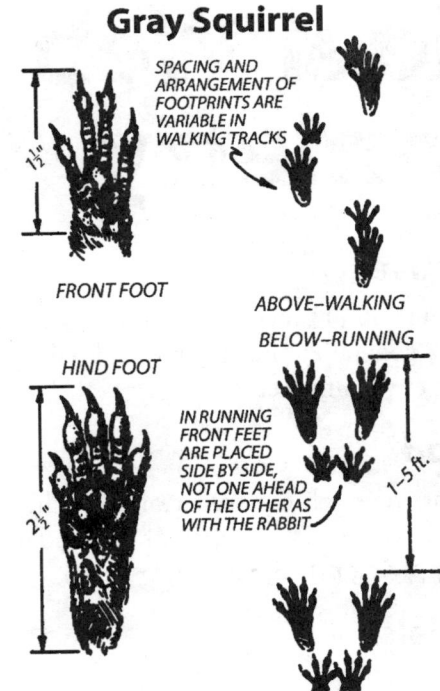

Black Bear

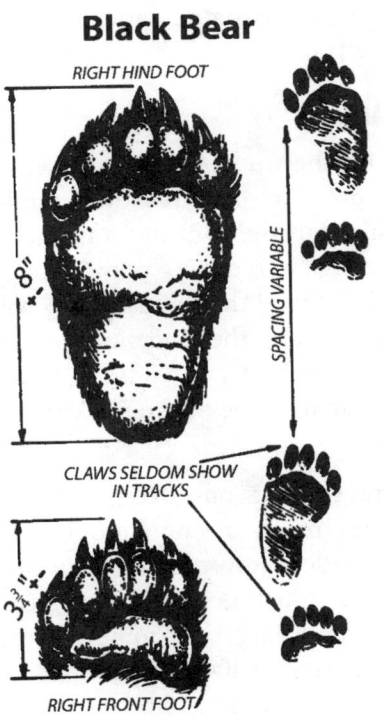

Cottontail Rabbit

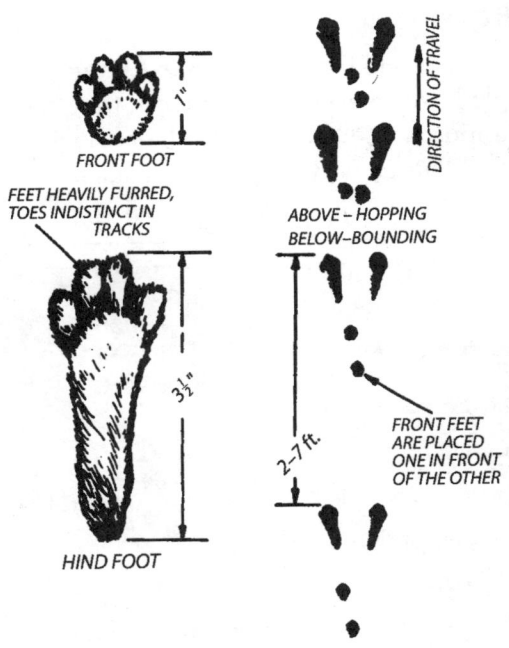

Source: J. J. Shomon
Reprinted from *Virginia Wildlife Magazine*

Spider Web Geometry

Objectives
Students will (1) recognize spiders as wildlife, and (2) generalize that people and wildlife share similar environments.

Method
Students research the spider of their choice and then construct a replica of the spider's web, applying principles of geometry.

Materials
Research materials on spiders, writing materials for use in research, measuring instruments, thread, glue; OPTIONAL: photographic materials

Background
Spiders are one form of wildlife. Although many people have an aversion to spiders, they actually are important contributors to the ecological system. This activity emphasizes spiders as one of the diverse range of animals included within a definition of wildlife. Wildlife includes all animals other than those domesticated by people. Wildlife ranges in size from microscopic forms, like amoebas, to many 100 feet in length, like the blue whales. Wildlife occurs in many forms, colors, and adaptations—from the muskox to the manatee, the mollusk to the myna. Wildlife includes spiders, insects, worms, reptiles, amphibians, fish, birds, and mammals, if nondomesticated. (See the Project WILD activity "Animal Charades.")

The major purpose of this activity is for students to identify spiders as one form of wildlife, developing and applying mathematical and research skills in the process.

Procedure
1. Talk with the students about spiders. Some may express dramatic reactions, while others will point out the contributions made by spiders (e.g., in reducing populations of insects). Expand the discussion to wildlife in general, assisting the students in establishing working definitions of wildlife and domesticated animals if they have not done so already.

2. Send the students on a 10-minute investigation of the room or school grounds, looking for any evidence of spiders. (Caution the students to touch neither the webs nor the spiders. In advance, determine whether any poisonous spiders live in your area. If they do, teach your students how to recognize and avoid them. Remind your students that they may not touch the spider or its web. That precaution can be as much for their sake as for the spider's.)

Grade Level: 5–8

Subject Areas: Mathematics, Science, Language Arts, Expressive Arts, Environmental Education

Duration: two 45-minute sessions

Group Size: individual or small group project

Setting: indoors and outdoors

Conceptual Framework Topic Reference: WPIA2

Key Terms: wildlife, spiders, arachnids, geometry

Appendices: Outdoors, Field Ethics, Animals in Classrooms, Metric Conversion Chart

3. Ask students to research a spider of their choice, investigating the appearance and characteristics of the spider and its web. Find out the spider's habitat needs and its common prey; then assess the spider's role in its environment. If they don't know already, ask the students to find out what makes a spider (an arachnid) different from an insect. They should design a replica of the spider's web as accurately as they can, using recognizable geometric shapes.

4. Next, the students should make the web using thread and glue. The webs should be constructed to scale and made as realistic as possible.

5. Ask the students to present their findings. What have they learned about spiders? What contributions do spiders make to the environment? For older students, what theorems of geometry were most useful in their web construction? Encourage the generalization that people and wildlife share environments—and that spiders are wildlife.

Evaluation

1. Identify five spider species that are common in your area.

2. List three characteristics that make an arachnid different from an insect.

3. For older students, write a proof to support the geometric theorems that you used in constructing your web.

Oh Deer!

Objectives

Students will (1) identify and describe food, water, and shelter as three essential components of habitat; (2) describe factors that influence carrying capacity; (3) define "limiting factors" and give examples; and (4) recognize that some fluctuations in wildlife populations are natural as ecological systems undergo constant change.

Method

Students portray deer and habitat components in a physical activity.

Materials

An area—either indoors or outdoors—large enough for students to run (e.g., playing field), chalkboard or flip chart, writing materials

---

Grade Level: 5–8

Subject Areas: Science, Environmental Education, Mathematics, Expressive Arts

Duration: one 30- to 45-minute session

Group Size: 15 and larger recommended

Setting: indoors or outdoors; large area for running needed

Conceptual Framework Topic Reference: WPIIA, WPIIA2, WPIIA2a, WPIIA2a1, WPIIA2a2b, WPIIA2a2ci, WPIIA2a2cii

Key Terms: habitat, limiting factors, predator, prey, population, balance of nature, ecosystem

Appendices: Simulations, Ecosystem, Early Childhood

Background

Carrying capacity refers to the dynamic balance between the availability of habitat components and the number of animals the habitat can support. A variety of factors related to carrying capacity affect the ability of wildlife species to successfully reproduce and to maintain their populations over time. The most fundamental of life's necessities for any animal are food, water, shelter, and space in a suitable arrangement. Without these essential components, animals cannot survive.

However, some naturally caused and culturally induced limiting factors serve to prevent wildlife populations from reproducing in numbers greater than their habitat can support. Disease, predator and prey relationships, varying impacts of weather conditions from season to season (e.g., early freezing, heavy snows, flooding, drought), accidents, environmental pollution, and habitat destruction and degradation are among these factors. An excess of such limiting factors leads to threatening, endangering, and eliminating whole species of animals.

This activity illustrates that

- good habitat is the key to wildlife survival,
- a population will continue to increase in size until some limiting factors are imposed,
- limiting factors contribute to fluctuations in wildlife populations, and
- nature is never in "balance," but is constantly is changing.

Wildlife populations are not static. They continuously fluctuate in response to a variety of stimulating and limiting factors. We tend to speak of limiting factors as applying to a single species, although one factor may affect many species.

Carrying capacity limitations can result in competition among domestic animals, wildlife, and humans.

Natural limiting factors, or those modeled after factors in natural systems, tend to maintain populations of species at levels within predictable ranges. This kind of "balance in nature" is not static but is more like a teeter-totter than a balance. Some species fluctuate or cycle annually. Quail, for example, may start with a population of 100 pairs in early spring, grow to a population of 1,200 birds by late spring, and decline slowly to a winter population of 100 pairs again. This cycle appears to be almost totally controlled by the habitat components of food, water, shelter, and space, which are also limiting factors. Habitat components are the most fundamental and the most critical of limiting factors in most natural settings.

This activity is a simple but powerful way for students to grasp some basic concepts: first, that everything in natural systems is interrelated; second, that populations of organisms are continuously affected by elements of their environment; and third that populations of animals are continually changing in a process of maintaining dynamic equilibrium in natural systems.

Procedure

1. Tell students they will be participating in an activity that emphasizes the most essential things animals need in order to survive. Review the essential components of habitat with the students: food, water, shelter, and space in a suitable arrangement. This activity emphasizes three of those habitat components—food, water, and shelter—but the students should not forget the importance of the animals having sufficient space in which to live, and that all the components must be in a suitable arrangement for wildlife populations to reach their maximum size.

2. Ask the students to count off in fours. Have all the ones go to one area; all twos, threes, and fours go together to another area. Mark two parallel lines on the ground or floor 10 to 20 yards apart. Have the ones line up behind one line; the rest of the students line up behind the other line, facing the ones.

3. The ones become "deer." All deer need good habitat to survive. Again ask the students what the essential components of habitat are (food, water, shelter and space in a suitable arrangement). For this activity, assume that the deer have enough space in which to live. The deer (the ones) need to find food, water, and shelter to survive. When a deer is looking for food, it should clamp its "hooves" over its stomach. When it is looking for water, it puts its "hooves" over its mouth. When it is looking for shelter, it holds its "hooves" together over its head. A deer can choose to look for any one of its needs during each round or segment of the activity; the deer cannot, however, change what it is looking for (e.g., when it sees what is available during that round). It can change what it is looking for in the next round, if it survives.

4. The twos, threes, and fours are food, water, and shelter—components of habitat. Each student is allowed to choose at the beginning of each round which component he or she will be during that round. The students depict which component they are in the same way the deer show what they are looking for (i.e., hands on stomach for food, and so on).

5. The activity starts with all players lined up behind their respective lines (deer on one side, habitat components on the other side)—and with their backs facing the students along the other line.

6. Begin the first round by asking all of the students to make their signs—each deer deciding what it is looking for, each habitat component deciding what it is. Give the students a few moments to put their hands in place—over stomachs, over mouths, or over their heads. (The two lines of students normally will display a lot of variety—with some students portraying water, some food, and some shelter. As the activity proceeds, sometimes the students confer with each other and all make the same sign. That's okay,

continued

although do not encourage it. For example, all the students in habitat might decide to be shelter. That could represent a drought year with no available food or water.)

NOTE: Switching symbols in the middle of a round can be avoided by having stacks of three different tokens—or pieces of colored paper—to represent food, water, and shelter at both the habitat and deer ends of the field. At the start of each round, players choose one of the symbols before turning around to face the other group.

7. When the students are ready, say, "Oh Deer!" Each deer and each habitat component turn to face the opposite group, continuing to hold their signs clearly.

8. When deer see the habitat component they need, they should run to it. Each deer must hold the sign of what it is looking for until getting to the habitat component student with the same sign. Each deer that reaches its necessary habitat component takes the "food," "water," or "shelter" back to the deer side of the line. "Capturing" a component represents the deer successfully meeting its needs and successfully reproducing as a result. Any deer that fails to find its food, water, or shelter dies and becomes part of the habitat. That is, any deer that died will be a habitat component in the next round and so is available as food, water, or shelter to the deer that are still alive.

NOTE: When more than one deer reaches a habitat component, the student who arrives there first survives. Habitat components stay in place until a deer chooses them. If no deer needs a particular habitat component during a round, the habitat component just stays where it is in the habitat. The habitat component can, however, change which component it is from round to round.

9. Record the number of deer at the beginning of the activity and at the end of each round. Continue the activity for approximately 15 rounds.

10. At the end of the 15 rounds, bring the students together to discuss the activity. Encourage them to talk about what they experienced and saw. For example, they saw a small herd of deer (7 students in a class size of 28) begin by finding more than enough of its habitat needs. However, because the population of deer expanded over two to three rounds of the activity until it exceeded the carrying capacity of the habitat, there was not sufficient food, water, and shelter for all members of the herd. At that point, deer starved or died of thirst or lack of shelter, and they returned as part of the habitat. Such things happen in nature also.

NOTE: In real life, large mammal populations might also experience higher infant mortality and lower reproductive rates.

11. Using an overhead projector, a flip chart pad, or chalkboard, post the data recorded during the activity. The number of deer at the beginning of the activity and at the end of each round represents the number of deer in a series of years. That is, the beginning of the activity is year one; each round is an additional year. Deer can be posted by fives for convenience. For example,

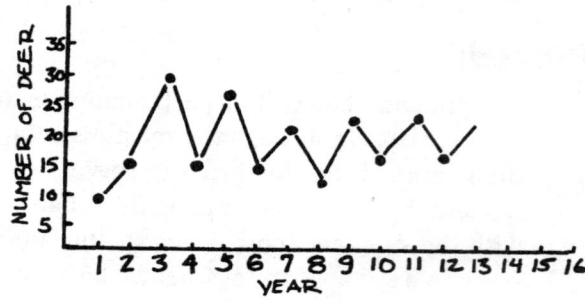

The students will see this visual reminder of what they experienced during the activity: the deer population fluctuated over a period of years. This process is natural as long as the factors that limit the population do not become excessive to the point where the animals cannot successfully reproduce. The wildlife populations will tend to peak, decline, and rebuild; peak, decline, and rebuild—as long as there is good habitat and sufficient numbers of animals to reproduce successfully.

12. What is realistic and unrealistic about this simulation? (Deer that do not survive **do** become recycled as nutrients but it is not instantaneous. Deer need **all** habitat components to survive. Poor habitat usually results in a weakened individual that succumbs to disease, not instant death.)

13. In discussion, ask the students to summarize some of the things they learned from this activity. What do animals need to survive? How do these components influence carrying capacity? What are some "limiting factors" that affect the survival of animals? How do factors that limit carrying capacity affect the health, numbers, and distribution of animals? How do these factors affect competition within a species? Why is good habitat important for animals? Are wildlife populations static, or do they tend to fluctuate as part of an overall "balance" of nature? Is nature ever really in "balance" or are ecological systems involved in a process of constant change?

Variations

1. After the students have played several rounds of "Oh Deer!," introduce a predator such as a mountain lion or wolf into the simulation. The predator starts in a designated "predator den" area off to the side. The predator has to skip or hop. This impediment reduces the possibility of violent collisions between deer and predator. The predator can tag deer only when they are going toward the habitat and are between the habitat and deer lines. Once a deer is tagged, the predator escorts the deer back to the predator den. The time it takes to escort the deer simulates the time it takes to eat. The "eaten" deer is now a predator. Predators that fail to tag someone die and become habitat. That is, in the next round the predators that died join the habitat line. They will become available to surviving deer as food, water, or shelter. During each round, keep track of the number of predators as well as the number of deer. Incorporate those data into the graphs.

2. Instead of drawing the line graph for students as described in Step 11, have the students create their own graphs. Provide them with the years and numbers of deer.

Extensions

1. When the students have finished tabulating and discussing the graph data, ask them if they have ever heard of the Hudson Bay trappers in American history. Tell students briefly who the trappers were.

There are a hundred years or more of records of the activities of these trappers. In those records are some interesting data. The data refer to pelts shipped from America to Europe, particularly the pelts of snowshoe hares and lynx. Researchers have found that snowshoe hare populations seem to peak about every seven to nine years and then crash, repeating the process over each comparable time period. A snowshoe hare population graph would look like this:

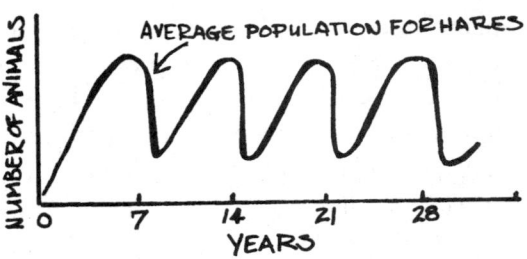

It also has been discovered that lynx populations do the same thing—except that they do it one year behind the hare populations. The combined graph would look like this:

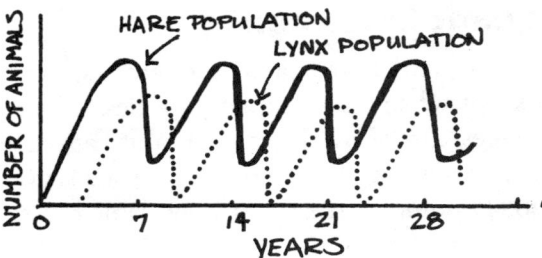

continued

Plot both sets of data on a graph, adding first the hares and then the lynx. Ask the students these questions:

- Which animal is the predator? Which prey?
- Are predators controlling the prey, or are prey controlling the predators? (The number of prey animals available is an indicator of how many predators can live in the area.)
- How is this graph similar to the one created in the deer habitat activity? Who controls the population fluctuations? (Sometimes the habitat—when the deer population is not too large; sometimes the deer—when the deer population destroys the vegetative food and cover.)

2. Some recent research has added a new dimension to the story of the snowshoe hares and the lynx.

It has been found that a major winter food of the hare is a small willow. As the hare population grows, the use of the willow plants grows too. However, when the willow plant has been "hedged" or eaten back so far, the plant generates a toxin (poison) so the hare can't eat it. That is when the hare population crashes, followed by the crash of the lynx population about a year later. Then the willow is able to grow again. The hare population begins to grow in response, and last of all, within a year or so, the lynx population follows. And the cycle has begun again—over and over—every seven to nine years.

3. Discuss the "balance" of nature. Is it ever in "balance"?

Aquatic Extension

Do the activity in exactly the same fashion, except substitute an aquatic species of wildlife. The essentials are the same. In this case, rather than assuming all the necessary space is available, assume all the water is available but space is needed, as is food and shelter. Hands on stomach is food, hands together over head is shelter, and arms out to the side is space. Otherwise, conduct the activity in the same fashion. The objective remains the same, except that now food, shelter, and space are the three essential components of habitat. Examples of possible aquatic species: manatee, salmon, frog.

Evaluation

1. Identify three essential components of habitat.

2. Define "limiting factors." Identify three examples.

3. Examine the graph below. What factors may have caused the following population changes:

   a. between years 1 and 2?
   b. between years 3 and 4?
   c. between years 5 and 6?
   d. between years 7 and 8?

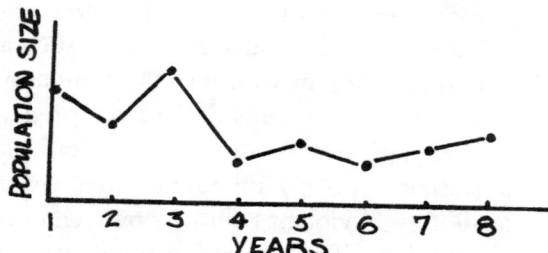

4. Which of the following graphs represents the more typically balanced population?

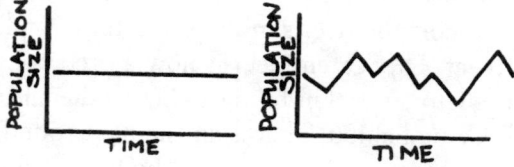

Wild Words

Objectives
Students will (1) research past- and present-day naturalists, and (2) analyze journals of the naturalists they investigated.

Method
Students create journals and then compare their entries to journals of naturalists they researched.

Materials
Construction paper for journal covers; blank, unlined writing, or computer paper; staples and stapler; hole punch; string or yarn; marking pens; crayons; pencils

Background
Those individuals who interpret the natural world through creative expression often are called naturalists. Naturalists spend most of the time outside, and they often record their observations in some form, from sketches, drawings, paintings, and photos to poetry and prose. Each naturalist's motivation for his or her career will be unique and may include sheer joy in learning more about natural systems, interest in contributing to scientific research, love for the art of writing as literature, and simple satisfaction in being outside.

People benefit today from the insights and observations of those who have been fascinated by the wonders of the natural environment. Although systematic inventories of plant and animal populations did not begin until after the 1930s, journals written by Captain John Smith, Meriwether Lewis, and Captain William Clark are historical records that reflect the considerable variation in historic population levels in the United States. Some of those early explorers and naturalists published their findings in formal publications. For example, John Muir, a wilderness explorer and founder of the Sierra Club, kept journals and sketched many of the smaller objects that he found on his travels. Aldo Leopold's book, *A Sand County Almanac*, was a compilation of his many years discovering the land near his home in Wisconsin.

Grade Level: 5–8
Subject Areas: Language Arts, Science
Duration: one 20- to 45-minute session
Group Size: any
Setting: outdoors
Conceptual Framework Topic Reference: WPIIA1
Key Vocabulary: journal, observation, naturalist
Appendices: Outdoors, Field Ethics, Simulated Field Trips

Procedure
1. Locate an open area on the school grounds, near a large tree in a park, or in any outdoor setting, from the school or organizational grounds to a remote, wilderness setting.

2. Ask the students to sit quietly, listening carefully for any sounds. Ask them to look with "soft eyes" or eyes that do not focus specifically on any one thing but broadly sense the environment. The students may move their heads at first in a scanning motion until they are accustomed to seeing without focusing on one thing at a time. "Hard eyes" are good

continued

for looking closely at a squirrel running up a tree. Encourage the students to try both "hard" and "soft" eyes, noticing the differences in how they feel and what they see. Both ways of seeing are useful.

3. Talk with the students about what they see, feel, and notice, or read an excerpt from the writings of a naturalist. Excerpts from *The Wilderness World of John Muir*, edited by Edwin Way Teale (Houghton Mifflin Company, Boston, 1954), are good. For example, the chapter "Windstorm in the Forest" is Muir's account of climbing a tall tree during a windstorm:

"It occurred to me that it would be a fine thing to climb one of the trees to obtain a wider outlook.... Under the circumstances, the choice of a tree was a serious matter.... Being accustomed to climbing trees in making botanical studies, I experienced no difficulty in reaching the top of this one, and never before did I enjoy so noble an exhilaration of motion. The slender tops fairly flapped and swished in the passionate torrent, bending and swirling backward and forward, round and round, tracing indescribable combinations of vertical and horizontal curves, while I clung with muscles firm braced, like a bobolink on a reed."

4. Distribute construction paper and either blank unlined writing or computer paper for the students to make their own journals. Simply fold the paper in half with the construction paper on the outside and the unlined paper inside. Staple along the seams so that the booklet stays together, or punch holes through the booklet and tie it with yarn. Provide marking pens and crayons so the students can put their name, a title, and a drawing on the cover of their book. Or make or buy more durable journals before going outside to start using them.

5. Give the students some time—about 15 minutes—to become accustomed to using their journal. Structured activities can be inserted at this point, or students can find a quiet place to make a drawing of something they see. The students could begin to write a few words of description or a poem about their feelings on being outside in that place at that time. The important thing to stress is that the journal is theirs—for them to fill with whatever they choose.

6. Have the students read and analyze selections from the journal of a well-known naturalist they have researched. Students may read the same selection or they may work in groups to analyze several works or authors. Ask the students to develop a personal response to the text selection. What new knowledge and what emotions did the author convey?

7. Have the students compare their journals to that of the naturalist. What differences in style do they notice? What differences do the students find between the environment described by the naturalist and the environment they described? Have the students try to write a short selection mimicking the style of the naturalist but describing their environment instead.

8. Discuss the value of journals. In addition to being a record of impressions, feelings, and observations, a journal can become a log of important data to be referred to later. It can reflect changes in ecosystems, vegetative types, and animal populations as well as attitudes about things. It can hold images as well as words. It can even hold artifacts—from leaves to grains of sand!

Extensions

1. See the Project WILD activity "Animal Poetry."

2. Select an animal habitat. Find a spot within that habitat. (The students should experience the habitat as closely as possible to the perspective of the animal they choose to be [e.g., lying on their backs looking skyward]. They should not damage the animal's habitat, and they should still be near enough to you to hear your instructions.) Write one word that describes the animal you have

chosen to be. On the next line, write two words that describe what you look like. On the next line, write three words that describe how you move or where you live. On the next line, write two words about how you contribute to the ecosystem where you live or how you live. On the last line, write another word that describes who you are. For example,

> Bird
> Large, Strong
> Soaring, Diving, Twisting
> Predator, Hunter
> Red-Tail

Aquatic Extensions

1. See the Project WILD Aquatic activity "Aqua Words."

2. Early explorers in North America often traveled by waterways. Lewis and Clark, LaSalle, and others were often the first to write in journals about what they saw. Pick a time period of your choice. Become a brave explorer venturing into unknown territory. Write an imaginary account of what you see—including the terrain, vegetation, and wildlife. Describe the water itself, its quality, and the plant and animal life directly associated with it, whether you are on a great river, a lake, or an ocean. Describe your feelings. Include an account of the "most hair-raising adventure" to date, and complete the sentence, "I find I am most often thinking about…".

Evaluation

Have students use the style of the naturalist they investigated as they do the following:

1. Have students write a description of a favorite place that they have not visited in a long time. Include details about what it looks like, how they feel when they're there, and what they like about it.

2. Take the students outside. Ask them to find a very small living organism and look at it as closely as possible without harming it. Ask them to write a short description or poem about this small living organism.

We're in This Together

Objectives

Students will (1) identify environmental problems of concern to both people and wildlife, and (2) generalize that people, domesticated animals, and wildlife are subject to similar environmental problems.

Method

Students interview people to identify environmental problems and then analyze, interpret, and summarize their findings.

Materials

Writing materials and a chalkboard

Background

Both humans and wildlife share the same basic needs as well as environmental concerns. The health and well-being of people, domesticated animals, like pets, and wildlife depends on an environment that has enough available food, water, shelter, and space.

The major purpose of this activity is for students to recognize that people and wildlife are subject to the same or similar environmental problems.

Procedure

1. Begin a discussion about environmental issues that are related to wildlife. Brainstorm a list on the chalkboard.

2. Tell the students that this activity focuses on planning an interview. Ask the students to develop a set of questions to use in interviewing people about environmental issues affecting wildlife.

3. Ask each student to interview 10 people using the list developed in Step 2.

4. Combine the concerns identified from all the interviews, including the students' original list. Rank the concerns from those mentioned most often to those mentioned least often.

5. Ask the students to try to categorize the concerns according to whether they are problems for people or wildlife. How are people and wildlife affected by these problems? How do they cope with them, if they

---

Grade Level: 9–12

Subject Areas: Social Studies, Science, Language Arts, Environmental Education

Duration: 45–60 minutes preparation, minimum, 45–60 minutes for interviews, plus additional 45 minutes for review

Group Size: any

Setting: indoors; outdoors optional

Conceptual Framework Topic Reference: WPIC, WPIIB

Key Terms: environmental problem, interview, components of habitat

Appendices: Using Local Resources, Guidelines for Interviewing People

do? Also analyze the problems according to components of habitat (food, water, shelter, and space in a suitable arrangement). For example, do the same issues affect humans and wildlife? This categorization is useful as an indicator that people and wildlife share the same needs and are subject to similar problems in environmental quality.

6. Ask the students to write an essay that summarizes what they learned in this investigation, emphasizing that people and wildlife are "in this together."

Extensions

1. Have class or group members read their essay, or short stories.

2. Publish a magazine or book that includes the results of the interviews, as well as the essays and short stories.

3. Develop a television news special featuring the common concerns of people and wildlife.

Evaluation

Choose a country and research how a citizen of that country would answer the questions developed for this activity.

Carrying Capacity

Objectives
Students will (1) formulate and test hypotheses related to wildlife populations and carrying capacity, and (2) describe the significance of carrying capacity.

Method
Students become herds of animals seeking food in a physical activity.

Materials
Five tokens per student, a kitchen timer

Background
Carrying capacity affects all living things, including humans. Carrying capacity may be seen as a type of dynamic equilibrium. It is typically expressed as the number of animals of a given type that can be supported in a given area.

Carrying capacity is also interpreted more broadly as the number of living things—plants and animals—any area of land or water can support at any one time. It is the dynamic equilibrium expressed by the availability of habitat components (quantity and quality of food, water, shelter, space, and the suitability of their arrangement) and the number of organisms that the habitat can support. Each area of land or water—and ultimately the planet—has a carrying capacity of plants and animals. The same area will have different carrying capacities for different life forms.

Carrying capacity for many species is in a constant state of change, both seasonally and annually. For example, terrestrial animals typically are most limited in the winter season when food supplies are reduced. Annual variations may result from factors such as natural disasters, changes in rainfall and temperature patterns, or human interventions. Factors that affect plant growth will affect animals because they either directly (as herbivores or omnivores) or indirectly (as carnivores) depend on plants.

Populations of living things tend to fluctuate naturally around some level. Carrying capacity is that level. A population may be below carrying capacity in the spring following a hard winter—or temporarily above it. The latter situation inevitably results in a decline of the population because of many natural limiting factors (e.g., mortality, disease, emigration, and lowered reproduction rate) and usually lasts for a short period. Biological carrying capacity is different from cultural carrying capacity, which is the number of a given animal that people are willing to tolerate. The carrying capacity of any area can be affected and adjusted by natural factors as well as by human intervention.

Grade Level: 9–12

Subject Areas: Environmental Education, Science

Duration: one 45-minute session or longer

Group Size: any, six groups of five students each is optimal

Setting: indoors

Conceptual Framework Topic Reference: WPIIA2a1, WPIIA2a2, WPIIA2a2cii

Key Terms: carrying capacity, population, management, habitat

Appendices: Simulations, Ecosystem

A population will, therefore, tend to fluctuate naturally, with or without human intervention. Humans may not always be willing to accept the consequences of natural events, however. Examples of intentional human intervention are reintroducing predators, feeding in winter, constructing nesting boxes, planting additional vegetation suitable for food, relocating animals, and hunting. Human intervention can increase or reduce a population or prevent its expansion to meet an expected natural reduction in carrying capacity. Such an intervention may result in a higher survival rate of individuals.

Intentional intervention may be based on a particular management philosophy or practice. Management of an area of land or water in relation to its carrying capacity for certain species can be subject to question and controversy. Whether or how it is appropriate for humans to intervene in natural systems is sometimes a part of such questions and controversy. Management may be defined as intentional choices based on human goals and objectives.

Procedure

1. Spread tokens out on a table in the middle of an open room. This arrangement of tokens represents a food supply that has been fixed by the end of a growing season.

2. Divide the class into "herds" of five students each, and have them all line up behind one member of their "herd" on the periphery of the open space.

3. Act as a timekeeper, and set the timer to ring at intervals of 1 minute or less.

4. During the intervals, members from each herd take turns coming to the table and taking one piece of food per turn, simulating the animal's need to eat reasonably regularly. When the round begins, all the first people in line from each herd will move at once to acquire food. Once they have obtained the food, they tag the next person in their herd line who moves to get food, who then tags the next person, and so on. This process continues until the timer signals the end of Round One. (The length of the round depends on the size of the physical area used for the activity as well as the size of the class of students. It should last just long enough so that some students do not get to the food supply before the timer rings and the interval ends.)

5. Record the names of students who did not acquire a token. Repeat the process until all of the food is used up. Any member of a herd going for three rounds without obtaining at least one food token "dies."

6. At the end of the activity, tell the students that because the food ran out before the next growing season could begin, additional animals died over the winter. Students without at least three tokens to last them through the winter "died."

7. Record the number of survivors from each herd on the board, flipchart, or overhead projector. Ask the students what happened to the competition level between the herds as the food supply diminished during the activity. Do they think other animals also will exhibit an increase in competition when a resource is limited?

8. Define "carrying capacity." Ask students to explain how they think this concept is related to the number of survivors in this activity. Why might knowledge of the carrying capacity for a species in a particular area be important? (These numbers might help determine management strategies when required.) What factors other than food might determine how many organisms an area might support? Do all land areas have an ultimate carrying capacity?

9. Discuss with the students what could be done or might happen to allow more of the population to live through the "winter" on the food available. Options may include reducing the population in various ways to match the carrying capacity (e.g., by redistributing some of the population to another area, introducing or increasing natural predator populations, or opening the area to

continued

hunting before the winter begins). Options to increase the carrying capacity could include bringing in or planting more "food" for the "herds." Another option is no action in the form of human intervention. Each option involves costs and benefits, and each may be controversial.

10. Repeat the activity two more times, incorporating two different options the students have discussed. What happens to the number of survivors that live to reproduce the next year?

11. Repeat the activity one more time, incorporating one of the options used above and also include five or six young animals born the previous spring. Designate one student in each "herd" to take two food tokens each time, one for themselves and one for an offspring to simulate this variation. How does this annual population increase affect the rest of the herd? What must now happen to re-establish the herd size within the area's carrying capacity?

12. Also record the number of "survivors" that result from the various manipulations of carrying capacity. What can be learned from this numerical representation? Which manipulation was the most successful? What criteria were used to determine success? What are examples of both cultural and natural influences on carrying capacity?

13. Ask the students to summarize some of the most important things they have learned about the concept of carrying capacity.

Evaluation

You are a scientist in the early 1900s. You have just learned of the following situation: All the natural predators of deer in the Kaibab Plateau in Arizona were removed from the area. Within a few years, the deer population had increased tremendously; within another few years, the population had collapsed to a very small number. Formulate a hypothesis that might explain the increase and decrease of the deer population related to carrying capacity. Explain how you would test this hypothesis.

Graphananimal

Objective
Students will identify characteristic life forms in two different environments.

Method
Students create picture collections of animals in two different habitats, and then "visit" the habitats by going on an indoor nature walk where they tally the number of animals seen, and then graph and compare the results.

Materials
Photos or pictures of animals (from magazines), cardboard for mounting photos, notebook paper, graph paper, pencils

Background
Different kinds of animals are found in different environments. Each environment is suitable for animals that are adapted to its climate, soils, water, vegetation, and other ecological factors.

Grade Level: Pre–K, K–4

Subject Areas: Science, Mathematics, Environmental Education

Duration: two 30-minute sessions, one 40-minute session if educators prepare wildlife pictures

Group Size: 15 to 30 students

Setting: indoors or outdoors

Conceptual Framework Topic Reference: HNIB

Key Terms: environment, habitat, graph

Appendices: Using Local Resources

Just as people need food, water, shelter, and space in which to live, so does wildlife.

The major purpose of this activity is for students to recognize that each environment has characteristic life forms (e.g., mountains and prairie, forest and desert, meadows and marsh).

Procedure

1. Pick two environments in your state. Ask students to make a collection of animals for each place by drawing pictures or cutting pictures out of magazines. Each student should find two animals for each habitat. Glue the pictures onto heavy paper or cardboard.

2. Ask the students to tell where their animals live. Make a pile for each habitat, and ask the students to put their pictures in the place where their animals live.

3. List the animals in each pile to show the students what species of animals live in each habitat. Some animals will appear on both lists. Ask the students to copy the two lists.

4. When the students are out of the room, place the animal cards in an area of the classroom that can hypothetically serve as the appropriate habitat. Label these habitats and place the pictures of the animals in the appropriate place. Some animals may be in both habitats. Put the animal pictures in all sorts of places—by a table leg, on a window ledge, etc.—to simulate where the animals might actually live. If possible, check with wildlife officials in your area to see what the actual proportions of animals are in each of the chosen environments and use the animal cards accordingly.

continued

© Council for Environmental Education 2001

Ecological Knowledge

Graphanimal

5. Bring the students back into the room for a "nature walk." Let the students use their lists to tally the animals they see in each place. At the end of the walk, students should total their counts and write that number on their lists. Have the students take turns walking along the "path." A sample list and tally might look like this:

FOREST	TOTAL	PLAINS	TOTAL
RABBIT 甶I	6	COYOTE 甶	5
COYOTE III	3	RATTLESNAKE III	3
DEER I	1	PRAIRIE DOG 甶II	7
JAY III	3	ANTELOPE II	2

6. Show the students how to make a bar graph for each of the environments:

RABBIT								
COYOTE								
DEER								
JAY								

Give the students graph paper, and show them how they can fill in each square for the number of each animal they saw. Or have them use a computer to compile and portray the data.

7. Using the graphs, compare the two environments. Which animals were seen the most? Which animals were seen the least? How could some animals live in both places? Why can't all the animals live in both places?

Variations

1. Skip having the students collect the animal pictures. If the educator collects the photos, the activity may begin with the nature walk.

2. Use the strategies for the nature walk when taking any field trip to areas where real animals can be observed.

Aquatic Extension

Choose two aquatic habitats, such as lake and river, or pond and stream, or freshwater (lake) and saltwater (ocean). Find or draw pictures of the animals that would be found in each of the two habitats. Put each animal on a separate card or piece of paper, and mix the cards together. See if a friend can correctly identify which animals live in which aquatic habitats. Do any of the animals live in both? If yes, which ones? Create a poster display to show the variety of animals that live in each of these two aquatic environments.

Evaluation

1. Identify five common animals that might be found in each of the following areas: forest, desert, prairie, stream, pond, ocean, seashore, park.

2. Two scientists went to separate parts of the world and studied the animals in each place. They made these graphs showing the species and numbers of animals they found. Why did the scientists see different animals? If the animals in one place were moved to the other place, would they survive? Why or why not?

Scientist 1	Number of Animals
Seals	
Whales	
Polar bears	

Scientist 2	Number of Animals
Lions	
Zebras	
Antelope	
Rhinoceros	
Hippopotamus	

Wildlife Is Everywhere!

Objectives
Students will (1) compare human and wildlife habitat, and (2) generalize that wildlife is present around the world.

Method
Students search their surroundings for evidence of wildlife.

Materials
None

Background
Many people think of wildlife as the large animals of Africa, such as the lion and elephant, or the large animals of the North American forests, such as the grizzly bear and elk. However, wildlife includes all animals that have not been domesticated by people.

What may be surprising is that wildlife includes the smallest animal organisms—even those that can be seen only through a microscope. Spiders, insects, reptiles, amphibians, and most species of fish, birds, and mammals may be considered wildlife. Even when animals are silent or not visible, they exist somewhere around us. Thousands of organisms live in and on human skin, hair, and bodies. In fact, the organisms that inhabit human bodies play a part in human survival. Some form of animal life is always near.

By investigating microenvironments or microhabitats, students will be able to generalize that wildlife exists in every country on the planet.

Procedure
NOTE: Ask students to observe, but not touch or disturb, any animals they may see.

1. Invite the students to explore the room looking for signs of wildlife. Even in the cleanest rooms, some signs of life can be found. It might be a spider web, dead insects near lights, or insect holes along baseboards and behind books. After the search and a discussion with the students about what they might have found, introduce the idea that people and other animals share the same environment. Sometimes people do not even notice that they are sharing the environment with other living things.

2. Take the search for animals outside. Divide the students into pairs, and give each pair five minutes to find an animal or some sign that an animal has been there. Look for indirect evidence such as tracks, webs, droppings, feathers, and nests (be sure not to harm or seriously disturb any evidence that is found). Afterward, sit down and discuss what everyone found.

Grade Level: K–4

Subject Areas: Science, Language Arts, Environmental Education

Duration: one 30- to 45-minute session

Group Size: any

Setting: indoors and outdoors

Conceptual Framework Topic Reference: HNIA, HNIB1, HNIB2

Key Vocabulary: wildlife, wild, domesticated, environment, evidence

Appendices: Field Ethics, Observations and Inferences, Early Childhood

---

continued

3. Discuss with the students what they have learned. Emphasize that the experience shows that people and wildlife share the same environment. Ask the students to predict where different kinds of animals are found all over the Earth—in the deserts, oceans, mountains, and cities. They may draw from their own experiences and talk about places they have been and have seen animals.

Extensions

1. Observe wildlife in yards, kitchens, neighborhoods, and city parks.

2. Search magazines and books for pictures of wildlife from all over the planet.

3. Invent names and descriptions for the wildlife found during wildlife searches. Students can observe the animals, write descriptions, and then check their invented names and descriptions against the scientific names and information found in reference materials.

4. Using state maps, look up towns, cities, and counties named after wild animals.

Aquatic Extension

Survey your school grounds or neighborhood for any aquatic wildlife habitats. Check puddles, sprinkler systems, and, if possible, streams, beaches, and ponds. Look for evidence—direct or indirect—of any wildlife that lives in or near these water-related areas. Tell or show someone what you find, taking care not to damage any wildlife or its habitat.

Evaluation

1. In which of the following places would animals be living: in a forest; in a hot, dry, desert; in a lake; at the top of a mountain; at the North Pole; in New York City? What kinds of animals would be found in those places? Name areas on Earth where animals would not be found.

2. What evidence did the class have (using the five senses) that showed that wildlife lives in any location where this activity was conducted?

3. Draw a picture of a place and include as many different animal species as possible that would be found living there. Explain your picture to a friend or adult.

4. Identify and describe three things that people could do to increase the numbers and kinds of wildlife living in an area that has little evidence of wildlife.

Habitracks

Objectives

Students will (1) identify the basic components of habitat as food, water, shelter, and space in a suitable arrangement; and (2) generalize that these components of habitat are needed by all animals—including people and wildlife.

Method

Students identify the components of habitat by using a map and exploring their surroundings.

Materials

Habitat maps, task cards and habitat components (see below), glue or tape, scissors, pencils, chalkboard, and small paper bags

Background

People and other animals share some basic needs. Every animal needs a place in which to live. The environment in which an animal lives is called "habitat." An animal's habitat includes food, water, shelter, and adequate space in an arrangement appropriate to the animal's needs.

Grade Level: K–4

Subject Areas: Science, Environmental Education

Duration: 30 to 60 minutes

Group Size: 3 to 10 groups of 3 students in each group

Setting: outdoors and indoors

Conceptual Framework Topic Reference: HNIIA1

Key Terms: habitat, track, survival needs, food, water, shelter, space, arrangement

Appendices: Outdoors

Procedure

Before the Activity

1. Draw a simple map of the school grounds, nature center, or wherever this activity is conducted. Besides the natural features on the site, include sidewalks, buildings, and other human-made structures on the map. Duplicate enough copies of the map so that every group of three students has a copy.

2. On each map, choose an animal and design a route of travel for the animal. Indicate the route by drawing the tracks or the marks left by the animal. For example, one map may have the hoofprint of a deer, while another map may have a footprint of a bird. Try to map the animals' travel as realistically as possible. For each map, write the name of the animal whose tracks appear on the map with the word "habitat" at the top of the page. For example: see Bird Habitat: What Birds Need to Survive.

3. Next, make a task card for each mapped animal. Each card should have the survival needs of the particular animal represented. The four components that need to be on each card include food, water, shelter, and space. See the line drawing below for a suggestion for a task card.

continued

Each task card may look similar, but could be a different color.

4. Make a set of food, water, shelter, and space pieces that will fit over the shapes on each task card. Again, these "habitat component" pieces need to be the same color as the task card they go with. For example, if you chose brown for the bear task card, the bear habitat pieces also should be brown. Just before the activity begins, go outside and place the habitat component pieces along the trail for the appropriate animals. (Be certain to tell other teachers and students about the trail and ask their cooperation in not disturbing it.) For example, food in the "BEAR HABITAT" might be found at a bush, water in a puddle near the drinking fountain, and space on a playground or vacant lot. For safety and convenience of the students, place several habitat pieces for different animals in the same general area. The color-coding works well to minimize confusion, because each group of students with a map and a task card is looking only for the habitat pieces that match that task card.

The Activity

1. Divide the class into teams of three students each.

2. Give each team a habitat map that indicates the name of the animal the students are tracking. Tell them that they have 10 minutes to track the animal they have been given, looking for the things their animal needs to survive. Give the teams the task card for their animal. Also, give them a paper bag or other container to put their habitat pieces in as they find them.

3. Have the teams go outside and track their animals. To share responsibilities, one student could hold the map, another the task card, and another the container for the habitat pieces. Tell the students they are going to find things that represent what their animals need to survive. When they find something that is the color of the task card they are holding, they should put it in their sack. They should find pieces that match what they see on their task cards.

4. Within 10 minutes, the students should all follow their maps back to the starting point.

5. Back in the room, give the students tape or glue so that they can affix their habitat pieces to their task cards.

6. Once the habitat task cards are completed, invite the student groups to report on what they found and where they found it. Ask the students if everyone found "food." When they say, "Yes," write food on the chalkboard. Do the same with "water," "space," and "shelter." Ask one of the students in each group to draw a line connecting the four habitat pieces. For example,

7. Tell the students that food, water, space, and shelter have to go together in a suitable arrangement for an animal to live. For example, animals need the right amount of space to survive. A bear needs more space than an insect. Animals must have the right amount and the right kind of food. Food, water, and shelter must be available when needed. (The line connecting food, water, space, and shelter represents the idea of a suitable arrangement for the animal in its habitat.)

Extensions

1. Label each student as "food," "water," "shelter," or "space." Using a piece of brightly colored ball of yarn, connect the "food," "water," "shelter," and "spaces" by having the students hold part of the yarn. The students all connected by the yarn represent a suitable arrangement of food, water, shelter, and space, to meet an animal's needs. First, use a very long piece of yarn that leaves the students standing a distance from each other. This arrangement can represent some animals' need for a large habitat in which to live—like a bear or a mountain lion. A short length of yarn that requires students to stand close to each other can represent some animals' smaller habitat—like an insect.

2. If possible, find real animal tracks. See the Project WILD activity "Tracks!" on page 30.

3. Look for components of habitat that meet the needs of some actual wildlife that might live there. Make a map that shows the components and their arrangement. Identify what animals might find this location to be suitable habitat. Look for evidence to see if they do.

Aquatic Extension

Have a student pick an aquatic animal. Have the student stand in the middle of the other students who are labeled food, water, shelter, and space. The student representing the aquatic animal should touch or hold onto the yarn to connect with every other student—indicating it is important for this and every other aquatic animal to have a suitable habitat in which to live.

Evaluation

Draw a picture of an animal in a suitable habitat. Identify and describe what the animal needs to survive, and show where and how its needs are met in the habitat.

What's That, Habitat?

Objectives
Students will (1) identify their own basic needs for food, water, shelter, and space in a suitable arrangement; and (2) generalize that wildlife and other animals have similar basic needs.

Method
Students draw pictures of human and animal homes, comparing basic needs.

Materials
Paper and crayons or chalk

Background
Humans and other animals—including pets, farm animals, and wildlife—have some of the same basic needs. Every animal needs a home. However, a home is not just a house where people live. Home, for many animals includes the out-of-doors. The scientific term for an animal's home is habitat. An animal's habitat includes food, water, shelter or cover, and space. Because animals need the food, water, shelter, and space to be available in a way that meets its needs, these things must be available in a suitable arrangement.

A house may be considered shelter for people. People build houses, apartments, trailers, houseboats, and other kinds of shelters in which to live. An animal's shelter might be underground, in a bush, in the bark of a tree, or in some rocks. Animals need a place to find food and water. They also need enough space in which to live and to find the food, water, and shelter they need. Home for an animal is more like a neighborhood that has everything in it that is needed for survival.

Procedure
1. Write the following words on a chalkboard: food, water, shelter, space.

2. Read each word aloud, asking the students to repeat the words.

3. Food and water will be easy concepts for the students to understand. Shelter and space will be more difficult. Ask the students to explain the definitions of shelter and space.

4. Give the students paper, chalk, pencils, or crayons. Ask the students to draw a picture of where they live, including pictures of

Grade Level: K–4

Subject Areas: Science, Language Arts, Expressive Arts, Environmental Education

Duration: two 20-minute sessions, or one 40-minute session

Group Size: any

Setting: indoors

Conceptual Framework Topic Reference: HNIIA1

Key Terms: habitat, survival needs, food, water, shelter, space, arrangement

Appendices: none

where they find food, water, shelter, and space. Ask the students to label the parts of their drawings where they find their food, water, shelter, and space. See the example on page 56.

Note on picture: Shelter could be shown in a number of ways. In this picture, it is shown by labeling the roof. Space can be shown as the area outside and inside the house or apartment. Shown here, it includes the house and yard. Space also can include the neighborhood (space actually includes all the areas used for survival).

5. Once the drawings are complete, write two more words on the chalkboard: arrangement, habitat. Say the words aloud, asking the students to repeat them.

6. Inform the students that food, water, shelter, and space arranged to meet an animal's needs is called "habitat." Ask the children if they could live in a home where the bathroom was 4 miles in one direction, the kitchen was 12 miles in another, and the bedroom was 9 miles in yet another direction. This arrangement is not suitable for a person, although some animals do travel great distances in their habitat.

7. Ask the students to write the word "habitat" in big letters at the top of their drawings. Discuss the meaning of habitat.

8. Give the students another piece of paper. Ask them to think of an animal. Ask a few students what animal they are thinking of and identify whether the animals are wild or domesticated. If both wild and domesticated animals are not a part of the grouping, ask the students to think of the kinds of animals that are missing. It is important to make sure the students are thinking about both wild and domesticated animals.

9. Ask the students to draw a picture of their animal in a place where it lives. Ask the students to make sure they include food, water, shelter, and space in an arrangement that they think would make it possible for the animal to survive.

10. Ask the students to talk about their drawings, pointing out the habitat components they have included.

11. Ask the students to write "habitat" in big letters on the top of this drawing as well. Discuss with the students how humans and other animals need food, water, shelter, and space. The arrangement is different for each but all have similar basic needs. When the students have an understanding of habitat, write a few sentences on the chalkboard defining habitat. As much as possible, make use of the ideas the students suggest.

12. Suggested sentences for older students: Food, water, and shelter must be within a useable range for each animal. Different kinds of animals need different kinds of food, water, and shelter and different amounts of space.

13. Ask the students to write these sentences on the back of one of their drawings. They may also read the words in the sentences on the board and write their own sentences about what habitat is, drawing pictures to go along with their words.

Aquatic Extension

Ask the students to think of an aquatic animal and to draw a picture of their animal in a place where it lives. Ask the students to make sure they include food, water, shelter, and space in an arrangement that they think would make it possible for the animal to survive. Ask the students to talk about their drawings and to highlight the habitat components they have included.

Evaluation

1. Choose the elements that wildlife species need to survive: food, water, shelter, space, and arrangement. Explain.

2. Choose the elements people need to survive: food, water, shelter, space, and arrangement. Explain. Write a sentence about what people and wildlife need to survive.

Beautiful Basics

Objective
Students will identify five basic survival needs shared by people and all other animals, including pets, and wildlife.

Method
Students list and organize needs of people, pets, and wildlife.

Materials
Chalkboard

Background
All animals—including people, pets, and wildlife—need food, water, shelter, and space in which to live. These needs must be in the quality and quantity required by the particular animal. Because animals need food, water, shelter, and space to be available in a way that is suitable to their needs, wildlife biologists say that these components must be available in a suitable arrangement.

Grade Level: K–4
Subject Areas: Science, Language Arts, Environmental Education
Duration: one 20-minute session
Group Size: any
Setting: indoors
Conceptual Framework Reference: HNIIA, HNIIA1
Key Terms: pets, wildlife, survival needs
Appendices: Early Childhood

NOTE: It may be helpful to do the Project WILD activity "What's Wild?" on page 7 before this activity so that students know the major differences between pets and wildlife.

Procedure
1. Draw a three-column chart on a chalkboard with the headings People, Pets, and Wildlife. Ask the students, "What do people need in order to be able to live?" List the students' ideas in a column under the word "People." Complete the same for pets and wildlife.

2. After the chart is complete, ask the students to cluster ideas together into larger themes. For example, warmth might be combined with physical comfort, and both might fit within the concept of shelter. Help the students to define the lists and to establish the essential survival needs for people, pets, and wildlife. The most basic survival needs will be the same for each of the three groups. The lists could include and be limited to these:

People	Pets	Wildlife
Food	Food	Food
Water	Water	Water
Shelter	Shelter	Shelter
Space	Space	Space
Arrangement	Arrangement	Arrangement
Sunlight	Sunlight	Sunlight
Soil	Soil	Soil
Air	Air	Air

Evaluation
1. List at least four things animals need for survival.
2. How do human needs differ from animal needs?

Everybody Needs a Home

Objective
Students will generalize that people and other animals share a basic need to have a home.

Method
Students draw a floor plan of their house and compare their needs with those of other animals.

Materials
Drawing paper; crayons, pencils, or chalk

Background
Humans and other animals—including pets, farm animals, and wildlife—have some of the same basic needs. Every animal needs a home. But a home is not just a house where people live. Home, for many animals, includes the out-of-doors. The scientific term for an animal's home is "habitat." An animal's habitat includes food, water, shelter or cover, and space. Because animals need the food, water, shelter, and space to be available in a way that meets the animals' needs, we say that these things must be available in a suitable arrangement.

A house may be considered shelter for people. People build houses, apartments, trailers, houseboats, and other kinds of shelters in which to live. An animal's shelter might be underground, in a bush, in the bark of a tree, or in some rocks. Animals need a place to find food and water. They also need enough space in which to live and find the food, water, and shelter they need. Home for an animal is more like a neighborhood with everything in it that is needed for survival.

Procedure

1. Ask the students to draw a floor plan of where they live or where a person they know lives. A floor plan will include the things the students need in their home— a place to cook and keep food, a place to sleep, and a source of water.

2. Once the drawings are finished, have a discussion with the students about what they drew. Ask the students to point out the things that they need to live and that they included in their drawings. Ask the students how their homes are similar to animals' homes. If a human home has several stories, it can be compared to a forest with an attic (the canopy), first and second floors (subcanopy), and basement (ground). How does the ground furnish the needs of humans and of animals?

Grade Level: K–4

Subject Areas: Science, Language Arts, Environmental Education

Duration: one 30-minute session or longer

Group Size: any, however, no more than 25 students is recommended

Setting: indoors

Conceptual Framework Topic Reference: HNIIA, HNIIA1

Key Terms: differences, similarities, survival needs, habitat

Appendices: Early Childhood

---

continued

3. Make a "gallery of homes" out of the drawings. Explain that everyone has a home, and all the homes together form a neighborhood. Neighborhoods and local services form a community. A community of animals includes animals (and plants) of different species. How are human communities like animal communities?

4. Ask the students to close their eyes and imagine a bird's home, an ant's home, a beaver's home, the President's home, and their homes. Show the students pictures of different places that animals live.

5. Discuss the differences and similarities among the different homes with the students. Have the students identify the components every animal needs in its home—food, water, shelter, and space in which to live—arranged in a way so the animal can survive. Summarize the discussion by emphasizing that although the homes are different, every animal needs a home.

Extensions

1. Select an animal and draw its home or habitat. Compare the animal's habitat to places where people live.

2. Take the students outside and look for animal shelters.

Aquatic Extension

Fish, aquatic reptiles, amphibians, aquatic insects, and aquatic mammals need food, water, shelter, and space in a suitable arrangement. Draw a picture of a home for an aquatic species.

Evaluation

1. Identify three reasons people need homes and three reasons animals need shelter.

2. Draw a picture of a suitable habitat for an animal. Write a paragraph to describe how habitat meets the animal's needs for survival.

Habitat Lap Sit

Objectives

Students will (1) identify the components of a habitat, (2) recognize how humans and other animals depend upon habitats, and (3) interpret the significance of loss or change in habitat in terms of people and wildlife.

Method

Students physically form an interconnected circle to demonstrate components of habitat.

Materials

None

Background

People and other animals share some basic needs. Every animal needs a place in which to live. The environment in which an animal lives is called a habitat. An animal's habitat includes food, water, shelter, and space in an arrangement appropriate to the animal's needs.

An animal will be affected if any of the components of habitat are missing or are significantly affected so that the arrangement for the individual animal or population of animals is no longer suitable. The impact will not necessarily be catastrophic, but it can be. There are additional limiting factors beyond those of suitable food, water, shelter, and space. For example, disease, predation, pollution, and climatic conditions can affect an animal's survival.

Within a biological community, there are interrelationships and interdependencies between plants and plants, between plants and animals, and between animals and animals. These interrelationships and interdependencies are important.

Procedure

1. Have the students form a circle, standing shoulder to shoulder. Ask them to name the components of habitat, with the first student saying food, the next saying water, the third saying shelter, and the fourth saying space. Continue around the circle until each student has called out a habitat component.

2. Ask the students to turn toward their right, at the same time taking one step toward the center of the circle. They should be standing close together, with each student looking at the back of the head of the student in front of him or her. (See the photos on page 63.)

3. Ask everyone to listen carefully. Students should place their hands on the shoulders of the person in front of them. At the count of three, ask the students to sit down slowly on the knees of the person behind them, keeping their own knees together to support the person in front of them. As the students are sitting say, "Food, water, shelter, and space in the proper arrangement are needed to have a suitable (good) habitat." The term "proper arrangement" is represented by the students' intact, lap-sit circle.

continued

Grade Level: 5–8

Subjects Areas: Science, Environmental Education, Expressive Arts

Duration: one 20-minute session

Group Size: 15 to 45 students

Setting: outdoors preferred; indoors possible

Conceptual Framework Reference: HNIIA1

Key Terms: habitat, food, water, shelter, space, arrangement

Appendices: Simulations

© Council for Environmental Education 2001

4. The students at this point may either fall or sit down. Discuss with the students the necessary components of suitable habitats for people and wildlife.

5. After the students have a better understanding that food, water, shelter, and space are necessary for any animal's survival, and that the appropriate arrangement comprises a suitable habitat, let the students try the activity again. This time ask them to hold their lap-sit posture. As the students lap sit still representing food, water, shelter, and space in their appropriate arrangement—identify a student who represents water. Tell the students, "It is a drought year. The water supply is reduced by the drought conditions." At this point, have the student who was identified as representing water remove himself or herself from the lap-sit circle. At this point, the circle will either collapse or suffer some other disruption. Other ways that educators can illustrate varying conditions could be to remove a student from the circle because of pollution of water supply, urban development that is limiting the availability of all habitat components, soil erosion affecting food and water supplies, and so on.

6. Ask the students to discuss what this activity means to them. Ask them to summarize the main things they have learned. They could include the following:

- Food, water, shelter, and space, in an appropriate arrangement, can be called habitat.
- Humans and other animals depend on habitat.
- Loss of any elements of habitat influence the animals living there.
- The components of habitat must be in an arrangement that meets the needs of the individual animals or populations of animals in order for the animals to survive.

Variation

Have the students form a circle, holding hands. Walk around the circle, first naming one student as an animal of a particular habitat. Name the next four students in the circle as food, water, shelter, and space for that animal. Repeat the process until all the students are involved. When all students have been designated as an animal or as components of an animal's habitat, comment on the fact that they are holding hands. This arrangement represents the idea that all things in an habitat are interrelated. Briefly discuss the idea of interrelationships. Then move the students into the lap-sit arrangement described in the Procedure section. Remind the students that they noticed all elements of the ecosystem were interrelated when they were holding hands. Do the lap sit to signify the dependence on one another. Discuss interrelationships and interdependencies in ecological systems.

Aquatic Extensions

Do "Habitat Lap Sit" from an aquatic perspective. Have students form a circle, holding hands. Name one student as an animal in an aquatic ecosystem. Name the next four students in the circle as food, water, shelter, and space for that animal. Repeat the process until all the students are involved. Finish the procedure as it is described in the Variation section. Do the activity more than once, picking a different aquatic ecosystem each time—to emphasize that all aquatic animals, in any aquatic ecosystem, need food, water, shelter, and space in a suitable arrangement in order to survive.

Evaluation

1. What are the five essential components of habitat?

2. Explain how the arrangement of food, water, shelter, and space is important to humans and other animals.

3. Which would probably have the greater long-term impact on the wildlife living on a farm in Iowa:
    a. a severe winter that killed many animals?
    b. the development of part of the farm into a shopping center?

Ecological Knowledge

Habitat Lap Sit

Who Fits Here?

Objectives

Students will (1) identify characteristic life forms in ecosystems, (2) describe the importance of adaptations in animals, and (3) generalize that each ecosystem has characteristic life forms adapted to live there.

Method

Students play an identification game using posters and cards.

Materials

Posterboard for 10 posters; crayons, paints, or magazine photos for posters; poster board, index cards, or construction paper for 50 adaptation cards

Background

Each environment is suitable to those life forms that have adapted to its climate, soils, water, vegetation, and other life forms and to other ecological factors over a number of years. Plants and animals tolerant of heat and little moisture are adapted to the desert, mountain goats to craggy hillsides and cold temperatures, and polar bears to ice fields and snowy vistas.

In this activity, students will research particular environments to discover characteristic life forms and then match those animals' adaptations back to the appropriate environment.

The major purpose of this activity is for students to recognize that each environment has characteristic life forms adapted to live there.

Procedure

1. Divide the class into two equal groups. Explain that each group will make a game for the other. The object of the game will be to match animals to the environment in which they live.

2. Ask each half of the class to choose five ecosystems they would like to know more about (e.g., desert, hardwood forest, coniferous forest, alpine, marine). Divide each half of the class into the five groups, one per ecosystem. Have students in each group research their ecosystem and learn its characteristic life forms, including adaptations of the animals that enable them to survive in that environment.

3. Ask students to make a poster showing the characteristic vegetation, terrain, and so on, in the ecosystem they are studying. Posters of each ecosystem can be made with crayons and paints or magazine cutouts.

Grade Level: 5–8

Subject Areas: Science, Environmental Education

Duration: two 45-minute periods or longer

Group Size: 10 to 30 students, fewer or more with adaptation of activity

Setting: indoors

Conceptual Framework Topic Reference: HNIB

Key Terms: adaptation, ecosystem, habitat

Appendices: Using Local Resources, Ecosystem

4. For each ecosystem, students should make five cards, one for each of five species of animals characteristic of the ecosystem. Put a description of the animal's adaptations to its environment on one side of the card and a coding number on the other side, so that the animal described can be identified later. Do not write the name of the animal on the card. The cards should describe adaptations that enable the animals to survive in the ecosystem. For example, for the desert environment, the five cards could read:

   "Hunts at night for warm rodents and sleeping birds; can climb loose, sloping sand by throwing loops of its body up like coils" (sidewinder rattlesnake)

   "Relies on agility and speed to escape predators, needs little water, gets water from plants it eats" (cottontail rabbit)

   "Hunts at night, lives in burrows of animals like gophers" (burrowing owl)

   "A bird that hibernates in winter to avoid desert cold" (nightjar)

   "Larvae feed on yucca flowers." (yucca moth)

5. When posters are made and cards completed, students in each half of the class should make a master list of the five ecosystems and animals that their cards represent. Next, they shuffle all their cards for their five ecosystems into one pile.

6. Each half of the class then exchanges posters and cards with the other half.

7. Each half of the class then tries as a group to decide to which ecosystem each card belongs.

8. Next, give students in each half of the class the master list for their posters. One student per group can read off the animals that correspond with each card for each poster.

9. Has each animal been placed in its proper ecosystem? If not, why not? Were there any animals found in more than one ecosystem? Are these ecosystems varied? How can some animals live in more than one ecosystem but not others? What are similarities and differences among the ecosystems and characteristic life forms? What are some of the most interesting animal adaptations? What functions do these adaptations serve? How do they relate to the nature of the physical environment? Ask the students what characterizes animals and the environments in which they live. (Each environment has characteristic life forms. These animals and plants are adapted to live where they do.)

Extensions

1. Look for rare, threatened, and endangered species in each ecosystem. Are there any? If not, why not? If yes, why? (usually habitat loss) See the Project WILD activity "Here Today, Gone Tomorrow."

2. Compare and contrast additional ecosystems and life forms from a variety of places on the planet.

3. Make an Ecosystem Quiz Show. Research the ecosystems, life forms, and adaptations—and then use a game show format to guess the animal and its environment.

Aquatic Extension

Do this activity again using only aquatic ecosystems—for example, pond, lake, stream, estuary, marsh, ocean, river.

Evaluation

1. Pick any three animals. Describe the ecosystem in which each animal lives, including identification of the animal's habitat requirements.

2. Describe the importance of adaptation in animals.

3. Design an activity or simulation that is for younger students and that teaches how wildlife is adapted for different ecosystems. This extension could be done in the form of a game. Have the younger people do the activity. Find out what the younger students learned.

Which Niche?

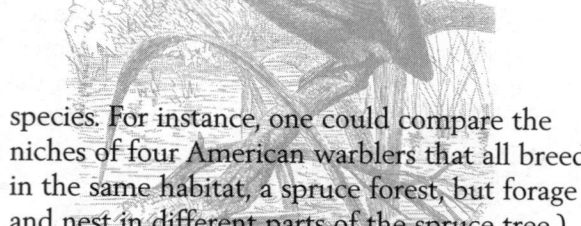

Objectives
Students will (1) define ecological niche, and (2) give at least one example of an animal and its ecological niche.

Method
Students compare ecological niches with careers in their community.

Materials
A guest speaker, chalkboard, reference materials

Background
Each animal has a role in the community. This role is called its ecological niche. The niche includes such things as where and how it gathers food; its role in the food chain; what it gives to and does for the community; its habits, periods of activity, and so forth. (Because a description of the complete ecological niche would include an infinite number of factors, the concept is most useful in terms of *differences* among species. For instance, one could compare the niches of four American warblers that all breed in the same habitat, a spruce forest, but forage and nest in different parts of the spruce tree.)

An animal's niche can be described as "what it does for a living." In a sense, this role can be compared to what people do for a living—that is, what their jobs or professions are in the communities in which they live.

The major purpose of this activity is for students to understand the concept of ecological niche, simultaneously learning more about potential careers in their own community.

Procedure
1. Explain to the students that in this activity they will be comparing human professions to the roles of animals in environments (animal "professions").

2. Select a few interesting jobs for discussion. Invite a doctor, dentist, social worker, truck driver or a cook to your class to talk about his or her work. Ask the speaker questions. Work with the students to develop the questions. Have the students take notes and record the answers during or immediately after the presentation, asking additional questions for clarification as necessary. Points to include are as follows:

   - What do they do for the community (the service provided)?
   - How do they provide the service?
   - What resources do they use to provide the service?
   - Where do they live and work?

Grade Level: 5–8

Subject Areas: Social Studies, Science, Environmental Education, Language Arts

Duration: one to four 45-minute sessions

Group Size: any

Setting: indoors

Conceptual Framework Topic Reference: HNIB2

Key Terms: ecological niche, career, community

Appendices: Using Local Resources

- What are the times during which they work?
- What other professions do they depend on for the functioning of their profession (janitor, delivery person, secretary, repair person)?
- What special adaptations (skills, tools, behaviors) do they use or are they required to have?
- What special habits do they exhibit?
- What other professions do they compete with, if any?
- What other professions do they cooperate with, if any?

Ask the students to produce a written summary of the information they acquire concerning each of the jobs they investigate.

3. Have the students brainstorm a variety of animals living in a particular community (forest, stream, desert, tundra). A photograph could serve as a stimulus. List representative members of this natural community on the blackboard. Make sure a variety of animals—including predator, prey, scavengers, and so on—are included.

4. Choose one of the animals listed and, as a group, begin discussing the same questions for it that were asked of the visiting professional. In this way, the students can see how the "profession" concept applies as a metaphor. Identify the animal's profession as its "ecological niche." OPTIONAL: As individual projects or in teams, students should select one animal, research the "niche" it fills and answer the same questions used for human jobs. As a culmination, each team can make a visual or verbal presentation about its animal and its niche.

Extensions

1. Have the students identify niches that are overlapping and that compete or cooperate for resources and services. Connections also may be made between niches to illustrate interdependency webs in the community.

2. Ask the class to investigate a variety of human professions in different communities or cultures for an emphasis on career awareness. Illustrate overlapping professions, competition, cooperation, and interdependency.

3. Have the students develop commercials or ads for "recruiting" individuals into given ecological niches, using special contributions or advantages, as points to highlight.

4. Students can select the animal they would most like to be from among those studied. They may base their selection on the contribution of the ecological niche to the community's health, as well as on other factors. Ask the students to describe the reasons for their choices. They could do this for human professions, too.

Aquatic Extension

See the Project WILD Aquatic activity "Blue-Ribbon Niche."

Evaluation

1. Define ecological niche.

2. Select any animal or person, and describe its ecological niche. Include what they do for the community, how they provide this service, what resources they use, where they live, when they do their work, what other organisms depend on them, what other organisms they depend on, what special adaptations they use or are required to have, what special habits they exhibit, what other organisms they compete with for the same niche, and anything else you think is especially interesting about this niche and how it is filled.

3. Create a poster that shows all the facets of an animal's niche.

What Did Your Lunch Cost Wildlife?

Objectives

Students will (1) trace some foods from their source to the consumer; (2) identify the impact those foods and their processing have on wildlife and the environment in general; and (3) recommend, with explanations, some food habits that could benefit wildlife and the rest of the environment.

Method

Students trace food sources, diagram environmental impacts, and apply the knowledge they gain by making changes in some of their consumer choices.

Materials

Writing and drawing materials

Background

Lifestyle choices made each day have some impact on wildlife and the environment. Many of those impacts are indirect and are, therefore, less obvious. The types of food people eat each day, for example, have many implications for wildlife and the environment.

The places and ways in which foods are grown have impact. Research has indicated that loss of habitat is one of the most critical problems facing wildlife. Habitat may be lost to agricultural use or development as well as to industrial, commercial, and residential uses. Given that people need food, the ways in which food is grown—and the ways that the land is cared for in the process—are very important. Eroded soil is a major nonpoint source pollution in the United States. This lost sediment can be detrimental to aquatic and terrestrial habitats. Farmers take measures to maintain and improve wildlife habitat as they grow and harvest their crops. They also pay close attention to the impact of their growing practices. Both inorganic and organic fertilizers commonly are used in industrial agriculture. These compounds may runoff or leach into water supplies. In lakes, for example, this run-off may increase nutrients that make algae grow.

The food transportation, processing, packaging, and marketing industries also are involved. Questions about the natural resources involved in getting the food from its source of origin to the consumer are critically important. One example is increased exploration for and development of fossil fuels used to transport the food from growing site to consumer, used often to fuel the processing, and frequently used in the packaging, as in the case of fossil-fuel-derived plastics.

Grade Level: 5–8

Subject Areas: Social Studies, Language Arts, Science, Environmental Education

Duration: one to three 45-minute sessions

Group Size: any

Setting: indoors

Conceptual Framework Topic Reference: HNIIA2

Key Terms: organic, inorganic, source, renewable, nonrenewable, impact

Appendices: Taking Action

Ethical considerations can also be raised concerning the impact on individual animals and plants by the methods used to produce food for people, as well as choices of which foods to eat.

Procedure

1. Select a food item. Identify the item's ingredients. In a discussion with students, trace the item's ingredients all the way back to their origins. Include where and how they grew or were formed and how they were harvested, processed, transported, packaged, and made available to the consumer.

2. Ask the students to generate a list of foods they either brought or bought for lunch. Be sure to include any packaging materials the foods came in.

3. Ask each student to pick one food to trace all the way back to its origins, including where and how it grew and how it was harvested, processed, transported, packaged, and made available to the consumer—the student. Ask the students to make simple flow diagrams of the path the food takes. (The students may want to do some research to obtain some additional information.)

4. Next, ask the students to create a picture, diagram, or chart to illustrate how food transportation affects wildlife and the environment.

5. Ask the students to report—using the diagrams as a visual aid as they describe the path taken by their food and its effects on wildlife and the environment along the way.

6. Ask the students to discuss and summarize their findings.

7. Ask the students to think of changes they could make in their own lunch-time eating habits that would be likely to have a beneficial—or at least less harmful—effect on wildlife and the environment. Describe the reasoning for this change, and evaluate its consequences. If, after examination, each change seems to be helpful, suggest that the students try making their changes for a week. At the end of the week, ask the students to report. Were they able to stick with the change? What happened? If they didn't make the change, why not? Did they forget? If they did make the change, did they find themselves making or thinking about any other possible changes? If yes, what were they?

Extensions

1. Map the energy used to grow and transport the food to the consumer.

2. Include the impact on other specified natural resources along the way.

3. Distinguish between renewable and nonrenewable resources.

4. Research genetically modified organisms (gmv) and their impact on agricultural practices such as pesticide, fertilizer, and irrigation use. Debate the "pros" and "cons" of gmv applications.

Aquatic Extension

Conduct this activity again asking the question, "What Did Your Lunch Cost Aquatic Wildlife?" Think of whole populations of species of aquatic animals and aquatic habitats.

Evaluation

1. Trace the possible route that a container of milk might take back to its probable source. What effect does this journey have on wildlife?

2. Identify three food habits that could reduce or increase effects on wildlife and the environment. Explain the reasoning behind your suggestions.

Urban Nature Search

Objectives
Students will (1) generalize that each habitat has characteristic life forms, and (2) suggest ways that the environment affects the life forms that occupy it.

Method
Students go outside to observe an environment and use a questionnaire to assist in gathering data.

Materials
Questionnaires (designed by educators or students), pencils, notebooks or journals, an outdoor setting to conduct this investigation

Background
For most people, wild birds and other animals are valued and appreciated residents of cities and towns.

Unlike the soil, waterways, or other ecological components of the urban environment, wild animals do not create but rather reflect environmental quality. They are an indicator of a diverse and healthy ecological community, and the positive values they impart to the urban scene must be emphasized through public awareness and education of both old and young concerning the potential richness and quality of their environment.

Every environment has its characteristic organisms (including animals) and the urban setting is no exception. Many urban organisms have adjusted as their habitat has changed from undeveloped to urban. Not only have people altered the environment, the human environment has been shaped by the ecologies within which people live.

The major purpose of this activity is for students to recognize that all environments have characteristic life forms and to identify ways that organisms are adapted for their environment.

Procedure
Before the Activity

1. Preview and select the route of the nature search. Note stopping places where students can observe and record information.

2. Design a questionnaire to be distributed to the students for use in the "search." The questions and tasks should encourage increased student observation. For example, many of the following phenomena can be designed into this activity:

Grade Level: 5–8

Subject Areas: Science, Language Arts, Environmental Education

Duration: one 45- to 90-minute session

Group Size: any

Setting: outdoors

Conceptual Framework Topic Reference: HNIB, HNIB1

Key Terms: investigation, observation, environment

Appendices: Outdoors, Field Ethics

- Tally, describe, and sketch different kinds of plants growing on the north and south sides of buildings. (The differences may be due to temperature variations, sun and shade-loving species of plants, and less evaporation on the north side of the buildings.)

- Look for birds. Tally the numbers of different kinds of birds. If they are migratory, sketch the pattern of their flying formation. Watch the birds. If they are feeding, what do they eat? Where do they nest? Would the birds eat the same food if they lived away from people? Where might they nest in a rural area?

- Look for animals establishing a "territory." Try to map the animals' territory. (During the mating season, birds sometimes can be seen choosing mates; males can be seen fighting, strutting, and dancing around the female species; and other birds can be seen nest building.)

- Look for evidence of predator and prey relationships. If any mammal, bird, or insect is seen, attempt to determine what animal is its predator or prey.

- Record evidence of plant disease and insect damage. It is always interesting to see insect galls or bag worms in their natural setting.

- Look for evidence of food chains. For example, if insects are observed, look for partially eaten, damaged, or mutilated leaves. Then look for who eats the insects. Draw a food chain and identify the parts.

- Try to observe a bee cross-pollinating flowers while gathering nectar for the production of honey. Note how pollen sticks to the hair on the bee's back and legs. Observe the specialized organs of the bee, and study them further (from diagrams and photos) back in the classroom.

- Sketch trees and list their contributions to the community. (For example, trees can be observed breaking the velocity or speed of the wind. Reducing wind speed in this way might save energy by reducing the winter heat loss from homes in the surrounding area. Trees also serve as part of the wildlife habitat, can increase the oxygen content of the air, and can have aesthetic value.)

- Who likes lichen? Predict what plants and animals have a direct or indirect relationship with lichen. (Lichen will be found growing on rocks, tree trunks, and even soil. Lichen is really algae and fungi functioning as a partnership in a symbiotic association.)

- Trace water's path in an area—such as on one street, around one tree, or down a hillside. (For example, draw the route of any visible erosion.) Look for evidence of freezing and thawing on sidewalks and buildings.

- Find mulch around trees and shrubs. Record any evidence or observation of life forms. Mulch allows the soil to absorb and retain moisture and to reduce evaporation. Mulch also reduces temperature extremes and contains earthworms as well as microscopic and other life forms.

- Look for evidence of components of habitat. Students can observe first-hand the basic wildlife needs. Match animals with their habitat needs (food, water, shelter, and space in appropriate arrangement). It can be a real challenge for students to determine if all basic needs can be met in the available habitat. Predict what animals should be able to live in the habitats identified.

continued

The Activity

1. On the field trip, each student should take a copy of the questionnaire, a pencil, and a notebook or journal. Remind students not to disturb or destroy any plants or animals they may see.

2. Discuss the diversity of wildlife. Make sure students understand that wildlife includes insects, spiders, and other invertebrates as well as birds, fish, reptiles, mammals, and amphibians. Also establish that students can identify wildlife species without knowing the animal's formal name. For instance, they can differentiate a black bird with a short tail from one with a long tail. As they conduct their urban nature search, students can invent their own names for the plants and animals they see.

3. What characteristic life forms did the students find that were most surprising? Which organisms might the students find in a rural setting? Do they think the behavior of the animals would be the same in both locations? Why or why not? Do they think the organisms' appearance would be different in the country? Why? How do they think the environment affects the species that live in it? Involve the students in a discussion of their observations, their techniques, and their conclusions. Encourage the generalization, warranted by the results of their investigation, that each environment has characteristic life forms.

Extension

Chart the characteristic life forms found on the search according to the environments in which they were found. For each animal listed, identify how its basic needs are met. Describe any animal adaptations that seem well-suited to survival in the urban environment. Note any interdependencies between plants and animals. Discuss ways in which people have altered the natural environment and ways in which natural forces have shaped the human environment.

Aquatic Extensions

1. Make a map to show all the public water areas in your community, if any. Streams, ponds, a lake, or river are all possibilities. If there are no such public areas of water in a natural or near-natural environment within your community, look next for water that people have introduced, but that is still accessible to the public. For example, count and map the location of the public water fountains in the community. Next, list and tally all the different kinds of wildlife that seem to depend on any single water source you identify. Remember—food, water, shelter, and space in a suitable arrangement are the essential components of habitat for any wildlife.

2. Look at urban ponds and lakes in parks, and compare those species living in concrete-bottomed ponds with those living in mud-bottomed ponds. What lives where? Where and how do they obtain their food?

Evaluation

1. List and describe 10 types of plants found in an urban environment.

2. List and describe 10 types of animals found in an urban environment.

3. Select any four animals found in an urban environment, and describe how these animals find food, shelter, and water in order to survive in the community. If these animals were not living in an urban environment, how might the way they meet their needs be different?

Rainfall and the Forest

Objectives
Students will (1) correlate rainfall data with vegetative communities, (2) correlate vegetative communities with animal life, (3) recognize interrelationships among living and nonliving elements of the environment, and (4) suggest ways that environments affect life forms that occupy them.

Method
Students work with state highway and vegetative maps to determine relationships among rainfall, vegetation, and animal habitats.

Materials
State highway map (one for each group of two or three students); one sheet of tracing paper the same size as the map (usually about 19" × 24" or 17" × 22"); four different colored pens or pencils per team; information including elevation and rainfall annually for 25 to 30 communities within the state; vegetation map of the state (one for each group of two or three students); OPTIONAL: range maps of selected wildlife species in the state

Background
NOTE: This activity is useful for understanding distributions of plant and animal communities in many, but not all, states.

Many natural systems affect wildlife survival and population fluctuations. Each year, 1 or 2 more inches of rain may allow a forest to grow instead of grassland, thus creating habitat for forest wildlife. Rain also may encourage or interfere with animal reproduction, depending on species and time and amounts of rainfall.

Rainfall is just one form of precipitation. The types and distributions of annual precipitation can influence which plants will survive in an area. Many plants would benefit more from a series of small rain showers than from a single thundershower that drops 5 inches of rain in less than an hour. Although precipitation has significant impact on an area's vegetative composition, other factors also influence what grows where. Those factors include elevation, latitude, soil condition and type, and the average number of frostfree days.

Food, water, shelter, and space in the appropriate arrangement are all fundamental to wildlife populations; all of these relate to plants in some way. Among other influences, plants are the product of rainfall amounts and temperatures. Rainfall is controlled by such factors as wind direction, elevation, proximity of an area to bodies of water, and other factors. Essentially, specific rainfall amounts create specific types of plant communities (e.g., grasslands, chaparral, or tropical rain forest). Each of these plant communities supports specific types of animals.

Grade Level: 5–8

Subject Areas: Science, Social Studies, Environmental Education

Duration: minimum of one one-hour session; preferably two to three one-hour sessions

Group Size: groups of two or three

Setting: indoors

Conceptual Framework Reference: HNIB1, HNIB2

Key Terms: vegetation, rainfall, rain shadow, elevation, community, habitat

Appendices: Using Local Resources, Ecosystem

---

continued

Ecological Knowledge

Rainfall and the Forest

For example, 25 or more inches of rain in northern Arizona commonly produce a fir forest that is not habitat for antelope or buffalo but is habitat for squirrels, blue grouse, and perhaps elk.

Comparable amounts of rain in other parts of the world usually will produce communities of similar but different plants and animals.

In this activity, students learn that specific habitats are the key to specific wildlife. Specific conditions (e.g., 10 inches of rainfall) will create specific vegetative types, and those specific plants will support certain animal types. Open grasslands, for example, created by approximately 10 inches of rain, tend to be suited to grazing animals like buffalo, antelope, and prairie dogs. Forests, created by more rainfall, may be more suited to Stellar's jays, fox squirrels, and porcupines.

The major purpose of this activity is for students to recognize some of the relationships among climate, vegetation, and wildlife species.

Procedure

1. Discuss the idea that all things, living and nonliving, are connected.

2. Divide the class into teams of two or three. Give each group a highway map of the state, one sheet of tracing paper the same size as the map, and four crayons of different colors. Also, supply each team with information listing 25 to 30 communities around the state, including their elevation and annual rainfall. (Students can develop this information in the form of a data sheet beforehand.)

3. Ask the student groups to outline the state on the tracing paper. Have students separate the list of communities into four rainfall-level groups, such as 0"–5", 5.1"–10", 10.1"–15", 15.1" plus. (0–10 cm, 10.1–20 cm, 20.1 cm–30 cm, 30.1 cm plus). These categories may need to be adjusted depending on the typical rainfall amounts in the state.

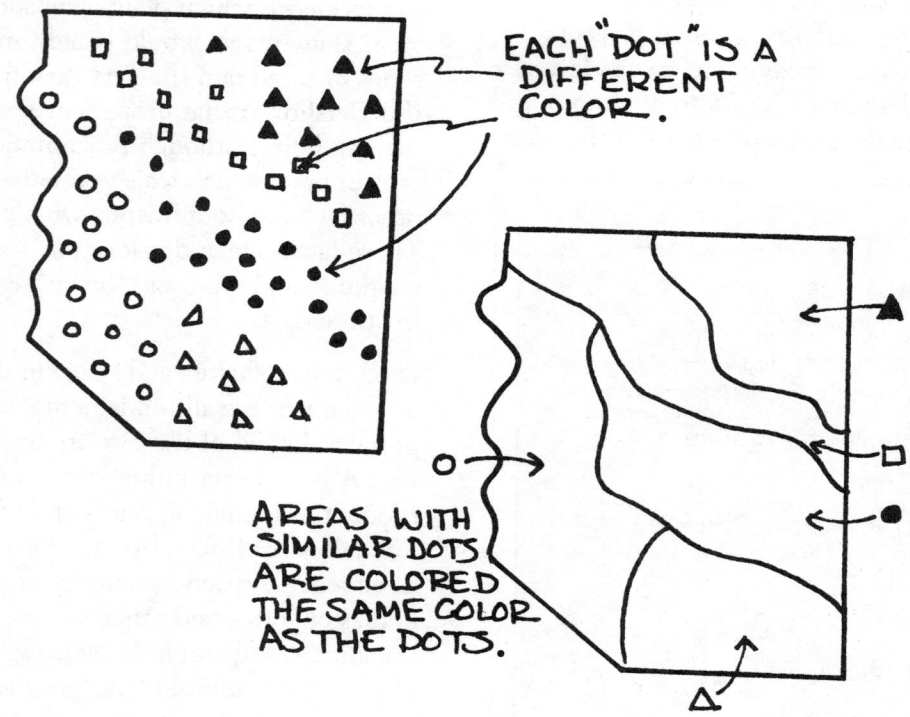

4. Assign a color for each level of rainfall. Ask the students to make a large dot of the appropriate color for each community at its location on the tracing paper over the map. Community names are not necessary on the tracing paper.

5. Consolidate each color into rainfall patterns. Lines between areas should run between dots of different colors, not from dot to dot. Color the maps.

6. Have students fold the highway maps and put them aside. Issue a vegetative map of your state to each group. These maps usually may be obtained through university agricultural extension services or botany departments. Highway and vegetative maps should be the same size, as nearly as possible.

7. Ask the students to find similarities in shapes created on their maps and those on vegetative maps. What rainfall level fits what vegetative type? The correlations will not be exact, but they should be graphic. Most of the time, more than one vegetative type will be covered by one rainfall amount. How much rainfall is needed for grassland, chaparral, or pine forest, for example? Have the students determine and list rainfall amounts for each vegetative community. Keep in mind that the student map has only 25 to 30 points of reference, but thousands of data points were used to develop the vegetative map. As a result, the two maps will not be identical, but they should be visibly similar.

8. Discuss local rainfall with the students: Where does your rain come from? What influences rainfall patterns in your state? Does elevation influence rainfall? Why? What is a rain shadow? Can they see where the typography influences rainfall in the state? Can they find two cities or towns that are at almost the same elevation, yet receive very different amounts of rain? Why is this? Would these rainfall and vegetative patterns be similar in other parts of the world? Would similar influences function all over the world?

9. Obtain information about the habitat needs of various animals in the state. If possible, obtain range maps of those species. Include animals such as crows, English sparrows, and starlings that thrive in most locations, as well as animals that are restricted to particular habitat types, such as spotted owls, prairie rattlesnakes, and flying squirrels. Ask students to identify suitable habitat for the selected species on the vegetation map. Have the students create a plastic overlay that shows those habitat areas. Or create a vegetation and habitat map without the use of an overlay by drawing symbols directly onto the vegetation map to represent the various animals.

10. If available, correlate official range maps with the student maps. Ask if anyone has discovered locations where an animal's required habitat is present but the animal itself is not. Ask for explanations for why this situation might exist. Possible reasons include disruptive human activity in the area. Competition from other species or circumstances in which a critical component of habitat, such as water sources or a specific kind of plant, is missing from the area even though the vegetative map does not convey this information.

Extension

Obtain habitat maps of several mammals in the state. Translate these data to another transparent overlay. Identify correlations between the animals on the overlay. Identify correlations between these data and the vegetative map. (Start with animals that are herbivores or omnivores. Save carnivores for last.) Habitats for reptiles and birds also will give good correlations. Have students make graphic representations, or write reports, about the interrelationships among rainfall, plant communities, and various species of animals.

continued

Aquatic Extension

1. See the Project WILD Aquatic activities "Watershed" and "Where Does Water Go?"

2. Have students add major bodies of water, if any, to the map. Also, add some way to identify watersheds. Ask the class to identify and discuss possible influences of these areas of water and watersheds on the vegetation and wildlife in the associated areas.

3. Looking at the interrelationships among all the kinds of data and gathered information, generate a set of hypotheses about the factors that seem to most directly affect the availability of suitable habitat for wildlife in the state. Direct the students to support their hypotheses by writing one or more paragraphs based on their findings from this study.

Evaluation

1. Write an essay describing the importance of rainfall and vegetative types to wildlife habitat.

2. Choose three wildlife species found in the state. Drop a handful of change, buttons, or other small objects onto your state map. Evaluate the habitat characteristics of each of the locations where each of the objects comes to rest. Determine how well each chosen species would survive based on the type of habitat found at those various spots.

Source: Adapted with permission from *Project Learning Tree. Pre-K–8 Environmental Education Activity Guide* (American Forest Foundation, Washington, DC, 1977).

Environmental Barometer

Objectives
Students will (1) observe and count wildlife in an area, (2) discuss why wildlife is or is not present, and (3) consider ways in which the presence of wildlife can be seen as an indicator of environmental quality.

Method
Students go outside to observe and count or to estimate wildlife in an area; they repeat the same procedures in another setting to compare findings and, as an option, make a school "environmental barometer."

Materials
Writing materials; poster board or construction paper; colored pens, pencils, or crayons

Background
Wildlife is an important indicator of the overall health of the environment. If there are few wild animals—or little evidence of wildlife—present in an area, it is likely there is little available food, water, or shelter in the area, or there may not be enough space.

Some species of animals are more adapted to difficult conditions than others. Some, in contrast, are so specialized that it is quite difficult for them to find the food, water, shelter, and other things they need.

Even if these necessary components of habitat are available, they may not be arranged to meet the needs of wildlife. The kinds of wildlife present are also important indicators—raptors, for example, are high on the food chain. Their presence in an area is an indicator that some variety of other animals and plants is also there.

The major purpose of this activity is for students to consider the importance of wildlife as an indicator of environmental quality.

Procedures
NOTE: Several possibilities may arise when doing this activity. The school or organization may be in an area where there are few, if any, wild animals present—with little access to any other area with much wildlife. If there is no significant difference between the observations in the two settings, talk with the students about what this means. It is also possible that the school is in a wildlife-rich setting—virtually as rich as any other setting in the area. Again, it is all right if there is no significant difference in the number and variety of wildlife observed in each area. Educators also may choose to make the observations and create the data charts for only one setting, simply analyzing and discussing the quality of the one environment—without using another for comparison.

Grade Level: Pre–K, K–4

Subject Areas: Science, Environmental Education

Duration: one or two 20-minute sessions, preparation time for students to bring family pictures to class

Group Size: small groups of three or four students each

Setting: outdoors

Conceptual Framework Topic Reference: IDIB

Key Terms: aquatic animals, grow, change, adult, young

Appendices: Outdoors, Field Ethics

---

continued

1. Before going outside, make sure students understand that the term "wildlife" includes insects, spiders, and other invertebrates, as well as birds, fish, reptiles, mammals, and amphibians.

2. Go outside and complete a wildlife count. Distribute writing materials to the students, and then have the students work alone. Ask each student to find a spot, sit quietly for 10 minutes, and observe. (Quiet is very important to increase the likelihood of seeing wildlife.) The students should record, either as a class or individually, the species and numbers of any wildlife they see. They can include evidence of wildlife in addition to actual sightings. Ask the students to total the number of each species of wildlife they observe and then make a grand total. If they find evidence rather than sighting wildlife, they should estimate the numbers. Put all the students' information on one master chart.

NOTE: Try working with an older student leader for each group of three or four younger students.

3. If possible, take the students to a setting where wildlife is more abundant. Repeat the process—with each student observing quietly for 10 minutes and recording observations.

4. Make a master chart of the information from this second environment.

5. Compare the information from the two charts. Was there any difference in the two settings? Why or why not? Which environment seemed to have the most varied kinds of wildlife? Where were there the most of any one kind of wildlife, such as the most birds? What kinds of food, water, shelter, and space were in each setting to support the survival needs of wildlife? If there were few animals or many in either setting, what might this lack tell us about the quality of the environment? What is environmental quality? Can wildlife be an indicator of environmental quality? Talk about whether it is realistic for every environment to be a good habitat for varieties of wildlife. Discuss the possibility and appropriateness of making efforts to improve environments as habitats for wildlife as homes for people.

Extension

Make a wildlife barometer to indicate the quality of the school or organization environment as a habitat for wildlife. Share your barometer with others. OPTIONAL: Show seasonal changes in the barometer's readings.

Aquatic Extensions

1. Make observations concerning the availability, apparent quality, and suitability for wildlife needs of the water you find in each of the habitats you investigate. Is more wildlife apparent in those areas where there is more water? If yes, what seem to be the contributing factors? If no, what seem to be the contributing factors?

2. Make a wildlife barometer comparing the quality of two different aquatic habitats as places in which diverse wildlife can successfully live. Explain the reasons for the differences in the two areas.

Evaluation

1. Each year thousands of birdwatchers participate in a National Audubon Society's bird count all over the United States. The information is kept and compared from year to year to see if changes occur in the total number of birds or in how many different kinds of birds are sighted. If a steady and long decrease in the bird populations occurred over a period of 5 years, should there be concern—and not just for birdwatchers? Explain your response.

2. Develop a list of things that tend to decrease and increase the number and species of wildlife in cities and towns.

3. Identify and describe three things that people could do to increase the numbers and kinds of wildlife living in an area that has little evidence of wildlife.

Habitrekking

Objectives

Students will (1) summarize evidence about the nature of habitats, and (2) generalize from evidence that people and wildlife have similar basic needs, share environments, and are subject to the same or similar environmental issues.

Method

Students go outside to conduct an investigation requiring observation, interpretation, and data-gathering skill; then they prepare and present their findings.

Materials

Copies of Habitrekking Evidence Lists on page 80, mixed media available for students to create visual and verbal reports

Grade Level: 3–4

Subject Areas: Science, Language Arts, Expressive Arts, Environmental Education

Duration: two or three 45-minute sessions

Group Size: three groups, with a minimum of two students each

Setting: outdoors and indoors

Conceptual Framework Topic Reference: IDIA1, IDIA2a

Key Terms: evidence, wildlife, habitat, environmental quality, pollution

Appendices: Outdoors, Field Ethics

Background

NOTE: It is recommended that educators use the Project WILD activities "Ants on a Twig," "Habitat Lap Sit," and "Habitat Rummy" prior to this activity so that the students are introduced to the various components of a habitat.

All animals—including people, pets, and wildlife—share similar basic needs. All animals need a place to live. The term for an area where an animal lives is "habitat." Habitat includes food, water, shelter, and space in a suitable arrangement. People, domesticated animals, and wildlife all need those elements.

Wildlife is all around, even though it may not be seen, heard, or sensed. Because people and wildlife share similar basic needs, it is likely that if people are without elements of their basic needs, wildlife will be as well. Wildlife habitat often is destroyed without people being aware of what has happened. The health and well-being of people, domesticated animals, and wildlife depend on a sustainable environment.

The major purpose of this activity is for students to recognize that people and wildlife share the same environment, have similar basic needs, and are subject to the same or similar environmental issues. Students are encouraged to generalize from their investigation into microhabitats so they come to these conclusions.

continued

Procedure

1. Divide the class into three groups. Have the students in each group pair off.

2. Each pair should be equipped with observation tools. Students could have one or more of these optional items: hand lens, trowel, camera and film, sketch pad, tape recorder, tape, string, meter stick, empty corked test tubes, microscope slides, paper bags, small containers with lids, video or still camera equipment, and so on. Given advance notice, students might bring in a variety of such "observation tools" from home.

3. Provide Habitrekking Evidence Lists for the pairs in each group.

4. Before starting, ask a student from each group to read his or her Habitrekking Evidence List to make sure each member understands what students are looking for. Make sure the students have a clear definition of wildlife and habitat. Establish the study sites where students will be looking for evidence. School grounds, urban city centers, forested parks, and vacant lots can be used as study sites. Establish a length of time for the investigations. Thirty minutes is recommended if the students stay near the school or organization where this activity began. Tell the students they should exercise their creativity because there are no real right or wrong answers. They may observe and infer. Both are sources of evidence.

**GROUP #1
HABITREKKING EVIDENCE LIST #1**

Caution: You may bring back evidence, but be careful not to harm the wildlife or environment.

Find Evidence That

1. Humans, domesticated animals, and wildlife all need food, water, shelter, and space arranged so they can survive.
2. All living things are affected by their environment.
3. Animals—including people—depend on plants—either directly or indirectly.

**GROUP #2
HABITREKKING EVIDENCE LIST #2**

Caution: You may bring back evidence, but be careful not to harm the wildlife or environment.

Find Evidence That

1. Humans and wildlife share environments.
2. Wildlife is everywhere.
3. Wildlife can be in many forms and colors, and can have special features that help it live in its environment.

**GROUP #3
HABITREKKING EVIDENCE LIST #3**

Caution: You may bring back evidence, but be careful not to harm the wildlife or environment.

Find Evidence That

1. Humans and wildlife are subject to the same or similar environmental problems.
2. The health and well-being of both people and wildlife depend on a good environment.
3. Environmental pollution affects people, domesticated animals, and wildlife.

5. Send the students "habitrekking."

6. When they return, ask each pair to present its evidence, including both pictures and words. The pairs within each group can compare their findings as they prepare for their group's report. Spend at least 45 minutes presenting and discussing reports.

7. In the discussion, ask the students to summarize what they learned. Emphasize the generalizations that people and wildlife have similar basic needs, share environments, and are subject to the same or similar environmental problems.

RECOMMENDATION: Check the observations and generalizations against resource books or other sources to verify the results and to correct false impressions.

Aquatic Extension

Adjust the "habitrekking" instructions to apply specifically to aquatic wildlife and aquatic habitats. For example, find evidence that humans and aquatic wildlife are subject to the same or similar environmental issues.

Evaluation

Using one of the Habitrekking Evidence Lists, conduct a similar investigation in a local environment. Write a brief summary of the findings.

Microtrek Treasure Hunt

Objectives

Students will (1) discover that humans and wildlife share environments; (2) recognize that humans do not have exclusive use of environments; and (3) discover that wildlife can be all around, even if it is not actually seen or heard.

Method

Students go outside on a "treasure hunt" for wildlife.

Materials

Hand lens, digging tool, pencil, photocopied instruction sheet for each group of two to five students

Background

Many people think of wildlife as the large animals of Africa, such as the lion and elephant, or the large animals of the North American forests, such as the grizzly bear and elk. But wildlife includes all animals that have not been domesticated by people.

What may be surprising is that wildlife includes the smallest animal organisms—even those that can be seen only through a microscope. Spiders, insects, reptiles, amphibians and most species of fish, birds, and mammals may be considered wildlife. Even when animals are silent or not visible, they exist somewhere around us. Tens of thousands of organisms live in and on human skin, hair, and bodies. In fact, the organisms that inhabit human bodies play a part in human survival. Some form of animal life is always near.

By investigating microenvironments or microhabitats, the students will discover that wildlife exists in every country on the planet.

This activity can be done almost anywhere with supervision—from city centers to parks to outdoor education sites. It is especially effective where students would not expect to find much wildlife.

Grade Level: 5–8

Subject Areas: Science, Language Arts, Environmental Education

Duration: 30 minutes to 2 hours

Group Size: small groups working simultaneously; any number

Setting: outdoors

Conceptual Framework Reference: IDIA2a

Key Terms: evidence, environments, wildlife

Appendices: Field Ethics, Observations and Inferences, Ecosystem

---

Procedure

1. Develop a list of items for the students to search for. They will be given a list of things to find, and they will go outside and find different kinds of evidence that wildlife exists. Review the concept that wildlife is diverse and includes insects, spiders, reptiles, amphibians and most species of fish, birds, and mammals.

2. Divide the group into teams of two to five. Provide each team with a small hand lens, small digging tool, pencil, and instruction sheet. The instruction sheet could look like the following:

> **WILDLIFE TREASURE HUNT**
>
> This is a treasure hunt to look for evidence of wildlife.
>
> **CAUTION: Be careful not to harm any animals or their habitats.**
>
> Find evidence that
> 1. Humans and wildlife share the same environment.
> 2. Humans and wildlife must adjust to their environment, move to a more suitable environment, or perish.
> 3. Wildlife is all around, even if it's not seen or heard.
> 4. Wildlife can be many different sizes.
> 5. People and wildlife experience some of the same problems.
> 6. Both people and wildlife need places to live.

3. Establish a length of time for the students to be outside. Educators can use 15-minute blocks of time for every one or two things the students are looking for. For example, the six-item treasure hunt used in the sample given in this activity could take anywhere from 15 to 45 minutes for the students to find their evidence. Every group should return with some evidence. Evidence can be things such as small drawings on a piece of paper or word descriptions of what they saw on the treasure hunt. It also can be small samples they bring back to class, if they can bring samples without doing damage to the habitat.

4. Before sending the students outside, make sure the instructions are clear. Discuss with the students what wildlife is, contrasted with other animals such as pets. Go through the list of items they are trying to find evidence of, so you make sure they have an understanding of what they will be looking for. With the time limits established, open the door, and begin trekking.

5. At the end of the designated time period, reconvene the groups and ask them to report their findings.

6. What are some of the most interesting things the students felt they learned? Encourage the students to come to the conclusion that people and wildlife share the same environment.

Extensions

1. Creatively write about the experiences of the treasure hunt.

2. Classify the types of wildlife found on the treasure hunt.

3. Tally the species of wildlife and the numbers of each species of wildlife found on the treasure hunt.

4. Use a microscope to examine some of the samples found on the treasure hunt, such as the underside of leaves with insect eggs, soil with a lot of plant matter, water, larvae, the inside of insect galls, bark, and a hollow plant stem.

Aquatic Extension

Adjust the "Wildlife Treasure Hunt" instructions to apply specifically to aquatic wildlife and aquatic habitats. For example, find evidence that humans and aquatic wildlife share the same environment, and so on.

Evaluation

1. Identify three things seen, heard, or smelled that proved that wildlife is all around.

2. Define "evidence." Give examples of how evidence can be used to interpret environments.

3. Create a chart showing the range of sizes of or the evidence of wildlife found on the treasure hunt.

continued

WILDLIFE TREASURE HUNT

This is a treasure hunt to look for evidence of wildlife.

CAUTION: Be careful not to harm any animals or their homes.

Find evidence that

1. Humans and wildlife share the same environment.
2. Humans and wildlife must adjust to their environment, move to a more suitable environment, or perish.
3. Wildlife is all around even if it's not seen or heard.
4. Wildlife can be many different sizes.
5. People and wildlife experience some of the same problems.
6. Both people and wildlife need places to live.

WILDLIFE TREASURE HUNT

This is a treasure hunt to look for evidence of wildlife.

CAUTION: Be careful not to harm any animals or their homes.

Find evidence that

1. Humans and wildlife share the same environment.
2. Humans and wildlife must adjust to their environment, move to a more suitable environment, or perish.
3. Wildlife is all around even if it's not seen or heard.
4. Wildlife can be many different sizes.
5. People and wildlife experience some of the same problems.
6. Both people and wildlife need places to live.

WILDLIFE TREASURE HUNT

This is a treasure hunt to look for evidence of wildlife.

CAUTION: Be careful not to harm any animals or their homes.

Find evidence that

1. Humans and wildlife share the same environment.
2. Humans and wildlife must adjust to their environment, move to a more suitable environment, or perish.
3. Wildlife is all around even if it's not seen or heard.
4. Wildlife can be many different sizes.
5. People and wildlife experience some of the same problems.
6. Both people and wildlife need places to live.

WILDLIFE TREASURE HUNT

This is a treasure hunt to look for evidence of wildlife.

CAUTION: Be careful not to harm any animals or their homes.

Find evidence that

1. Humans and wildlife share the same environment.
2. Humans and wildlife must adjust to their environment, move to a more suitable environment, or perish.
3. Wildlife is all around even if it's not seen or heard.
4. Wildlife can be many different sizes.
5. People and wildlife experience some of the same problems.
6. Both people and wildlife need places to live.

Stormy Weather

Objective
Students will generalize that humans and wildlife share environments and experience some of the same natural phenomena.

Method
Students will go on a simulated field trip to experience a storm.

Materials
None

Background
The major purpose of this activity is to have students recognize that people and wildlife coexist and sometimes experience the same natural phenomena. During a storm, for example, most people, pets, and wildlife need to seek shelter. This activity makes use of an instructional technique called a simulated field trip. Brain researchers and learning theorists tell us that the technique provides access to ways of processing information that facilitate long-term memory and comprehension of concepts. Have the students close their eyes as you read or describe in your own words a series of pictures for your students to visualize in their minds. Leave time between the phrasing of the words for the students to visualize the images that are being suggested.

Procedure

1. Provide the students with the following instructions:

   "Before we begin, I want you to decide who you will be during this activity. You may either be yourself or an animal. If you are an animal, you may be either a wild animal, a pet, or a farm animal. You don't have to do anything special if you choose to be an animal. It is just that you will be picturing things in your mind from the point of view of the animal you pick. Any questions? Okay, let's see by a show of hands how many people and how many animals we will have for this activity. How many of you are going to be farm animals? Pets? Wild animals? Yourselves?"

   NOTE: Be sure that there is some variety—some students should visualize things from their own perspective, some from the perspective of a domesticated animal, and some from the perspective of a wild animal.

Grade Level: 5–8

Subject Areas: Language Arts, Science

Duration: 20 to 40 minutes

Group Size: any

Setting: indoors or outdoors

Conceptual Framework Topic Reference: IDIA2a, IDIIA

Key Term: environment

Appendices: Simulated Field Trips, Early Childhood

---

continued

OPTIONAL: "Grand Canyon Suite" (Ferde Grofe, 1931) might be played to visualize the idea of the storm. Other music with a "storm" or natural environmental theme also might be played.

"Now, we are ready to begin. Get yourselves in a comfortable place. Don't worry about who is sitting next to you. All of you will have your eyes closed. Just be comfortable, and do your best to picture the things I will describe. Okay, close your eyes and picture this…. It is a late summer's night. There is a coolness in the air…. You hear the sounds of summer…. Somehow, you can feel some changes coming in the weather…. In the distance, the dark sky is broken by bright flashes of lightning…. The light is far away…. After a long wait, a rolling rumble is heard…. The lightning gets closer…. The rumbles are louder…. Suddenly, the lightning flashes and lights up the whole sky…. You need to find shelter, to find a safe place. The brilliant flashes of lightning pop and crackle all around you. The noise of thunder is crashing so that the earth seems to shake…. There are no longer times of quiet between the rumbles of thunder and flashes of lightning…. It becomes still…. You notice scents in the air, things you can smell and feel…. You begin to hear a new sound…. You are not sure what it is….You again have to find shelter, if you had come out thinking the storm was gone. You need to find a place to stay dry…. Suddenly, the rain is pouring down with a loud, rich sound. It rains…and rains…and rains…. And then stillness…. The storm has passed."

Here is an alternative or additional version.

"It is a late winter's night. There is a stillness in the air…. Bright stars twinkle in the cold, crisp, winter sky…. Somehow, you can feel some changes coming in the weather. A gentle breeze begins to stir the leafless trees. A quiet snow begins to fall…. The wind floats the snowflakes through the air. Around and around and down…. The snow touches you…. The wind grows stronger. You can hear the rustle of the branches. You feel the snow pelt you as it swirls faster through the sky. The snow falls heavier…. The wind blows colder…. Suddenly, a gust of wind kicks up and blows a huge, dead tree down to the ground. It crashes down beside you with a loud BOOM! and shakes the earth beneath your feet. The wind whips faster. You need to find shelter, a safe place…. Now the snow makes slapping sounds as the wind hurls it against the swaying trees. Branches creak and crackle all around you. Twigs and branches snap off. They strike the ground below and are covered by the deepening snow…. There is whiteness all around you as the blizzard fills the sky…. It snows… and it snows…and it snows…. And then there is stillness…. The storm has passed."

2. Wait a few seconds, and then tell the students to open their eyes. Ask what they saw and felt during the visualization. There is no reason for them to feel pressured to share. Most often, they are eager to describe what they experienced. Let the students volunteer, being sure to include if they were a wild or domesticated animal, or themselves. Ask what shelter they found, where it was, and what happened to them throughout the storm.

3. After the students have shared their descriptions, discuss the idea that people, pets, and wildlife share a common environment. Whether people live in the cities, in the country, in the desert, or on a mountaintop, people are not the only forms of life in those environments. Animals live all around—from the ant on the sidewalk to the spider in the garden. Events like summer storms, a strong wind, and a light or heavy snowfall send every animal seeking some kind of protection.

Extensions

1. Ask the students to draw pictures of what they experienced during the visualization.

2. Have the students dramatize the actions the animals took during the storm.

Aquatic Extension

Storms affect aquatic wildlife too. What happens to the fish in a stream during heavy rains? (Many tend to seek shelter near rocks or among underwater plants. Sometimes the storm washes large amounts of soil and rocks into the stream, making it difficult for the fish to breathe.) What about the fish and mammals in ocean waters during hurricanes? Sometimes scientists know even less about how storms affect aquatic animals because they cannot be seen easily underwater. Imagine yourself as an underwater animal in a storm, and describe what happens to you and your behavior.

Evaluation

Write a story that compares the ways a student and a wild animal might experience a drought, snowstorm, flood, tornado, fire, or earthquake.

Ants on a Twig

Objectives
Students will (1) identify similarities and differences in basic needs of ants and humans, and (2) generalize that humans and wildlife have similar basic needs.

Method
Students observe and demonstrate ant behavior.

Materials
Note pads, pens or pencils, food tokens, flat board

Background
Ants are members of a family of insects known for their highly organized social life. At least 8,800 known species exist, most of which live in the tropics. Ants are important to the environment. They contribute to population control of their prey, recycle plant material, aid seed dispersal, and turn the soil.

All ants are social, living in groups that range in size from a few individuals to colonies with half a million or more members. Ant colonies have two classes of individuals: reproductive and nonreproductive. The queen and the male ants are reproductive. They have wings and can fly, although queens lose their wings when they begin a colony. As in other hymenopterans, males arise from unfertilized eggs; fertilized eggs develop into females, most of which are workers. The largest workers are usually soldiers, and they may be equipped with oversized, muscular heads and sword-like jaws. Medium-sized workers forage for food, and the smallest workers are nurse ants that tend the young.

Ants are closely related to wasps and have a similar body structure. The ant's antennae are typically jointed in the middle. Some species of ants possess a sting that the workers use for defense; many species secrete formic acid, a potent repellent. The jaws of worker ants are used for tasks such as creating defense, building nests, and caring for larvae.

Ants consume a variety of foods, yet not all ants eat all foods. Ants can be herbivores, carnivores, or omnivores. Some ant species collect leaves that they use in a way similar to farming. They take the leaves to a nest where a fungus grows on them. The ants harvest the fungus and eat it. Carpenter ants dig elaborate tunnels in wood for shelter but they do not eat the wood pulp. Most

---

Grade Level: 5–8

Subject Areas: Science, Expressive Arts, Environmental Education

Duration: two 30-minute sessions or one 50- to 60-minute session

Group Size: teams of three to six; approximately 30 students total

Setting: outdoors

Conceptual Framework Topic Reference: IDIA1, IDIA2

Key Terms: basic or survival needs, observation, evidence

Appendices: Animals in Schools, Field Ethics, Simulations, Observation and Inferences, Early Childhood

of a carpenter ant's diet consists of aphid secretions. Ants will drink free-standing water. The moisture content in their food can also satisfy some of their water needs (ants get most of their water from their food).

Some ant species are ground dwellers. Ants can be found in neighborhoods and urban environments. Ant nests can go several feet into the ground and can spread out over several thousand square feet. Ants, like all animals, need water food, shelter, and space in which to live, all suitably arranged to meet their needs.

Procedure

1. Before going outside, have the students design a simple data chart or table to collect and summarize their observations. At least one student in each group could serve as a recorder, noting the students' observations. Included in their observations could be

   - evidence of how ants take care of their basic needs;
   - evidence of what their basic needs are; and
   - evidence of ant behavior, including how ants move in a line (this is important for a later phase of the activity).

   CAUTION: Remind the students to make their observations without harming the ants or their habitat.

2. Take the students outside and locate some ants—or even inside, if you can find some in the building. Check sidewalks, near the trash cans, and around windows. Look on trees, in flower beds, and in vacant lots. Divide the students into groups of three to six, and ask the students to observe the ants' behavior.

3. Observe the ants for approximately 20 minutes. Afterwards, bring the groups of students to a central location and ask them to report their findings. Close the discussion with a sharing of descriptions of ant behavior.

4. Place a flat board on the ground to represent a log. Next, have the students stand in lines facing each other. Instruct the student "ant lines" to start from each end of the "log" and walk to the other end. The student ant lines must pass each other without falling off the log. When they reach the far end of the log, they pick up a food token and carry it back across the log to their "home end." The students should simulate ant behavior using their earlier observations. Their arms and hands can serve as antennae, for example, touching as they pass each other.

   NOTE: Physical dramatization of concepts—in this case, ant behavior—is an excellent way to facilitate retention of concept understanding.

5. Ask the students to sit on the log. After they have investigated the ways that ants meet their basic needs for food, water, shelter, and space in a suitable arrangement, ask the students to describe similarities and differences between basic needs of ants, and humans. Assist the students in generalizing that humans, ants, and other animals—both wild and domesticated—have similar basic needs. Summarize the discussion by noting that, although humans and ants are obviously different, both species share the same basic needs, as do all animal species.

Extensions

1. Research additional printed and Internet resources for information on ants. Do the student observations match the printed references? Verify accuracy of observations, and check any discrepancies.

2. Commercial ant farms are available on the Internet and through nature or science supply companies. Establish an ant farm in the classroom for additional observation.

continued

3. Various humane experiments, stressing scientific observation, can be undertaken by the students. For example,

- Map the space used by an ant colony from the ants' shelter, through their travels, and back to their shelter again.
- Observe how ants find and use water. Put water out in various forms for a colony of ants (e.g., in a dish or in chunks of bread soaked in water). Observe and record what happens.
- Find ants moving in a line. Drop a small piece of food near the line. Record whether the ants will move off the line to obtain food. Repeat this process several times, varying the distance from the ant line to the dropped food.

Aquatic Extensions

1. Humans and aquatic wildlife also have similar basic needs. Pick an aquatic insect, spider, bird, reptile, fish, amphibian, and mammal. Make a poster or a chart with the common name for each; its typical habitat; and the food, kind of water, shelter, and space each needs to survive.

2. Many aquatic insects have fascinating means of locomotion. Find one, observe it, and demonstrate its movement to another student.

Evaluation

1. Describe three ant behaviors observed during this activity.

2. For one of these behaviors, describe why the ants behaved that way. How does the behavior help the ant to survive?

3. What five basic needs do humans and ants share?

Good Buddies

Objectives

Students will (1) define symbiosis, commensalism, mutualism, and parasitism; (2) identify animals that live in each type of symbiotic relationship; and (3) describe how symbiotic interactions can be cooperative or competitive.

Method

Students research pairs of animals, play a card game, and classify the pairs of animals according to three major forms of symbiotic relationships.

Materials

Copies of master cards on pages 94 and 95 (will need several decks), chalkboard, research materials

Background

Elements of any ecological system live in an intricate web of interdependence. When two species of organisms live in close association with each other, their relationship is called "symbiotic." In a symbiotic relationship, at least one of the organisms directly benefits from its close association with the other organism. There are three major forms of symbiotic relationships:

Commensalism: a relationship in which one species derives food or shelter from another species without seriously harming that organism or providing any benefits in return

Mutualism: a reciprocal relationship in which the two different species benefit and are dependent upon the relationship

Parasitism: a relationship between two species in which one species (the parasite) nourishes itself to the detriment of the other species (the host)

The major purpose of this activity is for students to become familiar with the concept of symbiosis as one example of interdependence in ecological systems.

Procedure

1. Reproduce several decks of the cards on pages 94 and 95. Each deck should contain 31 cards: 15 card pairs showing symbiotic relationships and 1 blank "good buddy" card. Use the information from the first column of the information chart found at the end of the activity to create a list of symbiotic partners. Post the list on the board, a flip chart, or an overhead projector.

2. Distribute one card to each student (do not include the blank "good buddy" card), and have each student determine his or her "buddy" according to the posted list.

Grade Level: 5–8

Subject Areas: Science, Environmental Education

Duration: two 30-minute sessions, one 45-minute session if background is properly provided, thus eliminating student research

Group Size: small groups of five or six students

Setting: indoors

Conceptual Framework Topic Reference: IDIIC1, IDIIC1c, IDIIC2

Key Terms: symbiosis, commensalism, mutualism, parasitism

Appendices: Ecosystem, Early Childhood

---

continued

3. Have the students research the buddy pairs to find out why they are buddies, and then answer the following questions: Why do they live together? What advantages and disadvantages do they provide one another? What would happen if one of the buddies were not there?

4. Have the buddy pairs give short reports describing their relationships.

5. Divide the class into groups of five to six students, and give each group a deck of cards. Follow these instructions to play Good Buddies:

   Deal out all cards. Play starts to the left of the dealer and rotates clockwise. Each player draws one card from the player to the left. After the player has drawn a card, that player may lay down all cards in his or her hand that form symbiotic pairs. When a player does not have any cards left, the game is over. The player with the largest number of pairs at the end of the game is the winner. One player is left holding the "good buddy" card at the end of the game.

6. To end the activity, discuss the definitions given in the background information for commensalism, mutualism, and parasitism. Go through the list of symbiotic pairs and, as a group, decide to which classification each pair belongs. Ask the group to determine which interactions are cooperative and which are competitive. "Good buddy" pair members may be called on to help decide the classification. Stress that symbiotic relationships are just one example of the interdependence of all elements of ecological systems.

Evaluation

1. Define symbiosis, commensalism, mutualism, and parasitism.

2. What are two examples of pairs of organisms that have these symbiotic relationships: commensalism, mutualism, parasitism?

3. Explain how cooperation and competition both exist in nature.

Animals	Relationship	Comments
Barnacle/Whale	Commensalism	Barnacles create home sites by attaching themselves to whales. This relationship neither harms nor benefits the whales.
Remora/Shark	Commensalism	Remoras attach themselves to a shark's body. They then travel with the shark and feed on the leftover food scraps from the shark's meals. This relationship neither harms nor benefits the shark.
Bee/Maribou stork	Commensalism	The stork uses its saw-like bill to cut up the dead animals it eats. As a result, the dead animal carcass is accessible to some bees for food and egg laying. This relationship neither harms nor benefits the stork.
Silverfish/Army ants	Commensalism	Silverfish live and hunt with army ants, and share the prey. They neither help nor harm the ants.
Hermit crab/Snail shell	Commensalism	Hermit crabs live in shells made and then abandoned by snails. This relationship neither harms nor benefits the snails.
Cowbird/Bison	Commensalism	As bison walk through grass, insects become active and are seen and eaten by cowbirds. This relationship neither harms nor benefits the bison.
Yucca plant/Yucca moth	Mutualism	Yucca flowers are pollinated by yucca moths. The moths lay their eggs in the flowers where the larvae hatch and eat some of the developing seeds. Both species benefit.
Honey guide bird/Badger	Mutualism	Honey guide birds alert and direct badgers to bee hives. The badgers then expose the hives and feed on the honey first. Next the honey guide birds eat. Both species benefit.
Ostrich/Gazelle	Mutualism	Ostriches and gazelles feed next to each other. They both watch for predators and alert each other to danger. Because the visual abilities of the two species are different, they each can identify threats that the other animal would not see as readily. Both species benefit.
Oxpecker/Rhinoceros	Mutualism	Oxpeckers feed on the ticks found on a rhinoceros. Both species benefit.
Wrasse fish/Black sea bass	Mutualism	Wrasse fish feed on the parasites found on the black sea bass's body. Both species benefit.
Mistletoe/Spruce tree	Parasitism	Mistletoe extracts water and nutrients from the spruce tree to the tree's detriment.
Cuckoo/Warbler	Parasitism	A cuckoo may lay its eggs in a warbler's nest. The cuckoo's young will displace the warbler's young, and the warbler will raise the cuckoo's young.
Mouse/Flea	Parasitism	A flea feeds on a mouse's blood to the mouse's detriment.
Deer/Tick	Parasitism	Ticks feed on deer blood to the deer's detriment.

continued

Ecological Knowledge

Good Buddies

Master Cards

GAZELLE			OSTRICH
CUCKOO			WARBLER
YUCCA			YUCCA MOTH
BARNACLE			WHALE
MISTLETOE			SPRUCE
OXPECKER			RHINO
REMORA			SHARK
			GOODBUDDY CARD

94 Project WILD K–12 Curriculum and Activity Guide

Ecological Knowledge

Good Buddies

Master Cards

ARMY ANTS	SILVERFISH
BASS	WRASSE FISH
COWBIRD	BISON
FLEA	MOUSE
DEER	TICK
HERMIT CRAB	SHELL
MARIBOU STORK	BEE
HONEY GUIDE BIRD	BADGER

© Council for Environmental Education 2001

95

What's for Dinner?

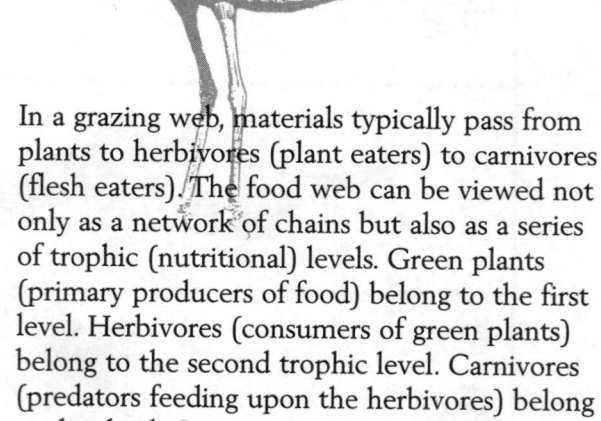

Objective
Students will generalize that all animals, including people, depend on plants as a food source, either directly or indirectly.

Method
Students list and analyze the sources of foods.

Materials
Writing materials, chalk board; OPTIONAL: poster board and drawing materials

Background
NOTE: The concepts in this activity are reinforced using pictures and verbal language skills and may be used effectively with English language learners.

Food webs are just one of nature's many cycles. In a food web, omnivores, herbivores, and carnivores comprise the organisms in an ecological community that ensures the continuation of food energy from one organism to another. These webs are made up of individual food chains.

In a grazing web, materials typically pass from plants to herbivores (plant eaters) to carnivores (flesh eaters). The food web can be viewed not only as a network of chains but also as a series of trophic (nutritional) levels. Green plants (primary producers of food) belong to the first level. Herbivores (consumers of green plants) belong to the second trophic level. Carnivores (predators feeding upon the herbivores) belong to the third. Omnivores (consumers of both plants and animals) belong to the second and third. Secondary carnivores (predators that feed on predators) belong to the fourth trophic level.

Animals, including people, either consume plants directly or depend on other species that, in turn, depend on plants.

Procedure
1. Ask students to make a list of everything that they had for dinner on a particular evening, or ask them to invent a dinner menu of their choice.

2. Ask the students to work alone or in groups to analyze where their food comes from. Every item from their dinner menu should be traced back to a plant. As each item on a menu is examined, ask the students to create a flow diagram or chain that shows the major sources of each food—from the product they eat all the way back to the plant origin (e.g., milk, cow, grass). Some chains will be short while others will be long. Sometimes the students may not be sure what particular animals eat for food, so they will want do some research.

Grade Level: 5–8

Subject Areas: Science, Language Arts, Environmental Education

Duration: one 20-minute session or longer

Group Size: any

Setting: indoors

Conceptual Framework Topic Reference: IDIA, IDIB, IDIIB2

Key Terms: food chain, plants, animals

Appendices: Using Local Resources

3. Discuss with the students some of the things they learned from this activity. After the students have described things they have learned, encourage them to make two generalizations about plants and animals. These generalizations may include that all animals, including people and wildlife, need food; all animals, including people and wildlife, depend on plants for food.

Extensions

1. Make posters of the menus created at the beginning of this activity, showing the food chains involved in each. Add soil, water, sun, and air, because those are necessary to plants, people, and all animals.

2. Create a master list of all the plants that were identified during the activity. Are there some plants that we are more dependent on than others? Ask students to research people who live in other parts of the world and to develop a list of plants on which they depend.

3. Did you know that everything you ate for breakfast (lunch, dinner, or a snack) started somewhere with a rock? Trace plants to soil and soil to its parent matter, which includes rocks.

Aquatic Extensions

1. See the Project WILD Aquatic activity "Water We Eating?"

2. Create at least two food chains that involve people, aquatic wildlife, and plants.

Evaluation

1. Construct at least three food chains using the following organisms: people, rabbits, grass, lettuce, mountain lions, robins, earthworms, hawks, mice, insects, wheat, cows, corn, pigs, deer, and acorns.

2. Which of these animals do not need food: horse, snake, frog, person, robin?

3. All of the food eaten by animals must first come from _____? (Although the objective of this activity stressed that animals rely on plants, please accept any reasonable response, such as soil or sunlight, if the students reasonably explain their theory.)

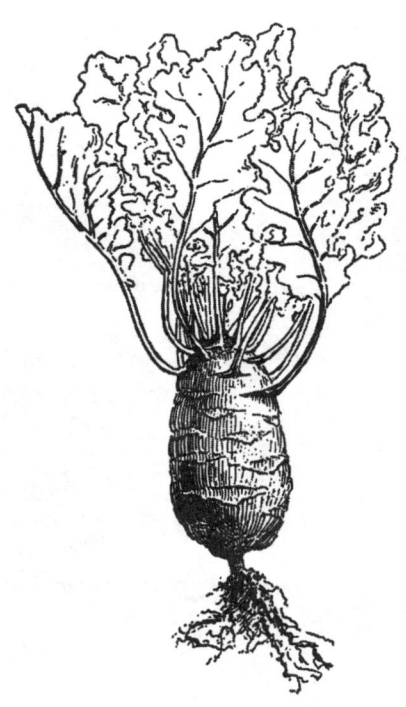

Seed Need

Objectives

Students will (1) explain how seeds are carried by animals, and (2) evaluate the importance of wildlife as contributors to ecological systems using this example of seed dispersal.

Method

Students gather seeds by going outside and by wearing socks over their shoes.

Materials

One large sock or a piece of masking tape per student (students can bring a large, old sock from home or educators can try to find an inexpensive or free source to obtain a sock for each student); paper or plastic bag; OPTIONAL: a shoe box, planting medium, cookie sheets, or trays

---

Grade Level: 5–8

Subject Areas: Science, Mathematics, Environmental Education

Duration: one 20- to 40-minute session or longer for gathering and analyzing data, minimal ongoing time in caring for planted seeds

Group Size: any

Setting: outdoors and indoors

Conceptual Framework Topic Reference: IDIA, IDIB, IDIIB2

Key Terms: ecosystem, dispersal, seeds, diversity

Appendices: Outdoors, Field Ethics, Early Childhood

Background

Wildlife contributes to the diversity and balance of ecological systems in ways that are not very obvious. One of these ways is in the process of seed dispersal. Animals carry many seeds—whether in the coats of fur-bearing animals or in seeds carried and dropped by some birds. Animals distribute seeds in other ways too. For example, pack rats and squirrels gather seeds and store them. Some of those seeds are not eaten, and the seed cache becomes a plant nursery. Many seeds are eaten but not fully digested. In those cases, animal droppings distribute and often fertilize seeds.

The major purpose of this activity is for students to understand one example of how wildlife contributes to ecological systems.

Procedure

1. Ask each student to put a sock over one shoe and to go on a walk through a grassy area or field—particularly one that is abundant in seed-bearing plants. (A piece of masking tape over the foot or around the ankle can also be used for this activity.) Have teams of students walk in different locations. Contrast seeds found in each location. Create an "environmental map." What ecosystem differences exist in the different neighborhoods or communities?

2. After they walk through the area, have the students take off their socks and examine them carefully. What has happened? Discuss briefly the seeds and other things that are attached to the socks. Place the socks in a paper or plastic bag, and return to the room.

3. Have the students remove the seeds and other particles from the socks. Talk with the students about the major kinds of things they seem to have—seeds, grass, small bits of twigs. Next, discuss the seeds in more detail, talking about the different kinds of seeds they have found: round, skinny, big, small, and so on. Make a data chart showing the types of seeds they found.

4. Have students record—with words and small drawings—the kinds of things on their socks. Also tally the number of each kind of thing on the socks.

5. Ask the students how different animals' fur might be similar to their socks. Has anyone ever brushed seeds or stickers out of a dog's or cat's fur? Discuss with the students how seeds are carried by animals which is similar to the way they carried seeds and things on their socks. Seeds may stick to an animal's fur in one location and fall off in another. Why is this process important? Evaluate the consequences. How does wildlife contribute to environmental diversity? OPTIONAL: Each student can plant his or her seeds in one of the shoe boxes filled with planting medium (soil or a commercial mix). Be sure the students put their names on their boxes. Water and care for the shoe box gardens regularly.

NOTE: Many wild plant seeds require freezing before they will germinate. Put the seeds in the freezer for several days, and then plant them. Even after freezing, some seeds may not sprout. Some seeds require scarring, scorching by fire, or digesting before they will grow. Also, some seeds are not viable and will not germinate or sprout.

Extensions

1. As the seeds in the boxes begin to sprout, measure the plants that grow. Take measurements every fifth day and plot these measurements on a graph.

2. Try similar experiments at home, using seeds the students find in their neighborhood. If you actually get the plants to grow, you can try to match the plants you grow at home from the "pet-carried" seeds to the plants growing outside. How far did the seeds travel on the animal?

Evaluation

1. Draw three different types of seeds that could be transported on an animal. Draw an arrow to show the part of the seed that makes this possible.

2. Write a paragraph to explain how fur-bearing animals are important to the types of plants that produce these seeds.

3. Choose a selection of sewing materials to demonstrate how seeds can attach to animal fur. (Buttons can represent the seeds. Attachment materials could include scraps of Velcro, string, rubber cement, and safety pins). Describe the characteristics of the kinds of wildlife that might disperse seeds in this fashion.

Owl Pellets

Objective
Students will construct a simple food chain.

Method
Students examine owl pellets, reconstruct prey skeletons, and hypothesize food sources of the prey.

Materials
Owl pellets (see information in the Background section), dissecting tools (toothpicks work fine), poster board, paper towels, glue, small animal skeleton diagrams and skull guide; OPTIONAL: hand lenses or magnifying glasses, gloves

Background
On the floor of abandoned buildings, beneath a grove of tall trees, or under other structures that offer shelter from inclement weather, tangible signs are left by a bird species that most people see only infrequently. Those objects are uniformly dark gray and measure from 1.5 to 3 inches long and .75 to 1 inch in diameter. The objects typically include bones, fur, and feathers. For those who can read them, they contain a wealth of information about wildlife. These objects are owl pellets.

Unlike certain other raptors, owls are not picky eaters. They swallow their prey as nearly whole as possible. Fur, feathers, and bones, however, cannot be digested, nor will they pass through the digestive system. About 12 hours after consuming a meal, an owl casts, or regurgitates, a "pellet."

Owls are not the only birds that cast pellets. More than 300 species of birds cast pellets. They include eagles and hawks as well as smaller birds like robins and tree sparrows.

Owl pellets are clean of all flesh and virtually odorless. After a short drying period, they can be handled easily by all age groups. Because they are found under the perch, they may occasionally be "whitewashed" by the bird. Pellets will keep almost indefinitely if dry and protected in a plastic bag or closed jar. Those collected on a field trip or during the summer can be saved for later examination. Pellets also may be purchased through scientific supply catalogs.

Owl pellets have been used for scientific study of small mammals and their distribution. With owls doing the collecting, the scientist must simply locate the owl roost to obtain the skulls and bones of the small prey living in the area. From those parts, the species can be identified. Owl pellets help map the areas occupied by certain small creatures that might otherwise have escaped detection.

Grade Level: 5–8

Subject Areas: Science, Environmental Education

Duration: one 20- to 45-minute session

Group Size: two or three students working in groups

Setting: indoors

Conceptual Framework Topic Reference: IDIIB, IDIIB2

Key Terms: owl pellets, food chain, cast, raptors, skeletons of songbirds, skulls of small animals

Appendices: Ecosystem, Field Ethics, Using Local Resources

Once the bones are separated from the mass of fur in the pellet, a number of anatomy lessons are possible. Hip bones and the upper leg bone with its large ball joint are identified readily. The scapula or shoulder blade, ribs, other leg bones, vertebrae, foot bones, and skull all are recognizable when sorted out.

For the Activity

To complete this activity, educators will need to purchase or collect actual owl pellets. Owl pellets can be located under trees or in abandoned buildings where owls may roost. Wear plastic gloves when collecting pellets. Local wildlife organizations may be able to help you identify possible roosting sites. Bird watchers and people who rehabilitate injured birds of prey may be of particular help. Identify the species of owl that cast the pellets if you can do so without disturbing the animal. To eliminate any parasites in the collected pellets, dry the pellets in an oven at 325°F for 40 minutes or 20 seconds on high in a microwave oven. Pre-dried pellets can also be purchased from scientific supply distributors such as Museum Products, 84 Route 27, Mystic, CT 06355, Tel: (800) 395-5400; or Pellets, Inc., P.O. Box 5484, Bellingham, WA 98227-5484, Tel: (360) 733-3012.

NOTE: Often the owl pellets acquired from a commercial source are pellets from birds that have been fed laboratory mice or rats. It's pretty hard to construct a food chain from this diet. It is worth the effort to secure wild owl pellets, if possible. A nongame biologist may be able to provide owl pellets.

Procedure

1. Divide the students into groups of two or three. Review safe lab procedures, including the need to wash hands before and after doing the activity and the importance of not eating or drinking during the activity. Give each team an owl pellet.

2. Have the groups separate the bones from the fur and feathers on a paper towel. Where possible, identify the skulls and jaws of the prey species. Use a hand lens or magnifying glass to look at the teeth. Consider how the teeth are arranged. Would they work best at tearing flesh, grinding seeds, or eating plants? Using the teeth as a guide, determine what kinds of food the prey species most likely ate.

3. Ask the students to determine if there are bones from more than one animal in the pellet. If there are, determine how many different animals and species are represented in one pellet.

4. Instruct the students to lay out the bones to form as many complete skeletons as possible. Skeletons may be glued to poster board for display and labeling.

5. From the evidence suggested by the skeletons, discuss possible food chains that include the owl, its prey, and what the prey eats.

Extensions

1. Investigate another bird of prey, its eating habits, and its food sources.

2. Write a poem that describes the interrelationships between owls, rodents, and the environments in which they live.

Evaluation

Draw a picture of a simple food chain that represents the eating habits of the owl and its food sources.

Eco-Enrichers

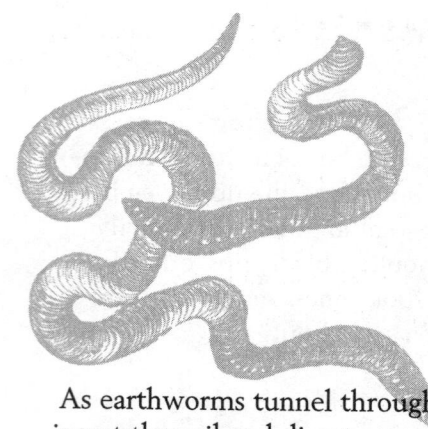

Objectives
Students will (1) evaluate the contributions of plant and animal matter to soil, and 2) recognize that wildlife in many forms contributes to the diversity and balance of ecological systems.

Method
Students experiment with soil and earthworms.

Materials
Enough soil from the same source to fill 3 cubic foot containers, earthworms, organic material (kitchen scraps and yard debris)

Background
Wildlife is an important contributor to healthy ecosystems. In this case, earthworms (not always recognized as wildlife) enrich the soil.

Grade Level: 5–8

Subject Areas: Science, Environmental Education

Duration: minimum of two 50-minute sessions, plus observation of soil boxes for 6 weeks

Group Size: whole class

Setting indoors

Conceptual Framework Topic Reference: IDIB, IDIIB, IDIIB2a3, IDIIC1b

Key Terms: ecosystem, soil, nutrients, fertility, acidity, alkalinity, porosity, organic, composting

Appendices: Outdoors, Field Ethics, Animals in the Classroom

As earthworms tunnel through the soil, they ingest the soil and digest any organic matter in it. Organic matter is dragged into their burrows and broken down. Although they are most numerous in the top 6 inches of soil, they also work in the subsoil, bringing mineral-rich soil from below to the surface. This process adds to the supply of nutrients available to plants. Research shows that in 100 square feet of garden soil, earthworms may bring from 4 to 8 pounds of dirt to the soil surface each year.

Besides incorporating organic matter into the soil, earthworms are good manufacturers of fertilizer. Castings have a nutrient level and organic matter level much higher than that of the surrounding soil. Earthworms convert nitrogen, phosphorous, potassium, and many micro nutrients into a form that plants can use.

Worms make other contributions, such as adding calcium carbonate, a compound that helps moderate soil pH. Over time, earthworms can help change acid or alkaline soils toward a more neutral pH.

Earthworm tunnels help to aerate and loosen the soil. This action allows more oxygen and water in, which not only helps the plant directly, but also improves conditions for certain beneficial soil bacteria. Finally, the tunneling of the earthworms provides access to deeper soil levels for the numerous smaller organisms that contribute to the health of the soil.

The major purpose of this activity is for students to recognize one example of the kinds of significant contributions from wildlife.

Procedure

1. Select some heavily compacted soil by a roadside or in an area where there has been erosion. Note that the soil may look infertile, but may be rich with inorganic nutrients. Take a large enough sample of the soil to fill 3 cubic foot containers.

2. With your students, do some simple soil tests to determine the quality of the soil. For example,

   - Look for signs of plant and animal matter in the soil. Count the number of species you can identify, examine a sample under a microscope, count the number of organisms in the sample, and estimate the number of organisms in the entire quantity of soil in the container using the number of the sample.

   - Test the soil acidity with pH kits.

   - Check soil porosity by determining how fast water will run through the soil.

   - Conduct a settling test to see what general proportions of soil components are present (i.e., sand, silt, clay, organic matter). For more detailed information on conducting soil tests, contact Global Learning and Observations to Benefit the Environment (GLOBE), toll free at (800) 858-9947, or on the web at **www.globe.gov**.

3. After the soil tests have been completed and recorded, divide the soil into the three containers. One container is the "control" and contains only soil. The second is for soil and organic material only. The third is for soil, organic material, and earthworms.

4. Begin adding organic material such as table scraps, grass clippings, leaves, and so on to the second and third containers. Add earthworms to the third container. Water the soil in all three containers occasionally to simulate a rainstorm. Decaying organic materials may have odors. Pick a location for the worm boxes where any unpleasant odors will not disrupt other activities.

NOTE: Students should be encouraged to harvest "wild" worms for this activity. If worms are purchased at a bait shop, request redworms because they are easier to care for and they survive longer in captivity than nightcrawlers.

5. Ask students to state the results they expect after 3 weeks of experimentation. Have them write down their hypotheses to compare with their findings.

6. Since the worms are in a limited environment, you and the students will need to keep adding food and other composting materials. Compost should be added to the second container also. Plan on adding materials once a week for 3 weeks and watering lightly once a week. Encourage the students to watch for changes in any of the boxes. Attach an observation sheet to the outside of each box for the students' reporting purposes.

7. At the end of the 3-week period, conduct the same set of experiments you originally conducted with the soil. Conduct the tests with all three boxes. In testing the soil in the earthworm box, make sure the students take care not to harm the earthworms; many may die anyway. Be prepared for this possibility, and add additional earthworms as necessary.

8. Discuss the findings. What differences are there in the three soil samples?

9. Now plant some seeds in all three soil boxes. Choose a fast-growing seed such as radishes. Seeds from plants native to the area might be available as well. Plant the same number of seeds in each of the soil boxes, and water them at the same rate. Record the date of planting. Record all watering procedures and changes in the boxes as the plants begin to grow. After 3 weeks, compare and discuss the results. Describe the importance of plant and animal matter as contributors to soil. Discuss how earthworms contribute to healthy habitats.

continued

Variation

Use two 2-liter soda bottles for the compost system. Cut the top off one and the bottom off the other. Invert one over the other so that the compost liquid will drain out. (The liquid can be used to water plants.) Use the cut bottom as a cover. Add vegetable scraps, water frequently, and occasionally add soil.

Extension

Many communities are encouraging citizens to compost their organic, nonanimal wastes. The study of worms and soils is an excellent departure point for studying about composting. Investigate local regulations about organic wastes. A master gardener program that is available through local cooperative extension services will be able to provide information on composting.

Evaluation

1. Identify three ways that earthworms have a positive effect on soil.

2. Explain how soil is important to plants and is a major factor in building wildlife habitat.

3. Write a story about what would happen to the soil, plants, and some types of wildlife if there were no earthworms.

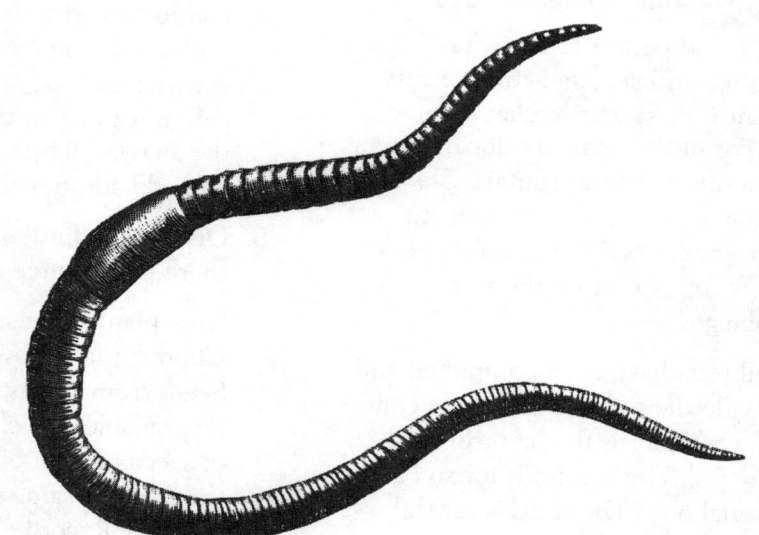

Energy Pipeline

Objectives
Students will (1) explain why energy dissipates at each trophic level, (2) contrast the transfer of energy and the recycling of organic material within an ecosystem, and (3) relate the role of each trophic level to ecosystem dynamics.

Method
Students simulate organic production and energy loss for major trophic levels in an ecosystem. The class acts as a "growth" assembly line that becomes increasingly complex with each round of play.

Materials
A large bucket of pea-sized gravel that may be purchased at larger hardware stores (tokens or dried beans also may be used), a large empty bucket labeled "Used-Up Calories," a box of reusable plastic sandwich bags, copies of the metabolism cards (may be laminated for future use) for each student pair, 52 plastic bowls or cups, one for each metabolism card, six small paper cups, 3" × 5" cards, transparency of the Total Growth Chart, transparency marking pens; OPTIONAL: whistle, colored gravel

Background
In every ecosystem, the biotic and abiotic components are linked by energy flow and material cycling to form a functional unit in which successive levels of consumers depend on organisms at lower levels. Each of these trophic levels is defined according to its major role at each level (producers, primary and secondary consumers, and decomposers). The trophic level that ultimately supports all others consists of autotrophs, the primary producers. These are mostly the plants that use sunlight to make organic compounds (sugars), which provide energy for their metabolic processes and growth. All other organisms are heterotrophs, consumers that are unable to make their own food. They are directly or indirectly dependent on the photosynthetic output of the producers. The primary consumers of the plants are the herbivores, and the secondary consumers that eat herbivores are the carnivores.

Energy flows through the ecosystem according to the laws of thermodynamics, and it determines the trophic relationships. Unlike materials such as water, oxygen, carbon, phosphates, and nitrates that are recycled, energy is lost at each level. Each successive trophic level contains less energy, less organic material, and fewer numbers of organisms. As a rule, about 90 percent of the available energy for any trophic level is lost through heat, movement, and other metabolic activities. Only 10 percent, on average, is available for transfer to the next level.

Grade Level: 7–8

Subject Areas: Science, Mathematics, Environmental Education

Duration: two 45-minute sessions

Group Size: 20-30 students

Setting: indoors

Conceptual Framework Topic References: IDIIB1, IDIIB1a, IDIIB1b, IDIIB2a, IDIIB2a1, IDIIB2a2, IDIIB2a3, IDIIB2b, IDIIC1a

Key Terms: trophic level, producer, herbivore, carnivore, decomposer, energy

Appendices: Simulations

---

continued

Consequently, food chains tend to be short, and the resulting energy pyramid has implications for human food supplies. Because humans are omnivores, they are capable of eating plants and animals. When humans (or any consumer) consume most of their food from a secondary or tertiary level, the transfer of energy is less efficient than it is when they consume at the primary level. There are relatively few top predators (secondary consumers) in an ecosystem because of this considerable loss of energy between levels. As much as a million calories in plant material may be needed to support 1,000 calories stored by a secondary carnivore. (A calorie is a unit of energy, generally defined as the amount of heat required to raise the temperature of 1 gram of water 1 degree Centigrade.)

The purpose of this activity is to demonstrate some of the complex trophic interactions resulting from the flow of energy throughout ecosystems. Although material substances such as water, nitrogen, carbon, and phosphorus cycle through ecosystems, energy takes a one-way course through an ecosystem and is dissipated at every trophic level. Energy from the sun and organic matter enter the animal world through herbivores. Either directly or indirectly, plants support nearly all forms of animal life, including humans. A relatively large quantity of plant material is required to support herbivores (primary consumers), and the herbivores can support only a smaller number of carnivores (secondary consumers).

The proportions selected for this activity are not meant to precisely reflect the complexity of food web interactions or the numbers of organisms and quantities of energy and organic matter involved. Instead, this activity provides an opportunity for the students to conceptualize the basic principles of energy flow in a manageable way. Educators will need to adjust the suggested proportions to accommodate different class sizes.

Procedure

1. Divide the students into pairs. These pairs should then be grouped into four "trophic level" categories:

   a. Six of the pairs will be plants (autotrophs) and will sit on one side of the room.

   b. Three other pairs will be grouped as primary consumers (herbivores) and will sit in the middle of the room.

   c. One pair will be a secondary consumer (carnivore) and will sit away from the plants on the other side of the herbivores.

   d. One other pair will act as the sun and will stand with the large bucket of pea-sized gravel near the plants. See Diagram A.

Diagram A

One possible arrangement for the energy system in a classroom:

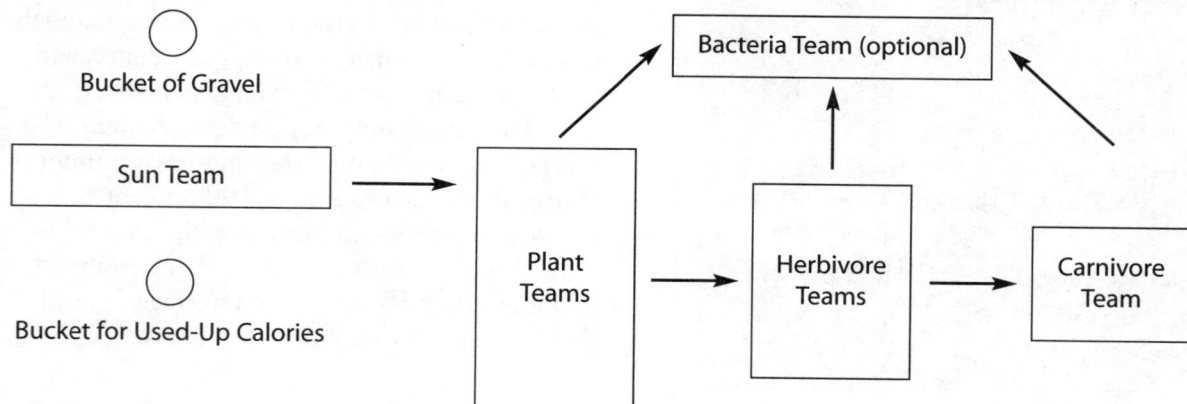

2. Distribute a set of five Plant Metabolism Cards to each plant pair, five Herbivore Metabolism Cards to each herbivore pair, and five Carnivore Metabolism Cards to the single carnivore pair. Give each of these pairs five bowls. Give the carnivore pair a whistle or some other device to signal the end of each round. Also hand out a 3" × 5" card for each pair to keep a record of its growth progress during the activity. The sun pair receives only two bowls or cups to carry gravel to the plants.

3. Tell each pair (except the sun pair) to place one of its metabolism cards in each of its bowls.

4. Explain that the sun pair will carefully hand out 10 pieces of gravel (in the plastic bowls or cups) to each plant pair. Each piece of gravel or stone represents a photon of sunlight containing one calorie of energy.* The plant pairs should place the gravel in their bowls as indicated by the metabolism cards. (See the metabolism cards on page 110 that describe each bowl and tell what the students are to do with the gravel.)

5. When a plant pair has placed all 10 stones in the proper bowls, those students ask the sun pair to supply another 10 stones. The plant pair then places those new stones in the bowls the same way. The students continue placing the "calories" (i.e., stones), 10 at a time, in their bowls until they have accumulated 10 "calories" in the "growth" bowl. At that time, the plant is sufficiently large enough that it may be eaten by a primary consumer (herbivore). A pair member then places the 10 growth "calories" in a plastic bag, hands the bag to one of the herbivore pairs and tallies the bag on the 3" × 5" card. The stones in the other bowls may now be discarded in the bucket labeled "Used-Up Calories." The sun pair should watch the various plant pairs and keep them all supplied with small amounts of gravel (calories), as needed.

*This is not to imply that one photon is equal to one calorie.

6. Once a bag has been transferred to an herbivore, the plant pair resumes the sorting activity and continues to produce bags of calories for herbivores until the end of the round.

7. Explain to the herbivore pairs that they will take the bags of gravel from the plants and sort them into their five bowls according to the directions on the corresponding Herbivore Metabolism Cards.

8. Each herbivore pair continues receiving bags from plant pairs and sorting them as before until they have accumulated 10 "calories" in the "growth" bowl. At this time, they place these 10 stones in a bag, pass the bag to the carnivore pair, and add a tally mark to their 3" × 5" card to record the number of bags the pair has created. Have the herbivore pairs discard the stones remaining in the other bowls by putting them in the large bucket labeled "Used-Up Calories." The pairs then resume as before: receiving bags from the plants, accumulating 10 stones, bagging the "calories," and recording the number of bags until the end of the round.

9. The carnivore pair will take the first bag given to them by one of the herbivore pairs and will sort the 10 stones according to the directions on their five Carnivore Metabolism Cards.

10. As soon as the final stone from this first bag is placed, a member of the carnivore pair blows the whistle or otherwise signals the end of the round.

11. The moment the signal is given, all pairs immediately halt their activities and count how many bags they have created. Project the transparency of the Total Growth Chart. Allow each pair to record its results on the chart.

continued

12. Ask the students to interpret the meaning of each step of the simulation.

    - Have the students interpret the total growth chart for the class. How many total bags were recorded by all pairs for each level? How are the calories distributed among the levels? What caused the difference? What are some of the ways energy is used up at each trophic level?

    - Where did the plants acquire their energy? Why were there no limits on the amount of "calories" given to them? How are plants limited in the real world?

    - How were the "calories" used by the plants? What are other ways (besides those listed on the metabolism cards) that organisms use energy?

    - What would happen to the numbers of bags needed for the entire system if the carnivore had been allowed to "grow" to full size? That is, how would the numbers have changed if the round had been allowed to continue until 10 calorie stones had accumulated in the carnivore growth bowl? (Ten times the number of bags would have been needed at each level.)

    - Why are food chains often short? (A 10-fold number of plants would be needed to support each level added above the primary carnivore. The number [biomass] of plants, therefore, is a limit to the height of the food pyramid.) Have the students consider the implication of this structure on human food supplies.

    - Could a lower trophic level pass all of its calories directly to a higher level? What would be the consequences for the organism if it did pass all of its calories on to the next higher level? Given the same initial amount of "calories," how could an organism transfer more calories to the next level and still survive? (An organism could reduce another metabolic activity, such as the number of seeds produced or the amount of movement.) What consequences would such changes in the metabolic distribution (e.g., reduction of seeds, lack of movement) have for the survival of an organism or species?

Total Growth Chart

	Round 1	Round 2 (optional)	Round 3 (optional)	
	Growth Calories	Growth Calories	Growth Calories	Nutrients
Carnivore				
Herbivore				
Plant				
Bacteria				

Extensions

Extensions are highly recommended for this activity. The following rounds may be added to demonstrate more complex interactions, or the teacher and students may design their own. Be sure to compare the interactions and energy flow from any new rounds they design with the basic simulation described here.

1. Bring decomposers into play. The decomposers, which interact with each of the other trophic levels, are the bacteria and other organisms that break down dead organisms and process nutrients. Have a bacteria pair receive bags (representing dead organisms that were not eaten by a higher trophic level) from both the plant and herbivore pairs and place their gravel in two bowls: one for metabolic process and one for growth. (The bacteria will not return gravel to the "Used-Up Gravel" bucket.) Direct both the producer and herbivore pairs to contribute alternating bags to this single bacteria pair. For example, a producer pair would give its first bag to the bacteria pair and the second to an herbivore pair, then to bacteria, then to herbivores, and so forth. At the end of the round, all calories in the growth bowls of the producers, herbivores, and carnivores go to the decomposers. The rest go to the "Used-Up Calories" bucket. The bacteria pair counts the number of growth stones and multiplies by two (to represent cell division) to determine the final numbers for the Total Growth Chart.

2. Contrast the recycling of nutrients with the one-way flow of energy through this simulated system. Add 15 to 20 colored stones or tokens to represent nutrients. Designate one of the students from the sun pair to act as "soil," and give this student the "nutrient" stones. Tell the class that these nutrients enter the system through the soil, and have the "soil" student give two "nutrient" stones to each plant pair and two to the bacteria pair. Each pair must include a nutrient stone in any bag of gravel it produces. Any extra nutrient stones that the bacteria pair accumulates must be returned to "soil," and "soil" periodically should give nutrient stones to the plants. Explain to the students that many plants live in close association with decomposers to take advantage of this nutrient cycling.

Evaluation

1. Draw a diagram that illustrates the energy flow in a simple ecosystem. Be sure the diagram illustrates how energy is dissipated at each level and that it reflects the complexity of interactions among organisms within the system.

2. Use Visual Vocabulary techniques (see Evaluating and Assessing Student Learning in the Appendices) to review terms and concepts introduced in this activity.

continued

Plant Metabolism Cards

Unused Sunlight

Not all sunlight can be converted into organic matter.

Place two calories in this bowl.

Reproduction

Plant uses energy to produce seeds.

Place three calories in this bowl.

Growth

Plant uses energy to grow.

Place one calorie in this bowl.

Photosynthesis

Plant absorbs energy from the sun and produces organic matter.

Place three calories in this bowl.

Respiration

Plants burn energy in the process of photosysthesis.

Place one calorie in this bowl.

Herbivore Metabolism Cards

Digestion

Herbivore uses energy to break down consumed food.

Place two calories in this bowl.

Movement

Herbivore uses energy to search for water.

Place three calories in this bowl.

Reproduction

Herbivore uses energy to create nest and raise young.

Place three calories in this bowl.

Growth

Herbivore uses energy to grow.

Place one calorie in this bowl.

Respiration

Herbivore uses energy to watch for predators.

Place one calorie in this bowl.

Carnivore Metabolism Cards

Digestion

Carnivore uses energy to break down consumed food.

Place two calories in this bowl.

Movement

Carnivore uses energy to search for prey and to hunt food.

Place three calories in this bowl.

Respiration

Carnivore uses energy to build a shelter.

Place one calorie in this bowl.

Reproduction

Carnivore uses energy for extensive courtship display and extra hunting to raise young.

Place three calories in this bowl.

Growth

Carnivore uses energy to grow.

Place one calorie in this bowl.

Birds of Prey

Objectives

Students will (1) interpret a graph of animal populations, noting changes over time; (2) hypothesize the relationship among temperature, ground squirrel behavior, and falcon populations; and (3) describe the importance of interdependence to the functioning of an ecosystem.

Method

Students interpret data on wildlife populations, generate hypotheses related to the data, and research potential explanations.

Materials

Graphs A–E (found in the Procedure section) enlarged for classroom use; OPTIONAL: photographs of predator and prey species

Grade Level: 9–12

Subject Areas: Mathematics, Science, Environmental Education

Duration: one or two 45-minute sessions

Group Size: large group, with small groups working with data and discussing

Setting: indoors

Conceptual Framework Topic Reference: IDIIB2, IDIIC

Key Terms: aestivation, population, hypothesis, prediction, interdependence, ecological systems

Appendices: Observations and Inferences

Background

In the Birds of Prey Natural Area in south-western Idaho, a large number of prairie falcons nest in late spring and early summer each year. The falcons mainly live off a large population of Townsend ground squirrels that live in the surrounding flatlands. Throughout the breeding season, the population of falcons increases as more and more birds move into the area to nest, until all available nesting sites are taken. Because the Townsend ground squirrels serve as the food base for the falcons, continued activity and availability of this prey base is crucial for the support of the nesting falcons. As the summer progresses, the daytime temperatures in the area increase to a point (around July 4) where it is too hot for the ground squirrels, and they go underground and undergo a form of summer sleep called "aestivation" or summer hibernation. Without available prey, the falcons and their new offspring must either leave or die. Within a day of the ground squirrels' aestivation, nearly all falcons capable of flight move out of the area in search of other food (other ground squirrel species and rodents). Most move to higher, cooler elevations where other species of ground squirrels (such as Columbian ground squirrels) remain active. This sudden seeming "loss" of falcons from the Birds of Prey natural area is directly tied to the important environmental factor of temperature.

The major purpose of this activity is for students to recognize that life forms and environmental factors interact in natural ecosystems to keep wildlife populations in long-term dynamic equilibrium with each other and their habitats.

continued

Procedure

1. Set the stage by giving students the following background information:

   The Birds of Prey Natural Area in Idaho hosts the largest concentration of nesting prairie falcons in the world each spring and summer. The birds nest along the cliffs above the Snake River and use the huge Townsend ground squirrel population for food. This prey species lives on the flat land above the canyon. Each year, the populations of these two species change from April through July.

2. Show the students Graph A. Have them look at the graph to see what happens to the populations of predator and prey. Then have them answer the following questions:

   - What do you observe happening?
   - What do you notice about the Townsend ground squirrel population in April, May, and June?
   - What do you notice about the ground squirrel population in July?
   - What do you think caused this drop in population? What might have happened to the squirrels?
   - What do you notice about the falcon population in April and May?
   - What do you notice happening to the falcon population in July? What do you think caused this population decline?
   - What might have caused the change?
   - How do these populations seem to be related?

   Ask the students to speculate, offer hypotheses, and develop questions to assist with finding a solution to this dilemma.

3. Show the students Graphs B, C, D, and E. Using the information provided on these graphs, encourage the students to discuss their ideas and hypotheses.

4. Ask the students to share those ideas that seem to be most reasonable given the information presented in the graphs.

5. Summarize the activity by

   - Closed inquiry approach—Review the sequence of events. Discuss the role of temperature in triggering aestivation. Ask the students to predict what the falcons might do if their food source "disappeared." Where might they find the falcons after they leave the area? Where would they go to obtain food? What kind of prey species might they use? Have the students suggest other physical factors that influence or limit wildlife activity. Have the students also propose some ways these same factors influence or limit human activity.

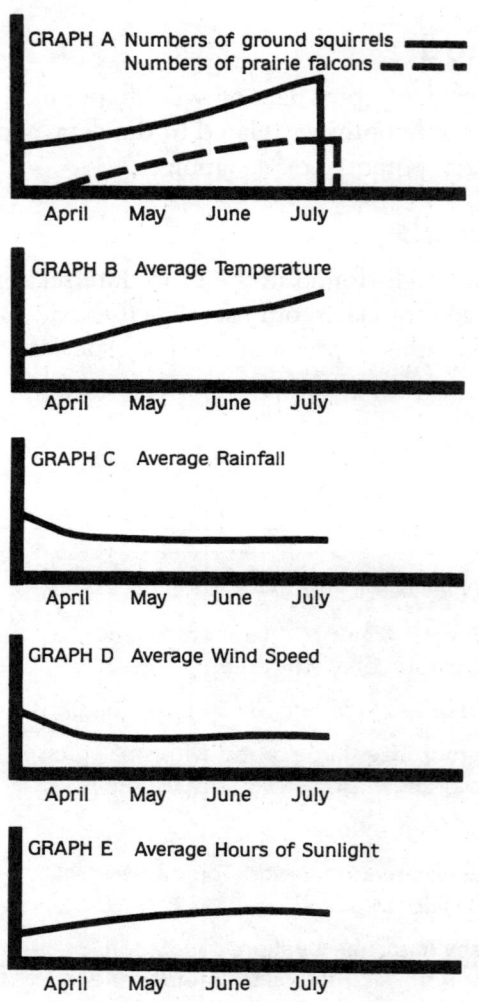

or by

- Open inquiry approach—Do not provide the above information, but allow student teams to research information on the squirrels and falcons.

6. Extend the discussion to the concept of interdependence in ecological systems. What was interdependent in this situation? Encourage the students to think of other examples of interdependence. Can they think of any ecosystems that are not composed of interdependent parts? Generalize that all ecosystems are made up of interdependent parts.

Extensions

1. The prey ordinarily used by the falcons at the natural area—the Townsend ground squirrel—is distributed throughout much of the plains area above the river, which is also potentially good agricultural land. Given this information, the activity could be extended to an investigation into competitive uses for the land occupied by the prey base, the legislation behind the establishment of the natural area, related controversies, or all three.

2. Investigate the process by which such natural areas are set aside, the agencies involved, and related issues.

3. Describe the usefulness of mathematical data in interpreting relationships between organisms in ecosystems; use the Birds of Prey Natural Area as an example.

Evaluation

1. Using Graph A as a reference, describe for each month between April and July:

   a. the relative population levels of squirrels and falcons,

   b. the behavior of the squirrels and falcons, and

   c. the role of temperature on a and b above.

Explain the importance of interdependence to an ecosystem.

Additional Resources

www.seaworld.org/birds/bird.html

www.ticcamp.com/kidspage/s4/j/hannah

www.raptor.cvm.umn.edu/raptor/rfacts/rfacts.html

Thicket Game

Objectives
Students will (1) identify examples of adaptation in animals, and 2) describe the importance of adaptation to animals.

Method
Students become "predator" and "prey" in a version of "hide and seek."

Materials
Blindfolds, outdoor area such as a thicket or other vegetated area free of poisonous plants and other hazards where students can hide safely, or a "thicket" built using desks, chairs, and blankets in a large room

Background
Animals are adapted to their environment in order to survive. Animals may also be adapted to changes in their habitats. For example, snowshoe rabbits have a white winter coat to blend with a snowy environment and a tan summer coat to blend with summer ground and vegetation colors. Chameleons change color to blend with their surroundings. The walking-stick insect can look like a twig or stick. Fawns have spotted hair that resembles dappled light on the forest floor in spring. Adaptations to predator and prey relationships may also include behavioral (e.g., hiding or flight) and physical (e.g., camouflage) variations.

The major purpose of this activity is for students to understand the importance of adaptation to animals.

Procedure
1. Take the group to a "thicket."

2. Blindfold one student who will be the "predator." The predator slowly counts to 20 while the other students, or "prey," hide. Students who are hiding must be able to see some part of the predator at all times.

3. After counting, the predator removes the blindfold and looks for prey. The predator can turn around, squat, or stand on his or her tiptoes, but cannot walk or change location. The predator should see how many students he or she can find, identify them out loud, and describe where they are. When identified, the prey students move to the predator's location and wait until the next round to become predators. Make sure the students do not tell the original predator where any of the students are hiding.

Grade Level: Pre-K, K–4

Subject Area Skills: Science, Environmental Education, Expressive Arts

Duration: one 30-minute session

Group Size: minimum of five students

Setting: outdoors

Conceptual Framework Topic Reference: CAIIA, CAIIA1, CAIIA1b

Key Terms: adaptation, predator, prey

Appendices: Outdoors, Field Ethics, Simulations

4. When the original predator cannot see any more students, a new round starts. All of the predators put on blindfolds and stand in close proximity to each other. Each predator has the same motion restrictions. Again, the original predator counts aloud to 20. At that point all the remaining prey must move at least 10 feet closer to the predators. Those remaining prey still try to remain hidden. All predators remove their blindfolds and take turns naming students they can see.

5. Play as many rounds as necessary until only one or two prey students are left. At that time, have the remaining students stand up and identify themselves. It may be surprising how close the prey got to the predators without being detected. The ability to remain undetected and to detect others is an example of successful adaptation. Introduce the term "adaptation."

6. Conduct the activity one or two more times.

7. Discuss what made predators and prey successful. Were they quiet, clever, camouflaged, or good listeners? Ask students to identify animals that are adapted with similar survival characteristics.

8. Ask the students how they could change to be more successful predators and prey. Some ideas that may come out are changing color (clothes), wearing clothing that does not stick to plants, being smaller, climbing a tree. Ask the students if animals can make any similar kinds of changes.

9. Talk about differences between physical and behavioral changes. Have the students identify which adaptations related to predators and prey are behavioral, which are physical and which involve both.

10. Ask students to summarize what they have learned. See if students can think of other examples of animal adaptations. Generalize that all animals are adapted to survive.

Aquatic Extensions

1. Imagine an underwater thicket. What would be the same, if anything, about predator and prey relationships in an underwater thicket? What would be different, if anything? Draw two different underwater thickets: one in a pond and one in an ocean. Include pictures of fish and other aquatic life that are hardly visible because of adaptations that make them hard to see and pictures of others that are easy to see.

2. Identify predators and prey in two or more aquatic environments.

Evaluation

1. Describe the importance of adaptations to animals. Give at least two examples of animal adaptations.

2. Create a play or skit that shows how both predators and prey are adapted to survive.

Seeing Is Believing!

Objective
Students will (1) identify vision as one example of an adaptation, and (2) describe the importance of vision adaptations to animals.

Method
Students use kaleidoscopes, binoculars or telescopes, and fisheye mirrors to imagine what animals might have such vision. Students then make posters showing these animals.

Materials
Three learning stations: one with a kaleidoscope, one with binoculars or telescope, and one with a fisheye mirror or photos taken with such a lens; magazines with wildlife photos or wildlife stamps; glue; poster material

---

Grade Level: K–4

Subject Areas: Science, Environmental Education

Duration: 5 to 10 minutes or longer at each learning center, one 30-minute session for discussion and posters

Group Size: one or two students at a time at learning centers, any size group in summary activity

Setting: indoors, at learning centers

Conceptual Framework Topic Reference: CAIIA, CAIIA1, CAIIA2

Key Terms: adaptation, vision, kaleidoscope, binocular, fisheye lens

Appendices: none

Background
NOTE: Also see the Project WILD activity "Thicket Game" for information about animal adaptations.

Vision is one example of an adaptation. Different animals have different kinds of vision that is well suited to the needs of that particular animal. For example,

Binocular: Predatory birds (eagles, hawks, owls) have acute distance and depth of vision similar to telescopic vision. Predatory birds do not have tunnel vision, however, as the word "telescope" might suggest; they have exceptional peripheral vision. This adaptation allows the birds to see their prey from great distances.

Kaleidoscope: Insects have compound eyes. Each facet of their eye functions like a separate eye, which gives insects exceptional peripheral vision. This adaptation allows insects to detect predators.

Fisheye mirror (or photos): Fish have eyes with wide-angle perception. They can easily see predators, prey, and other food sources.

The major purpose of this activity is for students to recognize the importance and the variety of adaptations in animals.

Procedure

Before the Activity

Establish three learning centers: one with kaleidoscopes (the kind you can see through), the second with either binoculars or telescopes, and the third with a fisheye mirror (or photos of objects taken with a fisheye lens on a camera).

1. Have the students visit each station, trying out the different kinds of vision. (Younger students may require assistance in using the equipment.)

2. Ask the students to predict what animals might have each of these three types of vision; emphasize that the way an animal sees is an adaptation.

3. Tell the class that adaptations are something animals have in order to survive in an environment. Ask the students to predict how the different types of vision help animals.

4. Divide the class into three groups, and have each group cut out magazine pictures and make a poster for one of the three stations, thus showing the kinds of animals that have that particular kind of vision.

Extensions

1. Write a paragraph with the title, "I'd like to see like a _____," in which you describe how you would like to see things and why you would like to be able to see that way.

2. Use poster board to make a pair of eyeglasses. Draw pictures or cut out photos from magazines showing the colors, shapes, or patterns of an animal's eye. Or create a small collage showing an animal's view of the world. Place the artwork on the lens of the eyeglasses.

Aquatic Extension

Compare the size of the eyes of many different species of fish, aquatic mammals, aquatic insects, or aquatic birds.

Evaluation

1. Each of the following animals has either kaleidoscope, binocular, or fisheye mirror eyes: trout, owl, fly, eagle, cricket. Identify which kind of vision each animal has.

2. How does an eagle's vision help it to hunt better?

What Bear Goes Where?

Objectives
Students will (1) identify three species of bears and their habitats, and (2) generalize that animals have adapted in order to live where they do.

Method
Students construct posters of three different bear habitats.

Materials
Pictures of the three North American bear species, three large sheets of paper with the outline of one bear species on each and labeled construction paper, pencils, scissors, glue

Background
Polar bears have long necks, slender heads, and are white in appearance. They live along the Arctic coasts, mostly on the polar ice. The carnivorous polar bears feed mainly on fish and seals. Their thick fur keeps them warm, and the webbing between their toes makes them good swimmers. Unlike other bears, they have fur on the soles of their feet.

Grizzly bears can dig up most of their food and can catch fish with their long claws. They also have a distinctive hump between their shoulders. They eat roots, tubers, gophers, marmots, and smaller rodents as well as carrion (rotten meat). They occasionally kill a larger animal for food. Grizzlies tend to live in the edges of forests but feed mostly in mountain meadows. They have wide heads and a "dished" face.

Black bears are quiet, shy animals that live in a variety of habitats from forests to brush or chaparral. They eat mostly nuts, berries, and fruit. They also eat rodents and insects, and they occasionally kill larger animals for food. The black bear may be black, auburn, or cinnamon. Black bears are smaller than grizzlies or polar bears and have heads that are more pointed.

The major purpose of this activity is for students to recognize that animals can adapt to living in different environments, as shown in the example of three different kinds of bears.

Procedure
1. Show the students pictures of the three different species of bears found in North America. Name the three bears. Ask students to discuss the similarities and differences between bears.

2. Ask the students to imagine the place where each bear lives. Talk about the similarities and differences of these regions. Ask the students to think about how each bear looks and whether its features help it to live where it lives. Talk about the different adaptations of each of the bear species.

Grade Level: K–4

Subject Areas: Science, Environmental Education, Expressive Arts

Duration: one 30-minute session

Group Size: three groups of three to six students each; increase groups as necessary for class size

Setting: indoors

Conceptual Framework Topic Reference: CAIIA, CAIIA1a

Key Terms: alike, different, adapt, survive, habitat

Appendices: Early Childhood

118　　　Project WILD K–12 Curriculum and Activity Guide

3. Distribute three large sheets of paper. Draw an outline of one of the bear species in the center of each sheet, and label it accordingly. (A photo of each bear will serve just as well.)

NOTE: The outline of each bear can be projected onto a chalkboard or a large piece of paper taped to a wall. Adjust the projected image until the bear's shoulder height is life size. The bear's outline then can be drawn by tracing the projected image.

4. Divide the students into three groups. Give each group one of the sheets of paper with the outline of a bear species and a supply of construction paper, pencils, and scissors.

5. Have students in each group draw and cut out elements of the habitat of their bear (trees, grassy meadows, and rocks for the grizzly; blocks of ice, snow, fish, and seals for the polar bear; forest trees, bushes, nuts, fruits, and berries for the black bear). Then glue these elements around the picture of their bear. (Make sure that examples of all major habitat needs are included: food, water, shelter, and space in which to live.)

6. Display the finished posters, and ask the students what they have learned about bears and where bears live. Discuss how each environment has characteristic life forms that have adapted to its climate, kinds of available food, and other factors. Emphasize that all animals are adapted to survive in their environment.

Aquatic Extensions

1. Look at pictures of three different species of fish and discuss their similarities and differences. Imagine the place where each fish lives. Draw a picture of each fish in a place where you think it could live.

2. Find out more about the adaptations of different kinds of fish that make it possible for them to live in certain environments. See the Project WILD Aquatic activity "Fashion a Fish."

3. Help make a bulletin board that shows "What Fish Goes Where?" Show fish that live in ponds, fish that live in lakes, fish that live in streams, fish that live in rivers, and fish that live in oceans. Include a picture of the appropriate habitat along with a picture of the fish. See the Project WILD Aquatic activity "Fishy Who's Who."

Evaluation

1. Describe the three species of bears, what they eat, where they live, and what each species looks like.

2. If someone took polar bears to Yellowstone National Park in Wyoming and took grizzly bears to the Arctic coast, do you think the bears would be able to live in their new homes? Why or why not?

© Pat Oldham 1993

Surprise Terrarium

Objectives
Students will (1) identify camouflage as an example of an adaptation, and (2) describe the importance of adaptations to animals.

Method
Students observe a live animal that uses camouflage techniques.

Materials
Terrarium with vegetation and one animal suited to the kind of habitat components represented in the terrarium (the animal should be one that uses camouflage as a form of adaptation to survive [e.g., leaf hopper, tree frog, tree lizard, walking stick, grasshopper, earthworm]); photos of animals using camouflage or magazines the students can use to find photos

NOTE: See the Guidelines for Responsible Use of Animals in the Classroom in the Appendices for suggestions concerning proper housing and care for animals in the classroom.

Grade Level: K–4

Subject Areas: Science, Environmental Education

Duration: one 20- to 30-minute session

Group Size: any

Setting: indoors

Conceptual Framework Topic Reference: CAIIA1b

Key Terms: adaptation, camouflage

Appendices: Animals in the Classroom, Field Ethics, Early Childhood

Background
One of the most important characteristics of an organism is its ability to adapt to climate, soils, water, vegetation, predator to prey relationships, and other ecological factors. Wildlife is adapted to its environment in ways that enable it to survive and maintain its populations. Adaptations may include behavioral (e.g., signaling, flight, freezing, hibernation, and migration) as well as physical (e.g., camouflage, mimicry, body coverings, and other specialized anatomical features) variations.

Animals that use camouflage can be particularly interesting and visually compelling to young students as a means of illustrating the concept of adaptation.

The major purpose of this activity is for students to recognize that organisms adapt to survive.

Procedure
Before the Activity

Make a "surprise terrarium" with an animal that is hard for the students to see at first because the animal is camouflaged in the terrarium.

1. Encourage the students to observe the terrarium, and ask them to describe what they see.

2. Ask the students to think of animals that blend with their environments and to talk about their ideas. Show photos or bring in magazines; then ask the students to look for pictures of animals that look so much like where they live that they are hard to see. Are the animals camouflaged? Camouflage is one adaptation animals might have that help them survive. Ask the students how camouflage helps an organism to survive. Can they think of other adaptations that help organisms survive?

3. If they have not found the animal that is living in the terrarium, encourage them to look very closely until they do.

4. Ask the students to summarize some of the things they have learned about adaptations and the importance of adaptations to organisms.

5. If the camouflaged animal was brought into the classroom from the wild, the students should participate in the process of returning the animal to its natural home. Talk about human responsibilities for proper care of animals that are used for instructional purposes.

Evaluation

1. Identify two animals that use camouflage and discuss how camouflage is important to those animals.

2. Pick a photograph of one kind of habitat from a selection of images. Draw an animal that would be camouflaged in that habitat.

Quick-Frozen Critters

Objectives

Students will (1) describe adaptations related to predator and prey relationships, (2) explain the importance of adaptations in predator and prey relationships, and (3) describe how predator and prey relationships limit wildlife populations.

Method

Students play an active version of "freeze tag."

Materials

Food tokens (pieces of cardboard), enough for three per student; vests or other labeling devices to mark predators; cones or objects to mark the corners of the playing field; four or five hula hoops to serve as "cover" markers; pencil and paper to record number of captures, if desired; OPTIONAL: bandannas or rag flags to use as tails (similar to what is used to play flag football)

Grade Level: 5–8

Subject Areas: Science, Environmental Science

Duration: one 20- to 45-minute session

Group Size: best with at least 10 students, one "predator" per every 4 to 6 "prey"

Setting: indoors or outdoors

Conceptual Framework Topic Reference: CAIIA, CAIIA1, CAIIA1a, CAIIA1b

Key Terms: predator, prey, adaptation

Appendices: Outdoors, Simulations

Background

Predator: an animal that kills and eats other animals for food

Prey: an animal that is killed and eaten by other animals for food

Limiting Factors: factors (e.g., disease, climate, pollution, accidents, shortages of food) that affect an animal when they exceed the limits of tolerance of that animal (Predators are limiting factors for prey. Prey are limiting factors for predators.)

Animals display a variety of behaviors in predator and prey relationships. These behaviors are adaptations to survive.

Some prey behaviors include signaling to others, taking flight, posturing in a fighting position, scrambling for cover and even "freezing" on the spot to escape detection or capture by predators. The kind of behavior exhibited partly depends on how close the predator is when detected by the prey. Each animal has a threshold for threat levels. If a predator is far enough away for the prey to feel some safety, the prey may signal to others that a predator is near. If the predator comes closer, the prey may try to run away. If the predator is too close to make running away feasible, the prey may attempt to scurry to a hiding place. If the predator is so close that none of these alternatives is available, the prey may freeze in place. The closer the predator comes to the prey animal, the more likely it is that the prey will "freeze" in place. This "freezing" occurs as a kind of physiological shock in the animal. (Shelter or camouflage also may make prey animals invisible to the predator when they freeze.)

Too often people who come upon animals quickly and see them immobile infer that the animals are unafraid when, in reality, the animals are "frozen" or, as the adage goes, "frozen stiff."

The major purpose of this activity is for students to recognize the importance of adaptations to both predators and prey and to gain insight into limiting factors that affect wildlife populations.

Procedure

1. Select any of the following pairs of animals:

Prey	Predators
Cottontails	Coyotes
Ground squirrels	Hawks
Deer	Cougar
Quail	Foxes

   Identify students as either "predators" or "prey" for a version of "freeze tag" with approximately one predator for every four to six prey.

2. Using a gym or playing field, identify one end of the field as the "food source" and the other end as the "shelter."

3. Place four to five hula hoops in the open area between the "shelter" and the "food." These represent additional shelter or "cover" for the prey and can be distributed randomly on the field. (If hula hoops are not available, string might be used, or chalk on asphalt.)

4. Food tokens are placed in the "food source" zone on the ground. Allow three food tokens for each prey animal. See diagram below:

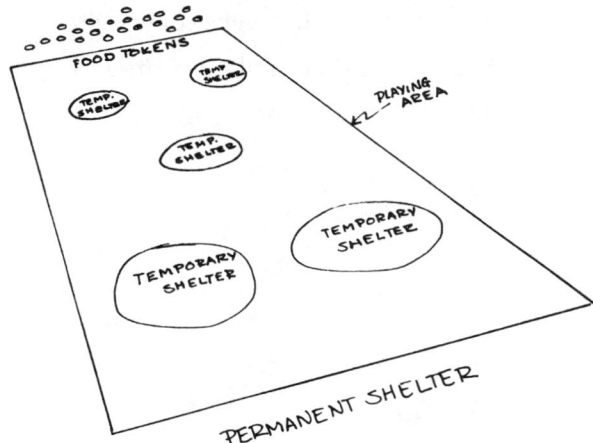

5. Clearly identify predators by using safety vests or other means.

6. Use a whistle or some other pre-arranged signal to start each round. When a round begins, have the prey students start from their "shelter." The task of the prey animals is to move from the permanent shelter to the food source, collecting one food token each trip and returning to the permanent shelter. To survive, each prey must obtain three food tokens. Travel is hazardous, however. Prey animals need to be alert to possible predators. If they spot a predator, they can use various appropriate prey behaviors, including warning other prey that a predator is near. All prey have two ways to prevent themselves from being caught by predators: they may "freeze" any time a predator is within 5 feet of them, or they may run to cover (have at least one foot within one of the hula hoops.) Frozen prey may blink, but otherwise should be basically still and silent.

7. Predators start the activity anywhere in the open area between ends of the field and thus are randomly distributed between the prey's food and permanent shelter. Predators attempt to capture prey to survive, tagging only moving (not "frozen") prey.

OPTIONAL: Prey can have bandannas in their pockets that the predators have to capture to represent the successful predation. Predators must each capture two prey in order to survive. Captured prey are taken to the sidelines by the predator that captured them.

NOTE: Establish a ground rule for student behavior: Behave in ways that are not harmful to other students, even when simulating predator behavior.

continued

8. Set a time limit of 5 to 7 minutes for each round of the game. (Captured prey on the sidelines will become restless if rounds are much longer.) Remind prey that they can remain frozen for as long as they like, but if they do not have enough food at the end of the activity, they will starve to death. In nature, an animal must balance the need to find food with the sometimes conflicting need for safety.

9. Play four rounds, allowing each student to be both prey and predator.

10. Discuss with the students the ways they escaped capture when they were prey. Which ways were easiest? Which were most effective? What means did they use as predators to capture prey? Which ways were best? What did the predators do in response to a prey animal who "froze"? In what ways are adaptations important to both predator and prey? Ask the students to summarize what they have learned about predator and prey relationships. How do predator and prey relationships serve as natural limiting factors that affect wildlife?

Variations

1. Conduct the activity for three or four rounds, recording the number of captures each playing period. Have the students who are captured become predators, and have each predator that did not acquire enough food in a round become a prey animal in the succeeding round. This feature quickly develops the concept of dynamic balance as prey and predator populations fluctuate in response to each other.

2. Have the students walk or assign different modes of locomotion to each animal.

Extensions

1. Select an animal, and research its behavior patterns for avoiding detection and capture. Reports or demonstrations of the behavior could be presented to the group.

2. Identify an adaptation used by a prey species to stay alive. Have each student create or tell a story about an imaginary person who might have used a similar adaptation to survive a difficult situation.

Aquatic Extensions

1. Conduct this activity using aquatic predator and prey species.

2. "Swim" toward your food while portraying trumpet fish, flounder, stonefish, or other marine organisms that "freeze" as a defense mechanism.

3. If possible, conduct the activity in the shallow end of a real swimming pool.

Evaluation

1. Choose any predator and its prey. Describe each animal's adaptations.

2. Explain the importance of adaptations in predator and prey relationships. What role do predator and prey relationships play in limiting wildlife populations?

3. Draw an imaginary animal that can escape the following:
   - a fast-flying predator
   - a stalking predator
   - a pouncing predator

   Justify your decisions.

4. Write about a predator that can capture the following:
   - a well-camouflaged species
   - a species with excellent eyesight
   - a species that has body armor or quills

   Justify your decisions.

Polar Bears in Phoenix?

Objective
Students will identify problems for an animal that has been moved from its natural environment to captivity.

Method
Students design and draw a zoo enclosure appropriate for the survival of a polar bear in a hot, arid climate.

Materials
Paper and drawing supplies (pens, markers, crayons); OPTIONAL: Students could construct a model using balsa wood or other material.

Background
NOTE: See the Project WILD activity "What Bear Goes Where?"

Polar bears are Arctic animals. They spend 90 percent of their time on floating ice, hunting seals for food. The remaining 10 percent of their time is spent on land. When awake, polar bears are active. They spend considerable amounts of time foraging and hunting for food. They are able to obtain their food from the sea during both of the Arctic seasons: the 3-month summer of continuous daylight and the 9-month long winter. They do, however, range on the tundra in summer, feeding on leaves and fruits of tundra plants and an occasional muskox or caribou, which a polar bear can outrun over short distances. In winter, these bears range over broad distances on the ice as they travel southward to stay near open water and shifting ice flows. They catch birds and seals that come up for air and occasionally dive for fish. When food is scarce they eat seaweed.

An increasing number of zoos are making an effort to display animals in a simulated version of their natural habitat. The local environment must be adapted to suit the animal's wants and needs in order for the animal to survive and thrive. In the case of polar bears, the habitat represents quite a challenge.

In captivity, polar bears do not like being enclosed, which makes it very difficult to gain access for maintenance of their enclosure. On smooth surfaces, they have a habit of twisting around on their hindquarters in such a way that the hind claws get very little use, can grow too long, and—because of the claw's curvature—can become imbedded in the bear's skin. Infant bears require warmth and the solitude of a den during their first several months of life. Male bears, if not kept separately, have been known to kill older cubs.

Grade Level: 5–8

Subject Areas: Science, Environmental Education, Expressive Arts

Duration: one 45-minute session

Group Size: any

Setting: indoors

Conceptual Framework Topic Reference: CAIIA1a, CAIIA1b

Key Terms: zoo, adaptation, survival

Appendices: Using Local Resources

---

continued

In the heat of summer, the bears spend most of their time in the cool recesses of their dens or in the cool, deep water in their pool. When the National Zoo in Washington, D.C. had polar bears, they air-conditioned the dens and installed windows in the side walls of their pool for sub-surface viewing of the animals. The zoo also changed the bear's diet in summer to reduce the thickness of the bear's fat layer, thus keeping the bears cooler.

In designing a zoo enclosure for a polar bear, students should take this information into consideration:

- Polar bears weigh 700 to 900 pounds at maturity, with a length of up to 10 feet. They can jump 10 to 12 feet into the air from a standing position.

- The enclosure should contain everything the animal needs to survive: a sleeping place, hiding place or den for solitude, pool, source of drinking water, food, and space for exercise. The enclosure should look as unlike a cage as possible. The bear's enclosure does not need to be entirely refrigerated. Polar bears need only a cool place in which to retreat. Also consider these elements:
  - temperature (day, night)
  - humidity
  - floor covering
  - slope of floor (for cleaning)
  - color
  - light intensity (day, night)
  - length of day
  - water
  - food, diet
  - plant life
  - air pressure
  - wind velocity and direction
  - maintenance

The major purpose of this activity is for students to recognize that animals are adapted to the environments in which they have lived for a long time. If people move animals to environments different from those for which the animals are adapted, then special attention must be paid to creating conditions in which the animals can live.

Procedure

1. Introduce polar bears to the students with a brief description of their habitat. Point out physical and behavioral adaptations of the polar bears to their natural environment and climate. Try to show the students pictures of both young and mature animals.

2. Tell the students they will each have the opportunity to design their own zoo enclosure for a polar bear that is being moved from its natural habitat in northern Alaska to the desert environment of Phoenix, Arizona. Students should create an environment that replicates (to the extent possible) the characteristics of the environment for which the bear is adapted. What do they need to consider? Compare and contrast the two environments. Identify and describe the bear's habitat needs. What can be done to meet those needs in Phoenix? Students may want to work individually or in teams.

3. Give each student a large piece of paper and drawing supplies. On a separate piece of paper before they begin to draw, have students list some of the major features they would like their enclosure to include, if possible.

4. Display the drawings on a bulletin board. Allow the class time to view the drawings and to discuss merits and drawbacks of the various enclosures.

5. As a summary, discuss some of the problems these bears might have in captivity. Talk about the responsibilities people have to meet the needs of animals that are put in captivity.

Extensions

1. If possible, visit a polar bear at a local zoo.

2. Visit several different kinds of animals in captivity. Where do the animals actually come from? How and why are they there? Compare the animals' natural habitats to those provided in the captive conditions. What differences are there between their quality of life in a zoo and in the wild? What was their original habitat range?

3. Discuss the purposes of placing animals in captivity, and discuss arguments for and against such captivity. What is the current status of their natural habitats? What conservation efforts exist to maintain wild places for each species? What conservation efforts are not being done?

Aquatic Extension

See the Project WILD Aquatic activity "Designing a Habitat."

Evaluation

Describe five challenges a polar bear would face if it were placed in captivity. Suggest possible solutions for each of these challenges, explaining your reasoning.

Adaptation Artistry

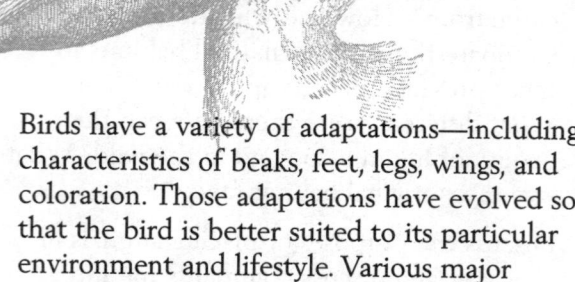

Objectives
Students will (1) identify and describe the advantages of bird adaptations, and (2) evaluate the importance of adaptations to birds.

Method
Students design and create imaginary birds and then write reports including descriptions of the birds' adaptations.

Materials
Drawing, painting, clay sculpture, or papier maché materials; construction paper and glue; pencil and paper

Background
All life forms exhibit adaptations to the environments in which they live. Wildlife species are adapted to their environment in ways that enable them to survive and maintain their populations. Each habitat is suitable only to those life forms that are adapted to their ecological conditions.

Birds have a variety of adaptations—including characteristics of beaks, feet, legs, wings, and coloration. Those adaptations have evolved so that the bird is better suited to its particular environment and lifestyle. Various major adaptations are listed on the next page.

The major purpose of this activity is for students to realize that there are advantages for birds in looking the way they do and for students to recognize some of the ways in which birds are physically adapted to their environments.

Procedure
1. Discuss with the students the various adaptations given in the background chart for this activity. Show the chart on a chalkboard or overhead display screen for reference by the students. Or the students could bring in pictures of birds along with information about their habitat and food. They could then group the data to make their own chart. Have the students brainstorm a list of bird characteristics, name the birds with such characteristics, and describe the advantage of the adaptation represented by the characteristic.

2. Tell the students they will each have a chance to design their own original bird that is adapted to its habitat. Each student should decide
   - where the bird will live,
   - what it will eat,
   - how it moves,
   - its gender or sex, and
   - how it raises its young.

Grade Level: 5–8

Subject Areas: Science, Environmental Education, Expressive Arts, Language Arts

Duration: one or two 45-minute sessions

Group Size: any

Setting: indoors (outdoors optional)

Conceptual Framework Topic Reference: CAIIA, CAIIA1, CAIIB

Key Terms: adaptation

Appendices: Early Education

3. Using these choices, have the students make a list of the adaptations that are necessary for their bird.

4. Using their list of adaptations, have the students create their own original bird by drawing or sculpting it (or by another artistic technique).

5. In conjunction with each drawing or sculpture, have each student write a short report that includes the name of the bird and its food sources, habitat, and lifestyle. Have the students include their lists of adaptations, the reasons for the adaptations, and the advantages provided by the adaptations for the habitat of the bird.

6. Completed projects may be presented to the group or displayed in the room. Ask the students to imagine their bird in a habitat different from the one identified in their report. What specific difficulties might the bird encounter in this new environment? Why? OPTIONAL: Go outside and identify adaptations displayed by real birds.

Extensions

1. Have the students make mobiles of the completed birds.

2. Prepare a slide presentation on an overhead projector or computer showing different types of bird adaptations.

3. Collect pictures of birds to develop a bulletin board showing some of the adaptations discussed. Look for pictures showing bird parts compatible with the "invented" birds. Display the invented birds.

Evaluation

Name two bird adaptations for each of the following body parts, listing their advantages: beaks, feet, legs, wings, and color. Assess the importance of each of these adaptations to a bird's survival in its environment.

Adaptation	Bird	Advantage
Beaks		
• Pouch-like	Pelican	Can hold the fish it eats
• Long, thin	Avocet	Can probe shallow water and mud for the insects it eats
• Pointed	Woodpecker	Can break and probe bark of trees for the insects it eats
• Curved	Hawk	Can tear solid tissue for the meat it eats
• Short, stout	Finch	Can crack the seeds and nuts it eats
• Slender, long	Hummingbird	Can probe the flowers for nectar it eats
Feet		
• Webbed	Duck	Aids in walking on mud
• Long toes	Crane, Heron	Aids in walking on mud
• Clawed	Hawk, Eagle	Can grasp food when hunting prey
• Grasping	Chicken	Aids in sitting on branches, roosting, protection
Legs		
• Flexor tendons	Chicken	Aids in perching, grasping
• Long, powerful	Ostrich	Aids running
• Long, slender	Heron, Crane	Aids wading
• Powerful muscles	Eagle, Hawk	Aids lifting, carrying prey
Wings		
• Large	Eagle	Aids flying with prey, soaring while hunting
Coloration		
• Bright plumage	Male birds	Attraction in courtship, mating rituals
• Dull plumage	Female birds	Aids in camouflage while nesting
• Change of plumage with seasons	Owl, Ptarmigan	Provides camouflage protection (brown in summer, white in winter)

Muskox Maneuvers

Objectives
Students will evaluate the effectiveness of some adaptations in predator and prey relationships.

Method
Students simulate muskoxen and wolves in a physical activity.

Materials
Two different colors of rag flags to use as tails (similar to what is used to play flag football); as many flags as there are wolves and calves

Background
NOTE: Although this activity does not illustrate all the complexities of predator and prey relationships, it does illustrate broad concepts.

Grade Level: 5–8

Subject Areas: Science, Expressive Arts, Environmental Education

Duration: one 20- to 45-minute session

Group Size: 15 to 50; procedures are based on 33 students

Setting: outdoors

Conceptual Framework Topic Reference: CAIIA, CAIIA1b

Key Terms: adaptation, predator, prey, defense, limiting factors, reintroduction

Appendices: Outdoors, Simulations

The muskox is a large, shaggy herbivore called "omingmak" or "the bearded one" by the Inuit. A male muskox weighs between 600 and 800 pounds at maturity and mature females weigh between 400 and 500 pounds. A young muskox may weigh only about 22–31 pounds at birth. These animals inhabit Arctic regions of Alaska, Greenland, and Canada where their long, thick fur protects them from -50° F temperatures and high winds.

Muskoxen often are found in herds of 20 to 30. Both sexes vigorously defend the young, usually forming a line or circle around them, while facing the threatening predator. Such a circle renders the animals relatively safe against natural predators, particularly wolves.

In Alaska, the original muskox population disappeared by 1865, primarily due to over-hunting. Wildlife managers established a reintroduction project to return muskoxen to their original range in Alaska during the 1930's. Thirty-four muskoxen were captured in Greenland and released on Nunivak Island between 1935–1936. The success of this effort is visible in Alaska today, where more than 7,400 muskoxen cover much of their historical range.

In this activity, the roles of bulls and cows are differentiated in ways not typical of actual muskoxen. Again, both sexes vigorously defend the young. They both have stout, pointed horns that help them do this.

The major purpose of this activity is for students to recognize adaptation and limiting factors in a predator and prey relationship.

Procedure

NOTE: This activity is best done outdoors in an open, grassy area; however, it is possible to do the activity indoors—even in a room—if tables, chairs, and desks can be moved to create a large space in which students can freely move, including "tag-like" running.

NOTE: Use the following chart as an initial guide for dividing the class into groups. Educators can vary the proportions in later rounds to respond to what happens in the simulations.

Total Players	Wolves	Bulls	Cows and Calves
15–18	2	3	Equal number or one more cow than calf
19–28	2	4	Equal number or one more cow than calf
29–35	3	6	Equal number or one more cow than calf
36–45	4	8	Equal number or one more cow than calf
46–50	5	10	Equal number or one more cow than calf

1. Divide the class into four groups. (For example, a group of 33 students would break down into 3 wolves, 6 bulls, 12 cows, and 12 calves.) Each will have a distinctive role.

2. Give the wolves and calves the appropriate flag, and have each one wear the flag so it is hanging out of a back pocket or looped over a belt in the back. The flags need to be visible and easily removable.

3. Next, tell the students the following information: Muskoxen are herbivores (plant-eaters) and often graze peacefully in meadows. While grazing, they spread out. Calves typically do not stray too far from their mothers, but the animals do not always stay clustered—except when predators appear. As the activity begins, the students representing muskoxen are grazing peacefully and the wolves are out of sight of the herd.

4. Show students that these are the behaviors each animal should exhibit:

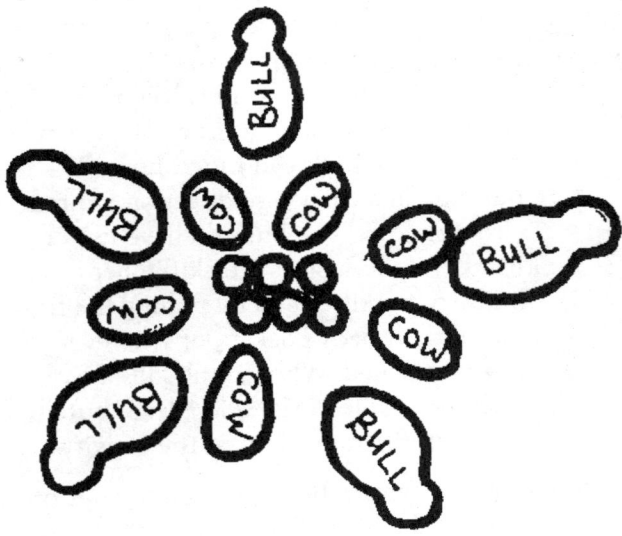

Cows: As soon as grazing begins, the cows should choose a lead cow to watch for predators. The cows should pick a signal that the lead cow will use to communicate to the rest of the herd that predators (wolves) are approaching. When the lead cow signals that predators are near, all the cows move to form a circle around the calves to protect the calves from the wolves. With the calves in the center of a circle, the cows stand with their backs to the calves, facing outward to watch the wolves. The cows can move very little. Mostly, they stay firmly in one place, moving their upper bodies to block the wolves from reaching the calves. The cows cannot touch the wolves with their hands or feet.

Calves: The calves depend totally upon the cows for protection. Each calf is to hold onto a cow with both hands on the cow's waist, and follow only the cow's lead. Calves cannot influence the cows' movement.

continued

Bulls: The bulls are the active defenders of the cows and the calves. As the predators near, the bulls form a circle around the cows, which in turn are forming a circle around the calves. The bulls form as tight a circle as they can around the cows and calves, never any farther than one step in front of the circle of cows. The bulls can move, however—but only in a clockwise direction around the circle of cows. The bulls do have use of their hands. As the wolves attack the herd, the bulls try to "kill" them by pulling the flags out of their back pockets, or wherever the flag is attached. When a bull kills a wolf, the wolf moves off to the side, "dead" but able to watch the remainder of the activity.

Wolves: Wolves begin the activity out of sight of the herd. They try to get as close as possible to the herd without being detected. Wolves typically work as a unit so they can attempt a strategy for surprising the herd in order to kill the calves for food. The wolves are mobile, able to move at any time in any direction. They can use any maneuver (except pushing and shoving) to break the herd's defenses. Once a wolf kills a calf— by pulling the calf's flag out of its pocket— temporarily stop the game and move the calf's carcass to the side, where it, too, can watch the remainder of the activity.

A Note About Sound Effects: Wolves can howl to communicate predetermined signals and to startle and confuse the muskoxen. The muskoxen can moo loudly.

5. Review these muskox maneuvers:

The muskox herd grazes quietly. The wolves are out of sight of the herd. The wolves move to attack the herd. When the lead cow spots wolves, the herd begins its defense. The muskoxen form a circle, with calves in the center, cows facing out in a circle around the calves, and bulls in an outer circle, also facing the wolves. Each should behave appropriately, as described above.

6. Remember that the activity can conclude in several ways. For example,
   - All the wolves could be killed.
   - All the calves could be killed.
   - The wolves could give up in frustration after a period of time with no success in killing a calf.
   - The wolves could kill one or more calves, and the activity would conclude because you know that the wolves are going to eat the calf (or calves) and the herd will move on.

7. Once the excitement and enthusiasm have peaked, sit down with the students to discuss what happened and what the activity represents in terms of animal adaptation and predator and prey relationships. Ask the students to describe and evaluate the predatory behavior of the wolves and the various defense behaviors of the muskoxen. What would happen if the wolves could not get into the herd? What would happen if the wolves always got into the herd? Ask the students to distinguish between what would be actual, typical behaviors of muskoxen contrasted with their behaviors in this activity.

8. Ask the students to brainstorm or research other examples of predator and prey relationships. Describe and evaluate the strategies of the predators and the prey in each example. How effective are these behavioral adaptations in enhancing the survivability of the species involved?

Variation

As mentioned earlier, this activity differentiates the roles of bulls and cows in ways not typical of actual muskoxen. To more naturally model muskox behavior, alter the activity in the following way:

Widely scatter food tokens (poker chips, drinking straws) across the playing field. Instruct the muskoxen to walk around the playing area and pick up food tokens. This action will simulate dispersed feeding patterns. The muskoxen may not group together in a defensive posture until receiving the signal from the lead cow that a wolf is near. Allow both cows and bulls to reach for a wolf's flag. Cows still cannot use their hands or feet to block wolves. Permit bulls to move in either direction. In real life, both cows and bulls aggressively defend their young. Have students brainstorm for strategies to work as a herd to protect the young. Repeat the activity. How did the group strategy change the outcome?

Extensions

1. A few students can research and report back to the class with more details about the life and times of muskoxen and wolves—acquiring additional information about their survival needs, habitat, and behaviors.

2. Investigate predatory and defense behaviors of different species in different habitats. For example, selected species of plains, forest, desert, and ocean animals can be compared.

Aquatic Extension

Many fish species also have effective adaptations that serve to protect them from predator species. Have one student be a predator and the rest of the students be prey. This time, the predator is a tuna, and the prey are herring in a school of fish. (Educators can pick their own example of predator and prey. Just pick a prey species that forms a school of fish.) Pantomime the school of fish moving through waters with the predator trying to catch at least one prey for food to survive. In a large open area, have the students move as the school of fish. Have three or four students inside the school of fish wear a bright-colored cloth or tie that the predator will try to remove in order to have successfully caught its prey. The school of fish must keep moving. See if the school of fish can successfully move the length of the open area at least once without any fish being caught by the predator. The predator may move in any direction and may stop and start moving at any time. The prey must move generally together and may not stop.

Evaluation

Identify a prey species and its predator species. Describe how each is adapted to the other. How does the prey protect itself? How does the predator overcome this protection? Describe the overall effectiveness of each animal's adaptations.

I'm Thirsty

Objective
Students will make inferences about the importance of adaptations in order for wildlife and other animals to survive.

Method
Students use data provided to perform mathematical calculations and to make inferences.

Materials
Paper and pencils

Background
NOTE: See the Project WILD activities "Adaptation Artistry" and "Muskox Maneuvers."

Desert bighorn sheep (*Ovis canadensis nelsoni*) are found from Nevada and California to western Texas and south into Mexico. Most populations move seasonally from upland areas in the summer to sheltered valleys during the winter. The availability of escape territory in the form of rocky cliffs is important to the survival of bighorn sheep. If a sheep can reach a rocky outcrop or cliff, it is usually safe from predators. Because they cannot paw through deep snow to feed, bighorn sheep also require drier slopes where there is less annual snowfall.

Bighorns have a complex digestive system that allows them to remove nutrients from poor quality food. Desert bighorns eat a variety of desert plants and get most of their moisture from the vegetation, although they still visit water holes every several days. If green vegetation is available, desert bighorn do not require drinking water.

Bighorn sheep can gather in herds of more than 100 individuals, although small groups of 8 to 10 are more common. Bighorn sheep are known for head-to-head combat between males. Horn size is a symbol of rank. The horns are used by the sheep to battle an opponent. Combat can last a full day until one of the males concedes. Males do not defend territories but fight over mating access to a particular female.

The major purpose of this activity is for students to manipulate simple data in order to heighten their awareness of the importance of adaptations to wildlife.

Procedure
1. Provide the students with the background information from I'm Thirsty, on the next page, which is about desert bighorn sheep.

Grade Level: 6–8

Subject Areas: Mathematics, Science, Environmental Education

Duration: one 45-minute session

Group Size: any

Setting: indoors

Conceptual Framework Topic Reference: CAIIA1, CAIIA1a

Key Terms: adaptation, inflow

Appendices: Metric Chart

Ecological Knowledge

I'm Thirsty

Animals can have incredible adaptations in order to survive in their environments. Use the following hypothetical example of the desert bighorn sheep: The desert bighorn live in dry, sparsely vegetated areas of the southwestern United States. Temperatures on summer days are frequently over 100° F (37.8° C). During the hottest months of summer, ewes (females) and lambs come to waterholes almost daily. The male sheep (rams) sometimes do not come to water for nearly a week at a time. Rams may roam 20 miles (32 kilometers) away from the available water supply. Add 20 miles (32 kilometers) to the approximately 5 miles (8 kilometers) traveled per day, and rams may travel almost 75 miles (120 kilometers) before they drink again. Rams are believed to drink approximately 4 gallons (15.2 liters) of water when they do come to water, while an ewe drinks approximately 1 gallon (3.8 liters) and a lamb drinks 2 pints (940 milliliters).

2. Given the background information, ask the students to carry out these calculations:

Questions for Students

1. How many miles to the gallon (or kilometers per liter) does a ram get?
2. How many gallons (or liters) of water would a ram drink in a month?
3. How many gallons (or liters) of water would a ewe drink in a month?
4. How many gallons (or liters) of water would a lamb drink in a month?
5. How much water must be available in a waterhole for 10 rams, 16 ewes, and 7 lambs in order for them to survive the months of June, July, and August?
6. What rate of inflow would a waterfall have to have to sustain the population given above if water evaporated at a rate of 10 gallons (38 liters) per day?

Answer Key for Teachers (English)

1. 75 miles/week ÷ 4 gallons/week = 18.75 miles/gallon

2. 52 weeks/year ÷ 12 months/year = 4.33 weeks/month
   4 gallons/week × 4.33 weeks/month = 17.32 gallons/month

3. 1 gallon/day × 7 days/week = 7 gallons/week
   7 gallons/week × 4.33 weeks/month = 30.31 gallons/month

4. 2 pints/day × 7 days/week = 14 pints/week
   Convert to gallons
   8 pints = 1 gallon
   14 pints/week ÷ 8 pints/gallon = 1.75 gallons/week
   1.75 gallons/week × 4.33 weeks/month = 7.58 gallons/month

5. June = 30 days, July = 31 days, August = 31 days, 92 days total
   This approach assumes there is no water evaporation and no rainfall—both of which are poor assumptions.
   Rams: 4 gallons/week ÷ 7 days/week = 0.57 gallons/day
           0.57 gallons/day × 92 days × 10 rams = 524 gallons of water for rams
   Ewes: 1 gallon/day × 92 days × 16 ewes = 1,472 gallons for ewes
   Lambs: First, convert daily water consumption to gallons.
           8 pints = 1 gallon
           2 pints/day ÷ by 8 pints/gallon = 0.25 gallons/day
           0.25 gallons/day × 92 days × 7 lambs = 161 gallons of water for lambs

   Total gallons for herd:
   524 (rams) + 1,472 (ewes) + 161 (lambs) = 2,157 gallons of water for herd

6. 2,157 gallons of water ÷ 92 days = 23.45 gallons/day for herd
   23.45 gallons/day + 10 gallons to make up for evaporation = 33.45 gallons/day rate of inflow from a waterfall

continued

Answer Key for Teachers (Metric)

1. 120 kilometers/week ÷ 15.2 liters/week = 7.89 kilometers/liter

2. 15.2 liters/week × 4.33 weeks/month = 65.8 liters/month

3. 3.8 liters/day × 7 days /week = 26.6 liters/week
   26.6 liters/week × 4.33 weeks/month = 115 liters/month

4. 940 milliliters/day × 7 days/week = 6,580 milliliters/month
   Convert to liters: 1,000 milliliters = 1 liter
   6,580 milliliters/week ÷ 1,000 milliliters/liter = 6.58 liters/week
   6.58 liters/week × 4.33 weeks/month = 28.5 liters/month

5. Rams: 15.2 liters/week ÷ 7 days a week = 2.17 liters/day
   2.17 liters/day × 92 days x 10 rams = 1,996 liters of water for the rams
   Ewes: 3.8 liters/day × 92 days x 16 ewes = 5,594 liters of water for the ewes
   Lambs: first convert daily water consumption to liters:
   1,000 milliliters = 1 liter
   940 milliliters ÷ 1,000 milliliters/liter = 0.94 liters/day
   0.94 liters/day × 92 days x 7 lambs = 605 liters of water for lambs
   Total liters for the herd:
   1,996 (rams) + 5,594 (ewes) + 605 (lambs) = 8,195 liters for the herd

6. 8,195 liters of water ÷ 92 days = 89 liters/day for the herd
   88.5 liters/day + 38 liters to make up for evaporation = 127 liters/day of inflow from a waterfall

---

3. Predict various complications that could develop if there were only one-half the amount of water calculated in Question 5.

4. Discuss the importance of adaptations to wildlife and other animals, as you use the example of the bighorn sheep in the southwestern United States.

NOTE: This activity can be used effectively as an extension or review for other activities about adaptation.

Extensions

1. Study topographical maps of typical desert bighorn sheep habitat. Predict the animals' food requirements on the basis of available vegetation. Research caloric value of available foods. Estimate the animals' caloric intake per day, per week, and per year.

2. Research the available seasonal water supply in a desert bighorn sheep's habitat area. Predict the seasonal maximum carrying capacity of the site according to water supply.

3. Compare the bighorn sheep's daily water usage to human daily water usage. Use as a point from which to discuss the importance of water conservation—to people, domesticated animals, wildlife, industry, and natural resources.

Evaluation

Discuss the importance of adaptation. Describe examples of adaptation and its importance to any species of animal other than bighorn sheep.

Forest in a Jar

Objective

Students will observe, describe, and investigate the concept of succession.

Methods

Students conduct a simple investigation using soil, water, seeds, a plant, and a jar; present their observations and findings; and design an experiment to further investigate the concept of succession.

Materials

Quart jar or clear 2-liter plastic soda bottle per small group, water, soil, aquatic plants (one per jar), two cups of bird and sunflower seed, writing materials for journals

Grade Level: 9–12

Subject Areas: Science, Environmental Education, Language Arts

Duration: 5 to 10 minutes for one or two days a week for several weeks; one class session for summary activities, presentations and additional designs implemented in class.

Group Size: any

Setting: indoors; outdoors optional

Conceptual Framework Topic Reference: CAIB, CAIB1, CAIB1a

Key Terms: evaporation, change, succession

Appendices: Outdoors, Field Ethics

Background

Succession is a term used to describe changes in an environment over time. Such changes affect the kinds of wildlife that live in the environment. Most forests, grasslands, deserts, and other lands are actively changing in character. Many of those changes happen slowly, giving the human observer an impression of a stable environment. Some changes literally happen overnight, as in the case of a fire.

Succession generally is thought of as an orderly process. Theoretically, succession begins with bare ground and is completed when a climax forest, grassland, or other environment becomes established. Seral or early successional plants are generally short-lived, thrive in sunlight, colonize rapidly, and spread their seeds far and wide. Roadsides, recent burns, forest harvesting, and other areas of recent disturbance are good places to find examples of early succession.

The first plants to become established in an area change the environment by adding nutrients to the soil from fallen leaves and other plant parts and by providing shade to the soil. This change allows different plants to grow. The presence of these newer plants changes the environment to allow even later stage successional plants to develop. Climax or late successional plants usually thrive in shade, live a long time, and reproduce more slowly. A plant community has reached a climax state when the plants present generally maintain the same population size over time. Old growth forests are good examples of a climax stage of succession.

continued

Succession influences what kinds of animals live in an area. As succession proceeds from a young system to an older one or vice versa, the habitat available to animals changes character. Therefore, the kinds of animals that live in the area are associated with the area's stage of succession.

Ponds provide another example of succession. As a shallow pond fills with sediment, marshy plants often are established. As the soil dries even more, land plants move onto the old pond shore. Eventually, what was a pond can become a forest many years later.

In this activity, students will be able to see in miniature how a wetland area can be succeeded by a forest habitat. The major purpose of this activity is for students to recognize the process of succession.

Procedure

1. Divide the class into small groups. Have each group of students place 2 inches of soil and 3 inches of water in a jar. Place the jar at a window, without a lid, and allow it to settle overnight.

2. Allow the groups to plant an aquatic plant in their jar. It should grow well in this environment. If the classroom has no windows, substitute with artificial light such as a grow-light.

3. Ask the students to predict what will happen to the plant and the environment in the jar if seeds are added on a continuous basis but water is not. Have the students begin a portfolio to record their predictions.

4. Once or twice a week, have students add three or four bird seeds to the jar. Do not replace the water that evaporates from the jar. While there is water in the jar, the seeds should germinate and then rot. Continue adding seeds even after the water evaporates. Have the students record their observations of the soil, water, and plants in their journals each day. Periodically provide specific questions to focus the attention of the students and to develop critical thinking skills. For instance, "Why do you think the seeds rot after germinating in the water?" The students should also draw or photograph their jars at regular intervals. If digital cameras are available, the groups can save this data in a file for their report later. Ask students to maintain a record of the numbers, types, or heights of certain plants.

5. As the water evaporates down to the soil, the aquatic plant will die. The bird seeds now will typically find the environment suitable for successful growth. Sunflower seeds, which grow large, can be added to represent forest trees. Now have the students add water as a substitute for rainfall. (They should all add the same amount—just enough to keep the soil damp and to keep things growing.)

6. Have each student make a poster, drawing, or other visual representation of what he or she saw happen to the "pond." The students can represent any numerical data in graph form. (If they have access to digital equipment, a computer presentation of the development would be possible.) Ask them to summarize in their journals what they learned about how environments can change. Introduce the term "succession." What parallels are evident between the "pond" in the jar and a real pond? What would have happened if the lid were left on the jar? Explain how this closed system would or would not represent pond succession.

7. Ask each group to brainstorm three questions the students have about the sequence of events that occurred in the jar. Have them design another investigation to answer one of their questions. Make sure that the students consider practicality and safety precautions in their designs. Pick one or more of the designs for the class to try. OPTIONAL: Take a field trip to a pond. What plants are growing in the water? What plants are growing on the shore? What evidence is there that succession is taking place? Compare the real pond to the pond in the jar.

Extensions

1. Establish several jars and vary the amount of water you add to each. One jar may be the "desert" jar that does not receive much additional water. The other extreme may be the jar that maintains its "pond" status. Several other jars would contain amounts of water somewhere in between. Identify and describe what the differences in "rainfall" mean to the plant communities that develop in each jar.

2. Experiment with different kinds of soils. For example, try three different kinds of soils and water each as if it were a "desert" environment. See what differences, if any, emerge.

Evaluation

The journals, presentations, graphs, and investigation designs serve as the evaluation.

Fire Ecologies

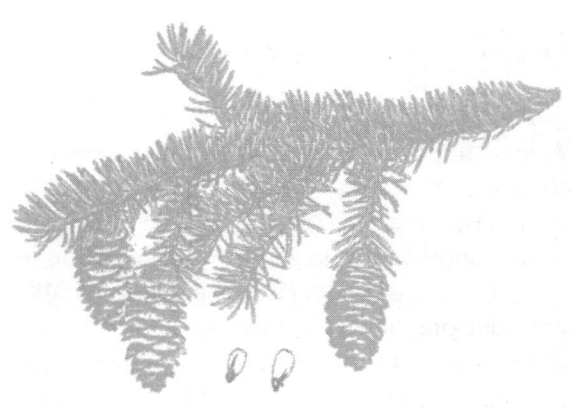

Objective
Students will identify, describe, and evaluate the positive and negative effects that forest and grassland fires have on wildlife.

Method
Students conduct a field investigation.

Materials
Soil analysis equipment (e.g., pH testing paper), containers for soil samples, plant and animal identification guides for field work, or classroom speaker, or access to library, Internet, and other reference materials

Background
NOTE: See the Project WILD activity "Smokey Bear Said What?" for a similar activity for younger students.

> **Grade Level:** 9–12
>
> **Subject Areas:** Science, Environmental Education
>
> **Duration:** three or four 45-minute sessions or longer, not including transportation to and from field sites
>
> **Group Size:** any
>
> **Setting:** indoors, outdoors if field research is possible
>
> **Conceptual Framework Topic Reference:** CAIB1b, CAIB1c, CAIB1d, CAIB2, CAIIB
>
> **Key Terms:** wild, controlled, prescribed fire, ecology, management, species, organic, inorganic
>
> **Appendices:** Ecosystem, Agencies and Organizations, Using Local Resources

The environment is always changing, sometimes subtly and sometimes dramatically. Fire is one of the important natural agents of change. Fire has helped shape North America's open spaces for thousands of years and has been essential for the survival of many plants and animals. (Source: U.S. Forest Service, 2000).

Whereas once all fires were suppressed or vigorously fought, today many fires are allowed to burn as part of a natural cycle within forest and grassland ecosystems. We have learned that the lack of periodic fire in many wild areas increases risks to society and the environment. In remote areas, some agencies monitor lightning-ignited wildfires and allow them to burn as long as they stay within "prescribed" limits of fire behavior and location. However, wildfires near populated areas still are fought aggressively. In fact, there has been a movement to "prescribe" fires under some conditions and in some places in an effort to replicate natural cycles that contribute to maintaining healthy ecosystems.

Such "prescribed burns" are planned and tended by qualified resource managers. Prescribed burns frequently are designed to reduce the fuel load in a given area. Reducing the fuel load in a forested area, for example, can prevent fires from becoming so hot that they eliminate virtually all life forms and even scorch the soil. That is, fires every 5 to 10 years in some forest types can clear the heavy under story without harming the larger trees in the forest. Accumulation of brush and under story can cause intensely hot and destructive fires. Intense and uncontrolled wildfire risks damage to soil, watersheds and air quality.

Objectives for use of fire as a management tool are variable. Objectives may include restoring fire's role in the natural cycle within a particular ecosystem, eradicating some plant species, and promoting the stimulation of plant species that are preferred food by some wildlife. In some areas, fire is the most cost-effective tool to manage habitats.

Prescribed burns are planned and initiated by qualified professionals who are trained in using fire for resource management objectives. Prescribed fires are used only after burn plans are approved. Those plans must specify objectives for the fire; its location, size, and type, how the fire will be started and controlled, and how the smoke from the fire will be managed. Fire plans set limits for weather parameters that control how hot a fire burns and in which direction smoke dissipates. Fires outside of those limits will not be started.

Students may ask why—if some fires are helpful—the U.S Forest Service's motto says, "Only you can prevent wildfires." This message is aimed at humans causing fires by error and accidents, such as carelessness in camping situations. The message also warns us about the terrible destructiveness of arson or fires set intentionally by people. Accidental and arson fires often are started near developed areas and occur during times of severe drought or high winds. This kind of wildfire can be terribly destructive.

Fires can have negative as well as positive effects. If a fire is too large, too fast, and too hot, wildlife can't move easily to safety. Individual animals may die or be displaced from their habitat. Short-term and long-term loss of vegetation can have a variety of effects, including loss of food and shelter for wildlife and an increase in silt and sedimentation in the waters.

Examples of positive effects and benefits are that fires can

- maintain and enhance fire-dependent habitats such as prairies, savannas, chaparral, jack pine forests, southern pine forests, and boreal forests;
- provide habitats for species that depend primarily on fire-driven ecosystems such as the jack pine warbler;
- increase soil productivity by releasing and recycling nutrients in litter and undergrowth;
- prepare soil for germination of some seeds;
- activate heat-dependent seed varieties such as lodgepole pines, jack pine, and black spruce;
- contribute to an "edge effect," providing a greater variety of food and shelter sources for some species of wildlife; and
- open up habitat, generating new growth, diversity, and abundance of food plants such as food for large herbivores.

The major purpose of this activity is for students to become familiar with positive and negative effects of fire on wildlife species and their habitat.

Procedure

1. Begin this activity with a discussion of forest and grassland fires. Students' reactions may be negative at first. Point out that while one harmful effect of forest and grassland fires is the destruction of habitat and the killing of wildlife, in some cases fire improves habitat and contributes to the long-term well-being of wildlife.

2. Brainstorm positive and negative consequences of forest and grassland fires for wildlife. Specify kinds of wildlife and give examples.

continued

3. Take a field trip to a forest or grassland where it is possible to see areas that have been recently burned, areas burned 10 or more years ago, and areas not burned in recorded history. Try to arrange to go with an ecologist or wildlife biologist who can point out and explain some of the similarities and differences among the various areas.

NOTE: If such a trip is not possible or additional information is needed, contact a regional forester, state wildlife agency, soil conservation district representative, or other resource person for information on the subject. It may be possible for a representative of the agency to come to the classroom and talk with the students about different circumstances under which fire can be helpful and harmful to wildlife—possibly bringing slides or a film on the subject. If neither the field trip nor the visit from a resource person is possible, the students will need to work from library and other reference materials on their own. The agencies mentioned above may be able to provide you with before and after photographs of such sites.

4. If the field trip is possible, prepare students to (a) make and record their observations (e.g., variety and quantity of vegetation, evidence of wildlife, actual sightings of wildlife); and (b) with permission of the landholder, take small soil samples in the various areas for testing purposes. Back in class, these soil samples should be tested for structure, organic and inorganic parts, chemical composition, and so on.

5. Ask the students to organize and present the findings of their research. For example, they could chart information as outlined in Table A.

6. Ask the students to summarize their findings, including short-term and long-term effects to wildlife in each area, both positive and negative, in a table. See Table B. They could include in their summary an assessment of the importance of fire in natural systems, as well as of its effectiveness as a management tool. In the situations they studied, ask them to evaluate the role of fire, including its positive and negative consequences. Their findings could include a listing of those situations and forest types in which fire generally is most beneficial, those in which it is most harmful, and those where it has little effect. Ask them to address any limitations to their study (i.e., any aspects of their research that prevent them from generalizing their findings to all fires affecting wildlife).

Table A

Field Investigation Data

	Recent Fire Area	Fire 10–15 Years Ago	No Recorded Fire
Soil Data			
Plant Species			
Associated Wildlife/ Evidence of Wildlife			
Wildlife Observed			

Extensions

1. Also discuss other impacts from wild and controlled burns. What is the public attitude toward fires in forest and grassland areas? What is the broad range of consequences from fires and lack of fires on the local economy, aesthetic value, ecological value, and agricultural value? What are the benefits and challenges in allowing and preventing fires?

2. Develop a set of recommendations for conditions under which fires should and should not be allowed. Check your recommendations against present guidelines used by the U.S. Forest Service, U.S. Fish and Wildlife Service, National Park Service, Bureau of Land Management, Bureau of Indian Affairs, local state foresters' office, and other state and federal agencies involved in fire management. (See "Agencies and Organizations" in the Appendices.)

3. Research the history of fire management in the United States. Contrast policies of the North Americans and federal agencies. Compare public attitude toward forest and grassland fires today with attitudes during the 1930s and 1940s.

4. Add a study of succession to this activity.

Evaluation

1. Describe two differences between forest land and grassland that is burned frequently and forest land and grassland that is never burned.

2. Identify 10 species of plants and animals that are frequently helped by fire and 10 that tend to do better when fire is absent in grasslands or forests—and describe the circumstances or reasons involved in each case.

3. The U.S. Forest Service has hired a new information specialist in one of the regional offices. It is evident that the general public in the region has little understanding of the role of fire in natural systems. How can the information specialist effectively communicate with the public in order to provide a balanced and informed view of the subject? Design a radio, television, or magazine advertisement that conveys that point of view.

Additional Resources

www.blm.gov/education/fire_and_weeds.html

Table B

Consequences to Species

	Short-Term Benefit	Long-Term Benefit	Short-Term Harm	Long-Term Harm
Plants				
Animals				

Move Over Rover

Objectives
Students will (1) list factors that influence the distribution of animals in ecosystems, and (2) generalize that each ecosystem has characteristic animals adapted to live there.

Method
Students play a game in which the object is to identify characteristic animals found in several ecosystems and to match those animals to the environment in which they live.

Materials
Animal Cards (pages 146–150), materials for creating eight ecosystem posters, Educator Answer Key (Educators may want to laminate Animal Cards for long-term use.)

Background
Ecosystem diversity is affected by many influences, such as climate and the level of human disturbance. Animal diversity is generally higher where there is a mild climate and an abundance of food and cover, or where ecosystems overlap. New ecosystems and ecosystems that are harsh tend to have relatively few species because not many species are adapted to the extreme conditions.

The most fundamental of life's necessities for any animal are food, water, shelter, and space in a suitable arrangement. Without these essential components, animals cannot survive. Most animals' requirements for food, shelter, and nesting and breeding sites are often tailored to their ecosystems. However, different kinds of animals respond differently to environmental variables. Consequently, few animals fit neatly into a single ecosystem. Some animals reside in certain ecosystems year-round, while others migrate to different altitudes or latitudes seasonally. Still other species move among ecosystems on a time scale of days to weeks, using one area for feeding and another for reproduction.

Procedure
1. Copy the Animal Cards and cut them apart.

2. Divide the class into eight teams, and have each team research the biotic and abiotic characteristics (temperature, precipitation, and vegetation) of one of the following North American ecosystems: forest (mostly conifers), woodland (mostly hardwoods), shrub land, grassland, aquatic/riparian, desert/semi-desert, tundra, and subalpine. (Unlike tundra, subalpine ecosystems have trees such as fir, spruce, and aspen.) Ask each team to write a paragraph and to make a poster depicting the ecosystem.

3. When the posters are complete, ask a member from each team to read the description of that ecosystem. Ask all students to listen carefully to the information presented.

Grade Level: 5–6

Subject Areas: Science, Expressive Arts, Environmental Education

Duration: two 45-minute periods

Group Size: eight teams of three to four students

Setting: outdoors or indoors

Conceptual Framework Topic References: BDIA1, BDIB1, BDIB3

Key Terms: ecosystem, diversity, habitat

Appendices: Ecosystem Concept

4. Divide the playing space into eight equal portions, and place one ecosystem poster in a visible place in each portion.

5. Divide the class into eight equal groups so that the original teams are evenly distributed among these new groups. Ask each group to stand under one of the ecosystem posters.

6. Explain to the groups that they will be playing a game in which the object is to match animals to the environment in which they live. Explain that each student will receive a card giving information about an animal that lives in a particular ecosystem. The class will need to decide if the animal is already in the ecosystem in which it could live or if it must "Move Over Rover" to another ecosystem.

7. Distribute the Animal Cards to the students.

8. One by one, ask students to read their cards and guess the animal depicted. If they believe they are in the wrong ecosystem, they can voluntarily move over to the proper one. If classmates think a student has made an incorrect choice, they say, "Move Over Rover" and then explain why the animal should move and to which ecosystem it should move.

9. When all of the animals have been placed in an ecosystem, discuss the following questions:

- Has each animal been placed in its proper ecosystem? If not, why not?
- Were there any animals that could be placed in more than one ecosystem?
- How can some animals live in more than one ecosystem, and why can't others?
- What are the similarities and differences between animals that live in a certain ecosystem?
- Which ecosystems had the greatest diversity of animals? What characteristics of these ecosystems were supportive of a higher diversity?
- What factors influence the distribution of animals among ecosystems?

10. Ask the students to work with their original team members and to research other animals that live in their ecosystems. What similarities in habitat requirements exist among the animals found there? How are their adaptations related to climatic conditions?

Evaluation

Pick any three animals from the leftover cards. Ask students to describe the ecosystem in which each animal lives, including identification of the animal's habitat requirements.

This activity was adapted with permission from "Wonders in Nature—Wonders in Neighborhoods" (W.I.N.—W.I.N.) Unit 5 Curriculum Guide, Colorado Division of Wildlife, and Denver Zoological Foundation.

continued

Ecological Knowledge

Move Over Rover

Animal Cards

1. This bird likes to fly close to the ground and lives in open or semi-open areas. It builds nests of mud and grass.

2. This mammal lives in deserts, forests, and grasslands near rocky outcrops. It feeds on crickets, grasshoppers, scorpions, and spiders.

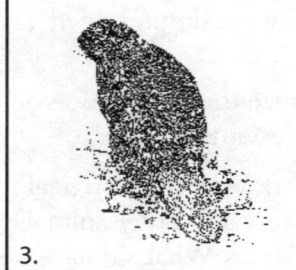
3. This mammal feeds on the inner layer of tree bark with the help of its large front teeth. It blocks streams and rivers with its dam.

4. This mammal must be sure-footed to reach the sparse grass upon which it feeds.

5. This mammal hunts at night and makes its den in rock crevices and hollow logs.

6. This amphibian is an incredibly small wood toad.

7. This bird hunts at night. It lives in underground burrows of animals.

8. This insect's larvae feed on crops of alfalfa.

9. This animal feeds on seeds and acorns near streams and is common around camp sites.

10. This mammal eats small rodents, rabbits, and birds. It also eats the remains of animals killed by wolves and mountain lions.

Project WILD K–12 Curriculum and Activity Guide

Animal Cards

11. This mammal nests in the ground, in trees, and in stumps. It eats seeds, nuts, and acorns, and it stores its food.

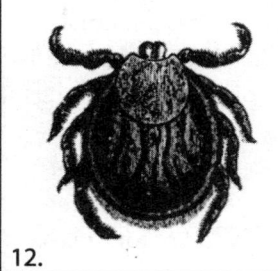
12. This tick feeds on the blood of mammals.

13. This insect lays its eggs in water. The mature insect can be seen flying and using its large wings.

14. This mammal's haunting mating calls echo through the high-country in late fall.

15. This bird hunts large rodents, such as rabbits, during the day. It uses its keen eyesight to locate prey as it soars in the sky.

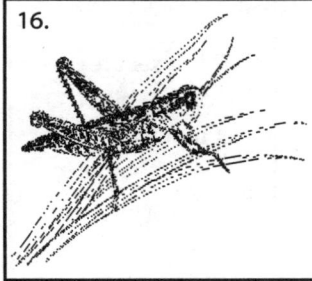
16. This insect eats large amounts of vegetation. It lives in places that produce lots of green plants.

17. This bird uses its long legs to walk through still water and to hunt fish and water snakes.

18. This bird hunts at night for rodents and snakes. It gets its name from the two tufts of feathers on the top of its head.

19. This mammal uses its strong hind legs to escape predators.

20. This mammal gets the water it needs from the plants it eats.

continued

Ecological Knowledge

Move Over Rover

Animal Cards

 21.	This mammal can live in many kinds of places near water. It often nests in the burrows of other animals or under wood or rock piles.	 22.	This mammal is a good swimmer. It often feeds on grasses, seeds, and bark.
 23.	This mammal is an excellent swimmer. It eats eggs, frogs, crayfish, birds, and fish.	 24.	This large mammal eats twigs and bark in winter and water plants in summer in areas where beavers are common.
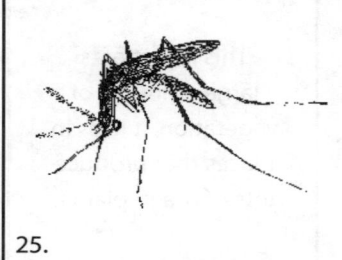 25.	This insect feeds on the blood of many animals. It lays its eggs in still water.	 26.	This mammal eats brush and sparse grasses. Its name comes from its large ears.
 27.	This mammal eats mostly aquatic plants but it may also eat frogs, clams, and other aquatic animals.	 28.	Once nearly extinct, this fast predatory bird has made a remarkable recovery since the ban of the pesticide DDT.
 29.	This mammal eats the bark of pine trees. It protects itself with its sharp, pointed quills.	 30.	This mammal's burrow provides homes for other animals, including burrowing owls.

Ecological Knowledge

Move Over Rover

Animal Cards

31. This mammal runs incredibly fast in the wide-open spaces it lives in.

32. This mammal eats many foods and may dunk the food in water before eating. It often lives in hollow logs.

33. This brightly colored fish has been stocked in many areas and has moved into the territories of many native species.

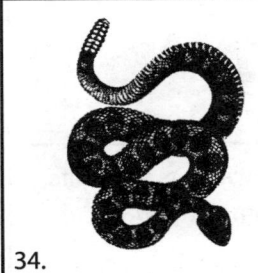
34. This reptile warns intruders to stay away with its rattling sound.

35. This mammal uses its hunting skills to catch deer mice and other small mammals.

36. This bird roosts in flocks near open water or in open areas.

37. This fish-eating mammal lives along streams, lakes, marshes, and rivers.

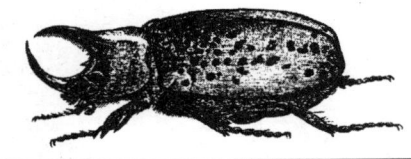
38. This insect does not develop large wings because of high winds.

39. This mammal comes out at night, and it sleeps in ground burrows, wood, or rock piles.

40. This mammal changes color with the seasons, which allows it to escape predators.

continued

Ecological Knowledge

Move Over Rover

Animal Cards

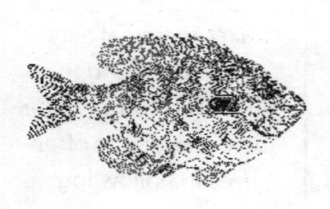 41.	This popular catch for anglers is very colorful.	 42.	This spider looks dangerous, but it hunts only insects.
 43.	This amphibian lives in or near water its entire life. It lives in mud at the bottom of the water during winter.	 44.	This bird survives the extremely cold winters by roosting in snow drifts and by eating energy-rich willow buds. Its plumage is snow-white in the winter and mottled brown in the summer.
 45.	This bird eats insects that live under the bark of trees.	 46.	Larvae of this insect feed on yucca flowers.

Educator Answer Key
(Answers may vary for local species.)

Animal	Habitat	Animal	Habitat
1. Barn swallow	Grasslands/Riparian	26. Mule deer	Woodland/Shrub land/Forest
2. Bat	All terrestrial ecosystems	27. Muskrat	Aquatic/Riparian
3. Beaver	Aquatic/Riparian (in forest)	28. Peregrine falcon	Shrub land/Woodland/Forest (near cliffs)
4. Bighorn sheep	Tundra	29. Porcupine	Forest
5. Bobcat	Forest/Riparian/Shrub land	30. Prairie dog	Grassland
6. Boreal toad	Subalpine (in forest)	31. Pronghorn antelope	Grassland
7. Burrowing owl	Grassland	32. Raccoon	Riparian/Woodlands
8. Butterfly	Grassland/Forest	33. Rainbow trout	Aquatic (in subalpine)
9. Chipmunk	Forest/Riparian/Woodland	34. Rattlesnake	Grassland/Semi-desert/Shrub land/Forest
10. Coyote	Woodland/Shrub land/Grassland	35. Red fox	Subalpine (in forest)
11. Deer mouse	Forest/Grassland/Woodland	36. Red-winged blackbird	Riparian/Grasslands
12. Deer tick	Shrub land/Forest	37. River otter	Aquatic/Riparian (in forest)
13. Dragonfly	Aquatic/Riparian (in forest, grassland)	38. Scarab beetle	Subalpine/Forest/Grassland/Shrub land
14. Elk	Subalpine (in forest, grassland)	39. Skunk	Shrub land/Woodland/Grassland
15. Golden eagle	Grassland/Shrub land	40. Snowshoe hare	Subalpine (in forest)
16. Grasshopper	Grassland	41. Sunfish	Aquatic
17. Great blue heron	Aquatic/Riparian	42. Tarantula spider	Shrub land/Semi-desert Woodland/Aquatic/Riparian/Grassland
18. Great horned owl	All terrestrial ecosystems	43. Tiger salamander	Aquatic/Riparian (in woodland/forest)
19. Jackrabbit	Grassland/Shrub land	44. Willow ptarmigan	Tundra
20. Kangaroo rat	Shrub land (semi-arid)	45. Woodpecker	Forest/Woodland/Riparian
21. Long-tailed weasel	All terrestrial ecosystems (near water)	46. Yucca moth	Grassland
22. Meadow vole	Grassland/Riparian		
23. Mink	Aquatic/Riparian		
24. Moose	Riparian (in forest)		
25. Mosquito	Aquatic/Riparian (all but tundra)		

Planting Animals

Objectives
Students will (1) describe reasons for "transplanting" animals, and (2) identify one animal that has been transplanted in their state.

Method
Students write letters to state wildlife agencies for information and to make models of transplanted animals in new habitats.

Materials
Writing materials, magazine photos, scissors, glue; OPTIONAL: boxes for models

Background
NOTE: This activity can be used independently or as an extension for the Project WILD activity "Here Today, Gone Tomorrow."

Wild animals sometimes are introduced or reintroduced to suitable habitat. This wildlife management technique is called "translocation." Translocation takes place for a variety of reasons, including providing a new home to species that were crowded elsewhere, reintroducing animals to historic habitats in order to provide a natural check and balance in an ecosystem, and restoring ecosystem diversity.

Reintroductions can have both positive and negative consequences. For example, reintroduction of predators can contribute to a healthy ecosystem because natural limits are placed on prey populations. Negative consequences also can occur. For example, some animals may go into shock and die from being translocated into a new environment. Animal species introduced where they have no natural predator can cause overpopulation of the introduced species and habitat degradation. A new species can also harm the native species by out-competing them for food, water, and shelter in the area.

The major purpose of this activity is to acquaint students with the concept of "translocating" animals.

Procedure
1. In a discussion, review what wildlife species are found locally and what wildlife species may once have been found there but are no longer present. How would the class find out if there was a new wild animal living in the area? How would it have gotten there? On its own? Put there by people? Why?

Grade Level: 5–8

Subject Areas: Science, Environmental Education, Language Arts

Duration: two 45-minute sessions, longer if a model is constructed

Group Size: any

Setting: indoors

Conceptual Framework Topic Reference: BDIIA, BDIIB, BDIIIC

Key Terms: habitat, transplant, introduced, niche, wildlife agency, management

Appendices: Using Local Resources

2. Help the class to write a letter to the state wildlife agency and to other informed organizations or individuals, so students can ask about newly introduced or reintroduced wildlife species in the region or local area. Have the students learn as much as they can from the wildlife agency's web page or publications before writing the letter. Request information not available from these sources. The following kinds of questions could be included:

- What animal species were translocated?

- Why were they introduced into that area? Did they once live there naturally? Where did they come from?

- Were other species displaced? Which niche did they fill?

- If the species were reintroduced, what had happened to the animals or habitat to cause the original disappearance?

- If habitat changes influenced this disappearance, have those changes been corrected?

- When were the animals plentiful in the area, and when did they disappear? How did this change take place?

- What indications, if any, are there that the transplant has been successful?

- What positive or negative effects, if any, have taken place for the translocated animals, for other animals in the area, and for the habitat?

3. Using the information the students have acquired, ask them to summarize what they have learned.

Extensions

1. Make a model of the animals in their "translocated" habitat. These models can be made in a large cardboard box, by the class as a group, by small groups of students working as a team, or by individual students using shoe boxes. Cut out magazine pictures of the animals and their habitat elements, back them with cardboard, and prop them up to create a diorama. Natural materials may also be used to create the background landscape.

2. Write a poem from the perspective of the animal.

Aquatic Extensions

1. See the Project WILD Aquatic activity "Aquatic Roots."

2. Focus this activity specifically on aquatic species in the state or region.

Evaluation

1. Identify and explain three reasons for translocating animals. Explain any major reasons for not translocating animals. Cite examples of species for your state.

2. Write a short report to illustrate potential pros and cons associated with translocating animals.

Here Today, Gone Tomorrow

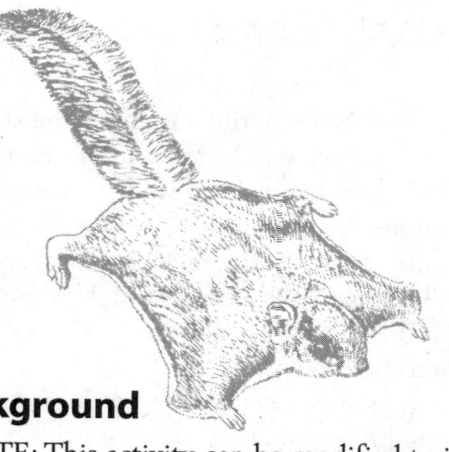

Objectives

Students will (1) identify and describe causes of extinction within animal species; (2) define "threatened," "rare," and "endangered" as applied to wildlife; and (3) identify any local threatened or endangered animals.

Method

Students become familiar with the various designations of animals such as "threatened," "rare," and "endangered;" conduct research; and make a master list of threatened and endangered animals locally or nationally, including factors that affect the animals' condition.

Materials

Information from state and federal agencies about threatened and endangered animals, poster board and other supplies for making posters, writing materials

---

Grade Level: 5–8

Subject Areas: Science, Environmental Education

Duration: two 30- to 45-minute sessions

Group Size: any

Setting: indoors

Conceptual Framework Reference: BDIA3, BDIIC

Key Terms: endangered, critically endangered, threatened, rare, extinct, peripheral

Appendices: Using Local Resources, Agencies and Organizations

---

Background

NOTE: This activity can be modified to include plant as well as animal species.

Pinpointing an exact number of species that become extinct each year is difficult. Many plants and animals still are unnamed and unknown. Controversy surrounds the estimates of the extinction rates for plants and animals. Some scientists estimate that human activity is responsible for the extinction of 100 plants and animals each day. Other scientists offer lower figures, but few experts disagree with the belief that the rate of species extinction is being accelerated by human actions.

As of December 1999, the U.S. Fish and Wildlife Service (USFWS) listed 939 plants and animals in the United States as being endangered, with an additional 266 listed as threatened. Many other species are under review for classification as threatened or endangered.

To list, reclassify, or delist a species, the USFWS must follow a strict legal process for proposing a new rule. The rule is first proposed in the *Federal Register*, a U.S. government publication. After a public comment period, the USFWS decides if the rule should be approved, revised, or withdrawn. (Source: U.S. Fish and Wildlife Service)

Although extinction is a natural process, excessive and intensive human activities in the environment have caused a dramatic increase in its rate. Loss of habitat as a result of human activity is considered to be the most pervasive cause of species extermination. Other major causes of species extermination and endangerment include habitat modification, unregulated or illegal commercial and personal use, disruption of migration routes and breeding behaviors, contamination by pollutants, human disturbance, predator control, competition or predation from introduced species, and natural causes.

Generally accepted definitions of the terms to be used in this activity are as follows:

extinct: complete disappearance of a species

critically endangered species: will not survive without direct human intervention

endangered species: in immediate danger of extinction

threatened species: present in its range, but threatened because of a decline in numbers

rare species: not presently in danger, but of concern because of low numbers (Some species always were rare because of their position in the food chain or because of habitat preference.)

peripheral: scarce in area because it inhabits the fringe or marginal habitat

Listings of animals in your state currently in these categories may be obtained from state wildlife agencies.

A list of species endangered in the United States is available from

> Director, Office of Endangered Species
> U.S. Fish and Wildlife Service
> U.S. Department of Interior
> Washington, DC 20204
> or on the Web at **www.fws.gov**.

State and federal listings of endangered, threatened, and rare species may vary because areas encompass different habitat conditions within their boundaries. An animal or plant may have been lost within one state's boundaries, but may be abundant in another and therefore, not considered threatened. The *U.S. Endangered Species Act of 1973* gives authority to protect endangered species to the U.S. Secretaries of the Departments of Interior and Commerce, with responsibilities further delegated to the U.S. Fish and Wildlife Service and the National Marine Fisheries Service.

The major purpose of this activity is to provide students with a working knowledge of the terminology and factors affecting potential elimination of wildlife species.

Procedure

1. Contact your state's wildlife agency, and request a list of animals that are classified as endangered, critically endangered, threatened, rare, extinct, or peripheral. Ask for information regarding the reasons that each of the species was placed in each of the classifications. For older students and those wanting more in-depth information, write to the U.S. Department of Interior regarding any comparable information available at the national level. (See the Background for the address.) Also contact local chapters of conservation organizations (e.g., National Wildlife Federation, National Audubon Society, Defenders of Wildlife) for additional information on species and habitats of concern.

2. Review and discuss with the students the definitions of threatened, endangered, rare, extinct, and peripheral—as used in wildlife conservation, as well as in a dictionary. Understand that words defined in a standard dictionary may have additional legal connotations. Ask each student or group of students to select an animal to research.

3. Ask one or more students to take the information accumulated from the wildlife agencies and private conservation groups and to develop a master list of the animals according to the category in which they can be classified, on state and national levels, and the principal factors affecting the animals. (See sample chart on page 156.)

continued

Ecological Knowledge

Here Today, Gone Tomorrow

Animal Name	State or Province						National						Factors Affecting Animal's Status
	Extinct	Endangered	Critically Endangered	Threatened	Rare	Peripheral	Extinct	Endangered	Critically Endangered	Threatened	Rare	Peripheral	

Or the educator can divide the class into teams so all students can participate in constructing this chart (e.g., one team classifying mammals; others classifying reptiles, birds, fish, insects, and so on).

4. Make copies of this information for all the students. Discuss the findings. What seem to be the most prevalent factors affecting the animals (e.g., habitat loss, pollution, impact from introduced species)?

NOTE: The U.S. Fish and Wildlife Service listed the following numbers of endangered and threatened species in the United States in 1999: Endangered—61 mammals, 76 birds, 14 reptiles, 9 amphibians, 69 fish, 18 snails, 61 mussels, 7 crustaceans, 28 insects, 581 plants = 939 endangered species; Threatened—8 mammals, 15 birds, 22 reptiles, 8 amphibians, 43 fish, 10 snails, 8 clams, 3 crustaceans, 9 insects, 140 plants = 266 threatened species.

Extensions

For Younger Students

1. Make a poster display showing the principal reasons that endangered animals are endangered. Poster displays could be made separately for both state and national endangered species.

2. Have a contest in which the students create posters honoring endangered species—from plants to wildlife.

3. Write a short essay, poem, or song about plants and animals facing extinction. What are these organisms "worth"? What are humans losing from the extinction of plants and animals?

For Older Students

1. Find out what is being done concerning the endangered plants and animals in your state or province, at the national level, at the international and worldwide levels. What can each of us as individuals do?

2. Have each student choose an endangered animal to research. What would be the consequences of the disappearance of this species? What are the benefits and challenges involved in saving it? What alternatives are available? What contributions does the animal make ecologically? Economically? Medicinally? Aesthetically? Intrinsically? Discuss the students' findings.

3. What animals and plants are known to be extinct? In each instance, what seems to be the causes?

4. Explore the possibility that extinction can apply to human cultural forms (e.g., traditional languages, native peoples).

5. In 10 minutes, name as many animals as you can that are not legally endangered or threatened. Find out what species have been taken off the endangered species list, how, and why.

6. Research, analyze, summarize, and interpret findings related to the following question: Why care about endangered species?

Aquatic Extensions

1. What kinds of habitats do aquatic species depend on? Research the conditions affecting each aquatic species, their current status, and projections for their future.

2. Are factors affecting threatened and endangered aquatic species significantly different from those affecting terrestrial species? If yes, why? If no, why not?

Evaluation

1. Arrange the following terms in a list so that they progress from the least amount of danger to a species to the greatest amount: endangered, rare, threatened, extinct, critically endangered.

2. Describe two reasons for possible concern when animal species become extinct.

3. Who decides what species are listed as endangered or threatened, and how do they decide?

4. Describe a principal cause for extinction.

Time Lapse

Objectives
Students will (1) describe successional changes in an ecosystem and the factors that affect these changes, and (2) relate species diversity to successional habitat changes.

Methods
Using computer technology if available, students create and analyze a series of sketches depicting changes in the variety and quantity of wildlife as an ecosystem undergoes successional change. Students research the kinds of animals that are found in each stage.

Materials
A copy of the Forest Diagram on page 162 for each of three student groups and one extra for class display (the diagrams may be enlarged.), copies of the Descriptions of Plants and Animals on page 165 for each group, copies of the Descriptions of Three Successional Stages on page 164 (cut into three sections—one stage for each of the three student groups), access to reference materials; OPTIONAL: copies of the sample animals on page 163 enlarged or reduced as needed and cut out for each group; computer access

Background
Ecological succession refers to the sequence of organisms that sequentially occupy an area over a period of time. Such changes can be observed over time in a plowed field or an area burned by a forest fire. Succession also refers to the process of change by which these communities replace each other and to how the environment becomes altered over time.

Succession occurs in every type of environment, although the details vary depending on the type of ecosystem. Succession can be categorized by three forces that may drive the change:

- physical changes produced by resident organisms, such as shading by trees or larger plants;
- geological processes, such as filling in of a lake with sediment; or
- biogenic changes, such as the introduction of a predator or consumer, invasive exotic plants or animals, or a disease.

Within any community of plants and animals, succession proceeds over time to result in a final stage called a "climax community". Even though the composition and structure of the climax community is determined by the regional climate, the pattern of stages to get to the climax

---

Grade Level: 5–8

Subject Areas: Science, Environmental Education, Expressive Arts

Duration: one 45-minute session

Group Size: any

Setting: indoors

Conceptual Framework Topic References: BDIA1, BDIA2, BDIB1, BDIB3, BDIB4

Key Terms: edge community, succession, climax community, biodiversity, exotic, invasive

Appendices: none

often is variable. Within any region, there is a variety of physical environments. The extremes of the physical environment eventually are modified by the combined activities of the organisms during the successional process. Also, many factors can intervene to prevent an area from reaching its climax condition, such as fires, special soils, introduction of exotic plants that outcompete the natives for sunlight and nutrients, and the activities of grazing animals. Agriculture and forestry plantations also set back succession.

Generally, natural vegetation within a climatic region tends to follow a characteristic pattern following a disturbance such as fire, flooding, plowing, mowing, and construction. These changes often involve a succession of communities dominated by plant species with a progressively greater maximum size, age, and shade tolerance, plus slower growth rates and dispersal abilities.

The purpose of this activity is to illustrate how habitats influence species diversity. Ecosystems undergo gradual successional changes that affect ecosystem diversity. New ecosystems and ecosystems that are harsh tend to have relatively few species, and species variety tends to be higher in the transition zone between ecosystems. In this activity, students will analyze the changes in species diversity that occur as an ecosystem undergoes succession.

Procedure

Before the Activity

Copy the plant and animal descriptions on page 165. Copy and cut the descriptions of the successional stages on page 164. Copy the Forest Diagram on page 162 and, if desired, enlarge it. OPTIONAL: copy and adjust the sizes of the animal sketches on page 163.

Part 1

1. Display the class copy of the Forest Diagram in the classroom. Leave space around the diagram for students to display their diagrams later.

2. Divide the class into three groups. Each group will study one successional stage: 3 to 5 years immediately after a fire, 15 to 25 years later, and more than 100 years later. (Educators may further divide the class to investigate additional successional stages, such as 8 to 10 years and 50 to 60 years later.) Provide each group with the Forest Diagram. Tell the students that the forest diagram represents an area of mature forest where a section has been recently harvested, abandoned, and later burned. (This section is on the left side of the diagram.) Ask the groups to discuss what the entire forest may have looked like before a section was harvested. What types of animals are currently present? What in the forest provides for their habitat needs? Where is each species located in the forest (i.e., in the tree tops, on the ground, on the edge, or in the center)? Have students look at the cleared area on the left. Why are no animals shown? Ask them what might still be there. (e.g., seeds, small insects, soil organisms) How soon could pioneer plants and animals begin to repopulate the area? What might happen to the cleared area during the next 5 years, 20 years, and 100 years if it is left alone?

3. Assign each group to one of the successional stages of a forest listed on page 164, and give students a copy of the description of their forest successional stage. Also give each group a copy of the Descriptions of Plants

continued

and Animals, which lists generic plants and animals that might be found in the forest. Local species may be different. Students need to research in which stage these plants and animals may occur, where they may be located (e.g., in the treetops, on the ground, on the edge) and the relative abundance of each species. Students may wish to research specific plants and animals in the stage they have been assigned.

4. Have students find pictures of organisms that may occur in their assigned successional stage and arrange them in the cleared area of the Forest Diagram. Each group may either cut and paste the plants and animals, or they may draw the plants and animals for that stage. OPTION: Scan the drawing of the Forest Diagram into a computer. Cut and paste clip art or "scans" of the animal sketches (on page 163) onto the electronic representation of the Forest Diagram.

   NOTE: If possible, adjust organism pictures to proper relative size.

5. When the groups have completed their arrangements, ask them to identify the successional stage and organisms in their diagram and to explain their reasons for placing the organisms where they did to the rest of the class.

6. For each group, ensure that the plants and animals are generally placed to reflect the different stages of succession.

7. Have the groups place their diagrams in the correct successional order next to the blank copy of the Forest Diagram that is displayed in the classroom and explain their rationale for the sequence.

8. Have the students analyze the sequence of diagrams by answering the following questions:
   - Where does the greatest variety of species live in their diagram?
   - How has the number of species in their diagram changed from the preceding diagram?
   - What species are present in their diagram that were not present in the preceding diagram?
   - What species are absent in their diagram that were present in the preceding diagram?
   - How have the sizes and types of plants changed in the forest?
   - How might the size of the clearing affect the rate of regrowth of the forest?

9. Ask the students to summarize changes that occurred in the population sizes, types, and locations of both plants and animals. What happened to the length of time for each of the stages represented by the diagrams? Discuss the concept of succession, and ask students to come up with a working definition. What differences would they expect in the various stages of succession represented in the diagrams if the area had been a desert climate? A tropical climate? A community at a high altitude? Had the area been harvested, but not burned, how would the diagrams have changed? What factors affect the rate and direction of succession?

Part 2

1. Ask students to bring in photographs that depict stages of succession. Photographs may be of the local community, and students can be encouraged to take their own photographs. As an alternative, you may want students to bring photographs representing stages from areas with a variety of climates.

2. Place a label on the wall for major stages of succession such as cleared, meadow, shrub land, young forest, and mature or climax forest. Have students place their pictures under the appropriate label and justify their decision.

Extensions

1. On the school grounds or a nearby lot, have students identify and count all plants and animals in a 1-square-meter area. Don't forget to look for soil organisms. Take a photograph of the area if at all possible, or have students draw the plot. With permission of the school or landowner, dig up and remove all plants and animals from the 1-meter square. Transplant them elsewhere. Photograph the area again and record the date. Mark the area to keep people out. Have the class or a group of students return a few days later and then once a week to photograph or draw the site and record the types and number of plants and animals that repopulate the area. Graph the data, and display the graphs with the photographs or drawings. Ask students to summarize the order of invading or pioneer plants and animals. Are they the same species that were there originally? Where did they come from? (If you have digital cameras or a scanner, the results from this activity can easily be added to a school web page.)

2. Some states have forest regulations that require (1) trees to be replanted on harvested forest land, (2) a certain number of seed trees be left per acre, or (3) cuts may be only a certain size. Check with the state natural resources agency to determine what, if any, requirements must be met. How would the regulations affect the successional changes in the diagrams?

3. Have students create a 3-D model of succession for use at a resources open house.

Evaluation

1. Describe stages of succession in a local ecosystem. Include examples of plants and animals.

2. Discuss factors that affect the rate and direction of succession. How do climate and level of disturbance influence the changes in species over time?

3. Relate succession of plant species in an ecosystem to succession of wildlife species. How do plants affect species composition?

4. Where does the greatest biodiversity occur? In developed or climax ecosystems? Disturbed or harsh ecosystems? (Harsh ecosystems are places that are very cold, dry, or subject to fire, flooding, or other major disturbances.) In the overlapping zone between ecosystems? Why?

continued

Ecological Knowledge

Time Lapse

Forest Diagram

Ecological Knowledge

Time Lapse

Sample Animals

Cardinal

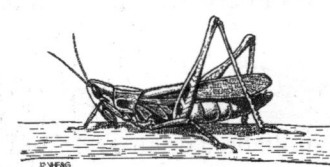
Grasshopper

Garter Snake

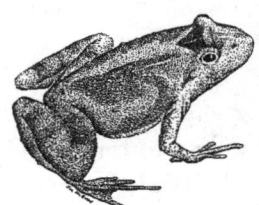
Toad

Owl

Robin

Bear

Sparrow

Songbird

Mouse

Squirrel

Fox

Rabbit

Deer

Turkey

Quail

continued

163

Descriptions of Three Successional Stages

NOTE: An area of the forest has been clean harvested and abandoned. A fire occurred on the site after it was abandoned.

3 to 5 Years

The first plants to invade prefer bright sunlight. The fire released many of the nutrients in stumps and branches left behind during the cutting of the area. Grasses—such as broom straw, golden rod, and other herbaceous plants—have taken over the area. The area is also green with sprouts from tree stumps that were not killed by the fire. Woody shrubs—such as blackberry, wild grape, sumac, and viburnums—are beginning to grow. Here and there, a young coniferous tree—such as red cedar or field pine—is beginning to reach above the grasses.

15 to 25 Years

The overall vegetation is dense as the plant community converts from shrubby field to forest. Maples, birches, oaks, and other hardwoods join pines and cedars. Few acorns and other nuts are being produced. Vertical layers are becoming distinct. At 25 years, the young hardwoods are approximately 40 feet tall and starting to shade out "sun-loving" shrubs such as blackberries and brambles. Other shrubs more tolerant of shade—such as blueberry, serviceberry, and spice bush—may continue to grow, although the blueberry will not produce as many berries. Hemlock and white pine, which thrive in under-story shade, may begin to grow.

More Than 100 Years

As taller plants occupy the site, less light is available on the surface of the forest. Plants tolerant of shading will out-compete plants that are intolerant of shading, and gradually the composition of the forest will change to favor shade-tolerant species. Distinct layers can be identified in mature forests. The canopy layer consists of trees 60 to 100 feet high, including mixed oaks, hickories, sugar maple, beech, birch, or other hardwoods, or hemlock and white pine. An understory layer 30 to 40 feet high has trees such as dogwood, hornbeam, and saplings. Below this understory, a shrub layer about 3 to 4 feet high, might include blackberry, arrowwood, spicebush, blueberry, or huckleberry. Poison ivy, Virginia creeper, and Japanese honeysuckle are vines that span all layers. An herbaceous (nonwoody) layer of perennial, annual, and biennial plants is found at the forest floor.

Descriptions of Plants and Animals

Grass/Herb: Grasses and herbs cannot tolerate excessive shade. They grow quickly, but have nonwoody stems and do not reach a great height.

Shrub: Shrubs have woody stems and are usually intermediate in height between grasses and trees. They can tolerate some shade.

Sapling: Saplings are trees that have not reached full height. They may be the size of large shrubs.

Mature tree: These trees have reached their full height and form the canopy layers.

Songbird: Songbirds in this area live in mature trees.

Squirrel: Squirrels build their nests in trees but are seen on the ground and moving through tree branches. They eat fruit, berries, and nuts.

Garter snake: This snake lives in grassy areas and shrubs. It eats toads, earthworms, small birds, and mammals.

Toad: Toads live in meadows and shrub lands. They eat insects and other invertebrates.

Wild turkey: Turkeys roost in trees and need clearings and brushy fields for nesting.

Mouse: Mice live in burrows and eat berries, grains, and insects.

Owl: Owls in this area nest in trees but hunt the ground for mice and shrews.

Black bear: Bears live in the thick forest where they have plenty of cover. They eat a variety of plant and animal matter.

Deer: Deer eat grasses, shrubs, and crops. They prefer an edge community where they can hide but also venture periodically into open areas to browse.

Grasshopper: Grasshoppers live in grassy areas and eat grass, clover, and other herbs.

Rabbit: Rabbits live in edge communities where there is plenty of shrub cover to hide, plus grasses and other herbs to eat.

Quail: Quail nest in shrub areas where they have cover, but they may feed in more open, grassy spaces that supply many insects.

Sparrow: Sparrows nest in shrub and tree areas where they have cover but may feed in more open spaces that supply many insects.

Cardinal: Cardinals are red to brownish-red birds that nest in the high branches of shrubs or low branches of trees. They feed on berries, seeds, and insects gathered from plants or from the ground.

Robin: Robins live in edge communities where there are open grassy spaces, shrubs, and small trees. They build their nests in the branches of younger trees and eat berries, worms, and insects.

Fox: Foxes live in burrows called dens. They prefer some ground cover for hunting, and they feed on birds, mice, rabbits, insects, and berries.

Ecosystem Facelift

Objectives

Students will (1) describe interactions or interdependency of organisms within an ecosystem; (2) articulate that managing an ecosystem as a whole, and not just for one or a few species, is essential for ensuring ecosystem diversity; and (3) relate the increase of wildlife populations to the improvement of habitats.

Method

Students simulate the restoration of a working ecosystem on the site of an abandoned shopping center or on an island in a river near an urban area. Students share their ecosystem designs, comparing and contrasting the two types of systems and the influencing factors on these systems.

Materials

Copies of the Student Guide Page on page 169; copies of pages 170 and 171 including scenario descriptions, potential plant and animal lists, and maps for the shopping center and island scenarios; markers; colored pens or pencils; plant and animal field guides

Background

Refer to "A Guide to the Ecosystem Concept" on pages 482 to 486 of this guide, and review the main concepts and vocabulary with students. For this activity, it is important to distinguish between "community" and "ecosystem." A community is all of the organisms that inhabit a particular area—populations of different species living close enough to each other to interact. An ecosystem is the natural unit that includes the organisms, their physical environment, and their exchange of energy and nutrients. An ecosystem has many small, or "micro," communities within it. The key to this activity is that an ecosystem is healthy if it is diverse over the range of communities that lie within the ecosystem. Management of wildlife areas must consider species diversity in this broader scope because improving habitat for one species may have negative consequences for another. This holistic approach, called "ecosystem management," also takes species interrelationships into account. To understand biodiversity, one must look at the bigger picture.

Greater diversity generally increases the stability of ecosystems. However, there are examples of ecosystems, such as dunes, that have an optimal level of diversity that may not be as high as a mature forest but that is, nonetheless, very stable.

Grade Level: 7–8

Subject Areas: Social Studies, Language Arts, Science, Environmental Education

Duration: two to three 45-minute sessions

Group Size: any (ideal of at least three groups of five)

Setting: Indoors

Conceptual Framework Topic Reference: BDIA4, BDIIA, BDIIB, BDIID

Key Terms: biodiversity, ecosystem, diversity, interdependency, habitat, niche, native, non-native, community, populations, competition, predation, management, topography

Appendices: Ecosystem Concept

For communities to thrive, it is important to look at the needs of the organisms within their physical environment. Even in an urban setting, plants and animals can flourish if they are adapted to its unique conditions or if their needs can be met by improving the habitat. Urban animal species must be able to tolerate people, eat a wide variety of foods, have a high tolerance for pollutants, have a rapid or high reproductive rate, and be able to adjust to relatively rapid changes in the environment. Urban plant species must be able to tolerate poor soil conditions and pollutants, be able to grow in diminished sunlight, have a high propagation rate (spread by root systems or produce a high number of seeds), and be able to tolerate damage to their systems.

In this activity, the students will work in small groups on either an urban island or an abandoned shopping center location. The topography and physical environment of the two locations are very different although both are the same size and urban. Students will find that the physical layout of the site influences their decisions as they restore ecosystems after a major disturbance at these locations. Another difference may be the effect of human impact if the shopping center site is planned for frequent or extensive access by people.

The purpose of this activity is to demonstrate that improving habitat improves wildlife populations. Habitat is the key to wildlife survival, and management of one species will affect other species. A biologically healthy ecosystem is diverse over the range of the ecosystem.

Procedure

1. Inform students that they will be designing an ecosystem on a 20-acre imaginary site that has been radically altered by natural forces and human actions. The students have the opportunity to develop the site, determining what living organisms and non-living components will be reintroduced, how these organisms will interact, and how the ecosystem will be managed.

2. Divide the class into six groups. Three will work on the shopping center site, and three will work on the island.

3. Provide each group of students with a description of either the island or shopping center site, the list of native and non-native species found on the island or urban site, the site map of the island or shopping center, and the Student Guide Page. The Student Guide may be given to student groups as they work on their designs to ensure that the discussion points are incorporated into student learning.

4. Have students look carefully at the topography of their site. Are there hills or low lands? Is there a water source? Is the soil probably moist or dry?

5. Have the students decide which plants would be most suitable for the area. They should research potential plants to find out which are native to the area, what conditions are required for their growth, and whether those conditions exist on the site. Have the students describe each plant's value to wildlife. Provide field guides and other related materials for this purpose.

6. Have the students list kinds of plants suitable for the growing conditions; for the required spacing; and for the soil, light, and water needs of each plant. Ask them if all areas of the site are suitable for every plant or if some areas of the site are better for some plants. Will improving water sources or soil fertility allow more species to be added to the design?

7. Have the students check to see if two plants have the same living requirements. Would these plants compete? Could just one be put in, or can the plants be managed to maintain both on the site simultaneously?

8. Next, have the students select animals. Again, have them research the needs of potential species using field guides or other sources. What other organisms (e.g., fungi, bacteria, and so on) besides plants and animals should be considered when developing the site?

continued

9. Considering the needs of the animals and the potential plants to be established at the site, which animals do the students think could survive best? Would some of the plant communities be better at supporting some animals over others? Have the students look into the possibility of predation or competition between two animals with similar needs and niches. How do they wish to manage the animals (i.e., not include one, set up two similar but separated communities, or manage to maintain both)?

10. Ask students to locate the animal and plant communities on their maps using symbols for each natural or constructed feature. Also, have students draw a food web diagram to represent the interactions of the various plants and animals in the ecosystem they designed.

11. Each group should present its food web and ecosystem design to the rest of the class. What are the relationships among the organisms that the group introduced to the island within the ecosystem? How did they attempt to maximize biodiversity within the limited space allotted? What challenges did they encounter? Did they solve their problems? Do they think their efforts and improvements eventually will improve the number and diversity of species from those that were found there originally, or not? Why or why not?

12. After all groups have made their presentations, discuss the differences between the two types of sites. Which type of location had the greater biodiversity initially? Why? Will one type of site probably have a greater biodiversity if the designs are successful? (Don't forget that both have the same acreage.) Why? Is a community with higher biodiversity necessarily more stable than a community with lower biodiversity? Students should support their position by referring to factors such as environmental conditions related to soil, water, and light and to human factors such as potential human impact and management concerns.

Extensions

1. Have the students consider the costs involved in restoring and maintaining the ecosystem they designed.

2. Visit an urban park. Have students study the history of the land before it was a park. What was the land used for in the past, and what species were found there? Have students observe and list the current species in the park and discuss management of the ecosystem with the park manager.

Evaluation

1. Critique the six ecosystems designed by the groups, select the preferred use, and defend the decision.

2. Describe how improving an ecosystem by creating suitable habitat helps or harms wildlife populations.

3. Give examples of how managing for one species can affect another species in a positive way or in a negative way.

4. How realistic do you think it would be for resource managers to design and actually develop an entire ecosystem "from scratch"? Support your answer by referring to the results from this activity.

Ecological Knowledge

Ecosystem Facelift

Student Guide Page

This guide may be given to the student groups as they are working on their designs to ensure that the discussion points are incorporated into student learning.

I. Topography

Consider the topography of your site.
- A. Locate hills.
- B. Locate lowlands.
- C. Locate sources of water.
- D. Locate areas of moist soils.
- E. Locate areas of dry soils.

II. Plants

A. Using the following chart, decide which plants would be most suitable for the site when considering the plant's requirements for space, soil, sunlight, water, and temperature:

Plant	Space	Soil	Sunlight	Water	Temperature

B. What improvements could be made to allow for a greater variety of species? (e.g., water sources?)

C. Consider two plants having the same requirements. How will competition between them be handled?

III. Animals

A. Using the following chart, decide which animals would be best suited for the site when considering the animal's requirements for space, food, shelter, and water?

Animal	Space	Food	Shelter	Water

B. What improvements could be made to allow for a greater variety of species? (e.g., water sources?)

C. Consider two animals having the same requirements. How can this competition be avoided?

IV. Interactions

A. Consider consumption of one organism by another. Can overpredation be avoided?

B. Which plant communities will be best at supporting which animals?

continued

Island Scenario
Belle Island

A 1,000-year flood has destroyed the plants and animals on Belle Island. The 20-acre island is in the middle of a tidal river. (Tidal rivers are open to the ocean and experience daily tidal fluctuations.) It has a large hill on the ocean side of the island (the side affected by the tides), and there is a low area capable of sustaining a marsh on the opposite side of the island. The island also has a flat plain that was formerly a meadow. The island has been used in many different ways since Europeans settled the area; originally it was used as a plantation. Later, industries powered by hydro-electricity were located on the island. Before the flood, the island was overgrown with a mixture of native and non-native plants and was inhabited by a variety of native and non-native wildlife.

List of Native and Non-Native Species Originally Found on the Island

Native	Non-Native	Native	Non-Native
Trees	**Trees**	**Animals**	**Animals**
Red oaks	Empress tree	Aquatic turtles	Starlings
River birch	Tree-of-heaven	Frogs	English sparrows
Pine		Snakes	Pigeons
Vines		Raccoons	Norway rats
Virginia creeper	**Vines**	Deer	Nutria
Trumpet vine	Japanese honeysuckle	Opossum	House cats
Poison ivy	Kudzu	Great blue heron	Stray dogs
Other Plants	**Other Plants**	Osprey	Carp
Jack-in-the-pulpit	Cordgrass	Cardinal	Striped bass
Cattails	Crabgrass	Dragonfly	
Wild rice	Dandelions	Mayfly	
	Purple loosestrife	Mosquito	
		Bluegill	

Belle Island

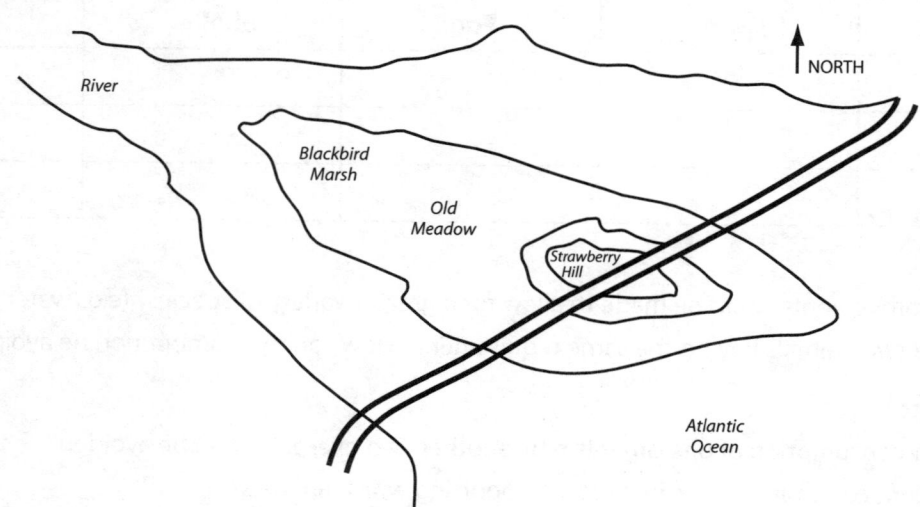

Shopping Center Scenario
Acme Acres

An abandoned shopping area is being torn down to make room for a new park. The area is currently 20 acres of asphalt and concrete that has been neglected for more than 10 years.

The city would like to develop a complete working ecosystem that benefits the people of the community by providing a natural setting that will attract wildlife. Different community needs and uses for the site have been identified and are being suggested to the city planning committee. Community members said that whatever the site is used for, the ecosystem that is established on the site must be healthy and sustainable.

List of Urban Species Normally Found in Surrounding Sites

Trees
Empress tree
Tree-of-heaven
Elm

Vines
Japanese honeysuckle
English ivy
Poison ivy

Other Plants
Crab grass
Dandelions
Milkweed
Lily of the valley

Animals
Starlings
English sparrows
Pigeons
Norway rats
House cats
Stray dogs
Carp/Goldfish
Crows
Raccoons
Gray squirrels
Bats
Mosquitoes
Ants

Acme Acres

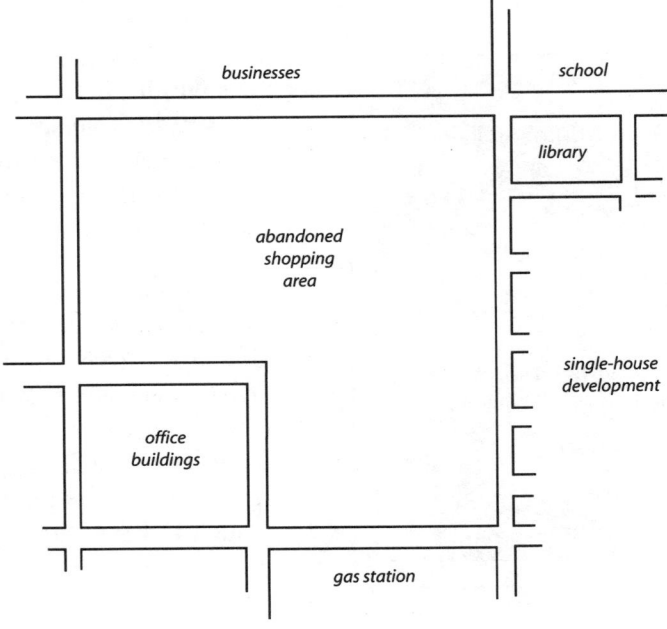

Bottleneck Genes

Objectives

Students will (1) describe biodiversity as it relates to natural systems, species, or individuals; (2) articulate that genetic diversity is essential to the health of a species because it facilitates adaptation to change and provides sources for new genetic material; (3) explain how natural selection favors individuals with traits adapted to their environment; and (4) explain that for a wildlife population to sustain itself, there must be enough habitat to support a healthy-sized population that will carry a healthy-sized gene diversity.

Method

Students will simulate the gene-pool analysis of a population of black-footed ferrets using colored beads.

Grade Level: 9–12

Subject Areas: Science, Environmental Education

Duration: one 40-minute session

Group Size: eight groups of two to four students each

Setting: indoors

Conceptual Framework Topic Reference: BDI, BDIA3, BDIB2, BDIC1, BDIC2, BDIIIE

Key Terms: gene pool, adapted, genetic diversity

Appendices: none

Materials

One large, long-necked glass bottle; eight sets of the Key to Environmental Situations cards (copy and cut) on page 175; eight copies of the Key to Genetic Characteristics on page 174; eight copies of the Black-Footed Ferret Bottleneck Scenario worksheet on page 176; beads of each of the following colors: yellow, black, orange, pink, blue, green, purple, red, and white (Pony beads, a type of craft bead, approximately $3/8"$ in diameter and $1/4"$ in length, or something similar, seem to work well.)

Background

Diversity is essential to the survival of a species. There are three kinds of biological diversity: diversity found in an individual, diversity within a species or given population, and diversity within an ecosystem. The ability of an individual to survive changes in the environment comes from the extent of genetic diversity the individual has, thus giving it the ability to adapt to those variations. Diversity within a population means that there are enough organisms to continue producing a variety of genetic combinations within the group. The third type of diversity, biodiversity, deals with the ecosystem. A diverse ecosystem provides a variety of food sources for those living there, which allows for a higher survival rate.

In the world of "survival of the fittest," an organism must have the genetic resources that allow it to survive immediate changes in its environment and that allow the species to adapt to long-term changes around it. The only way to ensure this will happen is to make sure that the genetic choices in the population are large enough to have the greatest variety of attributes passed along to individuals in the next generation. The best way to ensure a large and healthy population with enough gene choices is to have sufficient habitat to support it. When the number of individuals decreases, the genetic pool also decreases, causing what is called a "bottleneck" in the population, or a limited variety in gene diversity.

The purpose of this activity is to demonstrate what the importance of genetic variability is to health within a species and how this diversity facilitates adjustment to ecosystem changes. Students will simulate what happens when a population of black-footed ferrets begins to decrease in size, and they will examine how this decrease affects the gene diversity within the group. Following the simulation, the students will look at the effects of a limited gene diversity, or pool, on the population in a changing ecosystem over the period of a year.

NOTE: For information on the black-footed ferret, see the Project WILD activity "Back from the Brink" or visit www.blackfootedferret.org on the Internet.

Procedure

1. Divide the class into groups of two to four students. Give each group a copy of the Key to Genetic Characteristics, a Key to Environmental Situations and a Black-Footed Ferret Bottleneck Scenario.

2. Review the terms "genetic diversity," "biodiversity," and "population bottlenecks" as found in the Background section.

3. Review the gene color key. Discuss the benefits of the different attributes.

4. Place all of the genes (colored beads) into the glass bottle. Shake it gently to mix the colors. Explain to students that the genes will be distributed randomly, as would be found in a real population.

5. Distribute a small handful of beads to each group. These beads represent the genes available in the population of black-footed ferrets for each group. Have the students match their genes to the gene key and circle the colors or genes on the Key to Genetic Characteristics for their ferret population. (Please note that the students must be given a small amount of beads to ensure that they do not receive all nine colors.)

6. Have the students choose five Environmental Situation Cards randomly from the deck.

7. Students work with the Black-Footed Ferret Bottleneck Scenario worksheet to complete the following:

    a. Calculate the genetic diversity in their population.

    b. Describe their population according to its current genetic makeup.

    c. Develop and write a prediction for their population in the environmental situation they have chosen for approximately a 1-year period. Then address the following:

    - Is the population genetically equipped to survive in this environment? How well or how poorly?

    - How does a high or low percentage of genetic diversity affect the population's survival?

    - How do random changes in the environment affect the population? (Remind students that for this question they are concerned with how many beads of each color they have.)

8. Each of the groups should present their results to the class.

9. Discuss the following questions:

    - Why does gene diversity help protect a population?

    - Why would a smaller population have a higher risk of being eliminated than a large population?

    - Why do you think smaller populations have a harder time surviving disease? (Inbreeding depletes the gene pool that provides a variety of traits. If there are fewer genes that help an animal fight off disease, the population becomes more susceptible to pathogens.)

continued

Extensions

1. Discuss the impact of dominant versus recessive traits. Recessive traits have a much lower probability of becoming evident in the population unless the population becomes small enough to interbreed and bring forth those recessive traits, or unless that trait makes the animal better able to survive in its environment. Repeat the activity using two colors for each genetic characteristic (to represent dominant and recessive traits). For instance, dark blue beads could represent healthy jaw formation and light blue beads could represent a jaw malformation or deformity. Also use separate containers for each characteristic, and have students pick two beads from each of those containers. If the group receives only recessive color beads for a characteristic, then the recessive trait will be expressed. If the group receives only dominant color beads or if it receives a mix of dominant and recessive color beads for that characteristic, then the dominant trait will be expressed. (If the color selection of beads is limited, another token, such as colored paper squares, may be used.)

2. After the initial round, randomly pair the groups to see how combining genes from different populations affects diversity. Discuss how this relates to habitat fragmentation.

3. Visit a local zoo, and talk to staff members about their attempts to ensure genetic diversity with their breeding animals. Discuss any attempts they may be involved in to re-establish endangered species in the wild.

4. Have students choose an endangered or threatened species from a local zoo and design a plan for breeding that would ensure, or greatly improve, the chances for genetic diversity and, therefore, survival.

Evaluation

1. Steps 6 through 9 in the Procedure section can be used as an evaluation tool.

2. Have the students research a threatened species found in their area. Students can determine whether genetic diversity within the species had an effect on its depletion. They should also examine whether the species was placed on the threatened list because of degradation or loss of habitat. Have students check their conclusions with the state's natural resources agency or a local office of the U.S. Fish and Wildlife Service.

3. Ask students what challenges concerning genetic diversity many zoos face in trying to re-establish endangered animals.

Adapted with permission from Smithsonian Institution, Conservation & Research Center School Outreach Program, "Black-Footed Ferret Ambassador Program, Secondary School Program Teacher Guide," Jennifer Buff, Shannon Dodge, and Susan Peachey, 1999.

Key to Genetic Characteristics

Yellow	camouflage
Black	precise vision
Orange	accurate sense of smell
Pink	strong claws and forearms
Dark blue	healthy jaw formation
Green	agility
Purple	acute hearing
Red	healthy rate of reproduction
White	immunity to canine distemper

Key to Environmental Situations

1. A farmer has been trying to protect his wheat fields by exterminating prairie dogs. Very little prey is available. Given the genetic makeup, how would your population survive?

2. A golden eagle hunts from high above and will prey on available animals such as the black-footed ferret. Does your population have the gene for precise vision to avoid being captured? Given the genetic makeup, how would your population survive?

3. Black-footed ferret kits disperse from their home territory and are able to establish new populations in nearby prairie dog towns. Given the genetic makeup, how would your population survive?

4. An interstate highway has been built near your prairie dog town. How does this road affect your black-footed ferret population? Given the genetic makeup, how would your population survive?

5. Ranchers are allowing their dogs to run loose. Will your population's genes protect it against canine distemper, assuming the dogs carry it? Given the genetic makeup, how would your population survive?

6. A new generation of captive-born black-footed ferret kits has been preconditioned to live in the wild and are ready to be released at a nearby reintroduction site. Given the genetic makeup, how would your population survive?

7. A plague has hit your prairie dog town, and most of the prairie dogs die from the disease. How does your black-footed ferret population adapt to a reduction in food supply? Given the genetic makeup, how would your population survive?

8. As a coyote silently prowls nearby, only its odor might warn of its presence. Does your population have the gene for an acute sense of smell to warn about the coyote?

9. Black-footed ferrets eat prairie dogs and use prairie dog burrows for shelter. Does your ferret population have the agility gene to catch an aggressive prairie dog in its dark, narrow, winding tunnel system? Given the genetic makeup, how would your population survive?

10. Black-footed ferrets are nocturnal creatures that leave their burrows at night to feed. Does your ferret population have the camouflage gene to keep well hidden from the great horned owl hunting for its dinner? Given the genetic makeup, how would your population survive?

11. A badger is moving quietly around the prairie dog town. Does your population have the gene for acute hearing to avoid this predator? Given the genetic makeup, how would your population survive?

12. A prairie dog colony has just been established in a state park only a few miles away. How does the colony affect your populations of ferrets? Given the genetic makeup, how would your population survive?

13. It will be difficult for your population to take over and adapt to prairie dog burrows without the gene for strong claws and forelegs. Given the genetic makeup, how would your population survive?

14. Humans who are building homes have wiped out a prairie dog town 10 miles away. The surviving black-footed ferrets from that area are moving into your territory. Given the genetic makeup, how would your population survive?

continued

Ecological Knowledge

Bottleneck Genes

Black-Footed Ferret Bottleneck Scenario

Names of Team Members _____

On your Key to Genetic Characteristics, circle the **COLORS and GENES** that your population received through the bottleneck.

1. **Calculate the percentage of genetic diversity (heterozygosity) of your population.**

   Nine genes (colors) represent 100 percent genetic diversity in the original population.

   _____ genes received ÷ 9 original genes = _____ (decimal) x 100 = _____%

2. **List the genetic characteristics (colors) that your population received through the bottleneck.**

3. **List the genetic characteristics that your population lost when it came through the bottleneck.** (colors not received)

4. **Using the five environmental situations, write a prediction about what will happen to your population during the coming year.**

   Is the population genetically equipped to survive in its environment? How well or how poorly? How does a high or low percentage of genetic diversity affect the population's survival? How do random changes in the environment affect the population?

Section Two

Social and Political Knowledge

First Impressions

Objectives

Students will (1) distinguish between reactions to an animal based on myth or stereotype and those based on factual information, and (2) recognize the value of animals' contributions to ecosystems, even those that people sometimes respond to with fear.

Method

Students respond to a variety of images to study contributions of a range of animals.

Materials

Large photos, slides, or drawings of a variety of animals, including some the students might think are "cute" and some they might think are "scary"

NOTE: Animal pictures can be downloaded from many Internet sites. They can be printed or projected from a computer.

Grade Level: K–4

Subject Areas: Environmental Education, Language Arts

Duration: two 20-minute sessions

Group Size: any

Setting: indoors

Conceptual Framework Topic Reference: CPIIC1, CPIIC2

Key Terms: fear, environment, feelings, information

Appendices: Field Ethics, Animals in the Classroom

Background

People respond differently to different animals. For instance, some people don't like spiders. Their first reaction may be to recoil if they see a spider; their second may be to kill the animal as quickly as possible. Yet most spiders are harmless to people. In fact, spiders are important contributors to healthy ecosystems.

Spiders are not the only species of wildlife that will frequently cause a fright response in people. Wolves, snakes, and bats elicit fear among many people in a number of cultures. Bats, however, are viewed as signs of good luck among some cultures in China. Reactions to species may vary in different cultures.

This activity is designed for students to examine their spontaneous reactions to different animals, separating reactions based on information and experience from those based on misinformation and myth.

The major purpose of this activity is for students to recognize that all animals are important contributors to the ecosystem.

Procedure

Before the Activity

Prepare a series of cards showing a variety of different animals. The cards need to be large enough to show to the entire group and may be either photos or drawings of animals.

1. As each picture or photo is shown to the students, ask them to take turns saying the first word that comes to their minds as they look at the picture.

178 Project WILD K–12 Curriculum and Activity Guide

2. With younger students, write the name of the animal and the words the students suggest on the chalkboard. With older students, have at least two students serve as recorders, writing the words on the chalkboard for the whole group.

3. Ask the students to identify which animals on the list seemed to generate a response of dislike or fear and those that seemed to generate a generally favorable response.

For Younger Students

4. Ask the students to help choose an animal that seems especially scary. Tell them that this animal makes a contribution to the environment in which it lives. On your own or with the help of a local resource person, find out more about the contributions this animal makes to the ecosystem. If possible, and safe, bring in the animal for the students to get to know. See the Extensions. Talk about "first impressions" contrasted with reactions based on knowing more about the animal.

For Older Students

5. Divide the group into teams and ask each team to find out more about one of the animals. In their research, the teams should find out whether the reactions of the students to the animals were based on accurate information and experiences or were based on misinformation and inadequate information. Each team should prepare a report to present, including a description of the importance of the animal's contribution to the ecosystem.

6. Ask the students to present their reports. Talk about the values and contributions animals make—from ecological to aesthetic. Identify animals, if any, where the students change their feelings because they have additional and more accurate information. Identify animals, if any, where the students have not changed their views. Talk about "first impressions" contrasted with the importance of basing perceptions of animals, plants, people, ideas, etc. on the best information available.

Extensions

1. Have one or more live animals available, such as a nonpoisonous snake, nonpoisonous spider, toad, or caterpillar. Make sure the students do not hurt the animal and that the animal cannot hurt the students. Care should be taken in advance when removing any animal from the wild to make sure that it can legally be moved. If the animal was taken from the wild for this activity, see that it is returned safely—exactly to the place where it was found originally, if at all possible—at the conclusion of the activity. See the Guidelines for Responsible Use of Animals in the Classroom in the Appendices for additional guidance concerning care of the animal.

2. Draw a picture of a "favorite" animal and one of a "scary" animal. Write a short story about each, including the value of each animal.

3. Classify animal groups (e.g., mammals, spiders, insects). Which groups seem to be most "loved," "feared," and so on?

Aquatic Extensions

Prepare a series of large photos or drawings of a variety of different kinds of aquatic animals. Select a range so that there are likely to be some that provide a fearful or negative "first impression." Conduct the activity as described above.

Evaluation

1. What words would someone use to describe a snake, a spider, a wolf, and a deer if they liked the animal? What might someone say about each of these animals if they did not like the animal?

2. Write or tell a story that describes someone's first impression of one of these animals: brown bat, bullfrog, spider, garter snake, or northern harrier. How might that person's impression change as he or she learns more about the animal?

And the Wolf Wore Shoes

Objectives
Students will (1) distinguish between real and imaginary animals, and (2) give examples of real and imaginary animals and their characteristics.

Method
Students divide books into those about real and those about imaginary animals and then distinguish between real and fictitious animal characteristics.

Materials
A selection of children's books and comics about or including both real and imaginary animals

Background
The portrayal of animals in books, fairy tales, comics, cartoons, movies, and other media may have an influence on the perceptions people have of those animals.

The major purpose of this activity is to give students experience in actively distinguishing between realistic and fictionalized portrayals of animals in literature.

Procedure
1. Distribute several books to each group of two to four students. Each stack of books needs to include some books that portray animals realistically and some that give the animals unrealistic qualities, such as human attributes.

2. Let the students look through the books and separate the books into categories of those about real animals, animals that act in real ways, imaginary animals, or even real animals that act in imaginary ways. If necessary, help the students to make the distinctions.

3. Work quietly with each of the groups to check their classifications into "real" and "imaginary."

4. Ask one of the students to give an example of an "imaginary" animal. Talk about what makes that animal "imaginary."

5. Ask one of the students to give an example of a "real" animal. Talk about what makes that animal real.

6. Using a chart like the one on page 181, ask the students to fill in the blanks in the chart with examples from the books in their stack.

Grade Level: K–4

Subject Areas: Language Arts, Science, Environmental Education

Duration: two to three 20-minute sessions

Group Size: small groups of two to four students

Setting: indoors (or outdoors)

Conceptual Framework Topic Reference: CPIIC1, CPIIC2

Key Terms: real, imaginary

Appendices: Outdoors, Early Childhood

Social and Political Knowledge

And the Wolf Wore Shoes

	SHELTER	APPEARANCE	ACTIONS	FOOD	LOCOMOTION
REAL					
IMAGINARY					

7. Talk with the students about their ideas concerning the importance of being able to tell when something is real and something is imaginary. Talk about why that point is important to remember when you learn about animals and about how they live.

Extensions

1. Choose an animal in favorite stories such as *Stuart Little, Charlotte's Web, The Wind in the Willow,* and *Winnie the Pooh*. Are these animals real or imaginary? In what ways?

2. Tally the number of animals in familiar stories. For example, how many mammals, birds, reptiles, amphibians, fish, or insects can be found in a story? Are there more of some kinds of animals than others? If yes, why might this be?

Aquatic Extensions

1. See the Project WILD Aquatic activities, "Mermaids and Manatees" and "Micro Odyssey."

2. Establish categories of aquatic habitats or environments (e.g., pond, stream, river, lake, ocean). Do the activity as described above, except classify the aquatic animals according to what aquatic environments they are supposed to live in. Then indicate whether the portrayal you find in books is "real" or "imaginary."

Evaluation

Identify three things an imaginary animal often does that a real-life animal cannot do.

© Council for Environmental Education 2001

Museum Search for Wildlife

Objectives

Students will (1) identify wildlife portrayed as an art form, and (2) generalize that wildlife can inspire art.

Method

Students visit a museum, nature center, or other institution to find examples of how wildlife is presented in cultural art forms. Students may also use reference books on the Internet for additional information.

Materials

If conducted as a field trip, copies of "Museum Search for Wildlife Chart"; if conducted in the room, various art books, photographs, or slides featuring wildlife

Background

Wildlife has served as an inspiration for art throughout human history. Some art forms include cave drawings, pottery, baskets, costumes, paintings, sculpture, drawings, dances, photography, literature, and music. Artists are often inspired to capture wildlife in paintings, sculpture, drama, dance, literature, photography, and other means of creative expression. The major purpose of this activity is for students to recognize one aspect of the value of wildlife and its impact as a source of inspiration for varying art forms.

Procedure

1. This activity requires a trip to a local art, natural history, or anthropological museum.

   NOTE: This activity can be added to a field trip already planned as part of a social studies unit, for example. (If a trip to a museum is not realistic, have the students use a variety of reference materials to create a "museum.")

2. Survey the local community to see which museum, if any, would be appropriate. Make arrangements for your students to visit the museum.

3. Before the trip, discuss different kinds of art that people have created throughout human history, including cave drawings, pottery, baskets, costumes, paintings, sculpture, drawings, dances, photography, literature, and music. Ask the students what might inspire art.

4. At the museum, ask each student to find examples of wildlife represented in art. What kinds of wildlife? What kinds of art? Encourage the students to look closely because sometimes the image can be so stylized that it is hard to recognize. Ask each student to identify the art form and the wildlife and to make a small sketch as a reminder

---

Grade Level: 5–8

Subjects Areas: Social Studies, Language Arts, Expressive Arts

Duration: 30-minutes if using reference materials; 45-minutes or longer if at museum

Group Size: any size, up to 30 students

Setting: indoors

Conceptual Framework Topic Reference: CPIB, CPIB1, CPIIA, CPIB2, CPII

Key Terms: art, artists, inspiration, wildlife

Appendices: Using Local Resources

of what they see. (See the Project WILD activity "Wild Words." The students can put their sketches in their personal journals.) Or use a worksheet. For example, select one animal you saw represented at least three times. How did the artists portray it?

5. As a follow-up, discuss the students' observations with them. Identify the kinds of art that seem to include the most images of wildlife (painting, pottery, sculpture, etc.). Compare how one animal—like a deer—might look in different art works. Talk about the varying ways artists portrayed wildlife and some of the students' favorites. Talk about ways wildlife was portrayed during different historical periods. Talk about the relationships between people and wildlife during different periods. What are the clues? What if there were no wildlife?

6. Encourage the students to generalize that wildlife can serve as an inspiration and has aesthetic value.

Extension

Have the students make a wildlife art museum. Collect photos or copies of paintings, sculpture, pottery, petroglyphs, weavings, and so on.

Aquatic Extension

Have the students search through magazines or books for pictures of aquatic wildlife in art. Also look to see how frequently art with any kind of wildlife will include water. Make a list of the kinds of aquatic habitats found in art work, and tally how many times each is portrayed.

Evaluation

Groups of people were discussing endangered plants and animals—that is, those that are very close to becoming extinct. Some people felt that the plants and animals should be preserved and protected because of what might be learned about their capacity for uses in medicine, foods, and clothing, and as intrinsically valuable parts of the environment. Other people said that the animals and plants are not needed and that you should not to worry about them. Suppose you are an artist in the group and you want to express your opinion about the importance of plants and animals. As an artist, how would you present your case? Make that presentation.

Museum Search for Wildlife Chart

Place a check after the name of the animals found on the Museum Search for Wildlife.

Animal Group	Domestic Animals (Tame)	Wildlife (Untamed)

Saturday Morning Wildlife Watching

Objectives

Students will (1) discriminate between realistic and unrealistic portrayals of wildlife and other animals in cartoons, (2) identify possible influences on people's perceptions of wildlife from watching cartoons, and (3) make assessments about appropriate and inappropriate perceptions that can result from watching cartoons.

Method

Students watch, report, discuss, and evaluate wildlife in cartoons or comics.

Materials

A television, video recorder, and a videotape of a sampling of cartoons; a sampling of comic books

Grade Level: 5–8

Subject Areas: Language Arts, Social Studies, Environmental Education, Expressive Arts

Duration: one or two 20- to 30-minute sessions

Group Size: any

Setting: indoors

Conceptual Framework Topic Reference: CPII, CPIIC1, CPIIC2

Key Terms: wild, tame, influence, real, imaginary

Appendices: Field Ethics, Animals in the Classroom

Background

NOTE: This activity can be used as an extension for "First Impressions" and "And the Wolf Wore Shoes."

Donald Duck and Mickey Mouse are two examples of universally recognized cartoon characters who have come to us from the animal world. Many other animated wildlife and domesticated animal characters can be found in television and movie cartoons. Saturday morning television watching in the United States offers a wide range of "wildlife watching."

Television animals—including mammals, birds, insects, reptiles, spiders, one-celled organisms, and fish—animated and not, represent and misrepresent the real world. Sometimes the treatment of these animals models informed and responsible behaviors. At other times, it exaggerates the worst of ways to treat wildlife and other animals.

Cartoons regularly portray animals in anthropomorphic fashion (i.e., giving them human qualities or attributes). These traits may include walking upright, talking, thinking, and building things in a human manner. These impressions can carry strong implications for inappropriate future actions toward wildlife and other animals.

The major purpose of this activity is for students to discriminate between realistic and unrealistic portrayals of animals in cartoons and to make judgments about what they consider to be positive and negative influences of such portrayals in cartoons or comics.

Procedure

1. Have the students watch a variety of episodes of several cartoons. (Comic books may be substituted for watching cartoons. Daily newspapers, particularly the Sunday comics, may also be used for this activity.)

2. Ask the students to think about the following questions as they watch the cartoons:
   - Identify the names of three animal characters in cartoons or comics.
   - Identify whether the real animals on which these characters are based are wild or tame, or could be either (e.g., duck).
   - Describe each of the three cartoon animals: what it looks like, where it lives, what it eats, how it behaves, and how others treat it.

3. Ask the students to report on what they noticed about the ways animals are portrayed in cartoons. Identify whether the animal characters they watched were based on real-life animals. If so, were the animals wild or tame, or could they be either? (See the Project WILD activity "What's Wild?") Pick one animal, and make a chart that includes the above information.

   OPTIONAL: Describe what an animal would look like, where it would live, what it would eat, how it would behave, and how others would treat it if it were real contrasted with how it was portrayed in the cartoon.

4. Ask students to discuss how cartoons might influence people's perceptions of wildlife. What kinds of information do they provide? Is the information accurate and real, not real, or sometimes both? In what ways might cartoons encourage people to treat animals? Ask the students to think of one appropriate way to treat an animal and one inappropriate way to treat an animal that they have seen in cartoons. Conduct this discussion in small groups of two to four students. Ask each of the small groups to report back to the main group. After each group has reported, make a master list for all students to see and discuss that includes these:
   - real ways to treat real animals and
   - ways animals are treated in cartoons that they shouldn't be treated in real life.

   After looking at the completed lists, make any additions the students think are too important to exclude.

Extensions or Variations

1. Watch a cartoon—like Donald Duck, Bugs Bunny, Scooby Doo, Sylvester the Cat, or Mickey Mouse. Bring in a tame, real-life counterpart for the students to see, observe, and handle if possible, without harming the animal or the students. Discuss the similarities and differences between the imaginary and real animal.

2. Discuss how imaginary animals can symbolize human values and attributes. Consider what they tell us about our relationships, values, and behaviors.

Aquatic Extension

Be sure to look for any examples of aquatic wildlife portrayed in cartoons. Add these to the other examples of wildlife portrayed in cartoons, and conduct the activity as described above.

Evaluation

1. Describe five things that cartoon animals can do or that can happen to cartoon animals that are not true for wild animals or for pets.

2. Describe three ways that watching cartoons might affect people's perceptions of animals.

3. How can people distinguish between real and imaginary animals in cartoons and comics. Explain your reasoning.

4. Create two stories that portray the same animal in a major role. The stories can be acted out or drawn. In one story, show the animal realistically. In the second story, show the animal unrealistically. Explain how each of these two stories might affect how people perceive this animal.

Wildlife in National Symbols

Objectives
Students will (1) identify wildlife used in national symbols, and (2) hypothesize reasons wildlife are used in national symbols.

Method
Students research national symbols and make posters to depict their findings.

Materials
Access to reference materials, poster-making materials

Background
The lion is a good example of how wildlife has value as a symbol in many different cultures. It might be a national symbol, serve as a logo for an organization or cause, represent a youth or civic group, or be included in the symbols of a religious group. The lion, for example, is associated with regal qualities—courage, nobility, strength, and power. According to *The Cousteau Almanac* (Doubleday and Company, New York, 1980, 1981), "Lions appear on the United Nations coats of arms of more countries than any other animal—on those of India, Kenya, Malawi, Singapore, Burma, Burundi, Senegal, Sri Lanka, Swaziland, and several European nations." The Almanac continues to point out that lions no longer exist in the wild in most of these countries.

Many other animals that are national symbols of a country are on endangered or threatened species lists. Some examples are these:

Chile:	Andean condor
Dominica:	imperial Amazon parrot
Guatemala:	quetzal bird
United States:	bald eagle

The major purpose of this activity is for students to become acquainted with the diversity of countries and cultures that include wildlife in their symbols.

Procedure
1. Ask the students to develop a hypothesis about national symbols. Where do they come from? What do they represent? Strength? Natural resources? Cultural heritage?

2. Ask each student or group of students to select a country and research its national symbol or symbols. The more countries, the more interesting the results will be. Sometimes the symbols will be stylized, sometimes they will be literal and based on actual plants and animals, and sometimes several symbols will be combined. Ask the students to include in their findings information about the following:

Grade Level: 5–8

Subject Areas: Social Studies, Environmental Education, Expressive Arts

Duration: two 45-minute sessions

Group Size: any

Setting: indoors

Conceptual Framework Topic Reference: CPIIB1

Key Terms: symbol

Appendices: Using Local Resources

- what symbols the plants or animals are based on;
- whether those plants or animals are native, non-native, or nonexistent in the country;
- what characteristics the plants and animals have;
- whether the plants or animals are in abundance, threatened, or endangered where they exist; and
- what values they might represent that led to their use in the national symbol.

3. Ask each student or group of students to make a poster depicting their findings.

4. Given the hypotheses the students generated about why wildlife are used in national symbols, ask them whether the findings of their research supported those hypotheses. Discuss their findings and observations.

Extensions and Variations

1. Examine state or community symbols (e.g., state birds, animals, plants, seals) instead of national symbols.

2. Examine trademarks, logos, and product advertising campaigns for similar uses.

3. Many schools use wildlife or other animal symbols as mascots or in school emblems, team names, and so on. Survey the local community to compile a list of plants and animals used as school symbols. Contact the schools to find out how the names were chosen.

4. Study lyrics of state or school songs for references to wildlife.

Evaluation

1. Identify five animals or wildlife signs that are used as national symbols. What might each species have been chosen to symbolize?

2. Make a flag for a mythical country somewhere in the world using wildlife in the country's flag. Write a brief narrative explaining why the people of this mythical country chose the animal they did to represent them.

Prairie Memoirs

Objectives

Students will (1) interpret different cultural viewpoints, (2) describe how wildlife, and habitat affect cultures and societies, and (3) evaluate cultural factors leading to the endangerment of a species.

Method

Students analyze three literary selections about the bison.

Materials

Three literary selections (copies of Prairie Memoirs on pages 190 and 191)

Background

At one time, the Great Plains of North America, spanning from Canada to Texas and west of the Mississippi River, supported nearly 60 million bison. For centuries the indigenous people of the plains hunted the bison. They depended on the bison for meat, shelter, and clothing, as well as for other necessities such as rope and tools. Just as the bison relied on the prairie grasses for survival, native people, in turn, relied on the bison.

However, construction of the Union Pacific railroad created a conflict with the bison because stampeding herds were capable of turning over a train. Therefore, buffalo hunting became a regular feature for protecting the railroad. Also, during this time, a Pennsylvania tannery discovered that it could process hides into commercial leather; in 1871, buffalo hunting became a business. Bison hides became a valuable commodity.

The railroad and the Homestead Act opened the west to settlement. Many settlers thought the new land would provide an opportunity for an agriculture or cattle enterprise. Often, the settlers viewed both the bison and the indigenous people as a threat to their safety and economic well-being. This concern prompted settlers to develop grassroots cooperative support and to demand that the U.S. government provide long-term solutions by relocating the native peoples.

With the Oregon migration of the 1840s, the western expansion of the United States began. By 1890, the culture of the eastern United States had fully asserted itself over the west and the great bison herds of the plains were history.

The following selections are the fictional memoirs of Johnny Kincaid, Gray Hawk, and Catherine O'Riley. Their memoirs reflect three of the many differing personal views toward the prairie and the bison from the mid-1800s through the early 1900s. The purpose of the activity is to show that cultures affect and are

---

Grade Level: 5–8

Subject Areas: Science, Language Arts, Social Studies

Duration: 45 minutes for initial research, minimum 45 minutes for guided discussion

Group size: any

Setting: indoors

Conceptual Framework Topic References: CPIA, CPIIB, CPIIC,

Key Terms: ecology

Appendices: none

affected by wildlife and its habitat. The demise of the bison illustrates how wildlife and its habitat can be interpreted and treated differently by people viewing wildlife from different cultural perspectives and frames of reference.

NOTE: Consistent with common usage at the time, the reading selections in this activity use the term "buffalo" when referring to the bison (*Bison bison*) found in North America. True buffalo, such as cape buffalo or water buffalo, are not native to this continent. For more information on bison, see www.americanwest.com/bison/buffindx.htm.

Procedure

1. Have students research U.S. history (the Western Expansion) from 1840 to 1890. Students should investigate the culture of the indigenous people of the Great Plains and their dependence on the bison. Ask the students to consider the effect of the bison on the settlers who were moving west. What effect did the new settlers have on the bison? What was the natural history of the bison and its habitat?

2. Divide the class into three groups. Ask students in each group to read one of the three memoirs and to summarize the information found in the text.

3. Involve the students in a discussion guided by the following questions:

   - What is the main theme of each "memoir"? How are they different? What similarities are there in the themes of the three selections?

   - How did each author view the importance of bison? How did the culture of each author influence his or her perceptions? How did the bison affect the way of life for each author?

   - Using your research, do you think the experiences portrayed in the memoirs accurately reflect the people and events of the time? Why or why not? Do you see any biases in their writings?

   - The reading selections suggest a relationship between the people, the bison, the grass, and the soil. Underline sections of the three memoirs that suggest connections between these four elements. Describe how these elements are interdependent.

   - What lessons about the relationship of people and wildlife could be learned from reading these three selections? (Students might suggest a range of broad ideas, such as "Human activity affects and is affected by wildlife," "People disagree over the uses of wildlife and habitat," or "Wildlife is viewed and treated differently by people from various cultural perspectives.")

Extension

Have the students select and research the history of another region of the United States or world as well as the cultural factors that affected people's relationships to the wildlife of that region.

Evaluation

1. Contrast the apparent value and use of the bison and grassland by early settlers and the Native Americans as expressed in these selections.

2. What cultural factors led to the endangerment of the bison?

continued

Prairie Memoirs

Memoir I:
From the Stories of Johnny Kincaid

I was a scrawny kid who'd come to the Great Plains from Chicago looking for wealth and adventure in the spring of 1870. I didn't know what I would do when I got there, but I knew I would do something adventurous. When I arrived in Dodge City, I was penniless, tired, and hungry. I wandered the street, alone and scared. A huge man, about 6'4" with arms as big as two men and shoulders of steel, sauntered up to me. He wore buckskins and had a rifle flung across his shoulder. I was impressed.

He introduced himself as Sure Eye Jones (to this day, I do not know his real name). He asked if I was looking for work. He explained that he needed a skinner to go with him on a hunt the next day. He said he'd cover all my grub and pay me handsomely for each buffalo hide. I didn't know at that time what a skinner was, but it sounded like a good deal to me. Besides, I was desperate.

We headed out into the prairie land the next day looking for the big herd. Another man named Doug McKinnon, who was an experienced skinner, came along. He promised to teach me all he could about skinning. He gave me both a long bowed knife to hang on my hip and another short knife, something like a dagger, to strap on my boot. They were sharp enough to cut paper. Doug explained skinning to me while we searched for the herd. He told me we would prepare the hides for sale back in Dodge City and that my earnings would depend upon how many animals I could skin in a day. The more I did, the more money I would make.

As we traveled, I became excited about the hunt and the thought of making money. We came over the crest of a hill and saw the buffalo below us. It was a huge herd that covered the open plain as far as the eye could see. Some were young, some were calves, and some were heavy with young not born. It was an amazing sight. As my eyes lingered on the herd, a crack rang out in the air as a bullet shot into the herd and took out a yearling, which Doug whispered to me would be our dinner for the next few days. Sure Eye (now I realized how he got his name) took aim again and shot another. Crack after crack of the rifle rang out as Sure Eye killed buffalo after buffalo. It wasn't until he had killed 30 or so that he stopped.

Doug hollered at me to "Move it!" We raced down the hill and began our work. It took us all day and late into the night before we had skinned all the dead animals. Sure Eye came by and said, "Well done, boy! As far as I can figure, you just made yourself a whole heap of money. Well done." He slapped me on the back and moved on back to camp.

I continued to skin buffalo until there were no more to be found. I earned a great deal of money and was able to return to Dodge City to build a home; marry my wife, Sally; and work in town.

Some days I miss those grand herds of buffalo stretching across the horizon. It was quite an adventure, those early days on the prairie.

Memoir II:
From the Stories of Gray Hawk

Back in the days when the Earth was new, my forefathers hunted buffalo on foot. The buffalo flesh provided my people with food, and the skin became clothing and the sheltering cover of tepees. My people's daily life revolved around the buffalo hunt, and our rituals and worship were dedicated to its success.

Then the Spaniards brought horses, and many of these animals wandered over the plains. My people learned to tame and ride these wild animals. We became great horsemen. The horse allowed us to become great hunters; it helped us follow the buffalo herds. We also crafted tools to help us hunt. Hunters carried a short bow, a quiver for barbed arrows, and a long shear. Because the hunters were able to ride with hands free, they could feed and release the bow, and the hunts became more and more successful.

With the horse, our tribe was able to follow the buffalo and have a steady supply of food. The tribe grew. Often, small hunting groups would leave the larger tribe, but each summer all our people would reunite for the sacred ritual dance. This ritual lasted four days in which we honored the buffalo with offerings and ceremonial dances. Our dance celebrated the natural cycle of the grass, the soil, and the buffalo. We honored the buffalo, for it provided us with our daily needs.

The buffalo herds began to grow smaller. We had become skillful hunters, and settlers came to live on our land, build railroads, and hunt buffalo. The buffalo could not survive; the natural cycle had been changed. Then the settlers' government told my people we had to change our ways. We were told where to live and that we could not continue to follow the buffalo herds. The fact was that the buffalo herds were gone and that the ways of our ancestors would continue only in our stories.

Memoir III:
From the Diary of Catherine O'Riley

Early in the year of 1860, my husband and I left the forest lands of Missouri for the tall grass prairie of the area now known as Oklahoma. Our dream was to build a cattle ranch in this fertile grassland. We had been told that this was a wild area, but it was also rich in opportunity. However, in this land without trees, building a house, corrals, and barns became a problem. Providing water proved to be an even more difficult task. We soon knew that survival in this new land would require us to be strong and self-sufficient.

The first years on the ranch were tough. We were not prepared for what happened the first time a herd of buffalo moved into our cattle grazing area. The buffalo were large, aggressive animals, and the cattle scattered in fright. The buffalo depleted the grass and rolled in the dirt, creating great dust clouds. These large animals trampled anything that got in their path, and constructing barriers did nothing to change their course. Along with the buffalo came the native tribes. Many tribes had been relocated to the Oklahoma Territory, but they did not always stay on their reservation lands.

We thought the U.S. government with the soldiers from the area forts would make sure the tribes stayed on the land they were given. The government, however, was fighting a civil war. The only soldiers that we had to protect us and our property were untrained recruits, and they caused more problems than they solved. Many ranchers in the area met to discuss a way to handle the problem of the roaming herds of buffalo and the roaming tribes.

Someone had heard about the buffalo hunters hired by the railroad. Supporting these buffalo hunters seemed a good way to remove the threat of these animals. It was also suggested that if the tribes stayed on the reservations, the government could provide them with cattle. Then they would not need the buffalo, and we would have a new market for our animals. However, it was obvious that it was up to us to protect our property and livelihood.

By 1890, the buffalo and the native tribes were removed from the plains, and cattle freely grazed on the lush grass of the open public range. The best cows and bulls were kept and the breeds constantly improved. For the next few years, ranching was one of the most profitable industries in the country.

Cartoons and Bumper Stickers

Objectives

Students will (1) identify cartoons and bumper stickers designed to make a statement about some issue affecting natural resources and the environment, and (2) describe the influence of humor as a means for conveying information about such issues.

Method

Students find, analyze, and discuss cartoons or bumper stickers, or both.

Materials

Colored pens and strips of construction paper for bumper stickers, drawing materials for cartoons

Background

Humor may be one of the most profound and subtle tools used in influencing people's attitudes. The process of humor can be an efficient and pleasant means by which to communicate information. It can diffuse differences of opinion, although—if the joke isn't appreciated—it can make the differences seem even greater.

Humorous media are diverse, including monologues by stand-up comics, movies, plays, books, articles, photographs, dance, paintings, commercials, and more. Two of the most popular forms used in contemporary culture to make a quick political statement are bumper stickers and cartoons.

Stereotypes are a rich resource for the humorist. Stereotypes of animals frequently are used to get a laugh and may be accurately founded or sufficiently off-base to perpetuate misunderstanding. "The Big Bad Wolf" may be a classic case of the latter. Fine humor probably exploits realistic characteristics—based on the familiar—by comparison with what could be ridiculous or absurd.

Not all humor is meant to be funny. It may be poignant, angry, bitter, or sad. Political cartoonists, for example, frequently pull in a range of such emotions where, after the initial laugh, the response may be, "That's not so funny—it's true."

The major purpose of this activity is to examine two forms of humorous media in contemporary culture: the bumper sticker and the cartoon. Both may be seen to have some influence on people's attitudes. Some of this influence affects people's perceptions of issues affecting natural resources and the environment.

Grade Level: 5–8

Subject Areas: Environmental Education, Social Studies, Language Arts, Expressive Arts

Duration: one 45-minute session; time to look for cartoons or bumper stickers

Group Size: any

Setting: indoors (may be done outdoors)

Conceptual Framework Topic Reference: CPIB, CPIB2

Key Terms: stereotypes, media, attitudes

Appendices: Using Local Resources

Procedure

1. Ask the students to find examples of cartoons or bumper stickers that convey a message for an environment-related issue. Each student should find and bring in at least one cartoon or bumper sticker. Local newspapers can be accumulated preceding this activity, providing an opportunity to track the conditions leading to some of the reasons behind the cartoons.

2. Ask the students to post their cartoons or bumper stickers in the room. After the students have examined them, ask the following questions:
   - What is the major focus or topic of each of the cartoons or bumper stickers?
   - What organizations or people, if any, are involved?
   - What elements of the environment are involved?
   - What natural resources, if any, are involved?
   - What purpose does the cartoonist or author of the bumper sticker seem to have in mind?
   - What kinds of emotions or feelings seem to be elicited?
   - What actions, if any, do the cartoons or bumper stickers seem to be designed to promote?
   - What influence, if any, do you think these cartoons or bumper stickers will have?
   - Who will they influence? In what ways?
   - Do the cartoons or bumper stickers seem designed to mislead? Distort? Perpetuate negative stereotypes? If yes, in what ways?
   - Do the cartoons or bumper stickers seem designed to inform? To serve accuracy? To encourage constructive, responsible attitudes?

3. Ask the students to summarize their views of the effectiveness and appropriateness of the use of media such as bumper stickers and cartoons to attempt to influence people's attitudes.

Extensions

1. Have the students make cartoons, bumper stickers, or both inspired by some natural resource or environment-related issues. Put the cartoons in a book format or print the bumper stickers, using them as a source of income for some class project.

2. Write captions for existing magazine or newspaper photos.

3. Include an analysis of elements of propaganda (e.g., band wagon) in order to demonstrate components of persuasion.

4. Find humor in other communications media involving natural resources, the environment, or other issues (e.g., editorials in newspapers, radio, television, magazines; situation comedies; music; and so on).

Aquatic Extensions

1. Have the students create at least five bumper stickers or cartoons focused on important issues related to aquatic wildlife and aquatic habitats.

2. See the Project WILD Aquatic activities, "Aqua Words" and "Aquatic Times."

Evaluation

Describe the significance and usefulness of humor as a way to convey information about environmental topics. Describe its effectiveness as a way to influence opinion about environmental topics.

Power of a Song

Objectives
Students will (1) analyze popular music for environmental messages, and (2) interpret some influences of popular music and other art forms on people's environmental attitudes.

Method
Students listen to songs and analyze lyrics.

Materials
Radio; records, tapes, or song books as sources of popular songs

Background
Art reflects the artist. It also may influence one who sees, hears, or feels the art. Social attitudes toward environmental issues are affected by the communications media, including the classical and popular arts.

Artists may influence different people in different ways. For example, Sting and U2 are recognized as talented artists both by people who strongly agree and by those who strongly disagree with their political views on specific issues.

Historical and contemporary artists have expressed their views about issues, including environmental issues, and have influenced others in the process. The Transcendentalists of the 19th century, including Bronson Alcott, Ralph Waldo Emerson, and Henry David Thoreau, influenced some of their generation through their teachings and writings. Their influence continues.

John Denver was a popular songwriter and performer who consistently included what may be described as an environmental theme in much of his music and who made a statement with his music to public officials as well as private citizens. For example, Denver's song, "Rocky Mountain High," has been identified by some as having had a role in the decision not to bring the Winter Olympics to Colorado in the early 1970s. These words in that popular song spoke to the issue:

> Now his life is full of wonder
> But his heart still knows some fear
> Of a simple thing we cannot comprehend
> Why they try to tear the mountains down
> To bring in a couple more,
> More people, more scars upon the land...

From "Rocky Mountain High." Words by John Denver, music by John Denver and Mike Taylor. Copyright 1972, 1974 by Cherry Lane Music Company. All rights reserved.

Denver spoke and sang to the U.S. Congress in Washington, D.C., on the Alaska Land Bill issue. Denver was in favor of protection of Alaska lands as wilderness areas. He sang from a series of songs he had written about Alaska, including "To the Wild Country." Denver also spoke and

---

Grade Level: 5–8
Subject Areas: Expressive Arts
Duration: one 30- to 45-minute session
Group Size: any
Setting: indoors or outdoors
Conceptual Framework Topic Reference: CPIB1, CPII
Key Terms: music, song, lyrics, influence, attitudes
Appendices: Using Local Resources

sang before a meeting of the International Whaling Commission (IWC) in support of a cessation of worldwide commercial whaling. Denver sang "I Want to Live." Denver sang his song, "It's About Time," to a congressional subcommittee as part of his testimony in support of what became law as the National Environmental Education Act.

These are a few examples of the strong environmental statements in one songwriter's lyrics and performances. Look also at the musical writings of Dan Fogelberg, Jackson Browne, Joni Mitchell, Jimmy Buffett, Judy Collins, Stevie Wonder ("The Secret Life of Plants"), Paul Winter, U2, Alabama, Hammer, The Grateful Dead, Michael Jackson, Midnight Oil, Garth Brooks, Dolly Parton, and Sting. Students will be able to add other artists to this list. Traditional songs such as "Home on the Range," "Wild Mountain Thyme," "Woodsman Spare That Tree," and "April Showers" also could be used.

The major purpose of this activity is for students to examine the role of the arts and other communications media in influencing the attitudes of people. In this case, the influence is narrowed to people's attitudes about the environment and issues affecting it.

Procedure

1. Ask the students to listen to the lyrics of popular songwriters in contemporary music. Look for any artists who include lyrics with an environmental message.

2. Bring examples of music with an environmental message to class.

3. Listen to the lyrics. If possible, obtain written versions of the lyrics to at least one song. Identify the particular issues being written about in these songs. If necessary, find out more about the issues in order to attempt to better understand the perspective of the artist as conveyed in the lyrics.

4. The students may find that few contemporary artists include lyrics about environmental issues. Discuss why or why not. Talk about why some might and others don't. Discuss whether people are influenced by the work of popular artists, as in this case by the lyrics of songwriters' songs.

Extensions

1. Write an environmental song about a specific issue, a favorite animal, or general feelings about the environment. Share your song with family, friends, other students, a local politician, or anyone else who might enjoy musical expression.

2. Look for songs and lyrics with harmful environmental messages. Look for songs and lyrics with upbeat, hopeful messages. Look for those that seem to be calling for action.

3. Review music videos that have environmental themes.

Aquatic Extension

Aquatic themes are abundant in traditional songs as well as some contemporary songs. Sea chanteys, such as "Oh, Shenandoah" and John Denver's song "Calypso" are examples. Listen to a variety of songs with aquatic themes. Analyze the lyrics. Find examples of ecological concepts, historical information, political messages, and examples of the many ways that people value water and aquatic environments.

Evaluation

Describe the ways, if any, in which music and other art forms influence people's attitudes. In what specific ways, if any, do such art forms affect people's attitudes toward the environment?

Additional Resources

Dale and Linda Crider have written "The Watersong Book"—a book of songs about water, aquatic wildlife, and aquatic habitats. Information may be obtained by writing Anhinga Roost Music Company, Route 2, Box 342T, Gainesville, FL 32601.

continued

For Your Eyes Only

Objectives
Students will (1) observe the environment in which they live, (2) express environmental attitudes, (3) analyze viewpoints on the environment, and (4) listen to and respect the right of others to maintain different environmental attitudes.

Method
Students will observe, write, discuss, and make judgments about attitudes concerning the environments in which they live.

Materials
Writing materials, transparency or poster of "Factors That Influence Attitude/Viewpoint Toward the Environment" and "Three Major Types of Environmental Attitudes/Viewpoints" on pages 198 and 199, student copies of "Quotable Quotes" on page 202 (Additional quotes may be added.)

Background
Environmental issues tend to be complex and to have many ecological, political, social, legal, and economic implications. People interested in an issue bring many emotions, biases, beliefs, and needs to discussions. Attitudes are feelings, perceptions, or states of mind that are influenced by deep-seated values and principles. The views of individuals, for instance, may be influenced by their lifestyles; traditions; religions; and personal, political, and moral beliefs. Local and regional differences in values may exist. For example, the value placed on a pond may be higher in a dry environment than in an area along a river. Because of these varying perspectives, reaching decisions on environmental issues is seldom easy. A lengthy review process and opportunities for public input may be required.

An environmental attitude develops from the comparative value placed on something in the environment. These attitudes are expressed in the ways we act toward the environment, and they influence how personal and societal decisions are made. Listed on the next page are value factors that can influence our personal attitudes and viewpoints about the environment.

These factors may be interwoven and are not always easily recognized as distinct units. For instance, creation of a new park may come about because of political values, although the demand originated from the historical significance or educational value of the area.

Grade Level: 5–8

Subject Areas: Language Arts, Environmental Education

Duration: one 40-minute period for each part

Group Size: any

Setting: Part 1 outdoors and indoors, Part 2 indoors

Conceptual Framework Topic References: CPIA, CPIB, CPII, CPIIA, CPIIC

Key Terms: attitude, anthropocentric, biocentric, philosophical

Appendices: Taking Action

---

continued

© Council for Environmental Education 2001

197

Factors That Influence Attitude/Viewpoint Toward the Environment

political	pertains to the role or position of a governmental agency
economic	pertains to uses for food, clothing, shelter, and other benefits
religious	pertains to faith
ecological	pertains to roles in maintaining a natural ecosystem
scientific	pertains to providing an understanding of biological functions
cultural	pertains to societal customs, beliefs, and laws
educational	pertains to providing an understanding of a species and of the role people play in the environment
aesthetic	pertains to sources of beauty and inspiration
social	pertains to shared human emotions and status
recreational	pertains to providing leisure activities
egocentric	pertains to a focus on human benefit of resource
health-related	pertains to positive human conditions
ethical/moral	pertains to responsibilities and standards
historical	pertains to connections to the past

NOTE: For additional perspectives on environmental attitudes, see *Contemporary Values of Wildlife in American Society* by Stephen Kellert (1974); School of Forestry and Environmental Studies, Yale University: New Haven, CT.

For this activity, environmental attitudes are placed into three major categories. A person with an anthropocentric attitude views the value of the environment/resource from a personal need and interest. A person with a biocentric attitude considers all plants and animals to be worthy of consideration. A person with a philosophical attitude values the balanced system of living and non-living things.

Using the example of an untouched tract of wetland, the anthropocentric person would value the potential of the area for a human need such as agricultural production. The biocentric person would recognize the value of the plants and animals inhabiting the area. Finally, the philosophical person would recognize the value of the wetland as an ecosystem supporting life on Earth.

Procedure

Before the Activity

Set up an observation site. Mark borders with tape or other material (neon plastic tape strips work well). The area should be large enough for the entire class to use.

Part 1

1. Begin this activity outside; have the students take basic writing materials with them.

2. Describe observation site parameters to students.

3. Tell students they have 15 minutes to make observations about this site (tell them to write down descriptions about what they sense in the area). Students are to remain stationary (sitting or standing) while making all observations; they are not to walk around or through the observation site.

Three Major Types of Environmental Attitudes/Viewpoints

Anthropocentric   values personal need and interest
Biocentric   values all plants and animals as worthy of consideration
Philosophical   values a balanced system of living and non-living things

4. After 15 minutes, return to the classroom.

5. Give students a few minutes to review their observations and attitudes about the outdoor site.

6. Allow students the opportunity to share or orally present their observations made at the outdoor site. Remind students to respect the rights of others to express different attitudes toward what they saw.

7. Go over background information with students about how environmental attitudes develop. Review the three major types of attitudes—anthropocentric, biocentric, and philosophical—and the factors that influence attitudes about the environment.

8. Have the students evaluate the type of attitude they had toward this environment: anthropocentric, biocentric, or philosophical. Allow them time to discuss factors that may have influenced their attitudes toward the environment. Students can share why they chose to use a particular approach.

9. Read this quote from G. C. Lichtenberg (1765–1799), "We cannot remember too often that when we observe nature, and especially the ordering of nature, it is always ourselves we are observing." Allow students to reflect on and discuss the meaning of this quote in relation to their responses in Step 6.

OPTIONAL:

1. After all student presentations have been completed and self-evaluated, allow students to return to the site at a future time (could be immediately afterward or a few months later). Compare whether or not attitudes stayed the same or changed over time. Why or why not? Also compare whether or not behaviors (actions) toward the environment have changed over time. Why or why not?

2. Initiate Extension 2 found at the end of this activity. Upon completion of this component, determine whether *attitudes* toward the environment have changed. Determine whether *behaviors* toward the environment have changed. Was it easier to change attitude (how you think) toward the environment or behavior (how you act) toward the environment? If change did occur, what factors influenced the change?

Part 2

1. Distribute copies of "Quotable Quotes" on page 202.

2. Allow groups of three to four students to work together to read and discuss quotes by the authors. Categorize the authors' attitudes toward the environment: anthropocentric, biocentric, or philosophical.

3. Compile a whole-group consensus of how the quotes should be categorized. It can be compiled as a bulletin board display. Place copies of the quotes under the three headings: anthropocentric, biocentric, or philosophical.

4. Discuss how the authors of the quotes would react to current environmental issues. How would the anthropocentric group react? How would the biocentric group react? How would the philosophical group react?

continued

5. Discuss "Can a person have one attitude or viewpoint toward one environmental issue and have a different attitude toward a different environmental issue? Why or why not?"

OPTIONAL: Students can find and bring in other environmental quotes or writings and can categorize them on the bulletin board. Internet sites, such as **www.quotablequotes.net** often have designated sections for ecology- or nature-related quotes.

Part 3

1. Show the following quote on the overhead projector and read it to students, but do not disclose the author's name:

"The best remedy for those who are afraid, lonely, or unhappy is to go outside, somewhere where they can be quiet, alone with the heavens, nature, and God. Because only then does one feel that all is as it should be and that God wishes to see people happy, amidst the simple beauty of nature. As long as this exists, and it certainly always will, I know that then there will always be comfort for every sorrow, whatever the circumstances may be. And I firmly believe that nature brings solace in all troubles."

Anne Frank (1929–1945), German Jewish refugee, diarist. The Diary of a Young Girl (1947; tr. 1952), entry for February 23, 1944. *The Columbia Dictionary of Quotations.*

2. Allow students the opportunity to discuss what they think the quote means. What concerns and emotions are addressed in this quote? How does this quote make you feel? Who do you think the author is?

3. If students do not have an historical background on the story of Anne Frank, have them either gather biographical information or watch a video about Anne Frank's life.

4. Now that students know who the author is and under what circumstances the quote was written, show the quote to the students a second time. Allow the students to share any new reflections or interpretations.

5. Does background information about the author and her life change how you interpret what she wrote? Would background information change how you categorized the quotes in Part 2? Do you think it is important to know as much as possible about authors before trying to interpret what they wrote?

Part 4

1. Have students review and collect periodicals, news releases, newspapers, and other resources to identify local environmental concerns.

2. Have the class select a local environmental issue and track coverage of the issue over an extended period of time.

3. Ask the students the following questions: How much coverage did the environmental issue receive? Do you think the coverage was fair or biased? How much was the public involved in the review process? What concerns did the public interest groups have? How was the solution reached? Who will be affected by the final decisions(s)?

Extensions

1. Have students work with local environmental agencies to find an area in their community or on their school grounds where they can enhance or restore the natural environment for plants and animals. See the Project WILD publication *Taking Action: An Educators Guide to Involving Students in Environmental Action Projects* for ideas and considerations.

2. Provide a general topic (e.g., overpopulation of deer), and have students write sentences expressing each of the factors that influence attitude and viewpoint toward the environment.

Evaluation

1. Conduct a debate on current environmental issues. Throughout these debates students should be respectful of all student's right to express their own opinions. Encourage the students to defend their arguments with facts (not emotions).

2. Which of the three viewpoints—anthropocentric, biocentric, and philosophical views—do you feel most settlers had? Native Americans? Scientists? Which viewpoint do students take on current environmental issues? Do they take different stands on different issues? Why?

3. Present basic scenarios of several local environmental issues, and ask students to tell if they view those issues from an anthropocentric, biocentric, or philosophical standpoint. Students should be able to support their viewpoints. Do students take different viewpoints with different issues? Why?

4. Have students develop and write their personal environmental code of ethics, starting with the phrase " I believe that …" and share with the class.

continued

Quotable Quotes

"I am against nature. I don't dig nature at all. I think nature is very unnatural. I think the truly natural things are dreams, which nature can't touch with decay."
Bob Dylan (1986)

"After you have exhausted what there is in business, politics, conviviality, and so on—have found that none of these finally satisfy, or permanently wear—what remains? Nature remains."
Walt Whitman (1882)

"There are those who look at Nature from the standpoint of conventional and artificial life—from parlor windows and through gilt-edged poems—the sentimentalists. At the other extreme are those who do not look at Nature at all, but are a grown part of her, and look away from her toward the other class—the backwoodsman and pioneers, and all rude and simple persons. Then there are those in whom the two are united and merged—the great poets and artists. In them, the sentimentalist is corrected and cured, and the hairy and taciturn frontiersman has had experience to some purpose. The true poet knows more about Nature than the naturalists because he carries her open secrets in his heart."
John Burroughs (1906)

"Man masters nature not by force but by understanding. This is why science has succeeded where magic failed: because it has looked for no spell to cast over nature."
Jacob Bronowski (1953)

"Of all the things that oppress me, this sense of the evil working of nature herself—my disgust at her barbarity, clumsiness, darkness, bitter mockery of herself—is the most desolating."
John Ruskin (1871)

"You may drive out nature with a pitchfork, yet she'll be constantly running back."
Horace (8 B.C.)

"To sit in the shade on a fine day and look upon verdure is the most perfect refreshment."
Jane Austin (1814)

"There is in every American, I think, something of the old Daniel Boone—who, when he could see the smoke from another chimney, felt himself too crowded and moved further out into the wilderness."
Hubert H. Humphrey (1966)

"In a few generations more, there will probably be no more room at all allowed for animals on the earth: no need of them, no toleration of them. An immense agony will have then ceased, but with it there will also have passed away the last smile of the world's youth."
Ouida (Marie Louise de la Ramee) (1900)

"Nature has no mercy at all. Nature says, 'I'm going to snow. If you have a bikini and no snowshoes, that's tough. I am going to snow anyway.'"
Maya Angelou (1974)

"The tree which moves some to tears of joy is in the eyes of others only a green thing that stands in the way. Some see nature all ridicule and deformity … and some scarce see nature at all. But to the eyes of the man of imagination, nature is imagination itself."
William Blake (1799)

"The Laws of Nature are just, but terrible. There is no weak mercy in them. Cause and consequence are inseparable and inevitable. The elements have no forbearance. The fire burns, the water drowns, the air consumes, the earth buries. And perhaps it would be well for our race if the punishment of crimes against the Laws of Man were as inevitable as the punishment of crimes against the Laws of Nature—were Man as unerring in his judgments as Nature."
Henry Wadsworth Longfellow (1857)

"One swallow does not make a summer, but one skein of geese, cleaving the murk of a March thaw, is the spring. A cardinal, whistling spring to thaw but later finding himself mistaken, can retrieve his error by resuming his winter silence. A chipmunk, emerging for a sun bath, but finding a blizzard, has only to go back to bed. But a migrating goose, staking 200 miles of black night on the chance of finding a hole in the lake, has no easy chance for retreat. His arrival carries the conviction of a prophet who has burned his bridges."
Aldo Leopold (1970)

Ethi-Reasoning

Objectives
Students will (1) examine their own values and beliefs related to wildlife and other elements of the environment, (2) listen to and respect the rights of others to maintain different values and beliefs, and (3) evaluate possible actions they might take that have an effect on wildlife and the environment.

Method
Students read, discuss, make assessments, and write about hypothetical dilemmas concerning wildlife, natural resources, or both.

Materials
One set of the Dilemma Cards on pages 205 through 207 for each group of students

Background
This activity is designed to give students the opportunity to examine their own values and beliefs relating to wildlife and other elements of the environment. It is not the intent of this activity to prescribe "right" and "wrong" answers for the students. One exception is in the areas where information about laws is conveyed.

Variations in laws from state to state affect wildlife and the environment. Each state has an official public agency that is legally responsible for managing the wildlife within the state. This agency can be contacted in your state to request general information about laws that affect most wildlife in your area. For example, it is legal to hunt and fish for some animals in all states; however, what animals and under what conditions are specified by laws and regulations for which the state wildlife agency is responsible. There are also federal regulations that affect wildlife. The U.S. Fish and Wildlife Service can be contacted for information about such laws. For example, federal law protects all birds of prey—eagles, hawks, and owls—from shooting or any other intentional cause of death, injury, or harassment. All threatened and endangered species are protected by law. Songbirds are protected by law; that is, it is against the law to intentionally harm songbirds. It also is generally illegal to possess birds' nests, eggs, and feathers, even those found lying on the ground. It is generally against the law to pick up the carcass of an animal that has been killed by a vehicle along the highway or road. Instead, local wildlife authorities should be notified. In many cases, it is against the law to take an injured wild animal home to care for it. For example, birds of prey cannot be cared for by private citizens unless those citizens have a permit to do so. There are many laws, and they are complex. Again, it is useful and important to contact local authorities about the laws protecting and affecting wildlife in your area.

Grade Level: 5–8

Subject Areas: Social Studies, Environmental Education

Duration: one or two 45-minute sessions

Group Size: any, small groups of two to four students recommended

Setting: indoors or outdoors

Conceptual Framework Topic Reference: CPII, CPIIA, CPIIC

Key Terms: dilemma, responsibility

Appendices: Using Local Resources

---

continued

Whether right or wrong, questions of law can be separated from questions of ethics. On a personal level, an individual's choices as to what seems right or wrong for him or her in terms of values and behaviors may be described as a personal code of ethics. Hunting, for example, is controversial for some people from an ethical point of view. Some people say that although hunting is legal, it is unethical because a human being is taking the life of a wild animal. Others believe hunting to be a responsible and ethical form of enjoying recreation, acquiring food, or controlling an animal population. Those differences of belief may be sincerely held. Whether or not a person chooses to hunt is a personal choice dictated by one's personal ethics. Conflicts arise, however, when a person motivated by one set of ethics tries to force his or her ethics on others through activities such as arguments, harassment, or legislative action.

The major purpose of this activity is to provide students with an opportunity to reach their own judgments about what they think are the most responsible and appropriate actions to take in situations that affect wildlife and the environment.

Procedure

Before the Activity

Educators will need to copy and cut out the Dilemma Cards. Other dilemmas could be written that are more specific to regional issues. Students could also be involved in the process of creating the dilemma cards, with each student responsible for one card. Dilemmas can be left entirely open-ended, with no options suggested for consideration.

1. Divide the class into groups of four, and give each group a stack of Dilemma Cards. Place them face down at the center of the group.

2. The first student draws a card from the top of the stack. The student studies the situation, decides what he or she should do, and formulates his or her response.

3. When the students are ready—typically in less than 2 minutes—they each read the situation and the options aloud to the rest of the group. They each give the decision they have chosen and describe the reasoning involved. In turn, the other members of the group are invited to comment on the dilemma and what they would do in the situation. Discuss each dilemma for about 5 minutes. Make sure the person whose dilemma is being discussed has an opportunity to ask questions of the other members of the group and to offer clarification about his or her decision. The discussion gives the students experience in having ideas examined by peers and is intended to remind the students of the need to take personal responsibility for decision making. It is not necessary—and may not be desirable—for the students to reach consensus; there are legitimately ranging views of the most appropriate and responsible actions to take in many situations. The purpose is to provide students with an opportunity to examine, express, clarify, and take responsibility for their reasoning.

4. Return the card to the bottom of the stack, and have the next student select a card from the top of the stack. Continue this process until all students have had the opportunity to express their decision and rationale about a dilemma.

Evaluation

Choose a dilemma. Write a short paragraph on the positive and negative effects of all the options listed for that dilemma. Indicate what additional information, if any, is needed to make a responsible and informed decision. Give two opposing and convincing arguments for how to respond to this dilemma. Identify what response is the most responsible; explain your reasoning. Explain how someone else could reach a different, yet valid, opinion with the same information.

Dilemma Card

A deer herd has grown so large during the past 10 years that many of the deer appear to be starving. The herd is severely damaging the habitat, eliminating much of the vegetation that the animals use for food or shelter. There is a disagreement within your community as to what course of action is best to take. You personally are opposed to hunting. A limited legal hunt has been proposed to reduce the size of the herd in this area. Would you:

- Investigate and consider the situation to see what, in your judgment, seems the most humane and reasonable solution, including the feasibility of options such as moving some deer to other areas, even though you understand that they still may not survive?
- Attempt to identify the causes of this population increase and propose action to return the system to a balance?
- Allow the habitat degradation to continue and the deer to starve?
- Leave it to the state wildlife agency to work with the landholder to arrive at a solution?
- Do something else?

Dilemma Card

You are a homeowner in an area directly above a city. Local government officials have proposed diverting a small stream from the property of several homeowners above the city, including yours, to power a hydro-electric system that will benefit the entire city. As a homeowner, you are concerned with losing the aesthetic values of this stream from your property. You also are concerned about the effect the removal of this stream will have on the fish and aquatic habitat. Another concern is that your property may lose some of its value for resale. You realize that your city needs to supply electric power to all its citizens as cost-effectively as possible. Would you:

- Hire a lawyer and prepare to sue the city for loss of property value?
- Form a coalition of homeowners to meet with city planners and explore possible alternatives?
- Sell your property before the project is begun?
- Decide the needs of the city are more important than either the consequences to you personally or the ecological costs?
- Do something else?

Dilemma Card

Your family owns a 500-acre farm. A tributary to a high-quality fishing stream runs along the boundary of your property. The nitrogen- and phosphorous-based fertilizer that your family uses to increase crop production is carried into the stream by rain run-off. This type of fertilizer is increasing algae growth and adversely affecting the fish population in both the tributary and the main stream. Your farm production is your sole source of income, but your family has always enjoyed fishing and doesn't want to lose the fish from the streams. Would you:

- Change fertilizers even though it may reduce crop yield?
- Allow a portion of your land along the stream to grow wild, thus establishing a buffer zone (riparian area)?
- Investigate the possibility of gaining a tax exemption for the land you allowed for a buffer zone?
- Do nothing?
- Do something else?

Dilemma Card

You are a farmer. You have been studying and hearing about farming practices such as leaving edge areas for wildlife, no-till farming, and organic pest control. Although these practices may improve your long-term benefits, they may reduce your short-term profits. You are already having trouble paying your taxes and keeping up with expenses. Would you:

- Sell the farm?
- Keep studying farming practices but make no changes for now?
- Try a few methods on some of your acreage, and compare the results with other similar areas on your land?
- Do something else?

continued

Dilemma Card

You are fishing at a secluded lake and have caught 2 fish during your first day at the lake. Now, on the second day, the fishing has been great, and you have caught 5 fish in the first hour, all of which are bigger than yesterday's fish. The law allows you to possess 12 fish. Would you:

- Continue to fish and keep all the fish?
- Dispose of the smaller fish you caught yesterday, and keep the big ones to stay within your limit?
- Have fish for lunch?
- Quit fishing and go for a hike?
- Do something else?

Dilemma Card

You are finally able to build your family's dream house. Because of rising construction costs, you realize that you cannot include all the features you had planned for. You must decide which one of the following you will include:

- solar heating,
- recreation room with fireplace,
- hot tub and sauna,
- greenhouse, or
- something else.

Dilemma Card

You are a member of a country club that has recently voted to build a wildlife farm to raise animals for members to hunt. You are not a hunter, you think that hunting is okay only to do in the wild, and you are opposed to building the wildlife farm. Would you:

- Stay in the club and do nothing?
- Stay in the club, and speak out strongly against the subject?
- Resign from the club?
- Do something else?

Dilemma Card

You are an influential member of the community. On your way home from work, you are stopped by a police officer and cited for having excessive auto emissions. Would you:

- Use your influence to have the ticket invalidated?
- Sell the car to some unsuspecting person?
- Work to change the law?
- Get your car fixed and pay the ticket?
- Do something else?

Dilemma Card

Your class is on a field trip to the zoo. Although you know that feeding of animals by zoo visitors is prohibited, some of your friends are feeding marshmallows to the bears. Would you:

- Tell them that feeding marshmallows may harm the bears, and ask them to stop?
- Report their behavior to the nearest zoo keeper?
- Ask the teacher to ask them to stop?
- Do nothing?
- Do something else?

Dilemma Card

You are on a picnic with your family and you see members of another family leaving to go home without picking up their trash. It is clear the other family is going to leave litter all around. Would you:

- Move quickly, and ask them to pick up their trash before they leave?
- Wait for them to leave, and pick up the trash for them?
- Do nothing?
- Do something else?

Dilemma Card

You are walking in the woods and come upon a young fawn. There is no sign of the fawn's mother. Would you:

- Leave the fawn where it is?
- Move the fawn to a sheltered area?
- Take the fawn home?
- Do something else?

Dilemma Card

You have found a young screech owl and raised it to maturity. You have been told that you cannot keep the owl any longer because keeping it without the proper permit violates state and federal laws. Would you:

- Offer it to your local zoo?
- Keep it as a pet?
- Call members of the local fish and wildlife agency and ask their advice?
- Determine whether it could survive in the wild; if it appears the owl could, release it in a suitable area?
- Do something else?

Dilemma Card

You are president of a large corporation. You are very interested in pollution control and have had a task force assigned to study the pollution your plant is creating. The task force reports that you are barely within the legal requirements. The plant is polluting the community. To add the necessary equipment to reduce pollution would cost so much that you would have to fire 50 employees. Would you:

- Add the equipment, and fire the employees?
- Not add the equipment?
- Wait a few years to see if the cost of the equipment will drop?
- Hire an engineering firm to provide further recommendations?
- Do something else?

Dilemma Card

You love children and would like to have a large family. You are aware, however, of the world's population projections for the future. Would you:

- Plan to have a large family anyway?
- Decide not to have children?
- Limit yourself to one or two children?
- Do something else?

Dilemma Card

You are out in the woods with a friend when you spot a hawk perched on a high limb. Before you realize what is happening, your friend shoots the hawk. An hour later, you are leaving the woods and are approached by a state wildlife officer who tells you a hawk has been illegally shot and asks if you know anything about it. Would you:

- Deny any knowledge of the incident?
- Admit your friend did it?
- Make up a story implicating someone else?
- Say nothing, but call the fish and wildlife officer later with an anonymous phone tip?
- Do something else?

Dilemma Card

You have purchased a beautiful 10-acre property in the mountains to build a summer home. One hillside of the property has a beautiful view of the valley and lake below and is your choice for your home site. However, you discover an active bald eagle has a nest site on that hillside. The bald eagle is sensitive to disturbance around its nest tree and is a protected species. Bald eagles are highly selective in choosing nest sites and usually return to the same nest year after year. Would you:

- Select a different site on the property to build your home?
- Sell the property?
- Chop down the tree and build your home?
- Do something else?

Wildlife on Coins and Stamps

Objective
Students will describe coins and stamps as examples of ways that people have used symbols to represent values of wildlife.

Method
Students use reference materials to study portrayal of wildlife on coins and stamps.

Materials
Reference materials

Background
People of various cultures have used images of wildlife on their coins, other currency, and stamps. The images may represent real or imagined species. In any case, use of wildlife symbols represents recognition of human values.

Many countries have issued coins and stamps with animal images. Ancient Rome issued coins with wolves. China has issued coins with dragons (an interpretation of wildlife). Canada, Australia, and the Bahamas all have offered extensive issues of wildlife coins that can be obtained at face value.

The major purpose of this activity is for students to recognize that wildlife has value for people in a range of ways, reflected symbolically in the use of wildlife images on coins and stamps.

Procedure
1. Students can conduct their own research, or the educator can provide resource materials and establish a classroom learning center. The students can search reference materials for examples of coins and stamps with wildlife images. Encyclopedias often show pictures of coins, other currency, and stamps used in various nations. Coin collectors' catalogs and journals are also good sources of images.

2. The students can make copies of images they find by reproducing or sketching them, making sure to identify the country of origin and the value of the coin or stamp.

3. Next, have the students organize the coin and stamp images according to some characteristics. For example,
   - according to the kinds of animals pictured;
   - according to whether the animal is real or imagined, abundant or threatened, endangered or extinct;
   - animals pictured once, two to five times, or many times;

Grade Level: 9–12

Subject Areas: Environmental Education, Social Studies, Language Arts, Expressive Arts

Duration: 45 minutes or longer

Group Size: any

Setting: indoors

Conceptual Framework Topic Reference: CPIB1

Key Terms: symbol, value, culture

Appendices: Using Local Resources

- animals found in the United States, contrasted with those not found in the United States;
- animals shown on coins or stamps from two or more countries;
- animals shown in their habitat;
- unusual animals;
- animals used to represent power or military strength; or
- animals shown realistically.

4. Discuss with the students why wildlife has been used so often as a part of currency and stamps. Wildlife has historical and present-day value for people in many ways (as sources of food, clothing, and other products; as inspiration and recreation; as contributors to healthy ecosystems; as representation of virtues or fears; and so on). Many of these values are represented in symbolic form on stamps and currency.

Extensions

1. Have the students make a world map showing the countries that use wildlife in their coins and stamps. Look for regional similarities and differences. Analyze the wildlife images. Are there regional trends?

2. Compare the public attitude toward wildlife in different countries and parts of the world. What nations are active in worldwide conservation efforts? Why might these nations be involved and others not?

Evaluation

1. For each of the following emotions and values, list as many animals as you can that have been used on coins to express that emotion or value: love, power, or strength; beauty or grace; fear; pride; or freedom.

2. List the range of purposes for which wildlife has been portrayed in coins and stamps.

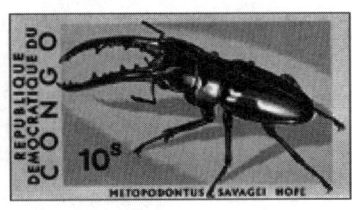

What You Wear Is What They Were

Objectives

Students will (1) identify principal resources from which their clothing is made, (2) distinguish between renewable and nonrenewable natural resources, and (3) recognize environmental consequences of clothing preferences.

Method

Students draw, label, and analyze their clothing according to the natural resources from which they are derived. Then they make assessments about appropriate uses of such natural resources using criteria that they establish.

Materials

Drawing materials or notebook paper

Background

NOTE: "Make a Coat" is a similar activity for younger students.

In all but the most tropical of climates, people need an outside covering to keep warm. When ice floes receded after the last Ice Age approximately 10,000 years ago on the North American continent, people used fire for part of their warmth. Skins from wild animals were also used. Saber tooth tigers, bears, woolly mammoths, and wolves were among the animals hunted for meat and clothing.

Native American tribes have used animals for food and covering, and some still do as a part of their present lifestyle. Elk, deer, bear, buffalo, seal, and almost all animals killed for food have also provided valuable skins for clothing.

When European settlers came to the North American continent, they brought with them a tradition of making clothing out of spun fibers such as linen and wool.

Today we have coats and other clothing made from many materials. We can divide the sources of those materials into two categories: renewable and nonrenewable natural resources. Definitions of renewable and nonrenewable natural resources are commonly used within the natural sciences. (Use of these terms is intended to describe inherent biological attributes, not to imply value judgments.)

Renewable natural resources are living things, with the capacity for regeneration. Trees and wildlife are examples of renewable natural resources. However, even renewable resources have limits. For example, although animals have the capacity for regeneration by mating and bearing offspring, they cannot do this if their habitat is destroyed or if environmental or human-caused pressures are too great to permit successful reproduction.

Nonrenewable natural resources are nonliving things. Minerals and fossils are examples of nonrenewable natural resources. Although such resources may be replenished over time

---

Grade Level: 5–8

Subject Areas: Environmental Education, Science

Duration: one or two 45-minute sessions

Group Size: any

Setting: indoors

Conceptual Framework Topic Reference: ECIB2

Key Terms: renewable, nonrenewable, natural resource

Appendices: none

by natural processes, the time span is enormously long as, for example, in the case of accumulations of fossils from which products such as petroleum are derived.

Cotton (from the cotton plant) and linen (from the flax plant) are two major clothing products derived from renewable natural resources—in this case, both from plants. Some clothing products come from animals. Wool, for example, comes from shearing the fleece off sheep and does not require killing the animal. Other domesticated animals (cattle) are used for clothing products (leather) and also are used for food products. Feathers from geese and ducks are used for down jackets.

In scientific terms, animals can be considered a renewable resource. In some cases, however, animal populations are endangered or threatened. In such cases, killing these animals is forbidden by law. It is also illegal to hunt many animals that are not threatened. Of those animals that are hunted, they are hunted only under laws and regulations. Some people raise ethical questions as to the appropriateness of the use of animals, particularly wild ones, for products such as clothing, food, tools, medicines, cosmetics, jewelry, and other ornaments.

In the United States, most animals that provide clothing products are raised in captivity. Some exceptions include snake skins, which may be used for shoes and purses, and deer antlers, which may be used for belt buckles, and so on.

Most synthetic clothing materials are derived from nonrenewable natural resources, such as fossil-based petroleum products. Some people raise ethical questions as to the appropriateness of using of nonrenewable resources such as fossil fuels, and consider questions such as their essentially finite availability as well as their cost to humans, wildlife, and the environment as they are obtained through mining and processing.

There are many aspects, aside from whether or not a resource is renewable, that influence the choice to use a particular material for clothing. For example, some materials (e.g., cowhide and petroleum-based synthetics) are derived as byproducts from the development of resources for other primary purposes (e.g., food, energy). Other sources (e.g., furs) tend to be developed primarily or solely for manufacture of clothing. In addition, nonrenewable resources, such as fossil fuels, are used in obtaining, manufacturing, and distributing clothes made from both renewable and nonrenewable natural resources.

The pros and cons of appropriate uses of renewable and nonrenewable natural resources are difficult and complex—and may raise social, economic, ethical, political, and biological questions. Even the concept that wildlife and other animals are renewable resources raises ethical objections from some people.

The major purpose of this activity is for students to distinguish, in scientific terms, between renewable and nonrenewable natural resources used as sources of clothing for people.

Procedure

1. Begin this activity with a discussion of how clothing is manufactured. Ask each student to look at what he or she is wearing. Using a piece of notebook or drawing paper, ask students to draw a simple picture of themselves, including the major exterior clothing being worn—from top to toe. Ask them to label each piece of clothing according to the major thing or things it is made of (e.g., cotton shirt, polyester shirt, leather shoes).

2. Now, turn the discussion to the concept of natural resources. Webster's *New World Dictionary* defines natural resources as "those actual and potential forms of wealth supplied by nature." We define a resource as "a portion of an environment upon which people have placed or assigned value, or see as being available for use." Such definitions are intended to be descriptive, not to make moral or ethical judgments about the appropriateness or inappropriateness of using portions of the environment that are designated as resources. Ask the students to define in scientific terms what might be considered renewable natural resources and what might be considered non-

continued

renewable natural resources. Using the brainstormed list of natural resources, put an "R" by those that can be considered renewable and an "N" by those that can be considered nonrenewable.

3. Returning again to their drawings, ask the students to label the clothing parts of their drawings according to the natural resources from which they are derived; also indicate whether the resources are renewable or nonrenewable.

4. Ask the students to divide renewable resources into plants and animals. Then ask the students to divide each of these categories into those that require killing the individual organism for use as a clothing resource contrasted with those that do not.

5. Discuss the students' findings. Consider questions such as these:
   - What effects do our preferences in clothing sources have on individual living organisms? On populations of organisms?
   - What effects do our preferences in clothing sources have on different aspects of the cultural and natural environments (e.g., on local economies, international trade, cultural tradition, global resources, wildlife, wildlife habitat, agricultural lands, water quality, oil shale development)?
   - In our assessment—as individuals, or as a group—which sources of clothing seem to us to be most appropriate? Under what conditions?

Ask the students to establish some criteria for their assessments, and to explain their reasoning.

Extensions

1. Have the students inventory their clothes closet. Tally the number of garments by each natural resource. Make a personal graph showing proportions of cotton, polyester, leather, and so on. Have them assess the number of clothes in their closet. What impact does the **amount** of clothing have on the environment?

2. Have the students write an environmental impact statement about the effect of their personal clothing preferences.

Evaluation

What effects do clothes made from renewable or nonrenewable resources have on the environment?

Does Wildlife Sell?

Objectives

Students will (1) identify use of wildlife and other natural images in advertising, (2) critically analyze and evaluate the purposes and impacts of using such images in advertising, and (3) recommend appropriate uses of such nature-derived images in advertising.

Method

Students evaluate and categorize advertisements.

Materials

Magazine or newspaper advertisements

Background

A cowboy boot manufacturer ran a series of advertisements for its boots showing boot wearers in conflict with wildlife. In this particular case, the wearer of the boot is about to kill a rattlesnake and a scorpion. There is a sense of drama in the ads—with the boot raised in the air ready to flatten the offenders. The advertisement portrays a person in battle with forces of nature and plays on the stereotype that some sort of virtuous strengths might accompany such actions. It also plays on the stereotype that some animals should be killed.

In contrast with the images chosen by that advertiser, the rattlesnake and the scorpion could be portrayed as integral components of natural ecosystems. The luster and patterning of the snake's scales and the grace in motion of both of the animals could be portrayed. Fewer boots would likely be sold because the marketplace may still be steeped in too many stereotypes of such animals to quiet the fears that the first ad played upon. One could contrast the kind of advertising campaign that authors Edward Abbey or Annie Dillard or that photographer Ansel Adams might design.

Contemporary advertising can exploit people's biases and emotional responses to elements of nature. Advertising, by design, is intended to evoke a response—usually one that will lead to some action, such as buying the advertised product.

The major purpose of this activity is for students to evaluate the uses and impacts of nature-derived images in advertising.

Procedure

1. Have a supply of magazines and newspapers on hand for the students to use in this activity. Ask each student to find at least one advertisement that uses some aspect of the natural environment in order to sell its product. The advertisement might show crystal waters, a soaring eagle, an elk standing majestically, a forested hillside, snow-capped

---

Grade Level: 5–8

Subject Areas: Language Arts, Environmental Education

Duration: one or two 45-minute sessions

Group Size: any

Setting: indoors

Conceptual Framework Topic Reference: ECIB1

Key Terms: stereotype, metaphor, advertising

Appendices: Using Local Resources

---

continued

peaks, and so on. If the advertisement is on a billboard, perhaps the student can bring in a photo; if it is from a television commercial, a sketch or description will work.

NOTE: Educators may want to establish a file of such advertisements, laminating them for future use.

2. As they work in small groups of two to four, ask the students to examine their advertisements according to questions such as the following:

- What is the advertiser's purpose?
- What image from nature is used to sell the product?
- Does the image have any direct relationship to the product?
- If yes, what is that relationship?
- If no, what purpose does the image serve for the advertiser in attempting to sell the product?
- What feelings, if any, does the ad elicit?
- What stereotypes, if any, does the ad encourage or build upon?
- Does the ad portray a stereotype based on people's reactions to the image, or does the ad portray a metaphor as a means to sell its product? If yes, describe its purpose. For example, a porcupine might be pictured alongside an electric shaver with, "Get rid of the bristles." The porcupine's quills serve as a metaphor for a stubby beard.
- Does the advertisement seem to portray the natural image in a realistic way? Describe what seems realistic and what does not.
- Identify and describe any ways in which the ad might contribute to practices that could be wasteful, destructive, inappropriate, and so on in terms of responsible use of natural resources and the environment.

3. As the students use criteria that they establish, ask them to categorize the advertisements as an appropriate or inappropriate means by which to attempt to sell products.

Extensions

1. For advertisements considered inappropriate (e.g., harmful or misleading), have the class do the following:
   - Redesign the advertisement to make it more appropriate in their judgments.
   - Write a letter to the advertising company explaining their concerns.
   - Write a letter to the managing editor of the magazine or newspaper in which the ad appeared.
   - Write an editorial about the ad for a city or school paper.
   - Call other people's attention to the ad and their reasons for concern.

2. For advertisements considered appropriate (e.g., constructive or accurate), the class could do these:
   - Write a letter to the advertising company in praise of the ad, explaining the basis for their opinions.
   - Call other people's attention to the ad and their reasons for praise.

3. Design advertisements to encourage responsible use of natural resources and responsible actions toward people, wildlife, and the environment. Send these ideas to the advertising departments of companies that would seem most able to benefit from them, along with courteous letters of concern and explanation.

Evaluation

1. Describe two examples of advertisements that portray animals in informative, accurate, or positive ways. Describe two examples of advertisements that portray animals in inaccurate, misleading, or negative ways.

2. How, if at all, does the use of wildlife or natural resources help the image advertisers wish to portray?

3. How, if at all, do the ways wildlife or natural resources are used in advertising help wildlife? Harm wildlife?

4. Describe a way that advertisers could use wildlife or natural resources to the best advantage of both wildlife and the advertisers.

5. Describe what you believe would be the most responsible and appropriate ways to include wildlife or natural resources in advertising, if at all.

6. Observe a television commercial or series of commercials that use wildlife. Compare the treatment of wildlife in video advertisements and print advertisements.

Pay to Play

Objectives
Students will (1) distinguish between consumptive and nonconsumptive uses of wildlife, (2) describe the sources of funding for wildlife areas, (3) relate usage to increased financial demand on managed wildlife areas, and (4) describe the impact of increased human usage on wildlife habitat.

Method
Students act as either consumptive or nonconsumptive users of wildlife as they move around a game board and land on designated private or public lands.

Materials
Dice; play money—$500 for each player (2 - $100, 2 - $50, 5 - $20, 8 - $10, 4 - $5), plus at least $3,000 in the Public Bank in various denominations; one game board for every four to five players (enlarge the game board included with this activity and laminate it for later use); one playing token for each player; Activity Cards (masters begin on page 221); different colored paper for each of two decks of cards—consumptive and nonconsumptive; 3" x 5" cards, one for each player to record the number of outdoor activities accomplished

Background
Consumptive uses of wildlife resources involve activities such as hunting, fishing, and trapping, as well as activities such as berry picking and shell collecting. Nonconsumptive uses of wildlife include watching birds, shooting photographs, hiking, and canoeing and do not involve the direct harvesting of wildlife. Both consumptive and nonconsumptive uses can have indirect impacts such as habitat loss or alteration. A great blue heron, for example, will leave its nest and young if it is startled by the presence of a photographer.

Wildlife-based recreation is important to many North Americans. Consumptive activities contribute millions of dollars to the economy through the sale of hunting and fishing equipment, firearms, ammunition, and boats. Nonconsumptive users may purchase items such as binoculars, photography equipment, canoes, bird food, off-road vehicles, gardening materials, and backpacking gear. In addition to the money generated for local economies, many of these items are subject to a federal excise tax that provides millions of dollars annually for conservation of wildlife. The Federal Aid in Wildlife Restoration and Federal Aid in Sport Fish Restoration programs, also known as the Pittman-Robertson and Dingell-Johnson Acts, are crucial funding sources. (See **www.restorewildlife.org** for more information.)

Grade Level: 5–8

Subject Areas: Social Studies, Science, Environmental Education

Duration: variable

Group Size: any, class divided into groups of four or five students

Setting: indoors

Conceptual Framework Topic Reference: ECIC, ECID, ECIIA, ECIIB, ECIIB1, ECIIB1a, ECIIB1b, ECIIB2, ECIIC, ECIIC1, ECIIC2

Key Terms: consumptive, nonconsumptive, private and public lands, resource, recreation, revenue

Appendices: none

Expenses related to hunting and fishing licenses and fees go to natural resources agencies to support operation of the state agency and the wildlife it manages. Entrance fees to publicly managed lands also contribute. Charging an access fee to hunt, fish, camp, or trap on private land is common in many states. These funds may or may not be used for wildlife and habitat management. Nonprofit organizations, such as The Nature Conservancy and Ducks Unlimited, contribute millions of additional dollars toward wildlife management and protection of wildlife habitat.

Funds provided by consumptive users, not general tax dollars, historically have been the primary source of income for most state wildlife management programs and some federal programs. As the population has grown over the past 25 years, the total number of people engaged in direct consumptive uses of wildlife (e.g., hunting, fishing) has remained relatively constant. At the same time, nonconsumptive use has doubled as leisure time and increased mobility have allowed the pursuit of outdoor activities. These economic and demographic trends are creating additional pressures on wildlife and habitat, while the revenue generated from consumptive fees has remained the same. As a result, many state natural resources agencies are becoming concerned about their ability to meet the demands on wildlife resources.

In the United States, wildlife is owned by the people and managed by the states on behalf of the citizens. State wildlife agencies are responsible for managing wildlife on both public and private lands. Private land owners, such as ranchers and farmers, own their land but not the wildlife on their land. A hunter wishing to hunt on private land must have a hunting license issued by the state and also may pay an access fee to landowners to hunt on their property. Access to public land typically is free, although user fees may be charged and a hunting license is required.

Procedure

Before the Activity

1. Copy and enlarge the game board on page 233. Educators may choose to laminate it for later use. Students may also wish to color and decorate the game boards.

2. Copy the Activity Cards using different colored paper to distinguish between consumptive and nonconsumptive decks. Cut the cards to size. Poker chips can be used for money, or play money can be purchased or borrowed from other board games. Colored paper can be used as tokens, or students may wish to create their own (e.g., miniature fishing poles, firewood, flowers, a berry basket, binoculars, a canoe).

As the Game Begins

3. Ask the students to suggest the meaning of the word "consume." From this informal definition, ask them to define what the phrase "consumptive use of wildlife" might mean and to give examples. Have the students also define and give examples for "nonconsumptive use of wildlife." Ask them to give examples of ways that nonconsumptive uses may affect wildlife. Explain that they will play a game that will help them further distinguish between these two terms. Have a discussion about the differences between public and private land; then give local examples of each.

4. Divide the class into groups of four or five students. Provide the groups with the game board, materials (tokens and currency), and instructions.

5. Establish two banks with the excess money. One bank, the Wildlife Management Fund, represents the state fund where fees and fines are collected by the state natural resources agency. This fund, in turn, is the source of revenue to manage state wildlife areas and parks. The other bank, the Public Bank, will handle revenues, fines, and fees for the private businesses. Put $200 in the Wildlife

continued

Management Fund and about $3,000 into the Public Bank. Identify student bankers for each.

6. Sort and shuffle the consumptive and nonconsumptive Activity Cards. Place them face down on the indicated spaces on the game board.

7. Each student should select a token and place it on "Start."

8. Use pairs of dice, give one die to each group of players. Before rolling the die, each player must decide whether to purchase a hunting license, a fishing license, or a parks pass. These items are valid for 1 year (one lap around the board). Require students to "pass" a hunter safety course before they can purchase a hunting license. To represent the course exam, ask each student applicant a question that is related to this activity, such as listing two consumptive or nonconsumptive uses of wildlife resources. The money for these documents is put into the Wildlife Management Fund and is used for wildlife management or parks. When the players reach "Year End," they must STOP. Their licenses and parks passes have expired and must be renewed to remain valid. Players may choose not to renew a license.

LICENSE FEES:

HUNTING LICENSE:	$100
FISHING LICENSE:	$ 30
ANNUAL PARKS PASS:	$ 40

9. The first player rolls the die to indicate the number of spaces to move. EACH TIME A PLAYER PASSES A "PAYDAY," HE OR SHE COLLECTS $100 FROM THE PUBLIC BANK.

10. The player then declares an intention to act as a consumptive or nonconsumptive user at this location. The player takes the top Activity Card from the corresponding consumptive or nonconsumptive deck, reads the top half of the card aloud, and follows the instructions.

11. Next, the player reads aloud the "Management Factor" at the bottom of the card and follows directions. Some cards are a positive action and some are a negative action. Players must keep the positive cards and discard the negative ones.

12. The next player follows the same procedure and play continues.

13. The game cannot continue if the Wildlife Management Fund runs out of money. If this possibility appears imminent, players must find ways to increase funding for wildlife management. They may decide to increase license fees, impose a tax, or perhaps encourage each player to contribute to a special fund for wildlife.

14. A time limit or the number of completed circuits on the game board can determine the end of the game. The winner is the player with the greatest number of positive Activity Cards at the end of the game. In case of a tie, the player with the most money is declared the winner. If the Wildlife Management Fund runs out of funds during the game, everyone loses.

15. After the students have had a chance to play the game for a while, ask them to list consumptive and nonconsumptive uses associated with wildlife. Record the responses on the board or a flip chart. What expenses can they identify with each of these activities? Why were some of the areas on the board identified as public or private? What is the difference between private and public lands?

16. Ask the students to remember the fees and fines they had to pay. Were most fees (not equipment or travel expenditures) related to hunting and fishing activities or nonconsumptive uses? Why were they charged those fees? Who do they think collects them? For what purposes do they think the money will be used? Let the students know that those fees, not tax dollars, are the primary source of income to run most state wildlife

management programs and some federal programs. In some cases, the fees are the only source of revenue.

17. Show students the Number of Participants for Three Wildlife-Associated Activities chart (see below). Ask students to discuss each of the following groups of questions:

    - How have each of the following changed between 1970 and 1996:
        a. The numbers of consumptive-use participants?
        b. The number of nonconsumptive-use participants?
        c. The total number of participants?
    - What specific impacts could the increased number of nonconsumptive users have on the environment and wildlife habitat?
    - What specific impacts could an increased number of consumptive users have on the environment and wildlife habitat?
    - Ask students to discuss funding sources for wildlife management. What new sources of funding would they recommend?
    - Has the increase in consumptive uses kept up with the increase in nonconsumptive uses? Which group pays the most in fees? How could these trends affect the revenue for natural resource agencies and their ability to maintain wildlife areas?
    - How do students think the following affect wildlife and habitat: (a) the economy, or (b) the increased use of wildlife lands for consumptive or nonconsumptive purposes?

18. After the discussion, have students play the game again, using some of the following activity modifications:

    - Fees and fines increase at the completion of a circuit because of increased costs associated with additional usage.

Number of Participants for Three Wildlife-Associated Activities

1970 versus 1996

Activity	1970	1996
Fishing	33,000,000	35,200,000
Hunting	14,000,000	14,000,000
Wildlife Watching	38,200,000	62,900,000
Total	**85,000,000**	**112,100,000**

Source: "1970 National Survey of Fishing and Hunting" and the "1996 National Survey of Fishing and Hunting and Wildlife-Associated Recreation," published jointly by the U.S. Department of the Interior, U.S. Fish and Wildlife Service, and U.S. Department of Commerce, Bureau of the Census.

continued

- Allow students to buy the private squares on which they land. Set a price beforehand (e.g., $100 a square). The owner-student now collects the fees and pays the fines. Allow students to form interest groups to purchase land. Have the tax bill be a percentage of the player's assets. Keep the taxes in a separate pile. When enough money has accumulated to purchase land, the students vote on a name and the use of the land. Allow a student to sell land to the government (money comes from the tax pile) at half the original purchase price.

- Label the squares to reflect state or regional public lands and private lands.

- Allow students to vote on changes to the fee and fine amounts.

Extensions

1. Use recreational maps to have students find local or state areas that allow certain activities. Contact county, state, or federal sources for park and forest maps with listings of permitted uses.

2. Investigate land uses for consumptive activities in other countries. For example, land used for consumptive activities in some European countries is privately owned.

3. Identify additional revenues, such as the sale of duck stamps, that support public or private lands.

Evaluation

1. Compare consumptive and nonconsumptive uses of wildlife.

2. Describe how fees, fines, and federal aid are used to support wildlife areas.

3. Relate specific examples that demonstrate how increased human use means increased financial demands on wildlife areas.

4. Explain how increased human use caused by increased leisure time and the pursuit of outdoor activities has affected wildlife and habitat.

5. Explain ways nonconsumptive users can contribute to wildlife management.

Activity Cards

CONSUMPTIVE **WILDLIFE MANAGEMENT FACTOR**	• Good fortune! You have won first prize in a fishing contest. Collect $50 from the Public Bank if you have a fishing license. Most states maintain a number of fish hatcheries to stock public fishing areas. Transfer $25 from the Wildlife Management Fund to the Public Bank. (Keep this card if you have a fishing license.)
CONSUMPTIVE **WILDLIFE MANAGEMENT FACTOR**	• Dry weather and poor forage have reduced the deer population in your hunting area. You must buy your meat this year. Pay $150 to the Public Bank. Deer management involves aerial surveys, habitat protection and improvement, and law enforcement. Transfer $50 from the Wildlife Management Fund to the Public Bank. (Keep this card.)
CONSUMPTIVE **WILDLIFE MANAGEMENT FACTOR**	• You just caught your favorite lure on a submerged stump. Pay $5 to the Public Bank for a replacement. There is a federal tax on fishing gear that helps pay for sportfish restoration. Transfer $50 from the Public Bank to the Wildlife Management Fund. (Keep this card if you have a fishing license.)
CONSUMPTIVE **WILDLIFE MANAGEMENT FACTOR**	• You spend most of the day collecting firewood that was used to cook the delicious fish you caught. Your energy level is so high that you get to take another turn if you have a fishing license. The trees for your firewood are a renewable resource that benefits both wildlife and people. For forest management, transfer $25 from the Wildlife Management Fund to the Public Bank. (Keep this card if you have a fishing license.)

continued

CONSUMPTIVE

WILDLIFE MANAGEMENT FACTOR

- This site is being used for the annual cut-your-own Christmas tree sale. Pay $20 to the Wildlife Management Fund for a tree of your choice.

This area is managed by the State Forest Service in an effort to benefit both wildlife and people. Transfer $30 from the Wildlife Management Fund to the Public Bank.

(Keep this card.)

CONSUMPTIVE

WILDLIFE MANAGEMENT FACTOR

- Your request to hunt on private property has been denied. Lose your next turn.

Private land is critical to wildlife management. Cooperation from landowners is an important part of a wildlife agency's mission.

(Keep this card.)

CONSUMPTIVE

WILDLIFE MANAGEMENT FACTOR

- A bountiful mussel harvest enables you to have a "mussel bake" for your friends if you have a fishing license. If you do not have a fishing license, pay a $100 fine to the Wildlife Management Fund for poaching mussels.

Aquatic wildlife populations are maintained through harvest limits. Law enforcement helps to make sure the limits are respected. Transfer $50 from the Wildlife Management Fund to the Public Bank.

(Keep this card if you have a fishing license.)

CONSUMPTIVE

WILDLIFE MANAGEMENT FACTOR

- The morel mushrooms you find today are a delicious addition to your dinner. A restaurant owner likes your dinner dish. He was so impressed that he bought your recipe for the La Petite Chateau for $100 (from the Public Bank).

Wildlife eat a variety of plants. A healthy habitat needs to have many different plant species. Transfer $20 from the Wildlife Management Fund to the Public Bank.

(Keep this card.)

CONSUMPTIVE	• Pay $20 to the Wildlife Management Fund for a firewood permit. Receive $100 from the Public Bank for a cord of wood that you were able to cut today on public land.
WILDLIFE MANAGEMENT FACTOR	Timber harvests affect wildlife in both positive and negative ways. Firewood collection helps reduce the fuel load of future forest fires. Harvesting also provides funding for public land management agencies. Transfer $100 from the Public Bank to the Wildlife Management Fund for timber sale. (Keep this card.)

CONSUMPTIVE	• A game warden observes you fishing. If you do not have a fishing license, pay $100 fine to the Wildlife Management Fund.
WILDLIFE MANAGEMENT FACTOR	Fishing license fees pay for producing and stocking game fish and other management activities. If you are fishing without a license, you are literally stealing fish from licensed anglers who have helped pay for them. (Keep this card if you have a fishing license.)

CONSUMPTIVE	• Increased development has resulted in cancellation of hunting at this site. Return to your previous location. DO NOT draw an additional card for going to that site.
WILDLIFE MANAGEMENT FACTOR	Thousands of acres of wildlife habitat are lost daily because of development. Sustainable development must include the protection of wildlife habitat and wildlife corridors within communities. (Keep this card.)

CONSUMPTIVE	• Improved road construction saves you time. Take another turn.
WILDLIFE MANAGEMENT FACTOR	The new highway affects critical winter range for deer. A deer fence must be constructed to keep deer off the highway. Transfer $30 from the Wildlife Management Fund to the Public Bank. (Keep this card.)

continued

CONSUMPTIVE **WILDLIFE MANAGEMENT FACTOR**	• Archery practice pays off. The resulting venison saves you $100 in meat costs. Collect this amount from the Public Bank if you have a hunting license. Hunters and anglers participate in a variety of hunting and fishing opportunities. Examples are archery, fly fishing, muzzle-loading, and spear fishing. License fees help pay for this management. (Keep this card if you have a hunting license.)

CONSUMPTIVE **WILDLIFE MANAGEMENT FACTOR**	• You want to go duck hunting, but first you must purchase a federal duck stamp. Pay $15 to the Wildlife Management Fund for the stamp. Money received from the sale of duck stamps is used to purchase and protect wetlands in Canada, the United States, and Mexico. As of 1995, federal duck stamp sales have generated more than $500 million that has been used to preserve more than 4 million acres of waterfowl habitat. (Keep this card.)

CONSUMPTIVE **WILDLIFE MANAGEMENT FACTOR**	• You choose to keep a bass that is below the legal size limit, and you get caught. Pay a $50 fine to the Wildlife Management Fund. In heavily used areas, wildlife managers impose regulations, such as size limits, to ensure quality fishing opportunities. Size limits usually allow fish to reproduce at least once before being taken. (Do not keep this card.)

CONSUMPTIVE **WILDLIFE MANAGEMENT FACTOR**	• In spite of spending $75 on camouflage clothing to hunt turkey, you went home empty-handed and ended up buying a frozen turkey for $25. Pay a total of $100 to the Public Bank. Thanks to an aggressive reintroduction program, turkey populations have increased dramatically across the United States. Transfer $30 from the Wildlife Management Fund to the Public Bank. (Keep this card.)

CONSUMPTIVE **WILDLIFE MANAGEMENT FACTOR**	• Because of a lack of funding resulting from decreased license sales, this area is closed. Move to the next square of the same type (move to the next public or private square), and choose another card. Seventy to eighty percent of the budget for most state wildlife agencies comes from sales of hunting and fishing licenses. Transfer $50 from the Wildlife Management Fund to the Public Bank. (Do not keep this card.)

CONSUMPTIVE **WILDLIFE MANAGEMENT FACTOR**	• An increase in the number of deer in this area results in your bagging a deer on the first day of hunting, saving you $100 because you do not stay to hunt the next day. Receive this savings from the Public Bank if you have a hunting license. Managing deer populations is beneficial to wildlife and visitors. Healthy habitat can support only a limited number of deer. To manage deer, transfer $40 from the Wildlife Management Fund to the Public Bank. (Keep this card.)

CONSUMPTIVE **WILDLIFE MANAGEMENT FACTOR**	• You left plastic bait containers and excess fishing line at the lake. You receive a citation for littering. Pay $50 fine to the Public Bank. Litter and other pollutants can harm wildlife. Educating the public is an important part of wildlife management. Take $40 out of the Wildlife Management Fund for the education budget. (Do not keep this card.)

CONSUMPTIVE **WILDLIFE MANAGEMENT FACTOR**	• Farmer Jones plants a hedgerow for wildlife. Your pheasant hunt on his land is successful. Your romantic pheasant dinner for two saves you $50. Collect from the Public Bank if you have a hunting license. Farmers can do many things to benefit wildlife including planting hedgerows, protecting wetlands, and delaying mowing until after nesting seasons. To date, Pheasants Forever has spent almost $10 million helping farmers protect more than 65,000 acres of farmland for wildlife habitat. (Keep this card if you have a hunting license.)

continued

CONSUMPTIVE

WILDLIFE MANAGEMENT FACTOR

- You travel to River Glen resort to fish in their private trout ponds. You land a 4-pound brown trout! Pay $15 to the Public Bank for the privilege of fishing here. Your fishing license is not needed at this private lake.

Although it cost $15 to fish here, private fishing lakes are not managed by state wildlife agencies. Therefore, the cost of your fishing license did not cover the fee.

(Do not keep this card.)

NONCONSUMPTIVE

WILDLIFE MANAGEMENT FACTOR

- You walk onto private property hoping for a glance at a rare bird but you forgot to ask permission. Pay $100 to the Public Bank for trespassing.

Whether you are a consumptive or nonconsumptive user, you must ask permission to enter private land.

(Do not keep this card.)

NONCONSUMPTIVE

WILDLIFE MANAGEMENT FACTOR

- Fees paid by hunters and anglers historically have been the prime source of funding in outdoor recreation areas. These funds are declining. Pay a $25 access fee to the Wildlife Management Fund to view wildlife in your favorite state wildlife area.

Managing current wildlife areas is a lot like farming and involves planting and thinning, fencing, and even constructing roads. Transfer $50 from the Wildlife Management Fund to the Public Bank.

(Keep this card.)

NONCONSUMPTIVE

WILDLIFE MANAGEMENT FACTOR

- Your tax bill has gone up to pay for free access to public land (i.e., U.S. Forest Service). Pay $100 to the Wildlife Management Fund.

Public lands are managed in a multiple-use manner. A portion of the cost for managing these lands helps wildlife. Transfer $30 from the Wildlife Management Fund to the Public Bank.

(Keep this card.)

NONCONSUMPTIVE	• Today is Memorial Day. Your favorite public campground is full. Move to the nearest private area, and pay a $20 camping fee to the Public Bank. DO NOT draw an additional card for moving to this site.
WILDLIFE MANAGEMENT FACTOR	To reduce bear problems in campgrounds, special garbage containers have been designed and installed. Transfer $10 from the Wildlife Management Fund to the Public Bank.
	(Keep this card.)

NONCONSUMPTIVE	• This area was featured in a recent newspaper article, resulting in increased use. You choose not to hike and camp as planned because of overcrowding. You have lost $50 in travel costs. Pay this $50 to the Public Bank.
WILDLIFE MANAGEMENT FACTOR	Public land managers must balance the needs of wildlife and visitors. Transfer $20 from the Wildlife Management Fund to the Public Bank to pay for research to identify and protect critical wildlife habitat such as fawning and nesting areas.
	(Keep this card.)

NONCONSUMPTIVE	• Today is the first day of hunting season. This area is closed except to licensed hunters. Return to your previous location if you do not have a hunting license. DO NOT take another card for going to your previous site.
WILDLIFE MANAGEMENT FACTOR	Different areas are often managed for different wildlife recreation opportunities. Not all wildlife areas provide recreation. Some are managed to protect critical habitat.
	(Keep this card if you have a hunting license.)

NONCONSUMPTIVE	• OOPS!! While trying to get a closer look at a bald eagle, you did not see the NO TRESPASSING sign. Pay the $50 fine to the Public Bank.
WILDLIFE MANAGEMENT FACTOR	The Endangered Species Act (1972) provides federal funds and protection for endangered species. These funds protect habitat and provide money for research. To protect endangered species, transfer $50 from the Wildlife Management Fund to the Public Bank.
	(Do not keep this card.)

continued

Social and Political Knowledge

Pay to Play

NONCONSUMPTIVE **WILDLIFE MANAGEMENT FACTOR**	• The poem you wrote while resting in this natural area earns you $100. Take your prize money from the Public Bank. The challenge of wildlife management is to provide opportunities to enjoy wildlife in different ways. Nature provides inspiration to writers, artists, musicians, and religions. (Keep this card.)
NONCONSUMPTIVE **WILDLIFE MANAGEMENT FACTOR**	• A new hiking trail opens near your home. You save $25 in transportation costs. Collect $25 from the Public Bank. Public land managers hire trail maintenance crews to build and maintain hiking trails. Transfer $25 from Wildlife Management Fund to the Public Bank. (Keep this card.)
NONCONSUMPTIVE **WILDLIFE MANAGEMENT FACTOR**	• You have won $50 in a wildlife photography contest. Collect your winnings from the Public Bank. Wildlife is managed for all types of uses. Game management money also supports wildlife viewing. Transfer $20 from the Wildlife Management Fund to the Public Bank. (Keep this card.)
NONCONSUMPTIVE **WILDLIFE MANAGEMENT FACTOR**	• You did not realize how much a recent temperature inversion had reduced the visibility on a wildlife photography trip. You lose the $20 it cost you for the wasted film and its development. Pay this $20 to the Public Bank. For many, wildlife serves as an inspiration for art and other means of creative expression. Without effective wildlife management, one may not be able to enjoy such activities. Money collected for license fees helps pay for those benefits. Transfer $20 from the Wildlife Management Fund to the Public Bank. (Keep this card.)

Social and Political Knowledge

Pay to Play

NONCONSUMPTIVE **WILDLIFE MANAGEMENT FACTOR**	• A birding club just put up a new observational blind, saving you time in spotting your favorite waterfowl. Join the National Audubon Society. Pay $25 to the Wildlife Management Fund, and take another turn. For more than a century, the National Audubon Society has been actively involved in bird research and education. Organizations like the National Audubon Society may choose to give grants to wildlife agencies. (Keep this card.)

NONCONSUMPTIVE **WILDLIFE MANAGEMENT FACTOR**	• You win $100 for obtaining a conservation easement* on old growth forest land. Keep it or donate a portion to The Nature Conservancy. (If you choose to donate some of your winnings, put them into the Wildlife Management Fund.) The Nature Conservancy, Ducks Unlimited, the Rocky Mountain Elk Foundation, and other nonprofit organizations contribute millions of dollars annually toward land acquisition and protection for wildlife. Transfer $100 from the Public Bank to the Wildlife Management Fund. * See Glossary. (Keep this card.)

NONCONSUMPTIVE **WILDLIFE MANAGEMENT FACTOR**	• You take your family of five to picnic in a state park. If you do not have a current parks pass, pay the $5 entrance fee times five individuals for a total of $25 to the Wildlife Management Fund. An entrance fee is one of the few ways for nonconsumptive users to contribute to wildlife management. (Keep this card.)

NONCONSUMPTIVE **WILDLIFE MANAGEMENT FACTOR**	• Because of extreme weather conditions, your guided snowmobile tour of this area has been cancelled. You lose the $50 down payment (no refunds). Pay this amount to the Public Bank. Especially in winter when food is limited, recreation can have an adverse effect on wildlife. Wildlife managers may limit public access to certain areas and may have to supplement wildlife food supplies during harsh weather. Transfer $25 from the Wildlife Management Fund to the Public Bank. (Keep this card.)

continued

NONCONSUMPTIVE

WILDLIFE MANAGEMENT FACTOR

- Today's canoe trip was fantastic! Show your appreciation by "adopting" a portion of the river. Pay $25 to the Wildlife Management Fund in an effort to support this clean-up program.

Rivers and streams are important to all wildlife species and must be managed for the benefit of both wildlife and people. Transfer $25 from Wildlife Management Fund to the Public Bank.

(Keep this card.)

NONCONSUMPTIVE

WILDLIFE MANAGEMENT FACTOR

- You have received a citation for littering. Pay a $50 fine to the Public Bank.

Litter and other pollutants can harm animals. Educating the public is an important part of wildlife management. Take $40 out of the Wildlife Management Fund for the education budget.

(Do not keep this card.)

NONCONSUMPTIVE

WILDLIFE MANAGEMENT FACTOR

- A game warden observes your dog chasing a fawn. Pay a $100 fine to the Wildlife Management Fund.

Pet dogs and cats can have serious impacts on wildlife. Dogs occasionally kill deer and other wildlife. A recent study estimated that house cats kill as many as one million birds every day in North America.

(Do not keep this card.)

NONCONSUMPTIVE

WILDLIFE MANAGEMENT FACTOR

- You donate $100 to The Nature Conservancy to purchase important land used as a prairie chicken breeding ground. Pay $100 to the Wildlife Management Fund.

Wildlife management is a partnership between state wildlife agencies and nonprofit organizations such as The Nature Conservancy. The Nature Conservancy has helped protect more than 70 million acres of habitat worldwide.

(Keep this card.)

NONCONSUMPTIVE **WILDLIFE MANAGEMENT FACTOR**	• The weather is so gorgeous that you decide to extend your bird-watching trip. Take another turn at this time. The Watchable Wildlife Program is a component of most state wildlife agencies. Transfer $50 from the Wildlife Management Fund to the Public Bank. (Keep this card.)

NONCONSUMPTIVE **WILDLIFE MANAGEMENT FACTOR**	• You contribute $25 of your tax return to the nongame check-off on your tax form for wildlife. Donate $25 to the Wildlife Management Fund. Many states have a tax "check-off" on the state tax form that allows taxpayers to contribute a portion of their tax return to wildlife. In Colorado, this option generates more than $2 million each year for endangered species. Transfer $50 from the Public Bank to the Wildlife Management Fund. (Keep this card.)

NONCONSUMPTIVE **WILDLIFE MANAGEMENT FACTOR**	• You don't hunt or fish, but you would like to contribute to wildlife management in your state. Purchase a special "conservation" license plate for your vehicle. Pay $25 to the Wildlife Management Fund. Many states generate wildlife funds by issuing conservation license plates for an extra fee. In Florida, these special "designer-type" plates generate more than $5 million per year for endangered species and habitat protection. (Keep this card.)

continued

**FISHING LICENSE
VALID FOR ONE YEAR
(ONE LAP OF THE BOARD)
FEE: $30**

**FISHING LICENSE
VALID FOR ONE YEAR
(ONE LAP OF THE BOARD)
FEE: $30**

**FISHING LICENSE
VALID FOR ONE YEAR
(ONE LAP OF THE BOARD)
FEE: $30**

**FISHING LICENSE
VALID FOR ONE YEAR
(ONE LAP OF THE BOARD)
FEE: $30**

**HUNTING LICENSE
VALID FOR ONE YEAR
(ONE LAP OF THE BOARD)
FEE: $100**

**HUNTING LICENSE
VALID FOR ONE YEAR
(ONE LAP OF THE BOARD)
FEE: $100**

**HUNTING LICENSE
VALID FOR ONE YEAR
(ONE LAP OF THE BOARD)
FEE: $100**

**HUNTING LICENSE
VALID FOR ONE YEAR
(ONE LAP OF THE BOARD)
FEE: $100**

**ANNUAL PARKS PASS
VALID FOR ONE YEAR
(ONE LAP OF THE BOARD)
FEE: $40**

**ANNUAL PARKS PASS
VALID FOR ONE YEAR
(ONE LAP OF THE BOARD)
FEE: $40**

**ANNUAL PARKS PASS
VALID FOR ONE YEAR
(ONE LAP OF THE BOARD)
FEE: $40**

**ANNUAL PARKS PASS
VALID FOR ONE YEAR
(ONE LAP OF THE BOARD)
FEE: $40**

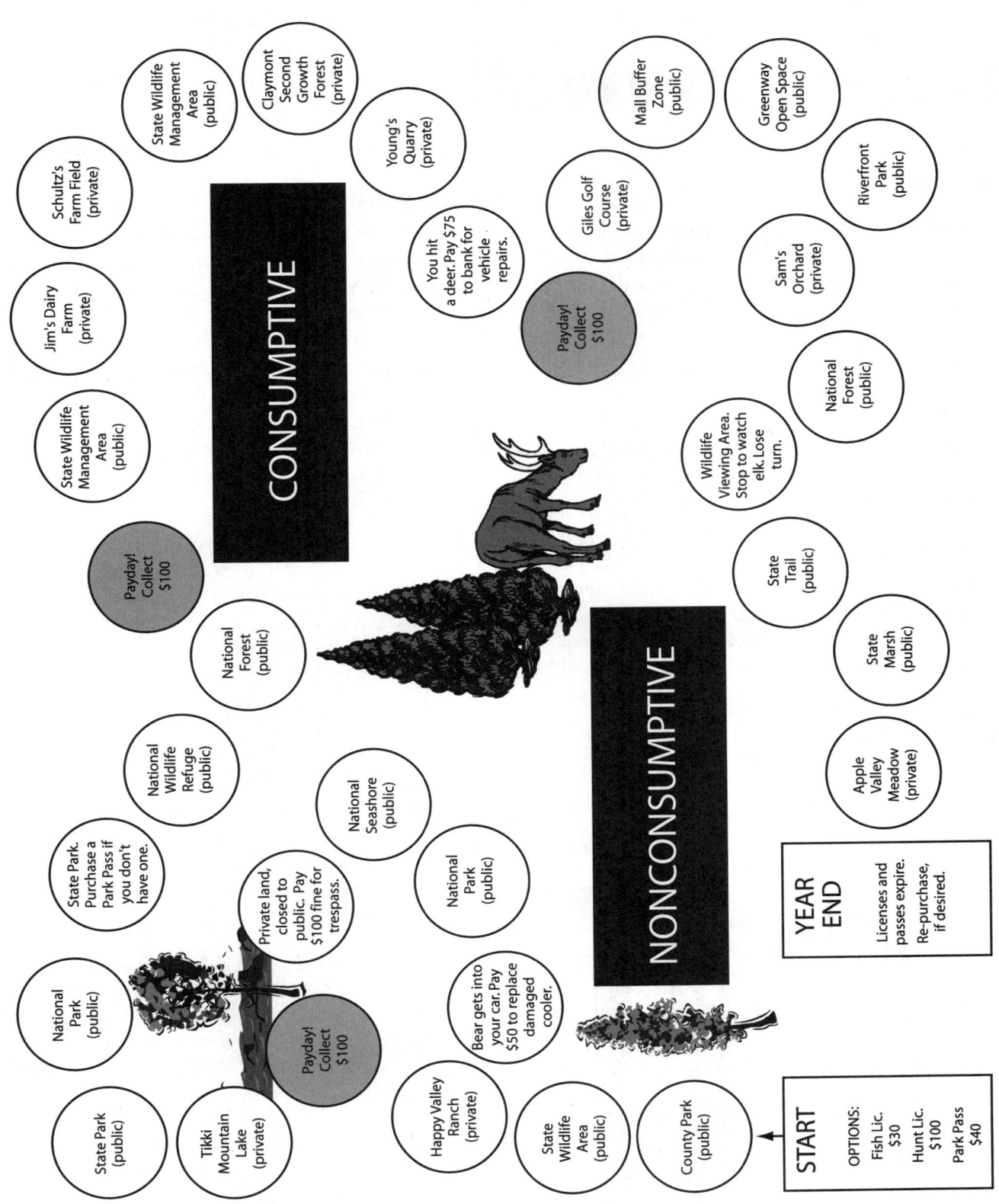

Arctic Survival

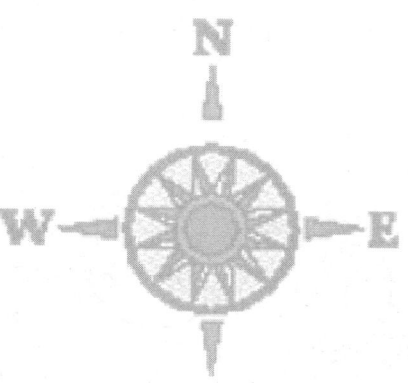

Objectives

Students will (1) describe how the available resources, including wildlife and habitat, affect the economy and culture of an area; (2) list natural resources; and (3) describe the difference between a nonrenewable and a renewable resource.

Method

Through a simulation, students will become hunters, gatherers, and traders in an attempt to gain food, water, shelter, and heat.

Materials

Tokens on page 239 made from multicolored construction paper, masking tape, an envelope for each student, four copies of Token Tally Data Sheet on page 242 for each group; OPTIONAL: a transparency of Token Tally Data Sheet to record class results

Grade Level: 9–12

Subject Areas: Social Studies, Science, Environmental Education

Duration: minimum two 45-minute sessions

Group Size: any

Setting: indoors

Conceptual Framework Topic References: ECIA, ECIA1, ECIA2, ECIB1, ECIC, ECID

Key Terms: renewable resources, non-renewable resources

Appendices: none

Background

One of the factors that drives the world's economy is the consumption of natural resources. A natural resource is anything that comes directly or indirectly from the earth. Natural resources include water, air, minerals, soil, fossil fuels, plants, and aquatic as well as terrestrial animals. This list includes homes, food, water, and income. In an analysis of the jobs of the world, it was found that many jobs are connected to the use of natural resources.

Economics is first about survival and then about power. If a country is aggressive in the sale, manufacture, or resale of natural resources, that country can provide jobs for its people who in turn can buy more natural resources to provide food, water, and shelter for themselves and their families. If the country is lacking natural resources but is able to buy them and resell them for a large profit, it will increase its opportunities for wealth and power. If a country has few natural resources and is unable to use them as a source of income, it may find itself unable to join the trade of international natural resources, making the economy depressed and with very little power.

Economic trends, as well as the increase of human populations and mobility, have important influences on wildlife and its habitat. During times when the value of money is high, people may find themselves buying more things made of natural resources. They may buy more fresh salmon, caviar, or lobster. They also may buy and develop more property, destroying natural habitats. Increases in wealth also allow greater mobility. As people move away from cities, rural areas become developed, too.

Natural resources fall into one of two categories: renewable or nonrenewable resources. Renewable natural resources are living things with the capacity for regeneration. Trees and wildlife are examples of renewable natural resources. However, renewable resources have limits. For example, although animals have the capacity for regeneration by mating and bearing offspring, they cannot survive if their habitat is destroyed or if environmental or human-caused pressures are too great. Nonrenewable resources are non-living things. Minerals and fossils are examples. Although such resources may be replenished over geologic time by natural processes, the time span covers millions of years. Although the better choice when using natural resources might be renewable sources, this choice may not be an option because of economic reasons or because it is consumed too quickly. For instance, although wood is a renewable resource and a good choice for heat, it may be too costly or labor intensive to use. Therefore, another choice may be natural gas, an easily accessible, low-labor, nonrenewable resource. People may sometimes choose nonrenewable resources over renewable ones as an investment. Generally speaking, nonrenewable resources are more scarce and, therefore, may be considered more valuable. An investor, for example, may choose to spend money on an oil company rather then investing in a corn farm.

The benefits and liabilities of appropriate uses of renewable and nonrenewable natural resources are difficult and complex and may raise social, economic, ethical and political—as well as biological—questions. Even the concept that wildlife and other animals are renewable resources raises ethical objections from some people.

The purpose of this activity is to illustrate how the economy of an area can affect and be affected by natural resources, including wildlife.

Procedure
Overview

In this activity, students will represent a group that has been lost in the Arctic in the fall. As they find food, water, shelter, and heat in order to survive the harsh conditions, economic principles unfold related to the availability of resources. The simulation will last several rounds. A new component will be added in each round. In the first round, students simply collect food, water, shelter, and heat; then students examine whether they survived. Next the student groups may trade to pool their resources and to increase their chances of survival. In the next round, a stress alters the available resources, affecting the economic dynamics. In the last round, the limitations of nonrenewable resources come into play as well.

Before the Activity

1. Divide the room into three sections with masking tape. Those sections represent the three boundaries of Groups A, B, and C. See Diagram A: Room Set Up on page 241.

2. Using construction paper, make the tokens indicated on page 239. Tokens should be about 2" across or large enough to find and grasp easily, but small enough to fit in the envelopes. Spread out the food, water, shelter, and heat tokens listed on page 239 (for Rounds 1 and 2) for each group in that group's section. Place tokens at the far end of each section.

The Activity

1. Explain to the students that the class represents a hunting club that has gone on an Arctic hunting trip in early fall. After a 4-day snowstorm, the club members have been separated into three groups, each lost within the same wilderness area. Each group must determine how to survive, finding food, water, shelter, and heat (it is getting very cold). Because the club planned on being gone for just a couple of days and because

continued

some equipment was lost or damaged in the storm, club members have only a small snow shovel, ax, rope, ammunition, rifles, hooks, string, matches, flint, knife, light-weight sleeping bags, some water bottles, and one backpack.

2. Divide the class into three groups. Place each group at one end of the section designated for that group. (The students should be standing at one end of their section, and their group's tokens should have been distributed at the other end.)

3. Give group members a Token Tally Data Sheet, and have them put their names and the round number in the appropriate blanks at the top of the form. Tell the students their group must collect enough food, water, shelter, and heat points to sustain their group for 2 weeks. This means they must earn 300 points each of food, water, shelter, and heat each round. Note that these point values and totals are shown on the Token Tally Data Sheets. Show students the different token shapes, and explain what each token represents.

4. Give group members a scenario card describing the habitat and resources in their section of the wilderness area. Ask the group members what types of animals they would expect to find in their section. What type of heat and shelter materials might be available?

NOTE: For more complete responses, have students research Arctic habitats before conducting the activity.

5. Give students the envelopes, and have them put their names and group numbers on the envelopes. Have them place their envelopes in a pile with those of their group members on a desk in the front of the room (away from the distributed tokens).

6. Round 1A: Basic Scenario

   a. Explain that each group will have three minutes to collect its tokens. Group members may work as individuals or as a team, but they must stay within their marked area. The envelopes must stay on the desk.

   b. Students must walk and collect tokens one at a time. Each one must be taken separately to the desk and placed in the envelope before another token can be gathered.

   c. Have students collect tokens for exactly three minutes. Make sure they collect one token at a time and put it in the envelope. At the end of the round, have each group add up its total number of points to determine if the group survived. Record the number of points on the Token Tally Data Sheets. Display the results (on the board or on a transparency) from each group for each category (food, water, shelter, heat) so the groups can compare their point totals and their available resources.

   d. Discuss which groups survived. (None will.) Ask each group to tell which resources it was missing and which were sufficient. Which resources did each group have in excess? Did any of the other groups have excess materials their group could have used?

   e. Collect all of the tokens for Round 1B. Keep Group A tokens together, Group B tokens together, and Group C tokens together. Do not mix group tokens.

7. Round 1B: Scenario with Trading Added

   a. Spread the food, water, shelter, and heat tokens as before. Have the students break into their respective groups. Give the students another Token Tally Data Sheet, and have them fill in their names and the round number.

b. Because no one "survived," the class will repeat Round 1, but this time the three groups will hear the gunfire from the other hunting parties and will manage to make contact with each other during the second week. They agree to meet to trade resources. They do not join but remain in one area in order to avail themselves of the varied resources, which are too far apart to access from one point. To simulate this scenario, the three groups will gather resources for two minutes but then they may cross boundaries and exchange some resources for an additional two to three minutes if they think doing so will increase their probability for survival. (Students may not take resources directly from another section.) Before beginning the round, give the groups a few minutes to develop a strategy or plan to gather resources and to trade with other groups.

NOTE: Late in this round, the students may begin to organize their trading into an informal stock market. If such activity becomes apparent, call attention to it as soon as the round ends.

c. At the end of the round, again ask each group to tally its points and record them on its Token Tally Data Sheet. Display the class results as before.

d. Which groups survived this round? (All may have.) Compare resources after trading. What does each group lack? Does another group have resources that still might have been traded? How has mobility affected the resources for each group? Was it a waste of valuable time or was it worthwhile because crucial resources were obtained?

e. Does any group still have excess items after trading? (If all groups have traded to the maximum extent, one group should have 50 extra food points.) If the survival needs of the group have been met, how could these items be used culturally (i.e., for clothing, decorations, art, religious ceremonies)? How can the availability of natural resources influence the culture of a community?

f. Collect the tokens for Round 2.

8. Round 2: Alteration of Renewable Resources

a. Spread the food, water, shelter, and heat tokens as before. Have the students break into their respective groups. Hand out another set of Token Tally Data Sheets, and let the students fill in their names and the round number at the top of the form.

b. In this round, explain to the students that Group B has harvested all of the bears from the area. (Remove all white food tokens from the Group B section.) At the same time, a herd of caribou migrated into Area C. (Add two black food tokens to Area C.)

c. Play the round as in 1B with the students gathering, trading, and tallying their points. Ask the students which groups survived Round 2. What was each group lacking? What did each group have in excess? How can the excess resources be used culturally?

d. How did the transfer of food resources from Group B (which lost bears) to Group C (which gained caribou) affect these two groups? (Group B still has adequate food, but now it does not have enough excess to trade for needed shelter

continued

with Group C. Group C has excess shelter available for trading, but now has adequate food and no longer requires an exchange with Group B, which previously supplied its food. Group A has no excess of either item.) At this time, Group C may ask to donate the extra shelter points to Group B to ensure its survival. If the class does not think of this alternative, you can bring it up in preparation for Round 3 when the food resources return to normal. (You also may want to discuss the role of charity organizations in society and the long-term economic strategy implied.) Ask students what the consequences might be to the other groups if Group B does not survive (and if the resources in this wilderness are so widely distributed that the other two groups cannot successfully gather from their own areas and also that of Group B).

e. Collect the tokens for Round 3.

9. Round 3: Loss of Nonrenewable Resources

a. Spread the food, water, shelter, and heat tokens as before. Have the students break into their respective groups. Again, distribute Token Tally Data Sheets, and have the students fill out the tops of the forms.

b. Tell the students that in this round some of the bears have returned and the caribou have moved on. (Remove all but the one black food token from the Group C section, and replace two white food tokens in the Group B section.). Tell the class that, unfortunately, Group A has used up its oil supply. (Remove all black heat tokens from the Group A section.)

c. Have the students differentiate between renewable and nonrenewable resources. Which type are the bears and caribou? Which type is the oil? The wood? Have the students quickly classify each of the other items. Ask the students to predict the effect the loss of the oil will have on Group A. (Group A will have enough heat from its wood, but will have nothing to trade for the other items it needs.)

d. Play the round as before with the students gathering, trading, and tallying their points. Ask the students which groups survived Round 3. What was lacking by each group? How is the effect of a loss of a nonrenewable resource different from the loss of a renewable resource? What might happen if Group B built a dam in its stream and used the power to mill its logs for more firewood? How would trade be affected? Who would benefit? Who would be hurt?

Extensions

1. Research the natural resources obtained in your area for commercial use. Determine how their value came to be.

2. Compare renewable and nonrenewable natural resources, and determine which group has more value in the world market. Describe why.

3. Research some wildlife species whose products are sold commercially.

Evaluation

1. Ask the students to design a fourth round that would simulate another scenario. They could develop the dam/mill idea from Round 3 or perhaps create another scenario such as what would happen if a forest fire destroyed the trees in the Group C area. Have them predict the results of the new round for each group.

2. Have the students research natural resources found in one country on each of the populated continents. What resources do each of these countries have that is either unique or in unique abundance? What resources does each lack? To what extent does it trade with other countries? Evaluate and explain the success or failure of each country in terms of the extent to which it maximizes its resources.

Total Tokens

EDUCATOR: Make the following tokens. Note the different shapes for each type. You may find that using small objects such as buttons or beans may be less labor intensive.

Animal Tokens

Animal	Renewable or Nonrenewable	Color Squares	Amount to Make	Value
Ptarmigan	Renewable	Orange	16	1
Rabbit	Renewable	Blue	12	2
Fish	Renewable	Red	30	4
Beaver	Renewable	Yellow	5	50
Duck	Renewable	Green	40	1
Bear	Renewable	White	3	50
Caribou	Renewable	Black	3	100
Moose	Renewable	Brown	2	200

Water Tokens

Water Source	Renewable or Nonrenewable	Color Circles	Amount to Make	Value
River	Renewable	Blue	20	25
Stream	Renewable	Green	12	25
Pond	Renewable	Brown	10	10

Shelter Tokens

Shelter Resource	Renewable or Nonrenewable	Color Triangles	Amount to Make	Value
Wood	Renewable	Brown	27	25
Stone	Nonrenewable	Gray	16	10
Earth	Nonrenewable	Black	13	5

Heat Tokens

Heat Source	Renewable or Nonrenewable	Color Rectangles	Amount to Make	Value
Oil	Nonrenewable	Black	25	20
Wood	Renewable	Brown	70	10

continued

Distribution of Tokens Per Group

Group A: pond, willows (shrubs), small animals, seeping oil

Item	Amount
■ Animals	16 orange, 12 blue, 10 red, 5 yellow, 20 green
● Water	10 brown
▲ Shelter	6 brown, 1 gray, 8 black
■ Heat	20 black, 40 brown

Group B: river, open area, large game, rocky

Item	Amount
■ Animals	2 brown, 20 red, 20 green, 3 white
● Water	20 blue
▲ Shelter	7 gray, 1 brown, 1 black
■ Heat	10 brown

Group C: stream, spruce forest, little game

Item	Amount
■ Animals	1 black
● Water	12 green
▲ Shelter	4 black, 20 brown, 8 gray
■ Heat	20 brown

ANSWER KEY

Total *Possible* Points for Each Group and Category in Round 1A Only
(None will survive.)

Category	Group A	Group B	Group C
■ Food	350	650	100
● Water	100	500	300
▲ Shelter	200	100	600
■ Heat	800	100	200

DIAGRAM A
Room Setup

```
(Front Desk)
Envelopes for
A    B    C
```

Group A	Group B	Group C
Tokens for Group A distributed here	Tokens for Group B distributed here	Tokens for Group C distributed here

Group Scenario Description Cards

Group A is lost near a murky pond surrounded by many small willow shrubs that are suitable for kindling. They have a lot of small animals to hunt, but with the number of mammals in the area, the water could be full of microorganisms and must be carefully filtered to keep everyone healthy. Oil can be found seeping from the ground in small puddles.

Group B is lost in an open area protected from prevailing winds by a large, rocky knoll. It has a clear river flowing through it and patches of snow from the previous winter. Larger animals can be found migrating through this area.

Group C is lost in a spruce forest. There are large animals in the area. A small stream flows through it.

continued

Social and Political Knowledge

Arctic Survival

Token Tally
Data Sheet

Name: _____   Round: _____

Animal Tokens ■

Animal	Color Squares	Value	Number Found	Points
Ptarmigan	Orange	1		
Rabbit	Blue	2		
Fish	Red	4		
Beaver	Yellow	50		
Duck	Green	1		
Bear	White	50		
Caribou	Black	100		
Moose	Brown	200		

Total Animal Points = _____
300 needed for survival

Water Tokens ●

Water Source	Color Circles	Value	Number Found	Points
River	Blue	25		
Stream	Green	25		
Pond	Brown	10		

Total Water Points = _____
300 needed for survival

Shelter Tokens ▲

Shelter Resource	Color Triangles	Value	Number Found	Points
Wood	Brown	25		
Stone	Gray	10		
Earth	Black	5		

Total Shelter Points = _____
300 needed for survival

Heat Tokens ▬

Heat Source	Color Rectangles	Value	Number Found	Points
Oil	Black	20		
Wood	Brown	10		

Total Heat Points = _____
300 needed for survival

Make a Coat!

Objective
Students will identify plants and animals as the sources for some historical and present-day clothing.

Method
Students make replicas of coats using different materials and representing varying historical periods.

Materials
Butcher paper or large shopping bags, scissors, paint, crayons, yarn, wool scraps, heavy thread, and needle

Background
NOTE: "What You Wear Is What They Were" is a similar activity for older students.

In all but the most tropical of climates, people need an outside covering to keep warm. When ice floes receded after the last Ice Age about 10,000 years ago on the North American continent, people used fire for part of their warmth. Skins from wild animals also were used. Saber tooth tigers, bears, woolly mammoths, and wolves were among the animals hunted for meat and clothing.

Native American tribes have used animals for food and covering, and some still do as a part of their present lifestyle. Elk, deer, bear, buffalo, seal, and almost all animals killed for food also provided valuable skins for clothing.

When European settlers came to the North American continent, they brought with them a tradition of making clothing out of spun fibers such as linen and wool.

Today we have coats and other clothing made from many materials. We can divide the sources of these materials into two categories: renewable and nonrenewable natural resources. Definitions of renewable and nonrenewable natural resources are used commonly within the natural sciences. Use of these terms is intended to describe inherent biological attributes, not to imply value judgments.

The major purpose of this activity is simply for students to be able to identify principal sources of clothing.

Procedures
1. Tell the students they are going to be making coats for themselves but they will first explore what coats are made of and why we need them. Have the students answer this question: "On cold days, we wear coats. Where do we get them?" Most students will say, "At a store." Some will say that someone at home made it for them or it was a gift. If

---

Grade Level: K–4

Subject Areas: Environmental Education, Social Studies, Expressive Arts

Duration: one 45-minute session; 60 minutes possible (two 30-minute sessions)

Group Size: small groups, up to a total of 20 to 30 students

Setting: indoors

Conceptual Framework Topic Reference: HGII

Key Terms: clothing

Appendices: none

---

continued

made at home, it will usually be from purchased materials. Children from families who hunt or raise sheep for wool may have coats made from animal materials. "How would you keep warm in a cold climate if you couldn't buy a coat at a store—or if someone in your family or neighborhoods couldn't buy the materials to make a coat?"

NOTE: If your students are from families that make their own clothes directly from plant and animal materials, change the question to " If we couldn't make our clothes...?"

2. Divide the students into groups of three or four. Assign, or have them choose, different historical periods and places in which to live.

3. Have each group make a coat. Cut a pattern out of butcher paper. Color and paint it to resemble a fur coat, a down parka, or another type of coat typical to their historical period. Use a simple pattern for all the coats. For example,

OR use a shopping bag. Cut neck and sleeve holes. If time and materials permit, each student could make a coat. Students can sew the seams with quilting or carpet thread and a crewel embroidery needle.

4. Have a fashion show or display the coats in the classroom. Ask the students to identify their coats, indicating the time period and place represented and the materials used. Older students should be able to distinguish whether the materials are from renewable or nonrenewable natural resources.

Evaluation

Where did the Native Americans and early settlers get the materials to make their clothing? Draw pictures to show how they made clothing.

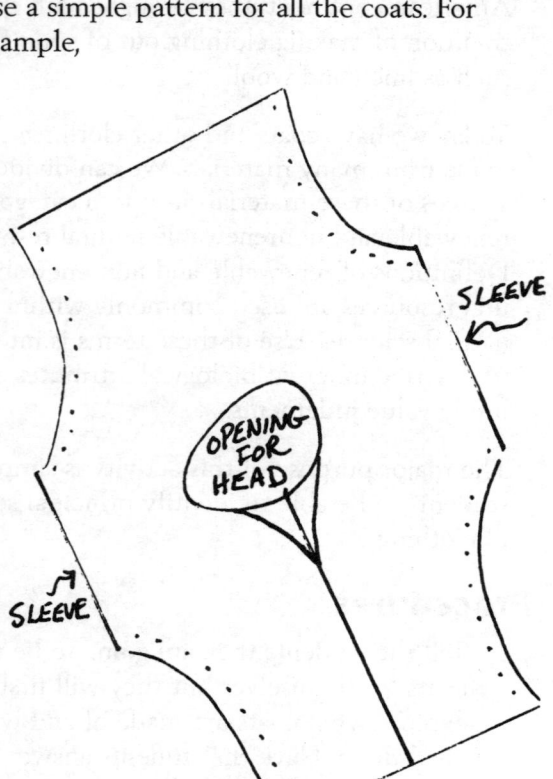

Lobster in Your Lunch Box

Objectives

Students will (1) identify the foods that are derived from plants and those that are derived from animals, and (2) articulate that all food sources are derived originally from wild plants and animals.

Method

Students plan and calculate the costs of a family's meals for one day; create a classroom chart; and analyze, discuss, and summarize their findings.

Materials

Supermarket advertisements, scissors, pencil and paper; OPTIONAL: a selection of cookbooks

Background

Humans consume food that comes directly or indirectly from wild sources. Plants—wild and domestic—support animal life. Domestic animals used as food were derived from wild animals. For example, most experts believe the chicken is descended from wild fowl that lived in the jungles of southeast Asia.

The major purpose of this activity is for students to recognize that all domesticated plants and animals have been derived from wild sources.

Procedure

1. Give the following directions to the students:

   a. You have been given the responsibility of planning meals for a family of four people for one day.

   b. Plan three meals for the day. Make a grocery list of all ingredients that you will need for those meals. Use newspaper advertisements to establish prices of the ingredients. Then cut or clip the ads and attach them to a piece of paper with the parts of the meal listed alongside the ads. Calculate the cost of each meal. Add up the total cost of three meals. What is the cost for four people? What is the cost per person? Use a chart to record your data. For example, see the chart on the next page.

2. Using the preceding chart, discuss the following questions:

   - What plants or plant products are on your menu? Place a "P" by those on the chart.
   - What animals or animal products are on your menu? Place an "A" by those on the chart.
   - Are the prices higher for plant- or animal-derived food?

Grade Level: 5–8

Subject Areas: Environmental Education, Science, Mathematics

Duration: three 30-minute sessions

Group Size: groups of two or three students

Setting: indoors

Conceptual Framework Topic Reference: HGII, HGIIA

Key Terms: domesticated, nondomesticated

Appendices: Observations and Inferences

continued

MEAL COSTS FOR FOUR PEOPLE

MEAL 1

PRODUCT	COST	
EGGS	.80	.20 each
TOAST	.24	.06 each
BUTTER	.12	.03 each
MILK	.60	.15 each
JUICE	.60	.15 each
	2.36	.59 each

For Older Students

- What percentage of food on the menu is derived directly from plants?
- What percentage of food is derived from wild animals, if any? From domesticated animals, if any?

3. Create a chart listing all the plants and animals. Discuss questions such as the following, noting results of the discussion on the chart:

- What do the plants and animals on the list need in order to survive?
- What plants do the animals depend on for their survival? Trace each animal back to its dependence on plants.
- Identify plants and animals that were once wild and are now domesticated. If possible, identify the original wild plants and animals that the foods were developed from. Place a "D" by any domesticated plants and animals.

- Why have plants and animals been domesticated as food sources (e.g., efficiency, convenience, cultural preference)? What are some of the consequences of domestication (i.e., on prices, energy, plants, animals, environment)?
- Summarize the discussion.

NOTE: Students may notice differences in eating habits and preferences; for example, some students may have chosen not to eat any meat or dairy products.

Extensions

1. Trace the life cycle of foods in the supermarket. Where do the foods come from? Are they locally grown and raised? Imported from foreign countries?

2. Have an "International Foods Day." Compare food preferences of different cultures. Look especially at whether food sources are primarily wild or domesticated.

3. Analyze foods for their nutritional value. For example, look at sources of protein. If possible, identify what you consider to be the most efficient producers of protein. For what reasons?

4. Explore the systems under which plants and animals are raised for food. Compare the various systems using a variety of criteria, including consequences to the plants and animals involved; impact on other plants, animals, and people; impact on the environment; efficiency; ethics; and so on. Consider short- and long-term costs, as well as primary and secondary consequences.

5. Examine your own eating habits. Consider overall healthfulness, as well as criteria such as those in Step 4 above.

Aquatic Extensions

1. Be sure to study foods derived from aquatic environments, such as rivers, streams, ponds, lakes, or oceans. Aquatic foods might range from fish to the kelp that is used in many foods, including ice cream, as a stabilizer.

2. See the Project WILD Aquatic activities "Kelp Help" and "Water We Eating?"

Evaluation

1. Examine a copy of a school cafeteria menu. Next to each menu item, mark "P" if the item came from a plant or plant product. Mark "A" next to items that came from animals or animal products.

2. Make a list of nondomesticated animals that are used regularly for food by people living in North America.

3. For each of these animals that are commonly domesticated and used as a food source for people, name a wild animal in North America that is similar: cow, chicken, pig, sheep, goat.

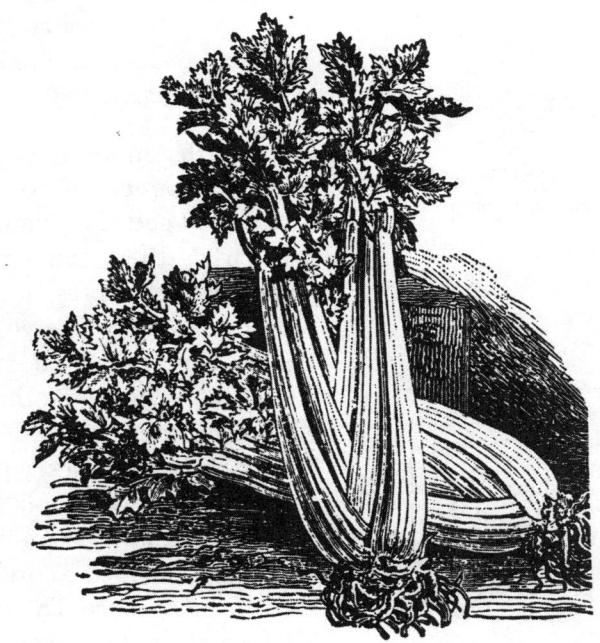

Let's Talk Turkey

Objectives

Students will (1) explain the origin and development of a domesticated animal; (2) evaluate the role and influence of the turkey on different cultures over time; (3) describe how human development affected turkey populations; and (4) identify the methods, laws, and management tools used to conserve turkeys in the wild.

Method

Students create a time line chronicling the historical use of wild turkey by societies through time and its ultimate decline and restoration in the wild.

Materials

Copies of the six Wild Turkey Cards on pages 250 to 252, approximately 20 feet of paper for time line (e.g., bulletin board paper), 125 index cards (seventy-five 4″ × 6″ and fifty 3″ × 5″), crayons, pens, pencils or markers, tape

Grade Level: 5–8

Subject Areas: Science, Environmental Education, Social Studies

Duration: one 45-minute session

Group Size: six groups of three to five students

Setting: indoors

Conceptual Framework Topic References: HGII, HGIIA, HGIIB, HGIIC

Key Terms: domesticated, wild

Appendices: none

Background

The wild turkey is an ideal species to study when showing how people affect wildlife and what the importance of wildlife is to people. The turkey is divided into two species. Currently, five subspecies of the wild turkey (*Meleagris pallopavo*) inhabit North America: the eastern wild turkey, the Florida wild turkey, the Rio Grande wild turkey, Merriam's wild turkey, and Gould's wild turkey. A sixth subspecies, the Mexican wild turkey (*Meleagris pallopavo gallopavo*) is now extinct. The other species of turkey, the ocellated turkey (*Meleagris ocellata*), is found in a 50,000-square-mile area comprising the Yucatan Peninsula of Mexico, northern Belize, and the El Peten region of northern Guatemala.

The North American wild turkey has been in existence for at least 10 million years. It has provided food and clothing to Native Americans and early settlers, and it provides recreational opportunities to present day hunters and wildlife watchers. The wild turkey was also the genetic source of the domestic turkey, favored for Thanksgiving and other holidays. Settlement of North America by Europeans led directly to a drastic decline in turkey populations but later various groups of people (writers, hunters, conservationists, lawmakers, and others) restored habitat and helped to bring the wild turkey back to its present range. The wild turkey provides a glimpse of the complicated relationship between society and natural resources. (For more detailed information, see the Wild Turkey Cards.)

Procedure

1. Ask the students what they think about when they hear the word "turkey." After recording all their thoughts, ask students if their thoughts are based on the wild turkey or the domesticated turkey. What is the difference between a wild animal and a domesticated one? Explain to students that in this activity they will be exploring the history of the wild turkey.

2. Divide the class into six groups. Provide each group with one of the six turkey cards. (It is recommended that each student have a copy of the card.)

3. Give each group 10–12 of the 4" × 6" index cards and 6–8 of the 3" × 5" index cards. Referring to the information on the Wild Turkey Card, each group should record the dates and key events/activities important for the turkey on the 4" × 6" index cards. Please instruct students to record only one date and the associated key event/activity on each card. In order to conserve space on the time line, it is best if the students orient the cards vertically with the date highlighted at the top and the key event/activity described under it. Have groups arrange their cards in chronological order.

4. On the 3" × 5" index cards, ask students to come up with phrases or words to describe how turkeys were viewed or used by people during the time period on the Wild Turkey Card.

5. Starting with the group that has Wild Turkey Card #1, have students briefly report their information to the class, as they lay out their cards—along with the associated phrases/word—in chronological order. Attach the cards to the long sheet of paper after all groups have reported to allow for the shifting around of dates.

6. Using spare index cards, ask students to record important facts, if any, about the turkey that are not already included on their time line. After this information is attached, have students decorate the time line with relevant illustrations.

7. After all presentations are completed, have students discuss the following questions: How did people view wild turkeys? Did all people view wild turkeys in the same way at all times? Are there any patterns in how wild turkeys were viewed or used? Is there any correlation between the views or uses of the wild turkey and the reasons for its decline, domestication, restoration, or all three? What laws helped wild turkey restoration? How did writers help set the stage for the restoration of wild turkey populations?

8. Ask students to divide the time line into "eras" or "ages" and to give the ages a name based on what was happening to the turkey (e.g., the "Golden Age of the Turkey", "Age of the Turkey Feather," and so on).

Extensions

1. Students can research the history of the wild turkey in their state and can place that information on the time line.

2. Students can research the history of another wild animal in their state and can compare and contrast its fate to that of the turkey.

3. Students can trace another domesticated animal to its origin.

Evaluation

1. Student presentations can be used as an evaluation tool.

2. Describe the differences between a wild animal and a domesticated animal.

3. Describe the contributions and importance of laws, agencies, organizations, and the general public in restoring the wild turkey to North America.

4. Write a poem or essay or create a video that illustrates the interdependence of people, wildlife, and natural resources.

continued

Wild Turkey Cards

Card 1

Scientists estimate that wild turkeys have been around for at least 10 million years. Wild turkeys are native only to the North and South American continents. Once there may have been as many as five different species, but if so, most of these became extinct in prehistoric times. Before European settlement, scientists estimate that 7 to 10 million turkeys were in North America.

Turkeys have been used as a source of food for thousands of years. At the Indian Knoll site in Kentucky, archeologists found large quantities of turkey bones, second only to the number of deer bones. Radiocarbon dating procedures indicated that these turkey bones existed before 3,000 BC.

The use of turkey as food varied among Native Americans. The Navajos, Tonkawas, and Lipans ate turkey, as did the Native Americans living in Connecticut. However, many Apache would not eat turkey, and the Cheyenne believed that eating turkey would make them cowardly.

Turkey feathers were used widely by Native Americans to make blankets, quilts, dresses, coats, and robes. The Cheyenne, as well as other native groups, used turkey feathers on their arrows. In 1612, Captain John Smith noted turkey spurs (from old gobblers) being used as arrow tips in Virginia. Feathers were also used to fashion ceremonial masks and headdresses and turkey bones were used to make spoons, beads, and other ornaments.

Many Native American groups—like the Cherokee, Chickasaw, and Mohawk—left turkey hunting to the children. Today's turkeys are very wary of people and are difficult to hunt. However, it appears that in the past turkeys were not shy of people and were considered too easy to hunt to waste the time of the experienced hunters.

Card 2

During the 1600s when Europeans began settling in North America, wild turkeys still were very plentiful. In fact, in 1709 there were reports of turkeys numbering 500 to 1,000 birds in one flock. The settlers began to rely on turkeys as an important source of food because turkeys were so plentiful and the meat was tasty. The turkey's primary feathers also were used for writing quills.

As the continent's population grew (more than 4 million by 1790), more forested land was cleared for farms, towns, cities, industries, roads, and railroads. Wildlife continued to provide food, clothing, and goods for trading and marketing. During this time, there were no effective laws regulating the use of land and wildlife. As expansion continued, wildlife became scarce near towns and cities; consequently, settlers were not able to go out easily to hunt for their own food.

From the late 1700s through the 1800s, market hunters helped supply food for settlers, selling deer, elk, turkey, bison, and other wildlife to markets and restaurants. Initially, wild turkeys sold for as little as 25 cents each. By 1900, turkeys were $5.00 each in Chicago. Continued habitat loss, combined with market hunting, which allowed hunters to sell their game to markets for profit, was taking a toll on many wildlife species.

By 1813, wild turkeys were gone from Connecticut. They were last seen in Vermont in 1842, in New York in 1844, in Michigan in 1897, and in Iowa in 1907. By 1920, the wild turkey was lost from 18 of the original 39 states of its ancestral range and from the Canadian province of Ontario.

Card 3

All turkeys in the world, including the domesticated turkey, are classified into two species. The wild turkey (*Meleagris gallopavo*) is the most common turkey and is found throughout North America. The ocellated turkey (*Meleagris ocellata*) is the other species and is found on the Yucatan Peninsula of Mexico, northern Belize, and the El Peten region of northern Guatemala. The wild turkey (*Meleagris gallopavo*) is divided into six distinct subspecies. Of these, the eastern wild turkey (*Meleagris gallopavo silvestris*) is the largest and most common subspecies. It originally ranged in the eastern half of the United States. Another subspecies, the Mexican turkey (*Meleagris pallopavo gallopavo*), is the forerunner of all domesticated turkeys we have in the world today. The Mexican turkey is the smallest of the six subspecies of the wild turkey, *Meleagris gallopavo*. Originally, it was found in southern Mexico, but it is now considered extinct.

Domesticating a species involves raising the animals in captivity and selectively breeding them for generations. Usually they are bred to benefit people (e.g., more meat, etc.). Eventually, they become very different from their ancestors in behavior and appearance.

When Hernando Cortes arrived in Mexico in 1519, the Aztecs already had large flocks of domesticated turkeys. The Aztecs had domesticated those turkeys from the Mexican wild turkey. How long the Aztecs kept domesticated turkeys is uncertain, but some scientists think those turkeys were introduced to Native Americans in the southwestern United States before 1350 A.D. The Aztecs used these birds mostly for their feathers and for sacrificial ceremonies. There are also reports that Montezuma, Aztec Emperor in 1519, fed about 500 domesticated turkeys daily to his menagerie of hawks, owls, and eagles.

By 1520, Spanish explorers took domesticated turkeys from Mexico to Spain. From there, the turkey quickly spread to Italy and France and then throughout Europe. By 1541, the domesticated turkey had reached England. By 1573, the turkey was so plentiful that it became part of the typical Christmas dinner. With selective breeding, new varieties of domesticated turkey were developed. By 1802, there were at least four standard varieties known in England.

Card 4

When the Spanish arrived in Mexico in the early 1500s, they were greatly impressed with the turkeys that had been domesticated by the Aztecs. Consequently, they took the domesticated turkey back to Spain, where farmers raised it throughout Europe.

Domesticated turkeys soon became part of the standard supplies sent with English colonists to America. In 1607, domesticated turkeys were brought back to North America with the settlers at Jamestown. Domesticated turkeys were also sent to help feed English colonists in Massachusetts in 1629. Soon small flocks of turkeys were being kept by many of the early colonists.

During the 1700s and 1800s, the propagation of domesticated turkeys stayed on a small, local scale. But even at this scale, changes were occurring to the domesticated turkey. The initial domesticated turkeys were smaller than the turkeys of today. They also were smaller than the eastern wild turkey (*Meleagris gallopavo silvestris*) found commonly throughout the eastern United States. During this time there were reports that local farmers captured wild turkey gobblers (males) and bred them with domesticated turkey hens (females) to obtain a larger bird.

In the 1920s, large commercial turkey farms were established in the United States. By World War II, turkey farming was a major industry. Over the years, selective breeding of domesticated turkeys led to today's domesticated turkey. Domesticated turkeys are now larger and plumper than wild turkeys. Domesticated turkeys come in a variety of colors, and they cannot fly. (Some of the early breeding of domesticated turkeys was done for feather quality and not necessarily meat.) Some of the most popular domesticated turkeys are the Beltsville, Small White, Black, White Holland, and Bronze.

Turkey farming continues to be a major industry. The United States raised about 275 million turkeys in 1999, with North Carolina producing more turkeys than any other state.

continued

Card 5

Before European settlement, scientists estimate that there were 7 to 10 million wild turkeys in North America. By the 1930s, there were about 30,000 turkeys in the wild. The habitat destruction, unregulated hunting, and market hunting of the 1700s and 1800s decimated the wild turkey population throughout North America.

Land and wildlife were affected as the number of settlers grew. A few laws were passed to try to protect land and wildlife but with the lack of consistent enforcement of the law throughout the country, most settlers did not realize that turkey populations were limited. By the end of the 1800s, the reduction in wildlife populations could not be ignored. By 1900, wild turkeys—along with deer, elk, bison, pronghorns, passenger pigeons, and other species—were reduced to small populations found only in a fraction of their original ranges. By 1914, the passenger pigeon became extinct. Many people feared that the wild turkey would suffer the same fate.

Scientists, hunters, foresters, bird watchers, and others interested in turkey conservation formed organizations to urge conservation. In 1875, the American Forestry Association was founded, emphasizing the conservation of trees and forests. Theodore Roosevelt and George Bird Grinnel established the Boone and Crocket Club, an association of hunters interested in conservation.

Naturalists and writers published books and articles promoting conservation. In 1876, John Muir wrote of the need for the government to protect the forests. Henry David Thoreau published "Walden" in 1854. In 1870, essays and stories were published in Harper's new *Monthly Magazine* deploring the destruction of American wildlife and attracting the attention of people throughout the country. In 1849, the Department of the Interior was formed and by the end of the 19th century, some states had formed wildlife agencies. These organizations, as well as popular writings, slowly began to influence the opinions of the general public and lawmakers. The stage was set for the recovery of the wild turkey.

Card 6

In 1891, the President of the United States was given the power to create forest reserves through the Forest Reserve Act. State laws and the Lacey Act of 1905—a federal law that limited interstate shipment of illegally taken wildlife—curtailed market hunting. The Pittman-Robertson Act of 1937 helped provide funds to states for use in wildlife recovery programs by placing an excise tax on hunting and sporting equipment. Many states established hunting regulations and seasons and, although still small, now had wildlife agencies and personnel to enforce those laws. Some states also established wild turkey refuges, setting aside land for turkeys until the population could rebound.

With the United States' entry into World War I in 1917 and the Great Depression of the 1930s, the conservation movement slowed. At the same time, abandoned farms and timbered forests reverted to the shrubs and forested land preferred by the wild turkey. After World War II, many state wildlife agencies started to make plans to restore wildlife populations, including the wild turkey.

Obtaining wild turkeys for use in restoration projects was difficult. One widely used method was to raise wild turkeys in pens and release them into the wild. This method was used for almost 20 years but ultimately was not successful. Pen-raised turkeys did not have the skills needed to survive in the wild.

In 1951, biologists began using the cannon-net method to trap wild turkeys for later transfer. A large net was concealed on the ground near bait and quickly propelled over feeding turkeys by an electronically detonated small cannon. Using this method, along with improving habitat for wild turkey, state wildlife agencies were able to increase the wild turkey population in the United States to 1.3 million birds by the 1970s.

Throughout the conservation and restoration movement, volunteer conservation organizations greatly contributed to conserving habitat and wildlife populations. Since 1973, the National Wild Turkey Federation has partnered with state and federal wildlife agencies to provide support in the restoration of wild turkey populations. Today nearly 5 million turkeys can be found in North America, including all states in the United States except Alaska. These birds provide opportunities for bird watchers, hunters, and other people who appreciate wildlife.

Wildlife Bibliography

Objectives
Students will (1) give examples of ways in which wildlife has influenced the development of human societies, and (2) describe wildlife as having important social and political value for people.

Method
Students research and construct annotated bibliographies.

Materials
Writing materials, access to library or Internet resources

Background
NOTE: See the Project WILD activity "Changing Societies."

Grade Level: 5–8

Subject Areas: Social Studies, Environmental Education, Language Arts

Duration: two 45-minute sessions plus research time

Group Size: any

Setting: indoors

Conceptual Framework Topic Reference: HGI, HGIA, HGIB, HGIC, HGII

Key Terms: society, historical, development, value

Appendices: Using Local Resources

The development of human societies has been affected by wildlife. Since the days of earliest humans, it might be argued that human society has affected the development, movement, and size of wildlife populations, rather than the reverse. However, there are examples throughout human history where human populations have followed, been influenced by, and were or are dependent on wildlife populations.

Human societies and cultures developed in various ways, partly because environmental factors produced different types of plants and animals in different places. Human populations in varying degrees have been dependent upon wild animals as a source of food, clothing, shelter, and utensils. All livestock and pet animals were domesticated and developed from wildlife species as humans sought to provide themselves with food, shelter, medicines, and companionship, and to satisfy other needs or wants. Wildlife has also played a significant role in the development of human culture through its influence in art, religion, and commerce.

Wildlife questions and issues have influenced alliances and conflicts among and within communities, societies, states, and nations. People have, and continue at times to, come into conflict over wildlife. Explorers and immigrants to North America came into conflict with native peoples over hunting grounds and fishing waters. Treaties and alliances between Native American nations and representatives of European nations, for example, sometimes were formed and shifted in struggles over wildlife resources. Some disputes continue today.

continued

The major purpose of this activity is for students to recognize that wildlife has social, historical, and political value in the lives of human beings.

Procedure

1. Begin a discussion with students about ways in which wildlife has influenced the development of human societies. For example, the abundance of wildlife as a source of food and of other products influenced the selection of sites for early human communities. Encourage the students to think specifically about the early development of the North American continent, with other areas of the world addressed optionally. Brainstorm ideas.

2. After the discussion, refine the list of brainstormed topics into a smaller list of general topics that could be researched. Include these topics, as well as others you find useful:

   - Historical influence of the availability of wildlife on the size and location of human communities.
   - Examples of issues and conflicts related to wildlife, historically and in the present.
   - Treaties and alliances involving wildlife within and between people and nations.
   - Creative portrayal of wildlife through art, literature, dance, music, and drama as an historic as well as a contemporary means of expressing human relationships with wildlife.

3. Ask each student to select one of the research areas. After selecting an area to learn more about, each student will need access to a library, the Internet, or other resource and reference materials. Ask each student to identify from three to six resources for the research topic, to briefly describe the contents of each resource, and to include one interesting quotation from each resource. Using an established bibliographic format, ask students to submit an annotated bibliography of resources for their research topic, including the author, title, publisher, copyright date, identification of kind of document (book, article, film), brief description, and quotation.

4. Conclude with a class discussion of the students' findings. Ask the students to summarize key relationships between the development of human societies and wildlife and to describe major social and political values to humans from wildlife resources. If possible, compile a master bibliography that is for all students to have, and that is based on the total of their individual contributions.

Evaluation

1. Write an essay describing the historical importance of wildlife. Support your ideas with examples of ways wildlife has influenced the development of human society and culture.

2. Create an annotated bibliography of at least two sources that explore a problem related to wildlife in your state and in a neighboring state.

Changing Attitudes

Objectives
Students will (1) give an example of a change in attitudes related to a wild animal or the environment, and (2) describe factors that may influence changes in attitudes.

Method
Students design, conduct, and compile community interviews then summarize their findings.

Materials
Paper for taking notes and/or tape recorders with blank tapes, information about local laws and regulations affecting wildlife

Background
Attitudes toward wildlife, the environment, and appropriate uses of natural resources have changed and continue to change over time. They also vary greatly from culture to culture, within subgroups of a culture, within communities, and among individuals.

For example, 60 years ago in the United States, predator control was more or less taken for granted, especially in the western United States. There were efforts to control grizzly bears, cougars, coyotes, wolves, hawks, and even bald eagles. There was even a bounty on many of those animals because they were considered a threat to domesticated animals and human safety.

Today, controversy still surrounds predator control. However, it is now more generally recognized that such animals have a role in the health of all ecosystems. Most predators now are protected by law. In some circumstances, predator control still is being carried out, but the trend is toward limiting control to the individual predators that cause damage.

The major purpose of this activity is for students to interview members of their community to gain information concerning changes in attitudes about wildlife and the environment.

Procedure
1. Initiate a discussion of whether or not the students think people's attitudes about some subjects might change, for example, over a generation. Fashions in clothing, furnishings, and food might serve as examples to begin the discussion. If students do not raise the issue, ask them if they can think of any examples of changes in attitudes about wildlife, the environment, uses of natural resources, lifestyles involving natural resources and the environment, and so on. Discuss their suggestions, and develop a list of the topics they suggest.

Grade Level: 5–8

Subject Areas: Social Studies, Environmental Education

Duration: minimum of three 45-minute sessions, additional time for interviews

Group Size: any

Setting: indoors and outdoors

Conceptual Framework Topic Reference: HGIIB

Key Terms: attitude, interview, community

Appendices: Outdoors, Using Local Resources, Field Ethics

---

continued

2. Working in groups of two to four, ask the students to generate a list of questions relating to wildlife and the environment that they might ask of adults in their community. For example,

   - How do you feel about wildlife?
   - Does wildlife live in your neighborhood? Did wildlife live in your neighborhood when you were a child growing up? What kind?
   - What animals, if any, do you no longer see that you once did?
   - What animals, if any, are more common now than they once were? What happened?
   - What were some attitudes you remember having about wildlife when you were younger? Which of these attitudes, if any, have you changed during the past 20 years? What has caused this change, if any?
   - When you were young, what laws, if any, did you know about that affected wildlife? What laws do you know about now that affect wildlife?
   - What are the reasons for such laws? Do you think we need laws protecting wildlife? Why or why not?
   - What general changes, if any, do you think there are in our society's attitudes toward wildlife—perhaps some changes you think are good and some you do not?
   - What problems, if any, involving wildlife are you concerned about?
   - What recommendations, if any, do you have about solving those problems?

3. Review the questions generated by each student or group of students before conducting interviews.

4. Ask the students—working alone or in groups—to interview at least one senior member of their community. The students should be prepared to take notes or tape-record the interviews. Instruct students to be sure to take time to listen to any of the stories that people might tell and that are slightly off the subject—out of courtesy and also in recognition that the slightly divergent topics will also be interesting and pertinent in some ways.

5. Next, ask the students to "interview" each other to record their own responses to those questions as a point of contrast for looking at some changes in their attitudes. OPTIONAL: Add other people to interview (e.g., family members, wildlife managers, members of city council, farmers, ranchers, animal welfare group members, hunting club members, agricultural agents, private conservation group members, members of preservationist organizations, office workers, people at community gatherings, neighbors, or other community representatives). In choosing people to interview, encourage students to seek diversity and a range of perspectives.

6. After the interviews are transcribed, analyzed, and summarized, compile the results of the interviews. Shorter approaches may also be taken where each group of students is responsible for summarizing the results of the interviews in a one-page format. Then a small group of students volunteers to prepare a summary representing the findings of all students.

7. Discuss the students' findings, including what changes in attitudes have taken place, if any, and what are some factors that might contribute to any changes in attitudes that they have identified.

Extensions and Variations

1. Expand the questions to include any changes in the local community and its natural resources. Include vegetation (i.e., what plants are here that were not here previously and what plants are no longer here), water (i.e., more, less, or the same in available quantity and quality), human population, and so on.

2. Identify a local controversial issue involving or affecting wildlife or other natural resources. What is the issue? How did it develop? What attitudes and information are involved? What possible solutions are available?

3. Start this activity by pretending you were settlers living 100 or 200 years ago. What animals, if any, did you see? How did you live? Day to day, week to week, season to season? After imagining yourself at that time, discuss what your attitudes might have been toward natural resources and the environment. Might they be different today? In what ways?

4. Look in literature for information about historic wildlife populations in your area, the United States, Canada, or other parts of the world. Compare it to present-day populations.

5. Explore Native American attitudes toward wildlife and other natural resources from historic times through today.

Evaluation

1. How do most people form their attitudes—what they know and how they feel—about animals?

2. Give two examples of attitudes that are about animals based on wrong information or not enough information.

3. Give an example of a change in attitude about an animal that has occurred in this country during the past 100 years. How did this change come about?

4. If you were going to try to change someone's attitude about snakes from negative (they do not like snakes) to positive (snakes are okay and contribute to ecosystems), how would you do it?

Changing Societies

Objectives

Students will (1) describe and give examples illustrating how wildlife resources have affected the development, movement, and size of Native American societies; (2) suggest ways that wildlife has influenced the culture of Native American groups; and (3) consider historical alliances and conflicts among North American groups that developed in relation to wildlife issues.

Method

Students portray members of Native American groups in three regions of North America.

Materials

Copies of Resource Cards beginning on page 262; three envelopes, labeled respectively A, B, and C; three copies of the Needs Chart on page 264; red pens or pencils; a copy of the Background Information Scenarios on pages 265 and 266 for each group (Educators may want to laminate the cards for multiple use.)

Grade Level: 7–8

Subject Areas: Social Studies, Science, Environmental Education

Duration: minimum of two 45-minute sessions

Group Size: any

Setting: indoors

Conceptual Framework Topic References: HGI, HGIA, HGIB, HGIC

Key Terms: resources, stress

Appendices: none

Background

Human societies and cultures have developed in relation to environmental factors that produced different types of plants and animals in different places. As a result, wildlife has influenced art, religion, and commerce, and has affected relationships among and within communities, societies, states, and nations.

Corn, for instance, helped to shape the cultures of the Native American groups from Canada to Chili. The economic life of ancient civilizations—the Aztecs, Mayas, and Incas—depended on the cultivation of this plant. Although there is one wild relative, *teosinte*, corn is known only as a domesticated plant; however, many varieties exist. Corn provided stability for early societies because it was a food that could be dried and stored easily, and because plant cultivation does not require mobility.

Bison also influenced the cultural development of those groups that depended on these animals. Bison once roamed from Canada to Mexico, grazing the Great Plains in such numbers that early explorers could not count them. Bison were the center of life for the native people, providing them with food, shelter, clothing, and spiritual inspiration. Because this crucial resource was mobile, the groups developed nomadic societies. Two events greatly affected the welfare of the Great Plains societies. First, the arrival of the horse with the Spanish explorers greatly improved the ability of such groups to hunt bison. However, as settlers later moved in from the east, the herds diminished, eliminating the subsistence base of the indigenous people in the area.

258 Project WILD K–12 Curriculum and Activity Guide

Another animal that greatly influenced cultural development in areas where it is found is the salmon. Six species of salmon swim into the rivers around the northern rim of the Pacific Ocean—and everywhere that salmon swim, they have become a part of the local culture. The Ainu, who live on the island of Hokkaido in Japan, made ceremonial robes of salmon skins. On the Kamchatka Peninsula of Russia, salmon bones have been found mixed with the remains of a human community that is 11,000 years old. From Alaska to California, salmon have formed the base of tribal cultures.

In this simulation, students are divided into three groups representing three Native American cultures found on the northwest coast, in the southeast, and on the plains of the United States. The three cultures differ in their main resource—one depends mostly on fish, another on corn, and the third on bison.

In each of the three rounds, student groups representing the three cultures send selected members to collect Resource Cards representing their primary food source. Each Resource Card is worth 250 Resource Points. At the end of the round, each group determines the total number of points accumulated and then decides how those resources are to be used by distributing their total points among five categories of needs: food, shelter, clothing, ceremonial, and tools.

The purpose of this activity is to illustrate how the availability of a resource can affect the development, welfare, and culture of a society. The simulated native cultures each have different resources that are enhanced and then stressed. Students are asked to relate the resulting developments in their society with the changes in wildlife resources available to them. Students also are encouraged to reflect on the relationship of wildlife resources to the history of Native Americans.

Procedure

Before the Activity

1. Divide the room into three sections (A, B, and C) as shown in Diagram A: Room Setup on page 262.

2. Place all of the Bison Cards at the far end of the Section A. Place the Fish Cards in the middle of Section B, and place the Corn Cards at the near end of Section C.

3. Place the three labeled envelopes at the front of the room where they are easily accessible to the students.

The Activity

1. Tell the students that they will be representing members of three Native American groups and that they will be discussing how resources affect the development of societies.

2. Divide the class into three equal groups, and distribute the Background Information Scenarios to each corresponding group. Ask a member of each group to read aloud the description of the culture it represents.

NOTE: Avoid name selections for the fictional groups described in the activity. Remind students to respect other cultures by avoiding derogatory speech or actions.

3. Tell the students that each group will collect Resource Cards unique to each group. Each card is worth 250 Resource Points, which can be converted into Needs Points for items each group must have to survive. Each member of their group needs 50 points for food, 50 for clothing, and 50 for shelter. When you know how many students are in each group, ask the groups to calculate how many points will be required for their survival. For example, if there are 10 members in the group, then the group must acquire 500 food points, 500 clothing points, and 500 shelter points, for a total of 1,500 points. If more points are accumulated, the points go toward the common good of the group.

continued

4. Hand out copies of the Needs Chart to each group. Ask someone in the group to draw a red line across each of the three *required* needs (the shaded columns for food, shelter, and clothing) for Round 1, indicating the minimum number of points needed in these three categories for that group.

5. Each group then elects three members to obtain food. The three selected members stand at the front of their section. During a timed 30-second period, these members are allowed to get the appropriate resources by picking up a single Resource Card from their section, returning to the front of the room with it, and placing it in their group's envelope. They may collect only one card per trip, but they may make as many trips as they can during the 30-second interval. Ask the students why the cards were not placed the same distance from the front of the room. What does this difference simulate in the real world? How do they think this complication affects the ability of the groups to obtain food? Have the students predict how it might affect their social development. Put the cards back at the end of the round.

6. Round 1: Basic Scenario

   a. Begin the simulation with the nine students quickly picking up their cards and returning them to their envelopes. At the end of the 30 seconds, have each group total the number of Resource Points accumulated. The group then decides how those Resource Points should be converted to Needs Points. Have them indicate their choices by drawing a line across each category in the Round 1 section of the Needs Chart. Extra points collected during the activity may be used in the tool and ceremonial categories if the group decides it wishes to do this. The students should decide specifically how those points will be used (e.g., decorations on clothing, medicine, decorations on houses, music instruments, weapons, and so on), consistent with the information on their Scenario Cards.

   b. Ask each group to announce its choices. Did each group have excess resources? Ask those who had extra points to describe how they were used. How did the three groups use their resources differently? How did the available materials affect their choices? Which group would eventually develop the richest culture if present conditions continue for many rounds (i.e., decades)? Why? (Consider factors such as abundance and diversity of resources, stability of resource availability, need to cooperate to maximize resources, mobility, and climate.)

7. Round 2: Resources Increased

   a. Tell the students that in the second round, the resources for each group are enhanced somewhat. The currents in the Pacific Ocean are favorable for an abundant return of salmon to Section B, and the weather is favorable for a good crop of corn in Section C. However, the most striking change is the arrival of horses in Section A, which allows the group to hunt more efficiently. Tell the students in Sections B and C that they may add one more card to their total at the end of the round, but the students in Section A may pick up two resource cards for *each* trip.

   b. Have each group elect three members to collect the Resource Cards for this round. Each group should indicate with a red line the anticipated number of points to survive on its Needs Chart for Round 2.

   c. Have the selected members collect cards for 30 seconds. When the cards are collected, have the groups determine their total points and the distribution of these points on the Needs Chart.

   d. Discuss the changes from Round 1. What new items were created with the extra points in all three groups? What was the effect of the arrival of the horse on the group in Section A? How do they think this event affected the indigenous people living on the plains? How did it affect their ceremonies, dress, and population size? How did their mobility affect trade and communication with other groups? What conflicts might have arisen as a result of their population expansion and greater mobility? Contrast the potential for change caused by an *additional* resource against the potential for change if *existing* resources are increased.

8. Round 3: Environmental Stress Introduced

   a. Run the game a third time with an environmental stress. Tell the class that a drought has hit Section C and that most of the corn and some other crops have died. Currents have diminished the salmon return for Section B, but other fish, such as cod and herring, are available. Diminishing herds have forced the group in Section A to travel farther to obtain bison. Remove all but three Resource Cards from Section A, remove half of the resource cards from Section B, and remove all but six cards from Section C.

   b. Ask the groups to elect three other members to obtain resources. Run the round as before and allow the group in Section A to pick up two cards per trip because they still have horses. When the groups have totaled their points and recorded their needs points distribution, discuss the results. Which groups survived? Did the horse help the group in Section A? Why or why not? Why was the group in Section B not as affected as the other groups? (diversity of resources) How can the group in Section C prepare for such eventualities? (Corn is easily dried and stored for long periods.) Speculate how these stresses might affect the social and cultural characteristics of each group.

Extensions

1. Research the history and culture of indigenous people from the geographic locations represented in this activity. Many Native American groups have their own Internet sites.

2. Collect traditional stories from various Native American groups, especially local ones. How many of these traditional stories feature wildlife? How did wildlife influence their culture?

3. Visit a natural history museum featuring Native American cultural history, and have the students look for wildlife themes in the artwork.

4. Have students create ornaments and decorations using Native American patterns and symbols featuring nature and wildlife.

5. Have students research or explore the relationship of their own culture to wildlife.

Evaluation

After the third round, have each group develop a story to explain the sequence of events during the three rounds. This history can be presented in an individual oral form (storytelling), group oral form (play), graphical format (series of drawings), written format, or combination of formats. The history should include the environmental stresses with the resulting changes in the social makeup of the group.

continued

Social and Political Knowledge

Changing Societies

Diagram A: Room Setup

```
              (Front Desk)
              Envelopes for
               A   B   C
```

Group A Selected members stand here Resource Cards for Section A distributed here	Group B Selected members stand here Resource Cards for Section B distributed here	Group C Selected members stand here Resource Cards for Section C distributed here

Resource Cards: Section A

Resource Card 1 BISON	Resource Card 1 BISON	Resource Card 1 BISON	Resource Card 1 BISON
Resource Card 1 BISON	Resource Card 1 BISON	Resource Card 1 BISON	Resource Card 1 BISON
Resource Card 1 BISON	Resource Card 1 BISON	Resource Card 1 BISON	Resource Card 1 BISON
Resource Card 1 BISON	Resource Card 1 BISON	Resource Card 1 BISON	Resource Card 1 BISON

Resource Cards: Section B

Resource Card 5 FISH	Resource Card 5 FISH	Resource Card 5 FISH	Resource Card 5 FISH
Resource Card 5 FISH	Resource Card 5 FISH	Resource Card 5 FISH	Resource Card 5 FISH
Resource Card 5 FISH	Resource Card 5 FISH	Resource Card 5 FISH	Resource Card 5 FISH
Resource Card 5 FISH	Resource Card 5 FISH	Resource Card 5 FISH	Resource Card 5 FISH

Resource Cards: Section C

Resource Card 25 bushels CORN	Resource Card 25 bushels CORN	Resource Card 25 bushels CORN	Resource Card 25 bushels CORN
Resource Card 25 bushels CORN	Resource Card 25 bushels CORN	Resource Card 25 bushels CORN	Resource Card 25 bushels CORN
Resource Card 25 bushels CORN	Resource Card 25 bushels CORN	Resource Card 25 bushels CORN	Resource Card 25 bushels CORN
Resource Card 25 bushels CORN	Resource Card 25 bushels CORN	Resource Card 25 bushels CORN	Resource Card 25 bushels CORN

continued

Social and Political Knowledge

Changing Societies

Needs Chart

Each Resource Card collected represents 250 points.

Each person in the group must have per round: 50 FOOD points
50 SHELTER points
50 CLOTHING points

Points	Round One — Food	Shelter	Clothing	Ceremony	Tools	Round Two — Food	Shelter	Clothing	Ceremony	Tools	Round Three — Food	Shelter	Clothing	Ceremony	Tools
4,000															
3,750															
3,500															
3,000															
2,750															
2,500															
2,225															
2,000															
1,750															
1,500															
1,250															
1,000															
750															
500															
250															

Draw a red line across the food, shelter, and clothing columns at the necessary level for the size of your group. Anything above that line represents an excess in that area, and anything below equals deficiencies. Include this information in your history.

Background Information Scenarios

Group Scenario for Section A

Your small group lives on the North American plains. Your group hunts game such as bison, deer, elk, and antelope, and roots and plants supplement your diet. It is a tedious process to herd and isolate the big animals. Dogs help, though, to transport the meat back to your band by dragging carcasses on wooden frames, or travois. Because you must move constantly to get game, your band is nomadic and lives in tepees that can be set up easily. For meat to be preserved, it is "jerked" or dried over a fire, or pounded with berries into pemmican. Not much meat is preserved in this way because of your need to travel lightly.

You have heard that some other groups have discovered horses moving into their area and that these groups are learning to use these strange animals for hunting. You do not see other bands from your group often because the area is sparsely populated. You trade little except for medicines and occasionally shells used to decorate clothing. Those from other groups whose language you do not speak communicate with you through sign language.

Although your group is not large, the boys work at war games and the girls learn to cook and sew. All adults instruct the children in tribal ceremonies; aggressiveness and individualism are encouraged. The group values "counting coup," or touching your enemy.

Clothing such as robes, leggings, shirts, dresses, and moccasins is made from hides. Decoration has been minimal in the past. Typically, decorations are made from porcupine quills that have been dyed with plants. You have used elk teeth and animal claws and have traded for shells from the sea. There is no headgear except for use in ceremonies. These items and tools usually are made from animals such as birds and bison.

Medicines and "visions" are important in your culture. Illness is caused by foreign substances in the body that can be exorcised by the medicine man, who has great powers. He may even walk on fire as proof of this power. Four and seven are sacred numbers.

Group Scenario for Section B

Your large group lives in the Northwest where the river watersheds are covered by great stands of trees. Your primary food is the salmon that migrate by your riverside village in the late summer. Other fish and game are also plentiful. Transportation by canoes allows you to trade and communicate with other groups. During the summer, the entire village concentrates on smoking and preserving as much fish as possible for the long, cold, snowy winter.

Because winter can be severe, you retreat indoors for social and cultural activities. It is the time for much celebration as your group honors the earth, ravens, seals, fish, and trees with song and dance. This is also the time that you carve totem poles to depict your history and traditions. Members of your group are artists who paint and carve on the wooden huts and who spend time decorating the furs and woven bark clothings that you wear.

The members of an immediate family live together in a large, square, wooden hut with plank walls and a roof. The social structure of your group is well organized, and rank is determined by hereditary closeness to the ancestral founder. Potlatch, a formal ceremony involving gift giving, confirms the social status of group members. Education is also organized formally through apprenticeships in which the children learn various skills, and all adults contribute to the transmission of etiquette, moral standards, and cultural traditions such as the Spirit Dance.

continued

Group Scenario for Section C

Your large group has about 500 members and lives in the southeast. The forests, meadows, and streams contain some wildlife, but the soil is especially rich. Your family is relatively self-sufficient, growing mostly corn, but also pumpkin, tomatoes, beans, and sunflowers. Corn is valued because it can be dried and stored easily; however, hunting and fishing in the winter and spring supplement your diet. The hunters, accompanied by their dogs, are gone for long periods of time because people have chased away the game. Mobility and a dense population, however, allow you much contact with other groups, bringing not only trade and communication but also war.

Hunting is a sacred act, because offending the animal spirits causes all death and disease. Antidotes for illnesses can be found in plants, which are friendly to humans. Green corn ceremonies are rituals of annual renewal, respecting the importance of plants in your society. Clothing and shelter are also constructed mostly from plant material. Your family lives in a rectangular, gabled, thatched house made of wattle (poles intertwined with twigs) and daub (mud covering).

Boys are trained for their role as hunters and warriors through hunting games; girls must learn to cultivate, to cook, and to preserve food, as well as to tend children. Skills are taught informally by all adults through a system of rewards and the granting of privileges, not punishment. Work and play are difficult to distinguish.

History of Wildlife Management

Objectives
Students will (1) define wildlife management, and (2) describe major trends in wildlife management philosophies and practices.

Method
Students generate questions, research websites, and contact agencies and organizations involved in wildlife management for information.

Materials
Research, writing, and skit materials; Internet access

Background
Wildlife management may be seen as environmental management of a natural resource. A natural resource is defined as "a portion of an environment upon which people have placed or assigned value or see as being available for use."

Wildlife in the United States is considered a public resource. So, even when lands or waters are privately owned, the wildlife is not. In some states, there are exceptions to this rule. This is notable with wild animal ranches where wildlife is raised by private individuals for hunting or fishing purposes. For the most part, however, wildlife is held in the public rather than private domain. Primary legal responsibility for managing and conserving most wildlife in the United States is delegated to government agencies, which serve on behalf of the public. A state wildlife agency has legal responsibility for managing most of the wildlife in your area, whether that wildlife is on public or private lands and waters. Federal agencies, primarily the U.S. Fish and Wildlife Service, in cooperation with state agencies, are legally responsible for managing wildlife affecting national interests such as threatened and endangered species, marine mammals, and migratory wildlife. The range of wildlife managed varies widely by states, agencies, and jurisdictions.

Wildlife management is defined as "the application of scientific knowledge and technical skills to protect, preserve, conserve, limit, enhance, or extend the value of wildlife and its habitat." Management is, by definition, a set of practices that involve intention to accomplish, predetermined goals. An example of a management practice is the adjustment of hunting permits with the objective of reducing, increasing, or maintaining a wildlife population in an area.

Grade Level: 5–8

Subject Areas: Environmental Education, Social Studies

Duration: three 45-minute sessions

Group Size: any

Setting: indoors

Conceptual Framework Topic Reference: PLIB2a, PLIB2b, PLIB3a, PLIB3b

Key Terms: resource, management, agency, law, regulation, game, nongame

Appendices: Using Local Resources

---

continued

Historically, the relationship among people, wildlife, and the land has been viewed by fish and wildlife managers and conservationists with varying degrees of importance. During the second half of the 19th century, conservationists realized that wildlife resources were limited and that hunting and related activities would have to be regulated to conserve declining wildlife populations. It was not until the 1930s that conservationists, led by Aldo Leopold, began to understand the importance of habitat and realized that regulating harvest alone was insufficient to ensure healthy wildlife populations. Much later, during the 1960s, biologists began to realize the importance of the human dimensions of wildlife management. Wildlife managers began to focus attention on the people who used fish and wildlife resources, as well as on the impacts humans were having on fish and wildlife populations. These impacts included things such as recreational impacts and habitat alterations. As time has progressed, the view on fish and wildlife management has changed from managing only fish and wildlife, to managing habitat and ultimately, to managing fish and wildlife, land and people. (Source: *Wildlife and the American Mind: Public Opinion on and Attitudes toward Fish and Wildlife Management*, 1998).

Wildlife management philosophies and practices have undergone changes as new information becomes available and as circumstances change. See the Project WILD activity "Philosophical Differences."

The major purpose of this activity is to provide students with some background about wildlife management, beginning by studying the development and present philosophy and practices of the public agency legally designated with responsibility for wildlife management in the students' own state and community. Also see the Project WILD activity "Pay to Play" for a focus on the sources of past and present funding of wildlife management in the United States.

Procedures

1. Ask the students to generate a list of questions to be directed to the agency responsible for wildlife management in the students' state and community. Their questions might include these:

   When was the agency organized? Why was it organized? How is it set up, and with what responsibilities? What is the agency's philosophy of wildlife management? How does it define wildlife management? What are its objectives? What major programs does the agency have in order to accomplish its objectives and responsibilities? Are these the same kinds of programs for which the agency has been responsible since it was established? What major similarities and differences are there in the programs, practices, and underlying philosophy of the agency since it was established? What major trends does the agency see in wildlife management philosophies and practices? What are the major sources of funding for the agency? What, if any, changes and trends in the major funding sources have there been over time? What regulations and laws affecting wildlife should we know and tell others about? What are the most difficult problems facing the agency at this time? What are the most important things we can know and do to be informed and responsible citizens concerning wildlife?

2. Once the major questions of interest have been identified, ask the students to research the topic. Check the web pages for the state natural resource agency to find out as much information as possible. Find out the address and phone number for the wildlife biologist. Write a letter to request information not found on the agency's web pages. Before the letter is mailed, be sure to review it for clarity and appropriateness. One concise letter to the nearest agency, with all the questions included, is recommended. The students should not send individual letters.

3. Ask the students to develop similar questions and letters to send to local offices for other agencies and organizations interested in wildlife management: federal agencies (U.S. Fish and Wildlife Service, U.S. Forest Service, Bureau of Land Management, National Park Service, and the U.S. Department of Agriculture), private organizations (American Fisheries Society, American Humane Association, Natural Resources Conservation Service, Canadian Wildlife Federation, Defenders of Wildlife, Ducks Unlimited, Fund for Animals, Izaak Walton League of America, National Audubon Society, National Wildlife Federation, Sierra Club, Sport Fishing Institute, The Wildlife Society, and Wildlife Management Institute), private industry (forest products, utilities, mining, commercial fishing), and associations like the International Association of Fish and Wildlife Agencies. Encourage the students to make a real effort to contact a diverse and representative range of groups.

4. Once responses have been received from the students' letters of inquiry, ask the students to summarize and interpret their findings. Allow a few weeks for responses.

Extensions

1. Compare similarities and differences among the wildlife management philosophies and practices of the agencies and organizations researched in this activity with those of Native Americans of the region—today and in early historical periods.

2. Construct a matrix comparing similarities and differences of wildlife management philosophies and practices among all the agencies and organizations researched as a part of this activity.

3. Create a visual interpretation of apparent trends in wildlife management.

4. Contrast the development and current status of wildlife management in the United States with that in other countries of the world today.

5. Look for wildlife references in historic journals to get a feeling for what people saw in earlier times. Interview senior members in the community who can describe changes they have seen in numbers, kinds, and range of wildlife in your area. How have attitudes changed, if at all?

Aquatic Extensions

1. In some states, fish are not managed by the same state agency that manages other wildlife species. In some states, freshwater fish are managed by one agency and marine fish by another. Find out what state agency is responsible for managing fish species in your state. Find out if that agency also manages all other aquatic species. If not, find out which agency does. Identify the major responsibilities of the state agencies responsible for managing fish and other aquatic species of wildlife in your state.

2. Develop a summary of all major laws and regulations that affect fish and other aquatic species of wildlife in your state.

3. Choose an aquatic organism. Investigate the laws and management practices affecting that organism. Are the regulations local, state, national, or global? Are they effective? Are there any areas in which improvements could be made? If yes, what?

Evaluation

1. Define wildlife management.

2. Who owns the wildlife on public and private lands in your area, and how is it managed?

3. If you have a question involving laws and regulations that affect wildlife in your area, to whom could you go for assistance?

4. What seem to be major trends in the management of wildlife?

5. What seem to be the most critical problems affecting wildlife populations in your area?

Wild Bill's Fate

Objectives
Students will (1) identify sources of information concerning legislation affecting wildlife, and (2) compare differing social and political viewpoints concerning legislation.

Method
Students investigate pending legislation affecting wildlife.

Materials
Writing materials, telephone, stamps; OPTIONAL: access to the Internet

Background
See the Project WILD activity "Know Your Legislation: What's in It for Wildlife."

State governments make decisions that affect wildlife. At the same time, protecting and managing the wildlife of any state is the responsibility of a state agency—usually a state wildlife department. Issues affecting wildlife are complex. Legislation affecting wildlife is no exception.

Some proposed laws directly affect wildlife. Other laws considered by a state legislature may have a strong effect on wildlife, although the laws may not relate directly to wildlife.

In this activity, students can study the legislative process while inquiring into wildlife issues. When state legislatures meet, the public can learn what bills are under consideration or visit the state legislature's website for more details. Usually, it is possible to contact the "bill" room at the state legislature. To find out what bills specifically are important to wildlife, contact your state wildlife agency and ask for the legislative liaison. Wildlife-oriented private groups and organizations will also be watching the legislature and can be asked to help identify wildlife-related bills. The major purpose of this activity is for students to recognize that there is a legislative process that affects wildlife.

Procedure
1. First, appoint one or two students to contact the state legislature—when it is in session—to find out what bills have been introduced that affect wildlife. One or two other students should contact the state agency responsible for management of wildlife. Another one or two students should contact representatives of a diverse and representative range of organizations interested in wildlife that might have information about any pending legislation. (Groups could include Defenders of Wildlife, Humane Society of the United States, International Association of Fish and Wildlife Agencies, National Audubon Society,

---

Grade Level: 9–12

Subject Areas: Social Studies, Language Arts, Environmental Education

Duration: two 45-minute sessions and then on-going work with occasional reporting for several months

Group Size: whole class in small groups of four to six

Setting: indoors

Conceptual Framework Reference: PLIA, PLIB1, PLIB2, PLIC

Key Terms: bill, law, legislation, legislature, amendment

Appendices: Using Local Resources

National Wildlife Federation, Sierra Club, The Wildlife Society, and Wildlife Management Institute).

2. These small groups of wildlife scouts could then prepare a report for the rest of the class, summarizing their findings. They should prepare a list of the bills under consideration, with a short paragraph of information about each, including the issues behind each bill.

3. Have the class divide into groups of four to six students, with each group selecting one piece of legislation to review and understand.

4. Each team should keep an information file on the bill they are studying that includes (1) the legislative bill number and title; (2) when it was introduced in the legislature, by whom, and where; (3) its route to and through committees; (4) when it passes through the house or senate; and (5) when it is signed into law or, if not signed into law, what happens to it. (A status sheet usually is published on a daily basis when a legislature is in session.) Pay particular attention to amendments. Amendments to the original bill may drastically alter the intent. See if amendments improve or hamper the intent. Then try to determine if an amendment is intended to improve or actually to "kill" the legislation.

5. Have each team prepare a list of questions its members have about their bill. Legislators, state agencies, and other groups originally contacted would be appropriate sources of additional information at this time. Before the students contact any organization or individual, make sure their questions have been reviewed. Educators may want to make sure that the students are adequately prepared to impose on these people for information. Educators should make sure that one group is not contacted by five or six groups of your students and that another group is not contacted at all. In addition to the legislative liaison at the state wildlife agency and members of private conservation groups, students might contact people such as the person who introduced the legislation; a representative of local business interests, as appropriate; and people "on the street" who may or may not know about the proposed legislation. Make sure students research the organization from which they obtain information because the mission and goals of the organization will influence its opinion of legislation.

6. Have the students report periodically (once a week) on the status of the legislation they are studying, its progress, and the issues affecting it.

Extension

Debate contrasting viewpoints concerning the proposed legislation. See whether the final disposition of the legislation matches the students' conclusions.

Aquatic Extensions

1. Focus on water-related legislation. Identify any possible effects on aquatic wildlife and aquatic habitats if the legislation is passed.

2. Write a letter to a legislator expressing your opinion about proposed legislation affecting aquatic wildlife. Include at least three statements that can support (with evidence) your perspective concerning the proposed legislation.

Evaluation

1. Identify one bill that has been introduced into your state legislature and that will affect wildlife. Describe the bill and explain its major purpose. Offer and support your opinion as to whether this bill should be passed.

2. Describe two opposing viewpoints, if any, affecting wildlife that relate to this bill.

3. Explain any possible unanticipated consequences from passage of this bill.

4. Identify two stages where you or other members of the public could influence the bill's passage or defeat. Describe what action citizens might take at those steps.

Know Your Legislation: What's in It for Wildlife?

Objectives
Students will (1) describe the legislative process in which a bill becomes law, (2) identify points when private citizens can have an effect on the legislative process, and (3) evaluate the effectiveness of the legislative process from the perspective of the students' personal experience.

Method
Students actively participate in the legislative process.

Materials
A copy of a bill being considered in a state legislature, butcher or poster paper, marking pens, writing materials

Background
See the Project WILD activity "Wild Bill's Fate."

Students can learn about the political process by becoming involved at a "grass-roots" level. Voting, letter-writing, and lobbying are among the direct ways used by adults to communicate their opinions to their governmental representatives. Young people can prepare themselves for their voting rights and responsibilities by monitoring the legislative process—specifically following a bill of interest to them in its course toward becoming a law. This activity is best done over a one- to two-month or longer period. The students should select a local wildlife or other environmental issue of interest to them with related legislation pending. Be sure that the students tackle a piece of legislation that is worth the effort.

Real-life—rather than simulated—experiences are important in learning such concepts and skills. Although role-play and simulation activities can be useful, they do not show students that they can influence policy making. Instructional benefits to students from this activity will vary depending on their own interest and abilities, their access to governing groups, and the amount of time available to work on this project.

The major purpose of this activity is to give students real-life experience in studying and participating in the legislative process. They are given an opportunity to have an impact on issues of concern to them.

Grade Level: 9–12

Subject Areas: Social Studies, Environmental Education, Language Arts

Duration: five 30- to 45-minute sessions to start the project, 45 minutes every 2 weeks, 15-minute updates each week

Group Size: any

Setting: indoors

Conceptual Framework Topic Reference: PLIA, PLIB1, PLIB3, PLIC

Key Terms: legislation, legislature, bill, law

Appendices: Taking Action, Agencies and Organizations, Using Local Resources

HELPFUL HINTS from a classroom teacher who has successfully done this activity with students:

1. By contacting legislators, students will make an impact. Four or five letters on a legislator's desk receive attention.

2. Students will really learn how a bill progresses—important knowledge in a democracy where citizens have rights and responsibilities.

3. This process might actually assist in passing or defeating a bill—and make an impact for the good of wildlife and the environment that will last a long time.

4. This process might not get the bill through or defeat it. Most pieces of legislation take three to five years to go through the legislature. It typically takes that long for a bill to receive serious attention and for the legislators to acquire sufficient information to consider its importance. If the outcome is not what you wanted, don't be discouraged. Ask students to join forces with next year's class in the same project. Their impact may not bring about the passage or defeat of a bill in one year, but it will hasten the process.

5. Appropriations bills that require allocation of money are much harder to get passed.

Procedure

Day One

1. Ask your students if they know of any laws that affect wildlife and the environment. They may be able to give a few examples. Initiate a discussion about how such laws came to be. Where do they come from, and how are they passed into law?

2. Ask for students to volunteer to contact local people about any legislation presently being considered that would affect wildlife or other aspects of the environment. One student could call the state wildlife agency and ask to speak to someone responsible for information about proposed legislation. Another could call a federal agency with responsibilities affecting wildlife. Another student could call a private organization—like a local chapter, affiliate, or representative of the Pheasants Forum, Defenders of Wildlife, Sierra Club, National Audubon Society, The Nature Conservancy, National Wildlife Federation, The Wildlife Society, or the Izaak Walton League—for information about proposed legislation they might be concerned in and working on. Industry can also provide valuable information. For example, the government affairs office of a large corporation might be able to assist. Check with the students before they make their calls or send letters. Stress that they make their requests clearly, concisely, and courteously. Make sure students research the mission and goals of the agency or organization they contact because this research will influence the group's perspective of the proposed legislation. Ask the students to be prepared to report back within two weeks about what they have learned. If possible, by that time the students should have copies of proposed legislation for review by other members of the class.

Day Two

3. Ask the students who contacted local people about proposed legislation to report to the rest of the class. After hearing the reports, ask the entire class to decide what one piece of proposed legislation they are most interested in finding out more about by following its route through the legislature to possible passage.

continued

Day Three and On

4. Once the students have selected the legislation they are interested in following, these are the next main steps:

- Know your legislation. Give each student a copy of the proposed legislation. Divide the class into committees. Ask each committee to take a section of the legislation, read it, interpret it to the best of their ability, and report back to the whole class. Ask each committee to outline its reports visually and verbally on a large piece of butcher paper for presentation in front of the class.

- Write the position paper. Ask the students to decide which areas of the legislation they wish to support or oppose with specific positions. Again, ask the students to work in committees to do research, bringing back information and expert opinions to substantiate their positions. All the information and concerns then should be compiled into a class position paper they will use to present their points of view to the legislators and allied groups.

- Get in touch with your federal representative or senator. Next, ask each student to write a letter to his or her state legislator. At least one copy of the students' position paper should be included with their letters. Be sure to check the letters for grammar and spelling errors—they have to be perfect!

- Establish a legislature contact person. Ask the class to appoint a student "Eagle-Eye" to be the contact person with the local legislator's office. If possible, the student should introduce himself or herself in person or by phone to the legislator or aide and should express the class's wish to keep track of this bill. It is the responsibility of the student "Eagle-Eye" to do as follows:

  ◆ Contact the legislator's office twice a week to determine where the bill is in the process and whether it has picked up any amendments.

  ◆ Keep a flow chart on the progress of the bill. This flow chart can be placed on a large piece of butcher paper on a bulletin board for the class to follow.

- Establish an organization contact person. The class already may have identified allied groups that might have an interest in this bill (e.g., when students volunteered at the beginning of the project to contact people for information about proposed legislation). Ask the students to appoint one class member to each group identified. It will be the responsibility of the student liaisons to contact, in person, the president or legislative chairperson of the local allied group for which they are the contact. Explain this class project, and give students a copy of the position paper. Student liaisons are to keep their allied groups informed, and—when the legislation reaches a critical point—student liaisons will contact the allied group leader, asking that the groups contact their general membership to write or call their local legislators about the bill. Keep a list of who is contacted.

- Identify a student whip. Ask the class to appoint another student to find out to what committees this bill will probably be assigned to. Wildlife bills usually go to the Natural Resource Committee and to the Appropriations or Ways and Means Committee if they cost money. The student whip should get a list of committee members and their districts from the legislature's Information Desk. Ask the student whip to list and display the names of these committee members and their districts. The student whip also should keep in constant contact with the student liaison in case the bill is relegated to some other committee unexpectedly.

- Student "Watchdog." Each committee member on the student whip's list should be assigned to a student Watchdog. Each Watchdog is to write his or her committee member a letter stating the class's position, including a copy of the position paper. Keep track of who is contacted, when, and how. It is the responsibility of each student Watchdog to call his or her respective legislator's office a couple of days before the bill goes into that committee to reaffirm the position of the students. Again, stress courtesy and clarity on the part of the students in making these calls. Student Watchdogs can also encourage relatives and friends who live in their committee member's district to write or call the legislator and to voice their opinions. Student Watchdogs should also work with student liaisons to contact the allied group leaders who live in their legislator's district.

- Make final efforts. When the bill is about to go into full committee or before the full House or Senate, it is time for the students, their friends, relatives, and allied groups to write or call (get the toll-free number for them) the legislators who will be making the decisions—making one last effort to make their views known.

- Get the results. The bill may or may not pass. In either case, the students have acquired valuable information and developed first-hand skills in working within the established political processes affecting wildlife and the environment.

Extensions and Variations

1. Draft your own proposed legislation, and debate it in a mock classroom legislature. Submit it for consideration to your state legislator or the appropriate committee.

2. Distinguish between laws and regulations. Regulations may have the same powers and penalties as laws, or may not. Look at similarities and differences. Obtain copies of state wildlife laws and regulations. They are normally free from the state wildlife agency.

Aquatic Extensions

Choose a piece of legislation related to aquatic species or aquatic habitats.

Evaluation

1. List five stages in the passage of a bill where citizens can influence the outcome. List the stages in order. Assume the bill begins in a House of Representatives. Briefly describe how citizens can have input.

2. What are three good places to go for information about legislation affecting wildlife, natural resources, and the environment?

3. How can a citizen find out the status of a bill that is being considered for legislation?

4. What impact does the legislative process have on people's perceptions and actions that affect wildlife and its habitat? Using your experience, what suggestions, if any, would you like to make that will improve the effectiveness of the legislative process? What are its strongest, most-valuable features? What are its weakest, most-negative features? What is your assessment of its overall importance?

5. What advice would you offer other students who want to influence the passage or defeat of legislation?

continued

Social and Political Knowledge
Know Your Legislation: What's in It for Wildlife?

Action Flow Chart for "Know Your Legislation" Activity

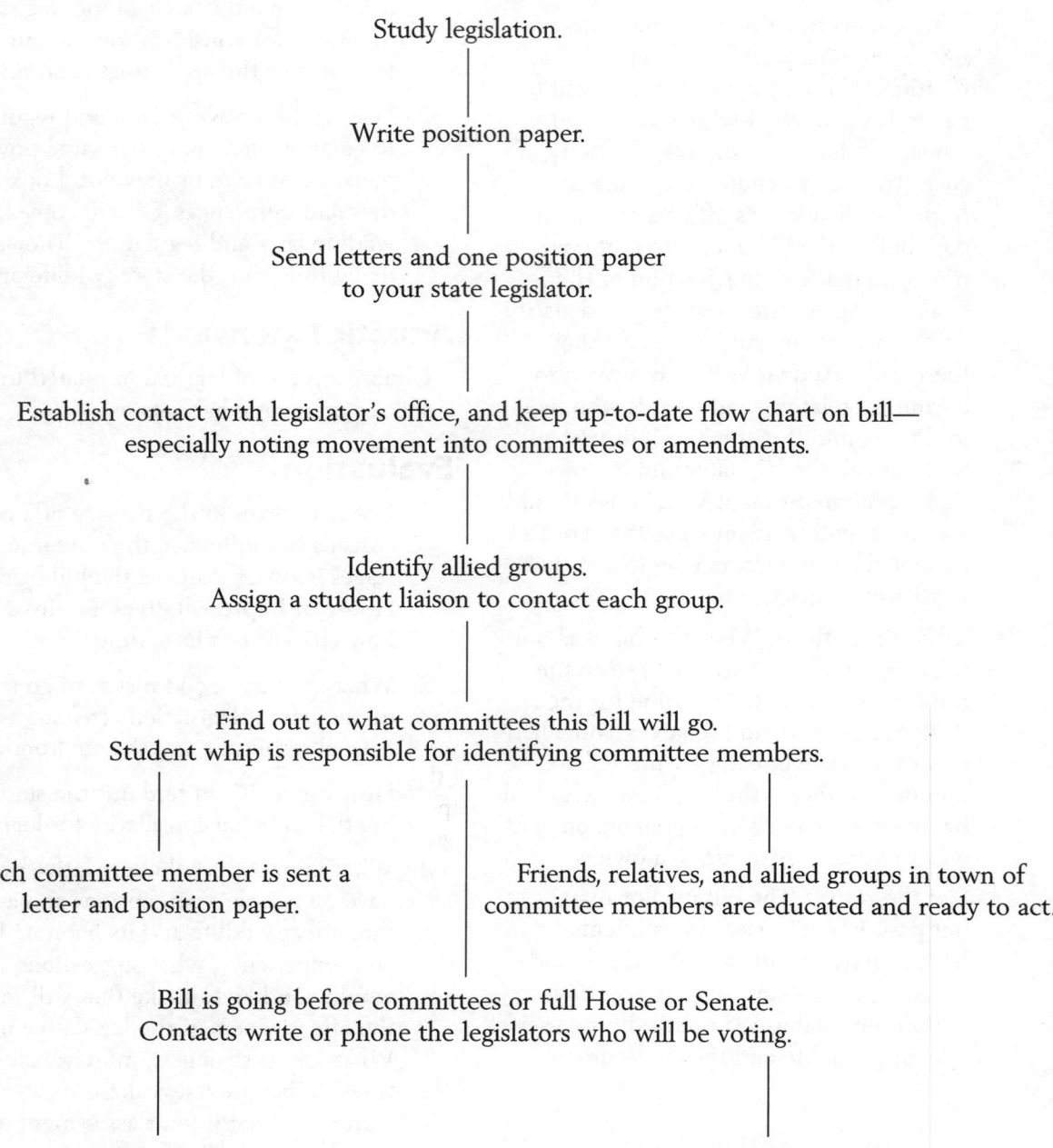

Study legislation.

Write position paper.

Send letters and one position paper to your state legislator.

Establish contact with legislator's office, and keep up-to-date flow chart on bill—especially noting movement into committees or amendments.

Identify allied groups.
Assign a student liaison to contact each group.

Find out to what committees this bill will go.
Student whip is responsible for identifying committee members.

Each committee member is sent a letter and position paper.

Friends, relatives, and allied groups in town of committee members are educated and ready to act.

Bill is going before committees or full House or Senate.
Contacts write or phone the legislators who will be voting.

IT PASSED.   IT DIDN'T PASS.

Section Three
Sustaining Fish and Wildlife Resources

Learning to Look, Looking to See

Objectives

Students will (1) describe differences seen in the environment as the result of casual and detailed observation, and (2) give reasons for the importance of looking closely at any environment.

Method

Students write what they remember seeing in a familiar setting, then check their accuracy and discuss the results. Next the students apply those experiences and new skills to an unfamiliar outdoor setting.

Materials

Note pads, pens or pencils

Background

Looking and seeing can be entirely different things depending on the purpose for looking. Students look at classrooms every school day, but if questioned about simple details, they may find that they are totally unaware of the existence of certain objects, colors, sounds, and textures. As students walk through a neighborhood, they probably have learned to notice only those things that are necessary in getting to and from a certain destination. Students may not see a soaring hawk although they may be looking at the sky. Students may not see a community of ants even though they are looking at the sidewalk. During a walk in the woods, students may leave the trail to see a tree better—and then not see the wildflower even though they are looking at the forest floor.

Observation skills are acquired easily. The three elements of observation are (1) to learn to be a careful observer, even if there is no sight to see; (2) to be aware of the surroundings; and (3) to recognize any part of the environment as being part of a larger whole. At a certain level, people are members of any community. When entering an ecological community, people are a part of that community just as if it were a school community or a neighborhood community. As a result, people have an opportunity and an obligation to be responsible members of each community.

Grade Level: Pre-K, K–4

Subject Areas: Language Arts, Environmental Education

Duration: one 20- to 45-minute session

Group Size: any

Setting: outdoors and indoors

Conceptual Framework Topic Reference: AAIA, AAIB

Key Terms: observe, see, appreciate, sense

Appendices: Outdoors, Field Ethics, Observations and Inferences

---

Procedure

1. *For formal classroom setting:* Begin this activity by covering a familiar spot such as a desk, bulletin board, other wall display, or table with a large sheet before the students come into the room. *For a informal setting:* Begin this activity with a discussion on observation; then ask the students to leave the room or just cover their eyes. Place a sheet over something that had been very visible to the stu-

dents during the observation discussion. *For both settings:* Distribute note pads, and ask the students to write down all the things they think are being covered by the sheet. When their lists are completed, ask them to turn their paper over on the desk. Remove the sheet. On the other side of the list, have the students make a list of what is actually under the sheet. What kinds of things did they remember? What kinds of things were most often missed? Ask why they think this happened.

2. Have the students go outdoors, and pick one spot near a tree, a fence, a playground, a vacant lot, or a field. Each student should find a spot alone, at least 50 feet from the closest human neighbor. Allow approximately five minutes for the observation. The students should look in a broad sense of the word—seeing, touching, listening, and smelling. Instruct them to record everything they "see." (Younger children can record in their minds.) Use an agreed-upon signal to indicate when it is time to return to the group.

3. Bring the students together for a discussion, centering on the process they went through as well as their list of sightings. Did they focus on any one area for a long time? Did they continue to shift their gaze? How did they focus their hearing and smelling? Cupping hands around their ears to simulate animal hearing has a dramatic effect on abilities to hear. Blindfolding a person seems to encourage better hearing as well. Moistening the undersurface of the nose and the entire upper lip area increases smelling ability. REMINDER: The role of an educator is to teach students how to look and see without telling them what to see.

4. Discuss with the students about the joy and importance of seeing as fully as possible. This is a way of appreciating, respecting, and learning more about the world.

Extensions

1. Squint your eyes. What patterns and shapes do you see?

2. What else did you see? Any living things? What were they? Were they plant or animal?

3. Categorize what was observed as living or nonliving—and/or as animal, plant or mineral.

4. Distinguish between qualitative and quantitative observations. Describe the differences between inferences and observations.

Aquatic Extension

What is the closest water source? It might be a drinking fountain, a sprinkler hose, a pond, a stream, or the beach. Try to imagine it clearly in your mind. Draw a picture showing as much detail as possible of the water and its immediate environment. Include any wildlife and vegetation that may be in the environment near and in the water. Now, or as soon as possible, go to the place in the picture. Make a written list of anything you did not include in your drawing. Add to your drawing to make it complete.

Evaluation

1. Think of three people in your life. Using your memory, write down the color of their eyes and a description of what they were wearing the last time you were together. Check to see if you were right.

2. Find and observe an insect. Pretend that you are making a report about what you observed to an entomologist (insect biologist). Include detailed observations. Explain the potential value of such detailed observations for two audiences: scientists and the general public.

Animal Charades

Objectives
Students will (1) define wildlife, and (2) distinguish between domesticated and wild animals.

Method
Students use charades to distinguish between wild and domesticated animals.

Materials
Chalkboard to be used by the recorder, small pieces of writing paper, a container (e.g., box, hat, wastebasket)

Background
An animal is a living organism other than a plant (or protist, fungi, algae, etc., as classified by some scientists). Wildlife are animals that live in a natural state, providing for their own food, shelter, and other needs in a suitable habitat. Wildlife also refers to animals that are not tamed or domesticated. Wildlife may be microscopic or as large as a whale. Wildlife includes, but is not limited to, insects, spiders, birds, reptiles, fish, amphibians, and mammals, if not domesticated.

Domesticated animals are those that humans have kept in captivity and bred for special purposes. The process of domestication takes place over a long period of time and involves genetic manipulation through selective breeding. All domesticated animals have wild ancestors. Cattle, sheep, dogs, cats, birds, and fish all are examples of domesticated animals.

Confusion can arise about animals that sometimes may be wild, sometimes may be tamed, and sometimes may be domesticated. If an animal, or population of animals, can live on its own, survive, and even reproduce, it probably is wild. Individual animals may be tamed—like some animals in zoos—while most of their numbers remain wild. A wild animal may appear to be tame, but still should be considered wild, unless it is both tamed and domesticated. Some animals that usually are considered domesticated—such as dogs, cats, horses, and goats—may become wild. The term "feral" refers to when once-domesticated animals become wild. For example, there are feral goats on California's Catalina Isle and feral horses roam in some areas of the western United States.

Where it is difficult to distinguish whether an animal is wild or domesticated, encourage the students to think in terms of what is usually the case.

Grade Level: K–4

Subject Areas: Science, Expressive Arts, Environmental Education

Duration: one 30-minute session

Group Size: 30 to 40 students or fewer

Setting: indoors or outdoors

Conceptual Framework Topic Reference: AAIA

Key Terms: animal, wild, domesticated

Appendices: Simulations, Early Childhood

Procedure

1. To begin this activity, create a space in the room that provides stage and audience areas.

2. Each student should take a small piece of paper and write his or her name on it, the name of the animal the student is going to portray, and whether the animal is domesticated or wild.

3. Collect the slips of paper and put them into a container. Charades are played in the order in which the students' names are pulled from the container. When a student's name is called, he or she goes to the designated stage area. A student timekeeper tells the performing student that he or she has 10 seconds to dramatize the chosen animal. (As an alternative procedure, students pick a paper out of the container and act out the charade for someone else's animal. The student who wrote the animal's name is identified and cannot guess during that round.) The audience members call out their guesses for the charade.

4. Follow the charades with a summary discussion, asking the students to clarify their definitions of wildlife and domesticated animals. Encourage the students to identify the range of forms found in wild and domesticated species. When assisting students in establishing definitions for what may be considered wild and domesticated species, both lions and trout can be considered wild. However, it is useful and important for the students to consider possible exceptions as they refine their understanding of distinctions between wild and domesticated animals.

Extensions

1. Ask the students to identify one or more animals that coexist. Have the students dramatize the animals, their relationships, and the ecosystems in which they live.

2. Classify the animals as appropriate or inappropriate pets, with reasons for the classifications.

Aquatic Extensions

Develop a list of several types of aquatic environments. For example, stream or brook, lake, pond, and river (freshwater environments), or ocean (marine environment). Announce the name of the aquatic environment in which the organism you will portray could live. Dramatize the organism's characteristics. Ask the audience to identify the aquatic animal being portrayed and match it to the appropriate aquatic environment.

Evaluation

1. Define wildlife.

2. Explain, using examples, how a species can be considered both wild and domesticated.

Animal Poetry

Objectives
Students will recognize and experience the inspirational value of wildlife.

Method
Students go outside to imagine themselves as animals and then write poems.

Materials
Writing materials: pens, pencils, paper

Background
Poetry is a form of imaginative literary expression that makes its effect by the sound and imagery of its language.

Poetry is one of the most ancient and widespread of the arts. Originally fused with music in song, poetry eventually gained an independent existence. Where poetry exists apart from music, it has substituted its own purely linguistic rhythms for musical rhythms. This rhythmic use of language most easily distinguishes poetry from imaginative prose.

Meter, the highly regular part of verse rhythm, depends, in some languages, on the different stresses on adjacent syllables and monosyllabic words. In some languages, poetic rhythm depends more on line length than on differences between syllables. Line length is determined by the total number of syllables in a line, by the number of stressed syllables in a line, or by some combination of number and stress.

Poetry may be divided into a number of types, including lyric; narrative such as epics, ballads, metrical romance, and verse tales; and dramatic (poetry as direct speech in specified circumstances). This activity develops the use of several forms of poetry: the Japanese Haiku, the Cinquain, and the Diamante.

Procedure
1. Locate a setting on the school grounds, in a park, wooded area, or other natural environment. Ask the students to choose a wild or domesticated animal for their poem. Ask them to close their eyes for a few minutes and imagine they are the animal, living in its natural environment. With students' eyes closed, educators can guide the students, imagining process with a few words or simply leave this process to the students' own imagination.

Grade Level: 5–8

Subject Areas: Language Arts

Duration: one 45-minute session

Group Size: any

Setting: indoors and outdoors

Conceptual Framework Topic Reference: AAIA

Key Terms: poetry, imagine

Appendices: Outdoors, Field Ethics

2. For five minutes, have the students "become" that animal. Imagine how long it lives, where it travels, and how other plants and animals look from its perspective. Afterward, ask the students to write a short poem about their animal. Poems can be free verse or rhyming. Cinquain and haiku are interesting forms of poetry and are explained in the Optional section below. Another form of poetry is a group poem. Everyone thinks of one animal. Each person contributes one word. One or more students can combine the words together to form the poem while the others discuss their experiences in "becoming" an animal.

OPTIONAL: Here are a few examples of other poetic forms that can be practiced.

Haiku Haiku, a Japanese lyric verse form having three unrhymed lines of five, seven, and five syllables, traditionally invoking an aspect of nature or the seasons. Traditionally and ideally, a haiku presents a pair of contrasting images: one suggestive of time and place, the other a vivid but fleeting observation. Working together, they evoke mood and emotion. The emphasis is syllabic, not rhyming. For example,

> The hawk soared over
> Spirit bird in my living
> Guide to harmony.

The haiku evolved from the earlier linked-verse form, known as the renga, and was used extensively by Zen Buddhist monks in the 15th and 16th centuries. In the next 200 years, the verse form achieved its greatest popularity and success.

Cinquain The word cinquain is derived from the French and Spanish words for five. The cinquain is a poetic form originated by the United States poet, Adelaide Crapsey (1878–1914), comprising five unrhyming lines of, respectively, two, four, six, eight, and two syllables. Each line has a mandatory purpose and number of syllables or words. These are (1) the title in two syllables (or words), (2) a description of the title in four syllables (or words), (3) a description of action in six syllables (or words), (4) a description of a feeling in eight syllables (or words), and (5) another word for the title in two syllables (or words). Here are two examples, the first using syllables and the second using words:

Panther
Vital, quiet
Moving swiftly to live
Endangered by human patterns
Near lost

Sea Otter
Mammal of living waters
Swimming, sleeping, eating, diving, basking, playing,
Sensitive indicator of the quality
of continuing life
Still here

Diamante A diamante is a poem shaped in the form of a diamond. It can be used to show that words are related through shades of meaning from one extreme to an opposite extreme, following a pattern of parts of speech like this:

> noun
> adjective adjective
> participle participle participle
> noun noun noun noun
> participle participle participle
> adjective adjective
> noun

continued

For example,

> egg
> light bright
> living stretching growing
> bird beak wing flight
> soaring seeing seeking
> feathered fluid
> raven

3. The completed poems can be typed or printed neatly and then displayed with a photograph or with black-and-white pen and ink drawing of the animal. For example,

The Goat, "Mazama"
Rhime ice coats my nostrils
The gale rages from peak to crag
Warm, white wool shaggily hugging my body…
Cautiously I move on rock
Barely noticing the fear
Of the valley below.
The eagle—the feel of snow—
This is my home.

Hal Neace, Teacher
Seldovia, Alaska

Excerpted and adapted with permission from Project Learning Tree (American Forest Foundation, Washington, DC).

Aquatic Extensions

1. See the Project WILD Aquatic Education activity "Aqua Words."

2. Create a poem in the shape of an aquatic animal. After drawing an outline of the animal, place words of the poem in order around the shape of the animal. Use words that describe the characteristics of this aquatic animal (e.g., where it lives, what it eats, how it moves, and other interesting facts).

Evaluation

1. Why do you think some people say that they would not want to live in a world without wildlife? Are you one of those people? Why or why not? Would you prefer to choose the types of wildlife you would like to live with? If so, which types would you want to live with and why?

2. Find an inspirational photograph, painting or other image that features wildlife. How does the artist portray wildlife in a way that you find inspiring?

Additional Resources

www.riverofwords.org

Drawing on Nature

Objective
Students will generalize that wildlife and other animals are an important inspiration for art and science.

Method
Students use techniques of observation and visualization to record wildlife by drawing.

Materials
Drawing materials

Background
Some significant breakthroughs have been made in recent years with respect to teaching drawing to young people and adults. Betty Edward's *Drawing on the Right Side of the Brain* and Robert McKim's *Experiences in Visual Thinking* are classics in this area, filled with actual instructional activities for use alone or with others.

Much of our understanding of science comes from interpreting visual images. The language of science is precise. The images that accompany scientific writing can enhance our knowledge of a subject and can add more precision to our perception. Drawings that accompany field notes offer researchers several paths through which to interpret their experiences. The subject is the same, but the information is different. Incorporating drawing into research improves one's observation skills. Good science requires keen observation skills.

Wildlife has been an inspiration for artwork of varying kinds throughout human history. Skills for observation of wildlife are also important to the poet and the scientist.

The major purpose of this activity is for students to recognize the value of wildlife as an inspiration for art and science, as well as to develop personal skills.

Procedure
1. This activity is best done in an outdoor setting and requires students to be able to observe an animal, preferably wildlife.
2. Provide each student with drawing materials.
3. Take the students to a park, a wooded area, a natural desert, an area of the school grounds, or a place where they can see animals. If sites are limited, the wildlife may be a line of ants, a cricket, or a grasshopper. If you can't find animals outside in a natural setting, perhaps the group could visit a zoo or an aquarium.

Grade Level: 5–8

Subject Areas: Environmental Education, Language Arts, Expressive Arts

Duration: one 45-minute session

Group Size: any; individual student project

Setting: outdoors

Conceptual Framework Topic Reference: AAIA, AAIB

Key Terms: observation, visualization, inspiration, art, science

Appendices: Outdoors, Field Ethics

---

continued

4. Give the students the following instructions:
   - Find an animal. Watch the animal as closely as you can. Look at its color, form, and body shape as if it were an outline against the sky.
   - Close your eyes and try to reconstruct the animal in your mind. See its color, body shape, etc., again in your mind. Remember—this time your eyes are closed.
   - If, when you open your eyes, that animal is gone—find another animal and start over. Find an animal. Watch the animal as closely as you can, etc.
   - After you've watched it very closely while paying particular attention to the shape of its body as if it were against the sky in an outline, close your eyes again and see the animal in your mind as clearly as you can.
   - Using a pencil, try to draw the body shape of the animal. Draw the outline of the animal as you would see it if it were surrounded by sky. Draw that outline of the animal's body on your sketching paper. Sometimes it helps to look at the animal—and not at the paper—when you are drawing the animal's outline.
   - Now that you have the body outlined, concentrate more on filling in some of the body parts than on filling in details.
   - Now fill in some of the details of the animal's surroundings—first closing your eyes to see the shape clearly before you outline it on your paper. You might outline the limb of a tree for a bird or the horizon line for an ant.
   - Now fill in as many details as you like. Your drawings may remain a pencil sketch, or you may use a felt-tip black pen for a pencil-and-ink impression, or you could use chalks or crayons to add color.

NOTE: Try to be supportive and encouraging to each of the students in this process without being too evaluative and judgmental. Several of the students who have never been able to draw anything with any feeling of success will experience some real delight with this activity. All of the students should be able to come up with something on paper they can be proud of. Encourage the students to keep using this technique for things such as keeping a journal of words and images.

5. Once their work is completed, talk with the students about what happened while they were working on their projects—what they saw, how they felt, etc. Talk with them also about the importance of wildlife and all of nature as a source of inspiration for varying forms of art and science.

Aquatic Extensions

1. Use these techniques for enhancing observations of aquatic wildlife and habitat. Include drawings of aquatic organisms in your own "Field Guide to Our School's Aquatic Wildlife" or "Field Guide to Our Community's Aquatic Wildlife."

2. If you have an aquarium or if you can visit one, use these visual techniques to record your observations.

3. At an aquarium, choose one feature of aquatic organisms to investigate. Make drawings of this feature in several different organisms. For example, try features used for locomotion in animals that live underwater.

Evaluation

Groups of people were discussing endangered plants and animals—that is, those that are very close to becoming extinct. Some of the people felt that plants and animals need to be preserved and protected because of the value they may have for medicine, food, and clothing or that they are a necessary part of our ecosystem. Other people said that plants and animals are not needed and that they would not worry about losing these species. Suppose you are an artist in the group and you want to express your opinion about whether or not plants and animals should be preserved. What would you say?

The Hunter

Objectives
Students will (1) describe their feelings about hunting, (2) compare their attitudes to those of other people, and (3) make personal judgments about the appropriateness of hunting.

Method
Students read and discuss a story.

Materials
Copies of the story, "The Twins", on page 290 through 293

Background
The following activity is about the hunting of wildlife. Students are asked to read a Depression-era (1930s) story about a young boy's experience with deer hunting. The story is open-ended so that the student can decide how the story ends. Educators are urged to use the activity as a way to teach students how to recognize and handle their emotions (and those of others) when controversial issues are discussed. It is important that the leaders of this activity provide a tone for discussion where each student's beliefs are acknowledged and respected.

Additional Project WILD activities that may provide enhanced background information on understanding controversial wildlife issues are "Pro and Con: Consumptive and Nonconsumptive Uses of Wildlife," "Philosophical Differences," "Deer Crossing," "History of Wildlife Management," "Wildlife Issues: Community Attitude Survey," "Too Close for Comfort," "Shrinking Habitat," "Planning for People and Wildlife," and "Ethi-Reasoning."

People have hunted animals since the earliest of times. Products of the hunt have been used for a wide variety of purposes including food, clothing, tools, bedding, medicines, and religious objects. Since that time, human populations have become increasingly urbanized, removing people from the necessity of daily contact with natural systems.

Hunter numbers have increased in the past century, but a smaller percentage of the overall population hunts today. Since we have become more urbanized, many people have lost the opportunity, knowledge, skills, and need to hunt. Today's supermarkets now provide people with most meat products. Even so, there are still those who hunt. Today in the United States, hunters pay fees to hunt and must follow all regulations of the agency responsible for wildlife

---

Grade Level: 5–8

Subject Areas: Environmental Education, Social Studies

Duration: one 45-minute session or longer

Group Size: any

Setting: indoors

Conceptual Framework Topic Reference: AAIIA, AAIIA1, AAIIA2

Key Terms: browse, habitat, edge effect, carrying capacity, adaptation, predator, prey, range, ecological niche, consumer, hunter, hunting, management, responsibility

Appendices: Using Local Resources

---

continued

management in their state or province. The hunters' fees, as well as a portion of taxes on certain hunting-related equipment, go directly to continuing management of wildlife resources, thus preserving non-game species, purchasing and restoring habitat, and enforcement of wildlife-related laws.

In recent times, hunting has been used by wildlife management agencies as a tool for managing some species of wildlife. Human activities in much of North America have greatly reduced the natural predators of many animal populations. Wildlife management practices often attempt to substitute human hunting as a check on the population growth of prey species. The effects of mortality factors such as predation and human hunting are subjects of debate and are in need of further study.

Why do some people hunt? Most hunters say that they hunt because they like to get outside. Some hunt to feed their families. Other hunters may find emotional, mental, and spiritual value in hunting. Many do so as part of their heritage. Most hunters feel they are making a significant contribution to the perpetuation of wildlife species and habitat.

Some people are opposed to hunting. They may believe that it is unethical or that it is biologically unnecessary and detrimental to the long-range health and genetic vitality of wildlife populations. Other concerns include the suffering of individual animals and the ethical right of humans to take the life of other animals. Some object to wildlife management practices they feel are aimed at producing wildlife for the benefit of hunters. Some who believe it is not appropriate to kill for sport or recreation may accept hunting as a tool in managing certain kinds of wildlife and under certain conditions. As with any controversial issue, there will be a range of views on this subject.

The major purpose of this activity is for students to examine their own attitudes about hunting.

Procedure

1. Ask each student to think about his or her personal feelings about hunting animals. The students may or may not choose to share their feelings in discussion. OPTIONAL: Ask each student to write a brief description of his or her feelings about hunting before proceeding with this activity.

2. Provide each student with a copy of the story, "The Twins," to read, or read it aloud to the students.

3. After having read or heard the story, ask each student to write an own ending to it. What does Jamie do? Why? How does he feel?

4. Next, ask the students to discuss the story and their endings to it. How do they think Jamie feels about hunting? How do they think Jamie feels about the animal he is hunting? How do they feel about animals and about hunting? Additional questions for discussion could include the following: Why is legal hunting allowed? What is the difference between hunting and poaching? Do you think hunting should be allowed? What reasons do people have for hunting? What reasons do people have who believe that hunting should not be allowed? In your judgment, what, if any, are appropriate reasons for hunting to be allowed? In your judgment what, if any, are appropriate reasons hunting should not be allowed? What responsibilities do you think people have if they choose to hunt? What responsibilities do you think people have if they choose not to hunt?

NOTE: Set a tone for discussion where each student's personal judgments are acknowledged and respected.

Extensions

1. Find out the following: Who sets the rules and enforces the regulations for hunting? (Regulations for legal hunting are established by the state agency responsible for wildlife. All wildlife in the United States, even on private property, is considered to belong to the public. It is managed on the public's behalf by state and federal wildlife agencies. Private organizations and individuals influence management, but legal responsibility belongs to state agencies, with some species and practices involving the federal government through the U.S. Fish and Wildlife Service and other federal agencies.)

2. Check with your state's wildlife agency to find out what kinds of hunting, if any, are allowed in your area—as well as when, why, by whom, by what methods, with what equipment, at what age, and under what regulations. Also find out what kind of hunter preparation or education is required, if any, for people who want to be allowed to hunt.

3. Check with a diverse and representative range of interested groups for their positions concerning hunting. Some groups may be for hunting, some may be against, and some may not take an official position. Investigate their reasons for their positions. Research the mission and goals, the inherent belief of each agency or organization, or both. Check each point of view for accuracy of information provided. For example, groups that could be contacted include the American Humane Association, Defenders of Wildlife, The Fund for Animals, Humane Society of the United States, International Association of Fish and Wildlife Agencies, National Audubon Society, National Rifle Association, National Wildlife Federation, The Wildlife Society, and Wildlife Management Institute, as well as state and federal wildlife agencies. Examples of position statements from a variety of organizations are included in this activity as optional background information.

4. Hold a series of debates. Argue and support positions for and against hunting.

Evaluation

Write an essay describing reasons for and against hunting. Include your personal feelings and recommendations about the appropriateness of hunting.

continued

The Twins
By Dr. Clifford Knapp and Suzanne Iudicello

The twin fawns were born on a May day when the sun dabbled the edge of the forest through the newly budding leaves and apple blossom petals fell in the abandoned orchard like fragrant snow. They were not the only twins that year; food had been plentiful in the valley and white-tailed deer were sleek and round-bellied.

Even as the doe licked her offspring clean, strength flowed into the young bodies. It hadn't hurt that she had been able, through the fall and winter, to slip into a nearby farm at night for corn, alfalfa and clover to add to the leaves, twigs, juicy weeds, acorns, and mushrooms the forests and fields offered to the white-tails.

The valley was a generous place for the herd of 60 animals. Where the hillsides dipped down to meet the farm fields, the shady forest ended. This edge meant that food was varied and abundant. It hadn't always been that way.

In the early 1700s, when the valley was first settled, the forests were widespread. Since white-tailed deer require a mixture of forest, openings and edge, they were present but not plentiful then. By 1900, however, the deer population had been almost eliminated by a human appetite for venison. Too much hunting had reduced the size of the herds. Much of the once abundant forest had been cleared for wood products and used as agricultural lands. This limited suitable habitat for the deer. Later, laws controlled hunting, and changes in land use practices led to a return of some of the forest. The mixture of agriculture and young forests provided an excellent environment for the deer herds and with the regulated hunting, they thrived. The young plants that grew in the open areas of the cut-over forest yielded an abundance of food, and by the 1930s, there were more deer in the valley than when the settlers first came.

That soft, May afternoon saw another birthday celebrated in the valley. The boy ran out to greet his father who was climbing down off the tractor after a day of making furrows for the spring planting. He looked up into the lined face of his father and barely contained his impatience while the farmer removed his hat and wiped the sweat from his forehead with a big, blue kerchief.

"Is it time?" the boy asked breathlessly.

The man smiled down at his son—a strong, wiry boy, made tough by summers of throwing hay bales and winters of chopping wood.

"Yes, Jamie," he grinned. "It's time." He put his arm across the boy's shoulders, and they walked up onto the wide porch where a table stood decked with early daisies and tiger lilies in a Mason jar, bright orange and yellow paper napkins, and a three-layer chocolate cake with 12 yellow candles. The boy's mother was already sitting at the table, pouring tall glasses of foamy, fresh milk.

"Do you want us to sing first?" She laughed as Jamie scraped the chair legs across the porch floor in his haste to get to the table.

"Nope. Where's my present?"

"Now, Jamie," his father scolded good-naturedly, "birthdays aren't just for presents. This is a special year for you and it brings with it not just a gift but some responsibility. You're no longer a little boy. You're a young man. This is not a birthday for toys."

Jamie looked down at his hands on his lap. "I know, Dad; I'm sorry."

But when he looked up again at his father, the excitement and expectation shining in his eyes were not those of a serious young man, but of a boy about to burst with anticipation.

As his mother cut the cake, Jamie's father took from behind the door a long, narrow box tied with a gold ribbon. "Okay, son, this is what you've been waiting for, and we won't keep you from it."

Jamie tore the ribbon from the box and lifted the cover. There, gleaming in the soft yellow cloth, lay the rifle. It wasn't new, but the gloss on the stock showed a new coat of oil and betrayed hours of careful rubbing, and the barrel shone with new bluing. The scratches he remembered on the dull gray were gone, but the initials his grandfather had carved on the stock were still there.

He drew the rifle from the box, taking care to point it away from anyone as his grandfather and father had taught him. It was much heavier than the .22 he'd lugged through the woods to stalk squirrels.

"It's yours now, Jamie, just as we promised," his father said. "You're 12 now and old enough to go deer hunting this fall."

Although Jamie thought the fall would never arrive, the summer passed quickly, filled with days of helping his father in the fields, fishing and swimming, and lots of practice with the rifle.

In the hills above the farm valley, the twin fawns gained strength quickly. By June, they followed the doe along the well-worn trails. As summer ripened, they roamed with the herd over the length of the valley and high on the hillsides. They were just two of 50 fawns that had been born that spring, swelling the herd from 60 to more than 100.

They fed on leaves, twigs, fruits, and nuts of the trees and shrubs in the forest and on the grasses and weeds along its edges. The summer habitat provided abundant food. The doe and her fawns grew strong and healthy on the bounty. This was fortunate, for the stark winter ahead would not offer such abundance.

November blew in rainy and cold, and Jamie was restless after the crisp, bright days of October. The harvest was complete, the fields lay in a stubble under the gray sky, and the few brown apples remaining on the trees were torn down by the wind. He sat in the warm kitchen and looked out at the glistening black branches scratching at the sky.

"Can I go out, Mom?" he asked. She looked up from the lunch dishes at her son, his dungaree cuffs well above the tops of the worn boots and the elbows frayed out of his plaid flannel shirt. The restlessness was about to burst his skin as his growing body had burst the seams of most of his clothes that summer.

"All right, but wear your father's poncho," she called as he was already halfway out the door, the rifle over his shoulder.

Jamie knew, from his summer forays and from past autumns when he'd been too young to hunt, that the deer often came down to the abandoned orchard to nip at the withered apples that grew on the overhanging trees. That part of the farm wasn't used now, and the orchard had long since overgrown, producing only tiny, bitter fruits, but the deer seemed to like them. He had watched, enthralled many an evening, as the slender, tawny forms moved delicately and then froze like shadows in the dusk.

continued

As he trotted away from the yellow light in the kitchen window, dusk gathered and the rain turned to sleet. The gray afternoon was threatening to turn bleaker yet. He scrambled over the crumbling remains of a stone wall and entered the orchard in a blast of wind that nearly took his breath away. "At least it's blowing toward me," he thought, settling in under a tree to wait. Just before nightfall, his patience was wearing thin, his foot was tingling where he had been sitting on it, the rain was trickling under his collar, and the sleet was stinging his face. He was about to stomp his foot to bring it back to life so he could walk home, when the doe entered the orchard; Jamie caught his breath.

The words of the wildlife license agent echoed in his ears as he raised the rifle to his shoulder. "We're going to open the season this year—bucks, does, fawns." The man had punched Jamie's slip of yellow paper for fishing and hunting—the first time he'd been the age to have a license for deer. "This is your first hunting season, son?" he'd asked. "Good luck."

Jamie watched the doe down the barrel of the rifle. She was stretching up, her front feet off the ground, trying to reach a last, wrinkled apple clinging stubbornly to a high branch. The slender neck glistened from drops of rain caught in the soft hair. His heart was pounding, and he wasn't sure if he was still breathing. He reached around with his thumb and gently pushed the safety off the rifle.

Just then the twin fawns stepped delicately into the orchard, melting from the darkened tree trunks like slightly smaller shadows of the doe. Jamie lifted his eyes from the barrel to the fawns. They, too, were stretching to try to reach the last brown leaves and few apples high in the branches but they were too short. They moved close to the doe, where her efforts at pulling on the branches had jostled a few apples to the ground.

Jamie refocused on the doe, sighted down the barrel and let out a deep breath to steady his hand. Just then, a blast of wind ripped through the orchard, carrying sleet and snow before it, ripping a tree branch in its fury. The branch tumbled down and the three deer bolted back into the thicket.

The boy reset the safety on the rifle and gingerly got to his feet. He looked into the darkening sky and the tossing branches and thought, "I'm glad. Maybe those three will make it through the winter."

Winter hit that night, lashing the valley with wind and snow that piled into high snowdrifts, and that froze into hard crusts and remained. The herd, trapped on the hillside, didn't move more than a quarter of a mile the whole winter. They competed for the dwindling food supply that remained poking above the snow and many fawns and does died.

Jamie thought often about the trio, as he looked out over the white landscape.

The grip of the season finally loosened one moist, February day. Rain pelted the snow, turning it to slush and pitted mounds where the mud showed through. Spring and summer returned to the valley and with them the activity that kept life for a farm boy busy and full.

For the herd, the winter had taken its toll. Most of the fawns had died of starvation and cold, as did many older bucks and does, weakened by age. The herd was reduced from the summer high of more than 100 to fewer than 50. Those remaining ventured down out of the hills to the greening valley where their favored plants sprouted anew. Throughout the spring and summer, they found plenty of food to go around among their reduced numbers, particularly since few fawns had been born after the harsh winter.

Summer's hazy, golden days burned into fall and as harvest time ended, Jamie's thoughts drifted again to the abandoned orchard and his rifle. One evening he took it out of its wrappings and cleaned and polished it, wondering if the twin fawns were among this autumn's yearlings.

The frosty straw stubble crunched under his feet as he made his way across the fields to the orchard. The passing of a year had seen more stones fall from the top of the wall and Jamie noted that the tree that had been his resting place last season was uprooted and lying broken. He concealed himself among the twisted branches and settled to wait.

The evening was still, the sky a pale salmon color where the sun had just slipped below the hills. Jamie hoped the slight varying breeze would not carry his scent. He slid a round into the chamber of the rifle, wondering how many times his grandfather had sat like this, in this very orchard, with this very rifle. He checked to make sure the safety was on.

Dusk fell with the twittering of a few last thrushes, and Jamie started at the sound of a snapping twig. A yearling doe stepped into the orchard, the brush rustling back to fill the space where she had emerged from the forest. Jamie exhaled quietly, trying to relax again, because this year was bucks only, the season restricted because the herd had so dwindled over the harsh winter. He watched the doe nosing among the brown weeds for fallen apples, wondering if she was the fawn of last autumn. He watched, still, admiring the sleek brown sides and graceful curve of the neck. The doe raised her head and listened, so close he could see her nostrils flickering to catch a scent. The deer glanced at the forest edge, tensed, and then bent her head to browse again as a yearling buck emerged from the same trail, disguised by the thick brush.

Jamie lifted the rifle to his shoulder, nestling it close against the rough wool of his jacket. He looked down the barrel at the young white-tail, wondering if these were the twins of that blustery evening a year ago. He questioned whether this time he would pull the trigger. "He made it through the winter; who am I to kill him now?" he asked himself.

The buck stepped away from the doe and began pulling apples from the drooping branches. It would be a clean shot, Jamie knew, well away from the doe, certain to be a quick kill. He exhaled, steadied his arm and concentrated on a patch of rusty brown hair on the animal's shoulder. "I can't look at his head," he thought. "I just have to keep thinking of him as meat for my family." As he thumbed off the safety, he allowed himself one last, stolen glance at the sculptured head, arching up to grasp an apple. Jamie swallowed and …

"The Twins" is adapted, with permission, from a story that originally appeared in Open Lands and Wildlife (Union, New Jersey: Pollution Control Education Center).

continued

The following statements were requested from organizations by Project WILD to be included in The Hunter activity. The contents of their statements do not necessarily reflect the views and policies of Project WILD, nor does mention of their organization constitute an endorsement or recommendation of the organization. Project WILD provides these statements to educators as examples of the diverse positions on the issue of hunting. For more information on these organizations, contact them through the listing on page 522 of this guide.

Defenders of Wildlife

The goal of Defenders of Wildlife is to preserve, enhance, and protect the natural abundance and diversity of wildlife, including the integrity of natural wildlife ecosystems. Defenders recognizes the intrinsic value of wildlife, the importance of its humane treatment, and the many benefits of wildlife to society. Defenders seeks to achieve its goals through education and reasoned advocacy of appropriate public policies.

Incorporated in 1947 to reform trapping practices, including banning the leg hold trap, Defenders has maintained its historic purposes while expanding its mission to match today's challenges to wildlife.

Defenders opposes the utilitarian notions that wildlife is most important for human consumption; opposes claims that wildlife, plants, and animals are "renewable resources" to be managed or harvested like crops; and opposes single species management plans where the primary goal is the production of more "game" for hunters.

Defenders of Wildlife advocates policies that are in the best interest of all wildlife by analyzing wildlife management programs to determine the appropriate response. Hunting is elevated by this standard to a case-by-case basis. Defenders has opposed hunting instances where such hunting has jeopardized sensitive species and their essential habitat.

Ducks Unlimited

Experts agree that habitat is the key to healthy wildlife. Without places to feed, breed, and find shelter, wildlife populations will inevitably decline. That thinking is at the heart of Ducks Unlimited's (DU) mission: to protect and restore habitat for the benefit of waterfowl and other wildlife. In 1937, DU was founded by a group of waterfowl hunters who were concerned about the dwindling numbers of ducks and geese in North America. They began raising money to help restore habitat in the key waterfowl breeding areas in Canada.

DU supports the concept of regulated sport hunting as an integral part of sound wildlife management and as a wise use of renewable natural resources. Sportsmen founded the conservation movement, and today hunters and anglers continue to provide most of the leadership and financial support for conservation around the world.

Although many DU members are hunters, the organization's focus is entirely on restoring and protecting habitat. Since its founding, DU has restored, protected, or enhanced more than 8 million acres of vital wildlife habitat in North America.

Fund for Animals

The Fund for Animals is a national animal protection society that actively opposes all sport hunting of wildlife. While some native cultures may still hunt for food, hunting in the United States is primarily for recreation. Unlike many conservation groups that focus solely on "populations" of animals, The Fund for Animals recognizes the value of all individual animals, whether their populations are endangered or thriving. Animals are not "resources" to be harvested like crops. They are living creatures that deserve our respect. All the benefits derived from hunting—spending time with family and friends, learning about the outdoors, following wildlife tracks, etc.—easily can be enjoyed without shooting animals.

The Fund for Animals advocates that the current system of wildlife management places too much emphasis on the propagation of "game" species for hunters. When money and resources are tied up in hunter education, game species research, and enforcement of hunting regulations, the non-game and endangered species programs receive little or no attention.

National Audubon Society

The National Audubon Society is an organization of more than 500,000 members working at the national, state, and local level for the conservation and restoration of natural ecosystems. It focuses on birds, other wildlife, and their habitats for the benefit of humanity and the Earth's biological diversity. For nearly a century, National Audubon has provided leadership in scientific research, conservation education, and environmental action.

The National Audubon Society historically has not assumed a position either for or against hunting. The Society does not promote hunting, nor does it oppose hunting so long as it does not adversely affect wildlife populations, is done legally, and is in keeping with the principles of good sportsmanship. The Society wants to ensure the continued viability of wildlife species. When sound scientific information demonstrates that the welfare of a species requires such action, the Society does not hesitate to advocate hunting restrictions.

National Rifle Association of America

The National Rifle Association (NRA), chartered in 1871, not only is the oldest shooting and hunting organization in America, but also is an educational, recreational, and public service organization dedicated to the right of responsible citizens to own and use firearms for all legitimate purposes. The NRA is a nonprofit organization supported entirely by its more than 3 million members and 10,000 affiliated clubs. It is not affiliated with any arms or ammunition manufacturers.

NRA states that well-regulated hunting is a beneficial use of renewable wildlife resources that, when left to nature, are lost to predation, disease, starvation, or old age. The hunting heritage predates recorded history by many centuries. The hunter's participation in the chase today is a healthy experience, both physically and spiritually.

NRA supports that the hunter's interest in wildlife has been the principal factor in fostering sound management and conservation practices. The commitment of the hunter's contributions of voluntary taxing, licensing, and regulation ensure propagation of all wildlife.

continued

National Wildlife Federation

The nation's largest conservation organization, with more than 4 million members and supporters, the National Wildlife Federation (NWF) attracts concerned citizens on both sides of the hunting issue.

While recognizing the concerns of those opposed on moral grounds, the Federation supports responsible, well-controlled hunting and fishing as appropriate uses of wildlife resources. Regulation of these activities should be based on sound, scientifically based wildlife management practices and should be designed to ensure the continued diversity and health of all wild species.

The real danger to wildlife populations today is rampant habitat destruction and degradation. In response, the NWF uses education, litigation, and advocacy to foster habitat conservation and healthy environmental practices worldwide.

By promoting commonsense conservation to concerned citizens on both sides of the hunting question, NWF is protecting habitat and natural resources for the benefit of wildlife and people everywhere.

The Humane Society of the United States

Organized in 1954, The Humane Society of the United States (HSUS) is a nonprofit organization dedicated to ensuring the protection and humane treatment of animals, both companion and wild. HSUS conducts programs oriented toward humane education and toward ensuring the welfare of companion, farm, and laboratory animals, as well as wildlife.

The HSUS is strongly opposed to the hunting of any living creature for fun, trophy or for sport because of the trauma, suffering, and death to the animals that results. The HSUS opposes such killing because of the negative effect upon the young who may learn to accept and live with the needless suffering and killing. The HSUS believes that a civilized society should not condone as sport the killing of any sentient creature.

The HSUS recognizes that the welfare and responsible management of animals may, on occasion, necessitate the killing of wildlife. When such killing is permitted, it must be used as a last resort, be demonstrably necessary, and be conducted by responsible officials, and the methods utilized must result in instantaneous and humane death. The HSUS also recognizes that the legitimate needs for human subsistence may necessitate the killing of wildlife. In such cases, killing must be accomplished in a humane and nonwasteful manner and must not involve endangered or threatened animals.

Wildlife Issues: Community Attitude Survey

Objectives
Students will (1) assess the values held by various groups and individuals regarding a selected issue, and (2) distinguish between beliefs, values, and attitudes.

Method
Students develop a questionnaire and conduct a community survey.

Materials
Writing materials to make questionnaires

Background
Individuals in a community may hold differing beliefs, attitudes, and values toward wildlife and the environment. There are many different reasons for any beliefs, values, and attitudes that people hold. Whatever the reasons or sources, the result may be strongly held differences of opinion related to the same issue in the same community.

Sometimes the best solution to a local issue may seem simple. More frequently, there are no clear "right" or "wrong" answers, yet emotions may be aroused and different solutions may have dramatically different impacts on all involved, including the environment.

For this activity, the following definitions are recommended:

belief: An information-based assumption. It may be right or wrong.

Example: Where there are more pheasants, there are more foxes.

Example: A given habitat will support only so many animals.

value: A worth attached to some event, place, idea, etc.

Example: Foxes are beautiful and important creatures.

Example: It is important to protect animals.

attitude: Based on an implied belief system or an implied value system, with a predicted behavior.

Example: Foxes should not be controlled. This statement implies a belief that human intervention in the populations of foxes will reduce some value that also is implied. The predicted behavior is opposition to control.

Example: Foxes should be controlled. This statement implies a belief that human intervention in the populations of foxes will enhance some value that is also implied. The predicted behavior is support of control.

Grade Level: 9–12

Subject Areas: Language Arts, Social Studies, Science, Environmental Education

Duration: approximately one week of class time, 45-minutes to one hour per day, plus time out of class to interview people in the community

Group Size: any

Setting: classroom and in the community

Conceptual Framework Topic Reference: AAIIA2

Key Terms: interview, survey, value, attitude, belief

Appendices: Outdoors, Observations and Inferences, Using Local Resources

---

continued

interest groups: Those groups or individuals who have an interest in an issue (e.g., for personal, ecological, or economic reasons). They may or may not have much information and may or may not have a strong opinion.

The major purpose of this activity is for students to acquire skills by which to analyze beliefs, values, and attitudes related to environmental issues.

Procedure

1. Ask the students to watch, read and/or listen to local media in order to identify environment-related issues of concern to people in their community. An issue most people have heard something about would be best.

2. Select one issue. Describe what is already known about the issue. Find out more about the issue (e.g., by contacting local spokespeople for involved interest groups, systematically clipping newspaper articles, taking notes on television and radio coverage, checking the library for pertinent information on related topics). Conduct a class discussion for students to share their findings about the issue.

3. Working in small groups, ask the students to prepare a questionnaire or questionnaire items that can be used to measure people's views about the issue. Questions should be constructed so that they can be analyzed according to people's beliefs, values, and attitudes. Questions that can be responded to in brief (e.g., "yes" or "no") will contribute to the students' success in getting people to take the time to cooperate in the survey. "Yes" and "no" questions are also easily quantified when the students are putting together the results. For example,

"Are you in favor of the proposed new hydroelectric project on the X River just north of town?"

47 Yes; 51 No; 67 Undecided

Questions can be designed to provide information about whoever is completing the questionnaire. For example,

"Do you use the river at present for recreational purposes? Yes or No?"

"If yes, do you fish on the river? White-water raft? Water-ski? Hike on the shoreline trails? Other?"

(People answer what it is they do. These responses, if any, can also be categorized and quantified, if useful.)

Such questions can be used to analyze the data and to distinguish among users and nonusers, consumptive users, nonconsumptive users, and so forth.

4. Students can sort and compile the questionnaire items generated by each group and can come up with a final version of the questionnaire. The educator should review the final draft before it is printed and used. When the questionnaire is printed, distribute enough copies so that each student has at least one copy for his or her own use as part of the survey. Each student takes the questionnaire and after school, on weekends, etc., will interview five individuals in the community. Students should work in pairs to conduct interviews. Do not send students out alone. The students record the responses by tallies on the copy of the questionnaire they are carrying.

NOTE: Students should be courteous, ask permission to interview whomever they contact, and briefly explain their purpose.

5. When the interviews are complete, the students may tally, analyze, and discuss the results.

NOTE: Here's an excellent opportunity to incorporate numerous exercises in mathematics. Depending on the level of your students, they could do everything from addition and division to finding the mean, median, mode, and standard deviation of the sample.

NOTE: It is very difficult to conduct what may be considered a scientifically valid community attitude survey. Such surveys require careful question construction, with questions tested on a pilot basis and statistically analyzed in special ways to ensure that they measure what they are supposed to measure. Who responds to the questionnaire is critically important before any generalizations can be made. For example, if the students question the first five people they see, or interview their parents and their next-door neighbors, they are likely to acquire what may be called a "biased sample." The students may validly say,

"_____ percent of the people we interviewed for our survey said ...,"

but—unless more precise procedures were followed than those described in this activity— it would be unlikely that the students could say,

"According to our research, _____ percent of the people in our community believe...."

6. Although "yes" and "no" questions will provide the best basis for quantifying answers, students may also consider asking several open-ended questions. By asking open-ended questions, students may gather insight into aspects of their community's underlying belief system. The answers they receive to the open-ended questions might cause the students to conduct a follow-up survey in which they revise their closed-ended questions. Those questions may also prompt them to qualify their interpretation of the data.

Evaluation

1. Choose one of the following animal populations and describe one belief, one attitude, and one value that might be held related to it: coyotes, deer, California condor, opossums, Norway rats, garter snakes, bald eagle, trout.

2. Why is it important that people understand how their own attitudes about wildlife develop their values and beliefs?

3. Mr. Smith is in favor of a dam that is being proposed to produce water for irrigation in the area. You inform him that the dam will have a drastic environmental impact on the river. He understands that, considers it, and votes in favor of the dam anyway. How would you explain his vote in terms of values and beliefs?

Too Close for Comfort

Objectives
Students will (1) describe possible negative consequences for people and wildlife under conditions of crowding, and (2) identify ways people can behave in order to reduce negative consequences of crowding for wildlife.

Method
Students experiment with physical distance and levels of comfort in humans, estimate appropriate distances between humans and wildlife under various conditions, hypothesize about indicators of animal discomfort, and summarize reasons to avoid animal discomfort through crowding.

Materials
None

Background
Sometimes wildlife seems to want to say, "Don't get too close!" From a tree branch, a bird watches a person approaching; when the person gets too close, the bird takes flight.

Grade Level: K–4
Subject Areas: Science, Environmental Education
Duration: 10- to 30-minute session
Group Size: any
Setting: indoors
Conceptual Framework Topic Reference: HIIA
Key Terms: crowding, disturbance, safety, behavior
Appendices: Simulations, Field Ethics

Animals are often threatened when crowded by humans, even though the humans may mean no harm and may merely want to observe the animal. Animals may display their discomfort by fleeing, grinding their teeth, coiling, hissing, stomping their feet, snarling, coughing, or wolfing. Flight is the usual way animals show stress. Noises may come when an animal is ready or threatening to attack.

Wildlife photographers have learned that when the wildlife they are photographing begins to act strangely, they probably have gotten too close. Animals may run away if you are inside a certain distance. At a closer distance, they may charge or in other ways respond aggressively to the threat of human presence.

One way of understanding the way wildlife acts is to recognize that many animals have certain distances that they keep from their own kind. Wolves may demand large areas of range that no other wolf outside of their own pack (family) may enter. Studies show that certain kinds of finches always leave a certain distance between themselves when they perch on a telephone wire or fence line.

When crowding occurs, many animals react with bizarre, aggressive, or disordered behavior, and they may develop skin diseases like mange. They may adjust to the crowded conditions, over time, by ceasing reproduction.

In the United States, great blue heron rookeries (colonies of nesting sites) have been disturbed by the mere presence of people. Rookeries are the birds' breeding grounds. Herons live most of the year alone; when they come together to breed, disturbances by humans during courtship and nesting can cause stress. Under circumstances of stress, they may not breed, may lay fewer eggs, or may abandon the rookery, leaving eggs or young birds to perish. The U.S. Fish and Wildlife Service recommends that nesting sites should be observed by humans at a distance of at least 660 feet (200 meters) to minimize disruption of the colony.

The purpose of this activity is for students to recognize the possible negative consequences for people and wildlife as a result of conditions caused by crowding.

Procedure

1. Introduce the concept of discomfort from crowding by asking one student to stand in front of the class. Approach the student slowly, asking the student to tell you when your closeness begins to make him or her feel uncomfortable. Ask the class whether they allow strangers to approach them as close as they do their friends or family. How do they feel in the middle of strangers on a crowded bus or elevator? Discuss what physical reactions they have in crowded conditions, such as avoiding eye contact, nervousness, sweaty palms, and so on.

2. Introduce the idea that animals in the wild might also be uncomfortable when approached by strangers. Talk about why they might be uncomfortable (e.g., fear of predation, need to protect young). Discuss what other conditions might increase or decrease wariness such as whether it can fly away, climb quickly, run fast, or swim fast; what the animal's size is; whether the animal is alone or with a group; and whether it is on a nest or has young.

3. Have the students make a list of animals they are likely to encounter and then estimate what distance should be maintained from each animal species, both for reasons of personal safety and for the comfort and safety of the animal. Emphasize that these are just estimates. As a rule, it is better to stay farther away than might be necessary than to get too close.

4. Have the students hypothesize about animal behaviors that might indicate discomfort, such as foot stomping, teeth grinding, raising up on hind feet, nervously looking around, and eventually flying away. OPTIONAL: Students can mime or portray such situations and have other students guess which animal they are and in what situation.

5. Discuss the ways in which wildlife harassment might occur unintentionally, such as getting too close when photographing, hiking near a nesting site, and using loud vehicles near newborn animals or in places where animals are unaccustomed to humans. Explain the possibility that there are certain times of the year when some animals are more sensitive to intrusion, such as during their mating season and during severe climatic conditions such as heavy winters or drought. How can communities minimize disturbances to wildlife? What can individual people do? Summarize reasons it is important to wildlife for people to minimize such disturbances.

Extensions

1. Have the students draw life-size outlines of some of the animals and display them on an outside wall of a building. Break into small groups; have each group establish a distance from each species that the group feels would be far enough for the animal not to be threatened by the presence of a person. Using measuring tapes, each group should measure the established "comfort zone" for each species under different conditions— and then present those suggested distances. Verify the accuracy of these distances by contacting a wildlife resource person. Discuss whether a general rule is apparent about the relationship of the size of the comfort zone to conditions such as size of the animal, presence of young, ability to flee, single animal or group of animals, and so forth.

continued

2. Why is it important to minimize such disturbances for domesticated animals, like pets, dairy cows, and so on?

3. Why is it important to minimize such disturbances for people? What actions can be taken to do so? With what consequences? With what benefits?

Aquatic Extensions

Because water is one of the essential components of a habitat, areas where water is available in the natural environment frequently are visited by many species of wildlife. Some live in or near the water. Others come to the water as needed. As a result, ponds, lakeshores, river banks, ocean beaches, streams, reservoirs, canals, irrigation ditches, and even city fountains can sometimes be places where people come "too close for comfort" when it comes to wildlife. Think of three examples of situations where people can come too close for comfort in aquatic habitats, with possible negative consequences for wildlife. Think of three examples of people and wildlife being able to successfully coexist near and in water.

Evaluation

1. Identify three examples of wildlife behavior that would indicate a human is too close.

2. Describe negative results of crowding for humans. Describe negative results of crowding for animals.

3. Identify several special conditions or times of year when wildlife are more sensitive to intrusion.

Ethi-Thinking

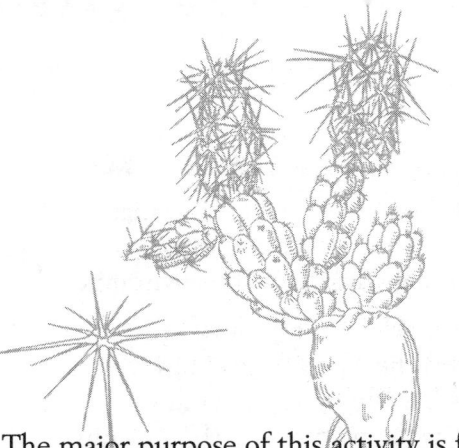

Objectives
Students will (1) generate a list of activities that are harmful to wildlife and the environment, (2) discuss reasons these activities are inappropriate, and (3) recommend alternate activities that are not harmful.

Method
Students list activities that might be harmful to wild plants and animals and use photos or drawings to picture, discuss, interpret, and evaluate these activities.

Materials
Art supplies (crayons, construction paper, magazines for photos) to make discussion cards

Background
NOTE: This activity can be used as an introduction to the Project WILD activity "Playing Lightly on the Earth."

Grade Level: K–4
Subject Areas: Environmental Education, Language Arts
Duration: one or two 20- to 40-minute sessions
Group Size: any
Setting: indoors
Conceptual Framework Topic Reference: HIIB, HIIIA, HIIIB
Key Terms: harm, wildlife
Appendices: Simulated Field Trips, Early Childhood

The major purpose of this activity is for students to discriminate between outdoor activities that are harmful to wildlife and the environment and those that are not.

Procedure
1. Ask the students to make a list of human activities that seem harmful to wild plants and animals. Ask them to think about things they've seen or know about that might be harmful. Some things could be these:
   - Pick up baby wild animals in the environment (birds, fawns, etc.).
   - Carve initials in trees.
   - Drive vehicles (cars, motorcycles) over fragile environments.
   - Remove plants from the environment, such as digging up cactus.
   - Destroy bird nests.
   - Illegally kill, collect, harass, or possess wildlife.

2. Have the students use photos or drawings to make cards showing these activities and describing what is happening. (Or the educator can prepare cards in advance, laminate them, and use them again.) Or students can dramatize the situation in skits, "commercials," songs, poems, and so on.

3. Collect the cards. Divide the group into teams of four students. Distribute one card to each group, and ask them to discuss (or present the skits, poems, and so on):
   - What is happening?
   - Does it harm wildlife? How?
   - Does it seem to be appropriate or inappropriate behavior? Why?

continued

© Council for Environmental Education 2001

- Is the person having fun?
- What else could people do that would satisfy their needs and interests without harming wildlife or the environment?

4. Ask each group to report to everyone else about (a) the students' feelings concerning what is happening in the outdoor activity shown in the picture and (b) a recommendation for an alternative activity the people could do that would not be harmful.

Extensions

1. Choose something you or your family owns such as a car, television, or refrigerator. Imagine you are that object, and explore how you—from invention to garbage dump—affect wildlife!

2. Distinguish between actions that are harmful to individual plants and animals and those that are harmful to large numbers of plants and animals. In what situations, if any, does it seem appropriate to harm a single animal or plant? In what situations, if any, does it seem appropriate to harm large numbers of animals or plants? In what situations, if any, does it seem inappropriate to harm a single animal or plant? In what situations, if any, does it seem inappropriate to harm large numbers of animals or plants? (Remember the definitions of wildlife and domesticated animals. Don't forget that wildlife includes but is not limited to insects, spiders, birds, reptiles, fish, amphibians, and mammals.)

3. Sometimes it is difficult to decide what is harmful and what is not. Usually if something is against the law, it is harmful in some way. Sometimes actions may be legal or there simply may be "no law against it." People will differ in their judgment as to whether the actions are harmful or not. Sometimes we may recognize that some of our actions are harmful in some ways—such as some of our choices for housing, transportation, and consumer products in our daily lives—and we still take those actions because of our perceptions of the importance of our wants and needs. One way to examine wants and needs is to categorize them according to "Luxury," "Useful But Not Necessary," and "Necessary for Survival." Think about personal ethics. What are ethics? How do we each make responsible decisions in our daily lives? (See the Project WILD activity "Enviro-Ethics" for an activity aimed at identifying a "Personal Code of Environmental Ethics.")

Aquatic Extensions

1. Generate a list of activities that are sometimes or always harmful to aquatic species of wildlife and aquatic habitats. Discuss the ways these activities are harmful. Discuss ways such harmful activities can be prevented.

2. Identify at least five examples of things people can do in aquatic environments that will not damage to populations of aquatic animals or the long-term health of aquatic habitats.

Evaluation

1. Identify five things people do that harm wildlife and wildlife habitat.

2. For each thing listed, describe what you can do about it.

3. Identify five things that people do that help wildlife.

4. Choose 10 photographs of people completing various actions or tasks. Examine each photograph and evaluate the potential environmental effects from the activities of the people portrayed. Explain the reasoning for your evaluations. What are the positive and negative effects of their actions?

No Water Off a Duck's Back

Objectives

Students will (1) identify ways oil spills can adversely affect birds; and (2) describe possible negative consequences to wildlife, people, and the environment from pollutants caused by humans.

Method

Students conduct an investigation using water, oil, hard-boiled eggs, detergent, and feathers.

Materials

Cooking oil, shallow containers, eye dropper, hand lens, feathers (natural); liquid detergent solution (made with one part dishwashing liquid to 100 parts water), hard-boiled eggs

---

Grade Level: 5–8

Subject Areas: Science, Mathematics, Environmental Education

Duration: one to two 45-minute sessions or longer

Group Size: small groups of three to four recommended

Setting: indoors

Conceptual Framework Topic Reference: HIIIB, HIIIB5

Key Terms: pollution, oil spill, trade-off

Appendices: Using Local Resources, Metric Conversion Chart

Background

The impacts of environmental pollution are often difficult to see. A major oil spill, however, provides dramatic evidence of potential harm to wildlife. Oil spills along coasts affect many parts of the environment, both nonliving such as water, ocean bottom, and shoreline and living such as sea birds, marine mammals, and shellfish. Examples include damaging feathers of waterfowl, killing embryos when oil seeps into eggs, suffocating fish when gills are clogged, and killing marine and terrestrial animals by ingesting food and water contaminated by the oil. Oil-soaked animals may try to clean themselves and, in so doing, often ingest oil that kills them.

Federal, state, and local spill-response teams, as well as organizations and industry representatives, have prepared contingency plans for oil spill emergencies. When a spill occurs, the teams swing into action using the plans. Trained responders try to keep oil away from animals and marshes with floating barriers called booms. They try to haze or encourage un-oiled animals, usually waterfowl, to move to safe areas away from the spill.

A rescue and treatment center is set up for animals injured by spilled oil. Oiled animals need trained people to collect, clean, and rehabilitate them in a facility with space, ventilation, controlled temperature, and hot and cold water. Professional bird-rescue organizations often have volunteers who have been trained in advance for oil spills. Efforts by untrained people may have unfortunate consequences, such as frightening vulnerable birds and causing further injury as the birds attempt to flee. The process of using

continued

detergents to clean oil from the feathers of birds caught in spills may also damage the birds' feather structure and arrangement, and thus the birds' waterproofing.

Large oil spills account for just one way oil can pollute the environment. Many people who work on their own vehicles dispose of their waste oil improperly. They pour waste oil into storm drains, into sewers, or on the ground. Many people are surprised to learn that they and their neighbors can account for more pollution than large corporations.

Oil spills are just one example of the kinds of pollutants that can have adverse short- and long-term effects on wildlife, people, and the environment. Excess fertilizers, herbicides, and insecticides from agricultural lands and residential areas run off the land and can get into lakes, rivers, wetlands, and coastal waters. Bacteria and nutrients from livestock, pet wastes, and faulty septic systems can likewise move over and through the ground into water sources and habitats. Soil from disturbed sites, including agricultural land and construction areas, is also pollution. It is a major "nonpoint source" pollutant (can't be traced to a single source) in our waters, and soil often carries other harmful substances with it.

The major purpose of this activity is for students to examine some of the possible consequences of human-caused pollution for wildlife, people, and the environment.

Procedure

1. Divide the group into teams of three or four. Each team needs a shallow pan partially filled with water. Add 1 teaspoon (5 milliliters) of oil to the water. Observe the interaction of oil and water. Measure the area covered by the oil. There are 768 teaspoons in a gallon (1,000 milliliters in a liter). Calculate how much area could be covered by 1 gallon (4 liters) of oil. Using this information, estimate the area that might be affected by an oil spill involving the following:

    a. A tanker truck holding 8,000 gallons (32,000 liters),

    b. A ship holding 300,000 gallons (1.2 million liters), or

    c. A supertanker holding 83,000,000 gallons (332 million liters).

    Discuss and compare estimates with other groups. Graph estimates and compute average figures.

2. Put enough oil in a small container to submerge three hard-boiled eggs. Add the eggs. Put the eggs under a good light, and watch closely. Remove one egg after 5 minutes and examine it—before, during, and after peeling off the shell. Try to remove the excess oil from the outside before attempting to peel the egg. Remove the second egg after 15 minutes and the third egg after 30 minutes, repeating the procedure, examining each carefully. Discuss the observations. What effect could oil have on the eggs of birds nesting near the water?

3. Have the students examine a feather with a hand lens and sketch their observations. Next, have the students dip the feather in water for 1 or 2 minutes, examine it again with a hand lens, sketch their observations, and compare them to the original observations. Place the feather in oil for 1 or 2 minutes; then examine it with a hand lens, sketch it, and compare the sketch with other sketches. Clean the feather in detergent, rinse it in water, and dry it. Examine it with a hand lens, sketch it, and compare the drawing with previous sketches. Discuss any changes in the feather after exposure to oil and then to detergents. What effect could these changes have on normal bird activity?

4. Discuss other possible effects on birds from an oil spill. Discuss possible effects on other wildlife species, on humans, and on the environment. What trade-offs are involved? Do we have to choose between oil and birds, as well as other wildlife? What are some alternatives? What are other examples of human-caused pollutants that can have negative

consequences for wildlife, people, and the environment? What is being done or can be done about these as well? OPTIONAL: Ask each student to write a report summarizing the findings of the experiment and providing recommendations on what can be done to reduce pollution caused by humans.

Extensions

1. A variety of oils—cooking oil, motor oil, crude oil—can be used to produce effects similar to the original experiment. Food coloring can be added to clear oils to observe their effects. Before to using motor oil, crude oil, or similar products, devise a plan for properly disposing of the waste materials including the oil, polluted water, and items used to clean the feathers. More oil is improperly placed in the environment by end users than commercial transporters. Take this opportunity to learn how to properly dispose of hazardous wastes in your own community. Research local laws pertaining to oil disposal.

2. Contact the local city or state environmental department to determine what forms of pollution cause problems in your area. A local wildlife rehabilitator or wildlife pathologist can provide insight into common pollution problems for nearby wildlife. These professionals may also be able to give information about the impact of improperly disposed of toxins on local wildlife populations.

Aquatic Extension

What are the consequences of oil spills for other species of aquatic wildlife (e.g., fish, marine mammals)?

Evaluation

1. How could an oil spill affect the success of birds nesting near the water?

2. Describe some possible effects of oil on a feather.

3. Explain why the effects of oil are different from those of water.

4. Describe some possible negative effects of three other human-caused pollutants on people, wildlife, and the environment.

Additional Resources

www.fhsu.edu/kga/lp/5/everhart.html

Migration Barriers

Objectives

Students will (1) define migration as it relates to wildlife; (2) describe possible impacts on wildlife migration patterns as a result of human activities; and (3) give an example of the importance of land-use planning as it affects people, wildlife, and the environment.

Method

Students draw murals showing deer migration routes and the consequences of developing a highway through an area.

Materials

Drawing materials, large butcher or poster paper, background information about deer or other animals that migrate seasonally, information about the animals' habitat needs (Check with local wildlife specialists for assistance.)

Age: Grades 5–8

Subject Areas: Social Studies, Science, Environmental Education

Duration: one or two 30- to 45-minute sessions

Group Size: any, small groups for mural making

Setting: indoors

Conceptual Framework Topic Reference: HIIIB2, HIIIC, HIIIC1, HIIIC2, HIIIC3, HIIIC4

Key Terms: migration, land-use planning, consequences

Appendices: Using Local Resources

Background

The purpose of this activity is for students to recognize that human actions can have an effect on wildlife. In this case, road construction through a deer migration route is used as an example.

Procedure

1. Divide the group into small teams, providing each team with drawing materials and a large piece of butcher or poster paper. Ask each team to draw a mural of a deer habitat (or habitat of another migrating land animal in your area) that includes a variety of environments from mountains to valleys. The deer herd in this habitat lives in the mountains in the summer and moves or migrates to the valleys in the winter. Ask the students to put in appropriate vegetation, water sources, and pictures of other animals in addition to the deer that might live in this environment. The students may choose the time of the year to be represented in their murals. Ask them to put their herd of deer in the area in which they think the deer would most likely be living at that time of year. Also ask them to draw a set of arrows to show the path they think the deer would likely take each year during the time they move from one feeding area to another (e.g., from the mountains to the valleys as winter nears and from the valleys to the mountains in the summer).

2. Once the murals are complete, either ask the students to describe what they have included in their murals, pointing out the deer migration pattern—or simply move on to the next part of this activity. The next step is to tell the students that a major highway has been

proposed for the area they have drawn. The highway is to be built somewhere between the mountains and the valleys that the deer travel to and from in their annual migration. An environmental impact statement indicates it is possible to build the highway in ways that can minimize the negative consequences for wildlife and other elements of the natural environment. The environmental impact statement is being contested in court; therefore, it is not clear whether the highway actually will be built. Introduce the concept of land-use planning to the students.

Students in each group attempt to plan for the land use in their area, which is represented by their mural. Ask students in each group to discuss how they could draw a highway on their mural in a way that they think would have the least possible negative consequences for wildlife and the environment. They could consider impact to the environment during actual road construction, ways to minimize runoff and erosion, replanting any areas where vegetation is destroyed in the building, and replanting with native plants. Ask them to pay particular attention to the herd of deer and its migration pattern, trying to figure out a way for the deer to move from their summer to their winter ranges and back again. Sometimes this can be done by building underpasses or overpasses for the deer to use so that they don't actually have to try to cross the highway. Sometimes the highway can be built in such a way that the migration route is avoided entirely. Teams that achieve a consensus—making a land-use planning decision—can draw the highway on their murals.

3. Ask each group to report. What land-use decisions did they make? With what consequences to the deer? To other wildlife? Vegetation? Soil? People? Ask students to identify solutions they think would be acceptable or those that would be unacceptable and give their reasons. What about transportation convenience for people? Other possible questions include the following: What are the costs to the builder of the highway? Who pays the builder? Is it actually taxpayer dollars? What are some of the factors to be considered in land-use decisions?

Extensions and Variations

1. Have the students choose an actual situation with similar concepts.

2. Use a topographical map rather than a mural. Provide each student with copies of the map. Compare similarities and differences in solutions, all working from the same visual reference (the maps).

3. Represent the area in three dimensions using clay, papier maché, or even mud.

Aquatic Extension

Many animals migrate and depend on available water and aquatic habitats. For two examples, see the Project WILD Aquatic activities "Hooks and Ladders" and "Migration Headache."

Evaluation

1. Define animal migration.

2. Identify three animals that migrate. For each, describe a human activity that might interfere with migration.

3. Offer one or more suggestions for decreasing the negative impacts of human land use on animal migrations. Explain the reasoning behind your suggestions.

Additional Resources

www.eco-action.org/dt/roads.html

Shrinking Habitat

Objectives

Students will (1) describe some effects of human development of land areas on plants and animals living or previously living in the area, (2) evaluate the importance of suitable habitat for wildlife, and (3) recognize that loss of habitat is generally considered to be the most critical problem facing wildlife today.

Method

Students simulate a process of land development.

Materials

Green and blue construction paper; classroom desks, tables, or chairs; five or six large bed sheets or blankets for a student group of about 25 (If this activity is conducted outdoors, hula hoops or string can be substituted for desks, tables, or chairs to designate habitat areas.)

Age: Grades 5–8

Subject Areas: Social Studies, Science, Environmental Education, Expressive Arts

Duration: one 45-minute session or longer

Group Size: minimum of six students with one developer, one carnivore, three herbivores, and one tree

Setting: indoors or outdoors, large area with room for people and props

Conceptual Framework Topic Reference: HIIA, HIIB2, HIIIB1

Key Terms: habitat, food chain, development, herbivores, carnivores, vegetation, consequences

Appendices: Simulations, Ecosystem

Background

All around us and all over the planet, wildlife habitat is being lost. Whenever an area of land is paved for a shopping center, divided and excavated for homes for people, or plowed to grow a crop, small animals lose their homes and frequently their sources of food and water. As these small animals disappear, so too do the larger animals that previously depended on the smaller animals in the food chain as a source of food. Animals that cannot tolerate human intervention for other reasons may also disappear (e.g., see the Project WILD activity "Too Close for Comfort"). Students can observe the changes in wildlife habitat near their homes, near schools, or in their region of the country either directly or by studying maps or historical photographs.

Development of land areas is happening in large ecosystems and in small ones all over the Earth. For example, many wetlands on the planet have been filled in and drained to make land for farms, homes, and businesses. In the coastal states of the United States alone, more than half (roughly 55 million acres) of wetlands have been destroyed, and most of the prairie potholes in the upper midwest and west have been lost. When those wetlands are gone, many kinds of water birds, reptiles, amphibians, crustaceans, and other life forms—including a wide variety of vegetation—are lost. Sometimes the animal forms can move on; most often they cannot. Nationally, more than half of the animal and one-third of the plant species listed under the Endangered Species Act depend on wetlands.

Tropical forests, whether evergreen rainforests or deciduous mountain forests, are being damaged by ever-expanding human populations. Unfortunately, this is happening before scientists have thoroughly studied those forests' contributions to Earth's natural processes. Scientists estimate that large tropical forests are home to numbers of plant and animal species that have not even been identified as yet. Such forests are tremendously important sources of Earth's biological diversity. It is estimated that together, the remaining tropical forests contain at least half of the world's biodiversity (estimated 3.5 to 30 million species of plants and animals), though they cover less than 7 percent of the land's surface.

The purpose of this activity is for students to simulate some of the potential impacts of land development on wildlife and its habitat, to recognize that this process is one that is taking place in areas all over the planet, and to understand that loss of habitat is generally considered to be the most critical problem facing wildlife today.

Procedure

1. Review with the students the elements necessary for a habitat (food, water, shelter, and space arranged suitably for the particular animal). After some discussion to make sure that the elements of habitat are clear, tell the students that in this activity they will be simulating wildlife in its habitat.

2. Divide the group into four teams: herbivores, carnivores, vegetation (e.g., trees, shrubs, grasses, etc.), and people who will be land developers. If students are not familiar with the terms "herbivore" and "carnivore," provide them with working definitions of those terms (herbivore: a plant-eating animal; carnivore: a meat-eating animal; and, although not needed for this activity, omnivore: an animal that eats both plants and animals). Plan for three times as many herbivores as carnivores, with a small number of developers in proportion to the other two groups. The numbers (amount) of vegetation may vary. For example, two developers, three carnivores, nine herbivores, and six trees or bushes (vegetation).

3. Establish a large area—either in the classroom with tables, chairs, and desks moved to the sides of the room, or outside—that can be used to simulate the wildlife habitat area before development. The "land developers" are to stay on the sidelines at this time, simply observing the undeveloped land and its wildlife inhabitants—or to meet on their own nearby, as they make plans for development.

4. Provide each "herbivore" with
   - two desks or chairs (or string or hula hoops) to use as "shelter,"
   - three pieces of green construction paper to represent food,
   - one piece of blue construction paper to represent water, and
   - some of the vegetation portrayed by students.

   Provide each "carnivore" with
   - one desk or chair (or string or hula hoop) to use as a "lair,"
   - space equivalent to that used by three herbivores,
   - three herbivores as a potential food source;
   - one piece of blue construction paper to represent water, and
   - some of the vegetation portrayed by students.

5. Ask the "herbivores" to arrange the food, water, and shelter—including the students who are "vegetation"—in a space to represent their habitat. Once the herbivores have arranged their habitat, ask the "carnivores" to move into the area to establish their lairs and water sources, keeping an eye on the herbivores as possible food sources. For

continued

added interest, suggest that the students identify what particular kind of animal they are and role-play its characteristics. (This phase takes about 10 minutes, with the developers planning while the herbivores and carnivores arrange their habitats.)

6. Once all the animals are established in their habitats, it is time for the developers to enter the picture. These developers have been given the opportunity to create a housing and shopping area. (They may use 3 to 7 minutes to construct their development, explaining their actions as they take them.) They are restricted in how much space they can use. They may use the space equivalent to that used by three herbivores. The developers may use the sheets and blankets to build their development. They may remove trees (represented by students) without physically hurting the students, shelter (represented by desks), food, and water.

7. Once they have constructed their development, engage all students in a discussion of what happened. What action took place? With what consequences? Would or did any animals die? From what causes? Could the developers have done anything differently to change the consequences? Could they have developed several scattered small areas instead of one large area, or vice versa, with what effects? Would it have reduced negative consequences for wildlife if they put the development in a different area of the habitat?

NOTE: See the Project WILD activity "Changing the Land" for information about habitat fragmentation.

8. Rather than negative consequences, were there positive consequences? If so, what were they? How were they achieved? Ask the students to consider and discuss what seemed realistic about the activity and what did not. For example, sometimes development can take place that enhances the area for some kinds of wildlife. Often, however, it will not be the same kinds of wildlife that were in the area before development. Planners and developers can sometimes add to the vegetation in an area, creating additional shelter and food for some kinds of wildlife and can make water sources available under some conditions, if there is insufficient water in the area.

9. Ask the students to summarize some of the possible effects on wildlife from human activities such as the development of land areas. Are there places in your community where wildlife habitat has been lost to human development? Are there places where wildlife habitat has been enhanced by human activity? What choices, if any, are there to the development of previously undeveloped areas? What trade-offs are involved, for example, in developing vacant areas within communities rather than undeveloped areas outside of communities? If development does take place, what kinds of actions can people take to minimize the negative consequences for wildlife, vegetation, and other elements of the environment? What about possible economic, social, ecological costs, or aesthetic costs and so on? Discuss loss of habitat as something that is affecting wildlife all over the planet. Ask the students to summarize the importance of suitable habitat for wildlife. Discuss the students' concerns and recommendations.

Extensions

1. Conduct this activity twice, with the students trading roles the second time. When the former wildlife become land developers, they could see if they could produce a development plan that could benefit the area for people and wildlife in some ways. The activity can also be conducted to show differences between developing the entire area, with a likely loss of much wildlife in the area, to developing only part of the area, with some wildlife likely to adapt and survive.

2. Ask students to complete the following sentence and discuss their response: "If I were going to build a house for my family in a previously undeveloped area, I would...."

Aquatic Extensions

1. Generate a list of possible human activities that can reduce or eliminate aquatic habitats (e.g., draining wetlands; building construction on shorelines; diverting waters for agricultural, domestic, or business purposes). For every example given, identify possible reasons both for and against taking such action.

2. Look at old and new maps of your area or state. Are there any areas where there used to be wetlands, forests, or prairies that are no longer there? If yes, what happened to those areas?

Evaluation

1. Identify and describe three animals or plants that used to live your area but no longer do.

2. Describe the changes that seem most responsible for eliminating each of these plants or animals.

3. Suggest and evaluate the advantages and disadvantages, if any, of possible actions that could have been taken to prevent the elimination of such plants or animals from the area.

4. Identify one species of wildlife that would benefit by living in an area where: (1) the trees have been harvested and grass has been planted, (2) a creek has been dammed to flood a valley, (3) a housing development with large lawns and many shrubs has been built, and (4) a city has been built on a lakeshore with crowded skyscrapers.

5. Identify one species of wildlife that would decline by living in an area where: (1) the trees have been harvested and grass has been planted, (2) a creek has been dammed to flood a valley, (3) a housing development with large lawns and many shrubs has been built, and (4) a city has been built on a lakeshore with crowded skyscrapers.

Smokey Bear Said What?

Objectives

Students will (1) identify positive and negative consequences of forest and grassland fires, and (2) describe some of the changes fire can make in ecosystems.

Method

Students brainstorm positive and negative effects of forest and grassland fires, conduct research, and create murals showing changes caused by fires in forest and grassland ecosystems.

Materials

Art supplies, butcher paper or other paper for mural display

Background

NOTE: See the Project WILD activity "Fire Ecologies" for a similar activity for older students.

Grade Level: 5–8

Subject Area: Environmental Education, Science, Social Studies

Duration: one 45-minute class session

Group Size: two groups, from 2 to 15 students each

Setting: indoors

Conceptual Framework Topic Reference: HIIIA1, HIIIA2

Key Terms: prescribed burn, management

Appendices: Using Local Resources

Open spaces are always changing, sometimes subtly and sometimes dramatically. Fire is one of the important natural agents of change. Fire has helped shape North America's open spaces for thousands of years and has been essential for the survival of many plants and animals. (Source: U.S. Forest Service, 2000)

At one time, all fires were suppressed or vigorously fought, but today many fires are allowed to burn as part of a natural cycle within forest and grassland ecosystems. Research has shown that the lack of periodic fire in many wild areas increases risks to society and the environment. In remote areas, some agencies now monitor lightning-ignited wildfires and allow them to burn as long as they stay within acceptable limits of fire behavior and location. However, wildfires near populated areas still are fought aggressively. In fact, there has been a movement to "prescribe" fires under some conditions and in some places in an effort to replicate natural cycles that contribute to maintaining healthy ecosystems. Such "prescribed burns" are planned and tended by qualified resource managers.

Prescribed burns frequently are designed to reduce the fuel load in a given area. Reducing the fuel load in a forested area, for example, can prevent fires from becoming so hot that they eliminate virtually all life forms and even scorch the soil. That is, fires every 5 to 10 years in some forest types can clear the heavy understory without harming the larger trees in the forest. Accumulation of brush and understory can cause intensely hot and destructive fires. Intense and uncontrolled wildfire risks damage to soil, watersheds, and air quality.

Objectives for use of fire as a management tool are variable. Objectives may include restoring fire's role in the natural cycle within a particular ecosystem, eradicating some plant species, and promoting the stimulation of plant species that are preferred food by some wildlife. In some areas, fire is the most cost-effective tool to manage habitats.

Prescribed burns are planned and initiated by qualified professionals who are trained in using fire for resource management objectives. Prescribed fires are used only after burn plans are approved. Those plans must specify what the objectives are for the fire, location, size, and type; how the fire will be started and controlled; and how the smoke from the fire will be managed. Fire plans set limits for weather parameters that control how hot a fire burns and in which direction smoke dissipates. Fires outside of those limits will not be started.

Students may ask why, if some fires are helpful, the national symbol of fire fighting agencies, Smokey Bear, says, "Only you can prevent forest fires."

This message is aimed at humans causing fires by error and accidents, such as carelessness in camping situations. The message also warns us about the terrible destructiveness of arson or fires set intentionally by people. Accidental and arson fires are often started near developed areas and occur during times of severe drought or high winds. This kind of wildfire can be terribly destructive.

Fires can have negative as well as positive effects. If a fire is too large, too fast, and too hot, wildlife cannot easily move to safety. Individual animals may die or be displaced from their habitats. Short-term and long-term loss of vegetation can have a variety of effects, including loss of food and shelter for wildlife and increased silting and sedimentation in the waters.

Some positive effects and benefits of fire are that it

- maintains and enhances fire-dependent habitats such as prairies, savannas, chaparral, jack pine forests, southern pine forests, and boreal forests;
- provides habitats for species that depend primarily on fire-driven ecosystems such as Kirkland's warbler;
- increases soil productivity by releasing and recycling nutrients in litter and undergrowth;
- prepares soil for germination of some seeds;
- activates heat-dependent seed varieties, such as lodgepole pines, jack pine, and black spruce;
- contributes to "edge effect," providing a greater variety of food and shelter sources for some species of wildlife; and
- opens up habitat, generating new growth and a diversity and abundance of food plants.

The major purpose of this activity is for students to become familiar with positive and negative effects of fire on wildlife species and their habitat.

Procedure

1. Begin this activity with a discussion about forest and grassland fires. Students' reactions may be negative at first. Point out that while the effects of fire may be detrimental to some wildlife species, the fire may benefit other species.

2. Brainstorm possible positive and negative effects of forest and grassland fires. Keep the list of brainstormed ideas posted for the students' reference.

3. Divide the class into two groups—one to find out more about forest fires and one to find out more about grassland fires. Using the brainstormed list as a beginning point, students in each group can volunteer to find out more about some of the topics. A few students might do this research, or all of the students may be involved. Possible topics for further investigation include the following:

continued

- terminology related to fires, such as "prescribed burn," "ground fire," "crown fire," and "wildfire";
- positive and negative effects of forest and grassland fires in various vegetation types under various weather conditions;
- U.S. Forest Service, National Park Service, Bureau of Land Management, Bureau of Indian Affairs, local state forester's office, and other state and federal agency policies toward forest and grassland fires;
- fire ecology information available from the agencies and organizations listed above;
- information about the number of different kinds of fires typical in specified areas during a year, such as those caused by human activity (e.g., fireworks, campfires, smoking, arson, and railroad-related ignitions), prescribed burns, and natural activity such as lightning;
- examples of historical and present-day cultural groups that use fire to improve wildlife habitat; and
- plant species that depend on fire for regeneration.

4. Once the necessary research has been done, divide the class into groups to make two murals: one of a forested area and one of grasslands. Each mural should portray the area before, during, and after a fire. Analyze and discuss positive and negative consequences of forest and grassland fires. Compare similarities and differences in the two areas.

Variation

Create the murals and then have the students research to find out if their murals are accurate. Correct and make additions to the murals after the research is completed.

Extensions

1. Contact a forester, wildlife biologist, or other resource person to come to talk with the students about different circumstances under which fire can be helpful and harmful to wildlife—possibly bringing slides or a film on the subject.
2. Take a field trip to study a forested or grassland area that has been burned.

Aquatic Extensions

If not already included, investigate the potential impacts on watersheds from forest and grassland fires.

Evaluation

1. Describe two differences between grassland that is burned frequently and grassland that is never burned.
2. Describe two differences between forested land that is burned frequently and forested land that is never burned.
3. Name 10 species of plants and animals that are helped by fire under some conditions and 10 species that usually do better when fire is absent in forest or grasslands.
4. Summarize conditions in which fire can and cannot be beneficial to some wildlife species.

Additional Resources

www.blm.gov/education/fire_and_weeds.html

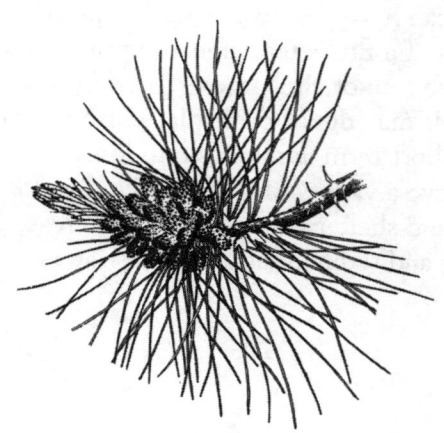

Noisy Neighbors

Objectives

Students will (1) identify noise levels that can adversely affect people, domesticated animals and wildlife; and (2) recommend ways in which people can change some behaviors in order to reduce negative effects from noise for people, domesticated animals, and wildlife.

Method

Students conduct an investigation of noise levels in their community, generate and test hypotheses, and make recommendations.

Materials

Writing materials, OPTIONAL: decibel meter (Many local zoning and code enforcement offices and state and local environmental departments may have decibel meters that can be brought to the class for demonstration.)

Background

People and wildlife are subject to similar environmental stresses. Loud noises, such as those from a motorcycle or snowmobile, a noisy group of people hiking, or a new road or dam construction, can affect both humans and wildlife. People, domesticated animals, and some wild animals living in metropolitan areas frequently learn to live with many loud noises. When animals in their natural habitat hear these and similar noises, they may react by running away, dying from the consequences of stress, or learning to adapt to such noises (as, for example, many animals in national parks have learned to do).

Many students may know that animals have hearing ranges different from humans. They may know from personal experience that dogs and cats can hear things that humans cannot. Loud music is easier for humans to hear than a machine's high-pitched whine, which may reach beyond our normal hearing range. Both sounds are real; although only one of them may be audible to us, both may be audible and disruptive to wildlife.

The major purpose of this activity is for students to recognize the effects that human-made noises can have on wild animals and to consider alternative behaviors that might have less-damaging consequences.

Grade Level: 5–8

Subject Areas: Social Studies, Environmental Education, Science

Duration: two or three 45-minute sessions

Group Size: any

Setting: indoors and outdoors

Conceptual Framework Topic Reference: HIIB

Key Terms: stress, noise, decibel, ordinance, hypothesis, correlation, consequences, responsibility

Appendices: Using Local Resources

---

continued

Procedure

1. Initiate a discussion about noise. What seems loud? What noises hurt your ears? Do any noises frighten or bother you? What is noise? Noise to one person may be music to another. Ask one or two students to research the questions and to report back to the group.

2. Find out about noise ordinances. (Some communities have regulations about allowable noise levels.) Find out about recommended health standards for sound levels. What levels are considered harmful to human ears and with what consequences?

3. With this information about allowable and recommended noise levels, students can do a "sound search" of the community. If possible, get a decibel meter from a community agency to record decibel levels around the school, shopping center, residential area, agricultural area, city park, entrance to national park or forest, and so on. Is there is any correlation between noise levels and the numbers of people, domesticated animals, and wildlife in each area. If there are large numbers of people or animals in an area with high noise levels, are they experiencing negative consequences (e.g., stress)? How are they coping; with what effects? Ask students to predict the impact of noise levels on people, domesticated animals, and wildlife. Consider the sources and consequences of human-made noise on wildlife. Here are a few examples to get you started.

Recreation—backpackers, hunters, woodcutters, motorcycles, dune buggies, snowmobiles, all terrain vehicles.

New Development—heavy construction equipment, automobiles.

Mining—drilling, explosions, construction traffic.

Generate a few hypotheses, and check them through research or by consulting local authorities.

4. Generate a set of recommendations: What is the individual's responsibility for noise control? Society's responsibility? What can students do personally—as individuals, groups, or families—to help increase and maintain an informed awareness and responsible behavior concerning the effects of noise on people, pets, and wildlife?

Evaluation

1. Identify four sources of noise that often can negatively affect wildlife. Describe the possible adverse effects.

2. Describe the process used to formulate and test one hypothesis concerning the effects of noise.

3. Explain three things that people can do to reduce the noise levels caused when they are visiting wildlife habitats.

Flip the Switch for Wildlife

Objectives

Students will (1) trace the route of electrical energy from source to use, (2) describe effects on wildlife and the environment derived from various kinds of energy development and uses, and (3) evaluate the effects on wildlife and the environment as a result of their own energy-use practices.

Method

Students illustrate the route of energy from its sources to human use, including environmental effects along its path, and then invent and try ways to lessen negative effects on wildlife through their personal energy-use practices.

Materials

Writing and drawing materials

> **Grade Level:** 5–8
>
> **Subject Areas:** Science, Social Studies, Environmental Education
>
> **Duration:** one to three 45-minute sessions, depending on students' prior knowledge of energy sources
>
> **Group Size:** any
>
> **Setting:** indoors
>
> **Conceptual Framework Topic Reference:** HIIIA3a, HIIIB, HIIIB5
>
> **Key Terms:** energy, development, generator, technology
>
> **Appendices:** Using Local Resources, Taking Action

Background

Electrical energy comes from a variety of sources. In the United States, a little less than 56 percent of electrical energy is produced from coal, 21 percent from nuclear power, 10 percent from hydroelectric sources, 9 percent from natural gas, and 4 percent from petroleum. Geothermal, wood, waste, solar, and wind account for less than .5 percent of the United States' electrical energy production.

Wildlife may be affected in both positive and negative ways as energy is obtained to fuel power plants. Hydroelectric dams may be built that supply energy and form lakes that are good for some fish, but block runs of other fish and that flood valuable wildlife habitat for land animals, but create more aquatic habitat for others. A power line through a forest may improve the habitat for some species and degrade it for others.

The major purpose of this activity is for students to compare the various sources of electrical energy as well as learn the positive and negative impacts on wildlife from each of these sources, including those they use each day.

Procedure

1. Ask the students, "What effects, if any, do we have on wildlife when we turn on a light switch?" Let them discuss the question and form opinions. As a way of testing their ideas (or hypotheses), assign groups of three or four students to research where their electricity comes from, identifying all steps from the light switch back to the land, and how they think each step along the way might affect wildlife. Also assign groups to research alternative technologies (e.g., solar, geothermal, tidal, wind power).

continued

NOTE: This activity is excellent as an extension to energy source activities students already are doing.

2. Ask the students within each group to draw and label their "power pathway" on a large sheet of paper. For example, coal would travel from the strip mine or tunnel by truck to the processing plant, then by train to the power plant, and finally over the electric power lines to their houses and their light switches. Have the students label points along the way where wildlife could be positively or negatively affected.

3. When the students have completed their power paths, have them show them to the rest of the class. Discuss the following questions with the students.
   - How is wildlife affected when a light switch is turned on? Are the effects positive or negative? Can any of them be reasonably changed?
   - Which type of fuel source has the greatest negative effects on wildlife? Which has the least? Why? Which has the greatest positive effect on wildlife? Why?
   - How could we minimize the negative effects?
   - Why don't we use the source of power with the least impact to a greater degree?
   - Which energy sources cost the least to develop and use? Which provide more jobs? Which seem to have the least negative overall impact on the environment?
   - What trade-offs are involved? Are there any reasonable solutions? If yes, describe some possibilities. With what consequences?
   - How can each of us help wildlife and the environment through our energy habits?

4. Ask each student to think of at least one constructive thing to do for wildlife that involves energy and its use.

Extensions

1. Create a large mural of a natural area complete with wildlife, trees, mountains, rivers, etc., but no human development. After completing the mural, brainstorm a list of things that would happen if a much-needed energy source (e.g., coal, oil, uranium, water) was discovered in that area. Draw pictures of those activities and facilities with one picture for each item listed. When all the pictures are completed, place them in appropriate places on the mural. For example, put the pictures where you think they should go if you were an energy developer. Pin, tack, or tape the pictures onto the paper. Discuss the positive and negative effects the "new development" will have on the environment and wildlife; then create a list of those effects. Now, redevelop the energy source and see if you can come up with ways that the development can have less impact on the environment and still acquire the energy needed at an affordable cost.

2. See if a similar situation exists in your area.

Aquatic Extension

If not already addressed, do the activity again, examining the possible positive and negative consequences for aquatic wildlife and aquatic habitats as a result of energy use practices and sources of energy used.

Evaluation

1. Trace energy from a burning light bulb back to the sun using two different pathways.

2. Describe two ways that wildlife or habitat might be affected by each of the following electric energy developments and uses: hydroelectric dam, nuclear-generating plant, coal-generating plant, oil-generating plant, wind-generating plant, tidal-generating plant, and active or passive solar facility.

To Zone or Not to Zone

Objectives
Students will (1) identify social and ecological considerations regarding human uses of land that are in conflict with each other and with wildlife habitat needs, and (2) describe the importance of land-use planning.

Method
Students portray a meeting of a county commission deciding a land-use issue.

Materials
Copies of Land-Use Dilemma scenario and Personal Data Cards on pages 323 through 325, props optional for role-play, room set up for mock county commission hearing

---

Grade Level: 5–8

Subject Areas: Social Studies, Environmental Education

Duration: two to three 45-minute sessions

Group Size: large group, depends on students assuming roles

Setting: indoors

Conceptual Framework Topic Reference: HIIA, HIIB, HIIIB1, HIIIB3

Key Term: land-use planning

Appendices: Using Local Resources, Simulations, Taking Action

---

Background
This activity uses a role-play strategy for studying the importance of land-use planning. It emphasizes the complexities of decision making where people with different points of view are involved.

Land-use decisions affecting wildlife have become a familiar issue where housing developments are concerned. The following land-use dilemma scenario is an imaginary conflict that corresponds to some real-life dilemmas.

The major purpose of this activity is for students to understand the importance, as well as some of the complexities, of land-use planning and decision making.

Procedure
1. Provide the students with copies of the Land-Use Dilemma on page 323.

2. Ask 15 students to serve as county commissioners, local residents, and business people, with each receiving a card describing his or her situation. The rest of the students will have roles as news reporters, outside experts, concerned citizens, etc. Those students may ask questions of people testifying at the hearing. They can be required to write letters to the editor or one of the commissioners in support of their particular points of view; write news articles about the hearing; or write personal impact stories describing the potential consequences for local workers, residents, schoolchildren, and so on; or pre-

continued

pare technical reports as researchers. Every student should have a role—either as one of the 15 people preparing testimony for the hearing or as active observers who prepare written questions, reports, or news articles.

3. To set the stage for the simulation, have each of the 15 participants read his or her personal data cards. The other students should each select a role; they do not need personal data cards although they may write their own. Students should be given time to prepare their presentations as members of the inquiry, or their questions, letters to the editor, and news stories as public observers. Students should be encouraged to improvise in developing their presentations and questions.

4. On the day (or days) of the hearing, the chairperson of the commission is to run the meeting. It is up to him or her to maintain order. All participants must be recognized by the chairperson before they speak. After all those presenting prepared testimony have spoken and have been questioned, the reporters, researchers, and concerned citizens will be asked to read their statements (articles, reports, letters to the editor, etc.). This is an excellent way to start the final day of the simulation. After all testimony, questions, and statements, the commissioners vote and give the reasons for their decisions.

5. Suggested time line for this activity:
   - Day 1: Read background information and select roles (approximately 30 to 45 minutes).
   - Homework: Prepare presentations.
   - Day 2: Conduct hearing (approximately 30 to 45 minutes).
   - Day 3: Continue hearing, including reading of news items and letters to the editor; vote; discuss results.

6. After the hearing and vote, discuss questions such as the following:
   - What are some things we have learned about land-use decision making?
   - What factors influence land-use decision making and planning?
   - What differences and similarities were there between how decisions were made in this activity and how they happen in our community? Other areas? Other parts of the world?
   - What responsibilities do we as citizens have in helping to make land-use decisions?
   - Why are land-use decision making and land-use planning important for people, wildlife, and the environment?

Extensions and Variations

1. Have the students identify a wildlife issue in their local area, gather data, and develop their own simulation.

2. Alter the role descriptions and repeat the simulation.

3. Use copies of a topographical map as common references for everyone.

4. Bring in real expert witnesses (e.g., local people who can add their perspectives and expertise). If you do, make an effort to get a balanced range of points of view rather than hearing from only one perspective on the issues involved.

5. Adapt this activity to a debate format.

6. Attend a local zoning board meeting.

Evaluation

1. Describe zoning laws. Identify and describe possible effects and values of zoning laws. Consider potential positive and negative effects.

2. How are local zoning laws passed? Write a short report describing how the Project WILD activity "To Zone or Not to Zone" is similar to or different from what really happens.

3. Describe how citizens can have their opinions considered in land-use decision-making processes.

4. Identify an example of how a zoning law might be good for wildlife.

Land-Use Dilemma

Pleasant Valley is a ranching and logging community on the western slope of the Snow Mountains. Silverton—a town of 20,000—is the trade center of the area. Cramer Lumber Company is expanding its operations. This expansion will provide 250 new jobs but housing is very limited. A 200-home subdivision has been proposed for an 80-acre plot of undeveloped land on the south edge of town. This forested area is bordered by Rattlesnake Creek on the west. Rattlesnake Creek provides excellent fishing for rainbow trout. Fifty-three species of birds have been sighted in this area, including some rare species. In the spring and fall, the area is used by migrating waterfowl, and deer feed in the area. Many small watchable species—such as ground squirrels and pocket gophers—inhabit the area. This 80-acre plot is currently zoned for agriculture and forestry and would have to be rezoned for residential by a vote of the county commissioners. The subdivision would be on a central water system but each home would have its own septic system.

continued

Personal Data Cards

Jack or Janet Thompson, Rancher (County Commissioner)

You are the third generation to run the "Rolling T" Cattle Company. You are proud to tell people that your grandfather was one of the first people to settle in this valley. Your spread covers 800 acres, and you have grazing rights to surrounding U.S. Forest Service land. You resent the increase in population of the area, and although you are involved in community affairs, you resent individuals moving into the area who do not share your values. Last winter, snowmobiles cut your fences three times, and in one case your cattle wandered onto the highway and caused a traffic accident.

Jelmer or Bertha Willas, Resident

You are a 68-year-old "old-timer" living on the land proposed for the subdivision. You have lived on Cornwall's land for 45 years, have built a home there with Cornwall's permission, and have raised seven children. You raise bees and chickens out back, and your garden covers one-half acre. You are settled in the middle of the area proposed for the housing development, and there is no question that you will have to be evicted and your house torn down. You have no legal claim to any of the land but have nowhere else to go.

Bob or Betsy Henderson, Farmer (County Commissioner)

You own and operate a large farm near the south edge of town and adjacent to the 80-acre plot in question. You have been interested in the possibility of buying the land to add to your family's agricultural operations. You've a keen interest in the environment, making efforts to use agricultural practices that benefit wildlife and minimize damage to other natural resources. Because you are an adjacent landholder, you may need to disqualify yourself from participation as a Commissioner in this meeting.

Tom or Mary Bennett, President of Chamber of Commerce

This is your 10th year as president of the Chamber of Commerce. You own a grocery store in the middle of town. Your greatest concern is the weak business climate in your community. The Chamber recently hired Smith & Wittigen, a business consulting firm, to evaluate the business potential of Pleasant Valley. Their findings indicate that the business community has overbuilt. Your profits and those of your fellow merchants have been declining steadily. You see this new lumber mill as the salvation of your business. You also have wondered about possible ways to improve the economy through increased tourism.

Oscar or Jan Sparrow, Local Audubon President

You represent more than 300 active Audubon members and are director of the annual bird-count competition. You have a list of 15 rare bird species found in the Rattlesnake Creek area. You are 37 years old and work at the lumber mill.

Len or Linda Olsen, Realtor (County Commissioner)

You started your business in Silverton 5 years ago. Your business is doing well, but you have difficulty relating to the "old-timers" like Thompson. Your real estate company is not developing this property. You have some questions regarding the credibility of the developer but you generally vote in favor of development.

George or Alice Long Wings, Native American Leader

You have an interest in the sanctity of the area in question because it is an ancient ceremonial site for your people.

Personal Data Cards

Harlie or Charlotte Jackson, Hunter

You are a 68-year-old "old-timer" and an avid hunter and angler. You have four children, and hunting always has been an important family activity. You are an influential member of Ducks Unlimited and the 80 acres proposed for development contain one of the prime duck hunting areas close to town.

Wallace or Wilma Cramer, Lumber Mill Owner

You own the nearby lumber mill. Operations have expanded, and you need inexpensive housing for new employees coming to the area. The wood milled is used locally and transported throughout the state. It provides an important source of income to the town.

Martin or Ethel Higgins, Developer

You own the largest development company in the area and can afford to buy the land outright. You will make a substantial profit if the housing that is needed for the lumber mill employees is built. You are successful and fairly competent but you have been criticized more than once for a lack of attention to landscape detail and design.

James Erma "Frosty" White, Snowmobiler

You are 30 years old and have just been elected president of the "Rattlers," the local snowmobile club. You feel that you should defend their interests in the area. The cost of gas is high, and your club doesn't want to have to drive long distances to ride snowmobiles. You would like to open a snowmobile repair shop but you might get a job at the new lumber mill.

Harold or Cornelia Cornwall, Landowner

You are a 63-year-old retired businessperson. You want to sell your land, move to Palm Springs, and live happily ever after under sunny skies. You want cash but your asking price is very reasonable. You own the 80 acres of prime wild land south of town.

Frank or Frances Study, College Professor

You teach at a nearby community college. You are an active member of several animal welfare organizations and are vocal in your opposition to hunting.

Harvey or Gladys Crow, Banker (County Commissioner)

You are a 50-year-old banker, and you are willing to finance new home loans. You are an art collector and former president of the local Chamber of Commerce. You also love bird watching and fishing. You think the whole area south of town has economically valuable recreational potential but are concerned about protecting environmental quality.

David or Wanda Dresser, Merchant (County Commissioner)

You are 46 years old and own a furniture store. You would like to sell furniture to all the new homeowners. You can also see the value of the 80 acres left in a natural and undeveloped condition. You are wondering if there might be another site for the development of this housing area.

Hazardous Links, Possible Solutions

Objectives

Students will (1) give examples of ways in which pesticides enter food chains, (2) describe possible consequences of pesticides entering food chains, and (3) describe how regulations attempt to control pesticide use.

Method

Students become hawks, shrews, and grasshoppers in a physical activity.

Materials

White and colored drinking straws; pipe cleaners; poker chips or multicolored, dry dog food—30 pieces per student, two-thirds white or plain and one-third colored; one bag per grasshopper (approximately 18–20)

Age: Grades 7–8

Subject Areas: Science, Expressive Arts, Environmental Education

Duration: two 30- to 45-minute sessions, with research time in between the two

Group Size: minimum of 10 students

Setting: a large playing area

Conceptual Framework Topic Reference: HIIIB4

Key Terms: pesticide, insecticide, herbicide, food chain, accumulate, toxic, chemicals, trade-offs, organic, inorganic, biomagnification

Appendices: Using Local Resources, Agencies and Organizations, Outdoors, Simulations

---

Background

Pesticides are chemicals—often synthetic, inorganic compounds—developed to control organisms that have been identified as "pests" under some conditions. Herbicides are pesticides that control unwanted plants; insecticides are pesticides that control nuisance insects and so on. Although pesticides are useful to humans when used properly, they frequently end up going where they are not wanted. Many toxic chemicals have a way of persisting in the environment and often become concentrated in unexpected and undesirable places—from food and water supplies to wildlife and sometimes people, too. The process where chemicals accumulate in organisms in increasingly higher concentrations at successive trophic levels is called "biomagnification." Biomagnification results in the storage of such chemicals in organisms in higher concentrations than are normally found in the environment. The results can be far-reaching.

For example, the insecticide dichlorodiphenyltrichloroethane (DDT) was applied to control insects that were damaging crops. In the early 1970s, it was discovered that DDT entered the food chain with damaging results. Fish ate insects that were sprayed by the chemical; hawks, eagles, and pelicans then ate the fish. The poison became concentrated in the birds systems, resulting in side effects such as thin egg shells. The weight of the adult bird would crush the egg in the nesting process. The impact on species, including the bald eagle and the brown pelican, has been well documented.

Laws in the United States have now prohibited the use of DDT. However, DDT use is not prohibited worldwide. Resident and migrating animal populations in the countries that still allow the use of DDT are at particular risk. Even after the application of DDT is stopped, DDT and its by-products can affect the environment for decades.

Concerns over the growing use of pesticides led to the establishment of the Federal Insecticide, Fungicide, and Rodenticide Act (FIFRA) in 1972. FIFRA gives federal government control over pesticide sale, use, and distribution. Under FIFRA, the U.S. Environmental Protection Agency (EPA) gained authority to study pesticide use consequences and also to require pesticide registration by farmers, businesses, and so on. FIFRA later was amended to require pesticide users to take certification exams. EPA must register pesticides used in the United States.

Congress also enacted the Toxic Substances Control Act (TSCA) in 1976 to regulate, test, and screen all chemicals imported or produced in the United States. TSCA requires that any chemical in the market place must be tested for toxic effects before commercial manufacture. TSCA also tracks and reports chemicals that pose health and environmental hazards. Authorization for toxic material cleanup has been placed under TSCA. TSCA supplements the Clean Air Act and the Toxic Release Inventory. Like FIFRA, TSCA is a balancing law, which says that the EPA is to make decisions on any chemical by comparing the risks it poses against the benefits it produces for firms and consumers.

Public pressure continues to force changes in the application and availability of pesticides. For example, there now is growing interest in integrated pest management. This agricultural approach considers the entire farm and garden ecosystem. Integrated pest management can include using a pest's predator as well as other biological controls to reduce crop damage. Integrated pest management can include the selective use of naturally occurring and synthetic pesticides, as well as habitat manipulations. One concern with this approach is the possible introduction of non-native species.

The major purpose of this activity is for students to recognize the possible consequences of accumulation of some pesticides in the environment and to evaluate measures to control pesticide use.

Procedure

1. Discuss the term "food chain" with the students. (Food chain: a sequence or "chain" of living things in a community, that is based on one member of the community eating another, and so forth [e.g., grasshopper eats plants like corn, shrews eat grasshoppers, hawks eat shrews])

2. Divide the group into three teams. In a class of 26 students, there would be 2 "hawks," 6 "shrews", and 18 "grasshoppers." (This activity works best with approximately three times as many shrews as hawks and three times as many grasshoppers as shrews.) OPTIONAL: Have grasshoppers, hawks, and shrews labeled so they can be identified easily. For example, a green cloth flag (tied around the arm) for grasshoppers, red bandannas for "red-tail hawks", and a brown cloth flag (tied around the arm) or caps for shrews.

3. Distribute a small paper bag or other small container to each "grasshopper." The container is to represent the "stomach" of the animal.

4. With the students' eyes closed, or otherwise not watching where the food is placed, spread the white and colored straws (or whatever material used) around in a large open space. Outside on a playing field (if it is not windy) or on a gymnasium floor will work; a classroom will also work if chairs and tables or desks can be moved.

continued

5. Give the students the following instructions: the grasshoppers are the first to go looking for food; the hawks and shrews are to sit quietly on the sidelines watching the grasshoppers. After all, the hawks and shrews are predators and are watching their prey. At a given signal, the grasshoppers are allowed to enter the area to collect as many food tokens as they can, placing the food tokens in their stomachs (the bags or other container). The grasshoppers have to move quickly to gather food. At the end of 30 seconds, the grasshoppers are to stop collecting food tokens.

6. Next, allow the shrews to hunt the grasshoppers. The hawks are still on the sidelines quietly watching the activity. The amount of time available to the shrews to hunt grasshoppers should take into account the size area in which you are working. In a classroom, 15 seconds may be enough time; on a large playing field, 60 seconds may be better. Each shrew should have time to catch one or more grasshoppers. Any grasshopper tagged or caught by the shrew must give its bag or container of food to the shrew and then sit on the sidelines.

7. Next, allow from 15 to 60 seconds (or whatever set time) for the hawks to hunt the shrews. The same rules follow. Any shrews still alive may hunt for grasshoppers. If a hawk catches a shrew, the hawk gets the food bag and the shrew goes to the sidelines. At the end of the designated time period, ask all students to come together in a circle, bringing whatever food bags they have with them.

8. Ask students who have been "consumed" to identify what animal they are and what animal ate them. If they are wearing labels, this will be obvious. Next, ask any animals still alive to empty their food bags out onto the floor or on a piece of paper where they can count the number of food pieces they have. They should count the total number of white food pieces and total number of multicolored food pieces they have in their food sacks. List any grasshoppers and the total number of white and multicolored food pieces each has. List the number of shrews left and the number of white and multicolored pieces each has. Finally list the hawks and the number of white and multicolored food pieces each has.

9. Inform the students that there is something called a "pesticide" in the environment. This pesticide was sprayed onto the crop the grasshoppers were eating in order to prevent a lot of damage by the grasshoppers. If there were substantial crop damage by the grasshoppers, the farmers would have less of their crop to sell, and some people and domestic livestock might have less of that kind of food to eat—or it might cost more to buy the food because a smaller quantity was available. This pesticide accumulates in food chains and can stay in the environment a long time. In this activity, all multicolored food pieces represent the pesticide. All grasshoppers that were not eaten by shrews may now be considered dead if they have any multicolored food pieces in their food supply. Any shrews for which half or more of their food supply was multicolored pieces would also be considered dead from chemical side effects. The one hawk with the highest number of multicolored food pieces will not die. However, it has accumulated so much of the pesticide in its body that the egg shells produced by it and its mate during the next nesting season will be so thin that the eggs will not hatch successfully. The other hawks are not visibly affected at this time.

10. Talk with the students about what they just experienced in the activity. Ask for their observations about how the food chain seems to work and how toxic substances can enter the food chain with a variety of results. Introduce the term "biomagnification," and discuss how it can result in the accumulation of chemicals in species higher in the food chain. The students may be able to give examples beyond those of the grasshopper—shrew—hawk food chain affected by the pesticide in this activity.

11. Divide the class into two, four, or more groups. Ask one or two groups of students to research other chemicals—such as tributyltin (TBT), polychlorinated biphenyls (PCBs), or dieldrin—that have demonstrated the ability to persist and accumulate through food chains. What are the effects of such chemicals on organisms? What limitations have been set on the use of such substances? Have the other groups research legislation such as FIFRA and TSCA to determine how these laws work to control toxic chemicals. Allow all groups to present their findings in class, and then have the students hypothesize the effectiveness of the laws in controlling the various chemicals that were researched.

Extensions

1. Consider and discuss possible reasons for use of such chemicals. What are some of the benefits? What are some of the consequences?

2. Offer and discuss possible alternatives to uses of such chemicals in instances where it seems the negative consequences outweigh the benefits. For example, some farmers are successfully using organic techniques (e.g., sprays of organic, nontoxic substances; crop rotation; companion planting); biological controls (e.g., predatory insects); and genetic approaches (e.g., releasing sterile male insects of the pest species) in efforts to minimize damages to their crops.

3. What research is being developed and tested on the effects of pest control efforts—from effects of possibly toxic chemicals to nontoxic alternatives? What are the benefits? Consequences? Potential?

4. Review news media for relevant local, national, or international examples of such issues.

Aquatic Extensions

1. See the Project WILD activity "What's in the Water?"

2. Have the students describe how pesticides can enter an aquatic food chain. Also, describe how pesticides can enter aquatic environments and can end up in food chains of terrestrial environments (e.g., mosquito larvae, fish, birds). Show how pesticides can enter the food chains in terrestrial environments and can end up in aquatic environments (e.g., grasshoppers, small fish, large fish).

Evaluation

1. Identify examples of how pesticides could enter a food chain.

2. Discuss two possible consequences of pesticides entering the food chain for each of the examples given above.

3. A group of ecologists studied the presence of a toxic chemical in a lake. They found the water had one molecule of the chemical for every 1 billion molecules of water. This concentration is called one part per billion (ppb). The algae had one part per million (ppm) of the toxic chemical. Small animals, called zooplankton, had 10 ppm. Small fish had 100 ppm. Large fish had 1,000 ppm. How do you explain this increase in this toxic chemical to 1,000 ppm for the large fish? Use a drawing to help support your answer. The ecologists found the chemical was a pesticide that had been sprayed on cropland 100 miles away from the lake. How did so much of the chemical get into the lake?

4. Evaluate the effectiveness of at least one law that regulates hazardous chemical usage.

Additional Resources

www.ma.org/classes/oceanography/swong/ddt.html

ww.chem.ox.ac.uk/mom/ddt/ddt.html

www.pmac.net.wildimp.htm

World Travelers

Objectives

The students will (1) identify native and exotic plant and animal species through local investigation, (2) interpret graphs and maps of the concentrations of native and non-native species, and (3) identify the effects of introduced species on ecosystems.

Method

Students conduct field research, develop graphs or pie charts and maps depicting the proportions of exotic species, and create reports on the effects of these species on native populations.

Materials

Writing materials to create a report and a graph or pie chart; field guides; tape measures; string to mark plots; reference materials (Internet, natural resource agency publications, newspaper articles, etc.); copies of the Dominant Species Chart on page 334 for each group

---

Grade Level: 5–8

Subject Areas: Science, Mathematics, Environmental Education

Duration: two to three 45-minute sessions

Group size: any size class divided into groups of three or four students

Setting: outdoors and indoors

Conceptual Framework Topic Reference: ITIIA2, ITIIA2a, ITIIA2b

Key Terms: exotic, introduced, native, dominant species, invasive species

Appendices: none

Background

Definitions

- **non-native:** in conservation biology, a plant or animal that has been brought into a new area, synonymous with "exotic" (Examples from the United States include the house mouse, common carp, Eurasian watermilfoil, Australian pine, feral horse, alewife, and ring-necked pheasant.)
- **introduced:** an organism that is brought into a community
- **native:** a species that naturally occurs in an ecosystem; not introduced by humans
- **dominant species:** plant or animal species that exerts major controlling influences on a community (Dominants generally make up the greatest total biomass [living material] in a community in terms of numbers and/or total weight.)
- **invader:** in conservation biology, a species that spreads into a community where it did not previously exist

A non-native species does not occur naturally in a specific location. While species always have migrated from one place to another, natural land barriers have prevented indiscriminate movement. Over time, human modification has changed those barriers. For example, organisms and seeds can be transported in a ship's ballast water, on clothing, and in cars or on boats as humans move from one place to another.

Zebra mussels were introduced into the Great Lakes in the ballast water from ships. Female zebra mussels are capable of laying over one million eggs each year. Unlike native freshwater mussels, they attach to solid surfaces using tiny thread-like fibers and, as a result, clog the water systems of power plants and water-treatment facilities and cover the shells of native mussels. They also compete with other mussels and larval fish for food.

Sea lampreys, common to the Atlantic Ocean from Florida to Labrador, swim inland into fresh water to spawn. They reached the Great Lakes through human-made canals. Lampreys are parasites of many native fish species, including paddlefish, lake trout, and whitefish. They attach to fish and feed upon them. Although this action usually doesn't kill the fish, it makes them susceptible to disease and illness.

Some plants and animals that were introduced intentionally have also caused problems for native ecosystems. Purple loosestrife was brought to the United States from Europe in the 1800s for use as a landscape plant and to provide nectar for honeybees. It has no natural predators here, reproduces rapidly, and grows quickly on disturbed soil. Purple loosestrife has taken over wetlands, marshes, pastures, and riparian meadows. The result is the degradation of habitats where native plants grow, fish spawn, and wildlife live and breed.

Another example of an introduced non-native species is the gypsy moth. This moth was brought to Massachusetts from France to crossbreed with silkworms. These voracious eaters can be responsible for the defoliation of millions of acres of forests, slowing the growth of trees, making songbirds vulnerable to predators, and increasing the water temperature of local streams.

Why do these invaders have such success? While not all non-native species succeed, those that do are aided by their ability to out-compete native species for resources and by the lack of natural predators and parasites to control them.

The main objectives of this activity are for students to identify native and non-native plant and animal species through field surveys and to examine the positive and negative effects of their presence.

Examples of Six Non-Native Plant Species

Purple loosestrife (*Lythrumrum salicaria*)

Russian olive (*Elaeagnus angustifolia*)

Black locust (*Robinia pseudoacacia L.*)

Tree-of-heaven (*Ailanthus altissima*)

Multiflora rose (*Rosa multiflora*)

White poplar (*Populus alba*)

The above species are described at **www.nps.gov/plants/alien/common.htm**. A picture of each plant is included.

Examples of Six Non-Native Animal Species

House sparrow (*Passer domesticus*)

Brown tree snake (*Boiga irregularis*)

Mediterranean fruit fly (*Ceratitis capitata*)

European starling (*Sturmus vulgaris*)

Rusty crawfish (*Oronectos rusticus*)

Gypsy moth (*Lymantria dispar*)

The above species are described at the following Web sites: **http//invasives.fws.gov/Index5A.html** and **www.nbii.gov**. A picture of each animal is included.

continued

Procedure

Before the Activity

1. Identify six non-native species found in your community. Students will target or focus on these species for this activity. Information on local species may be obtained from natural resource agencies, field guides, Internet sites, or library references. Collect information and pictures of these species for the class.

2. Divide the class in groups of three or four students. Explain to the students that they will be identifying plants on the school grounds or at a local city park. Make sure they understand the meaning of the words "native," "non-native," and "introduced." Demonstrate the different terms used to identify trees and plants, such as leaf shapes, leaf arrangements, flowers, buds, and bark. Describe the six local target non-native species (Step 1). Show additional examples of different non-native and native plant species in your area.

3. Explain that each group will be working in a designated plot so that each group is not identifying the same organisms. A 10-foot by 10-foot plot is recommended; however, the size of the plot can vary depending on the space available. Each group's plot will border another group's plot so the result is one large inventoried plot.

4. Make copies of the Dominant Species Chart on page 334. Review the categories with the students before the field trip: SPECIES (common and scientific name); NUMBER FOUND (the number of individuals found); CHARACTERISTICS (students should name at least three characteristics they used to identify the plant); REMARKS (where the plants were found, do they seem healthy, apparent age, or anything unusual about the population); and NATIVE/NON-NATIVE.

In the Field

1. Take the students to a school ground or a local city park. Have each group measure its plot and mark the boundaries with string.

2. With the aid of field guides, all groups then identify the four dominant species in the plot. In this situation, dominance is based upon which species is the most numerous. Make sure the students also record any of the target non-native species found. It also will be helpful to include any large tree (a diameter of 3 inches or more at breast height) within the section even if it is not one of the four dominant species. In addition, make sure students do not assume that just because a plant is not one of the target non-native species that it is native. Many landscape plants, including turf grasses, are not native. If the students encounter other dominant non-natives in their plot, they should refer to their field guides. Do not remove any leaves or twigs from the specimen.

3. If there are too many individuals of one species to count, show the students how to estimate the number by counting the individuals in a 1 square-foot subplot and then extrapolating for the total area. A section at the bottom of the Dominant Species Chart is provided to compute the percentage of the identified individuals that were native and non-native.

4. While students are identifying the specimens in their plots, have them diagram the major features of their sites and include the locations and names of plants they found. Also have them include any features that could affect the health or makeup of the site.

Analyzing the Data in the Classroom

1. Students may analyze the data from each group or from the class as a whole by developing pie charts and vegetative maps.

Pie charts: Each group calculates the percentage of the non-native species and the percentage that were native. Combine the data from all groups to develop a classroom pie chart.

Vegetative maps: Groups combine their plot diagrams showing the locations and identities of plants. Group members will need to agree on what symbol represents each species.

2. Have students conduct research on the non-natives found. Ask them to write short reports explaining how the non-natives arrived here, what positive and negative impacts they have had on the environment and wildlife, and what management techniques are or have been used to control their populations.

3. Ask the students to share the findings from their research with the class. Compare the role of wildlife managers and citizens. How do citizens contribute to the dispersal of non-native species? What can citizens do to retard dispersal? Ask the students to reflect on the importance of habitat evaluation in managing exotic species.

Extensions

1. Follow the same procedure but observe and identify insects instead.

2. Establish some long-term control plots for the activity. Establish two plots, each 10 feet by 10 feet. Leave one plot as the control, and let it develop without disturbances. For the second plot, try a management technique such as hand removal of a non-native species. This long-term project demonstrates how ecosystems change over years. Have classes observe the plots over several years and record, draw, or photograph the changes.

3. Take a field trip to a wetland or marsh to do the observations and identifications. Repeat the trip annually. Keep a record of the charts and maps done each year so that students can see how the presence of non-natives alter the ecosystem and so that students can become a valuable part of recording natural history.

4. Make this activity aquatic by researching some of the local non-native species affecting waterways and by having the students keep an inventory of what they find. Use the same methods of recording and evaluating the data. To identify some species, students may need to collect samples. It may be helpful to ask a local naturalist or biologist to speak to your class concerning safety issues and different ways of collecting the data.

5. Increase public awareness by creating a brochure, web site, or newspaper article documenting the class findings.

6. Have students research and develop a native species garden for an outdoor classroom. The students also could focus on native plant species that attract native animal species that may be declining in population.

Evaluation

1. What impact do non-native species have on their native counterparts?

2. What methods are there for controlling populations of non-native plant and animal species?

3. What are the pros and cons of having non-native plants and animals?

4. How can you help prevent the spread of non-native species?

5. Do non-native species affect humans? How?

6. Describe methods used to identify plants.

Additional Resources

plants.usda.gov/plants/cgi_bin/topics.cgi

www.seagrant.umn.edu

continued

Sustaining Fish and Wildlife Resources

World Travelers

Dominant Species Chart

TEAM _____

PLOT _____

Species	Number Found	Characteristics	Remarks	Native/ Non-Native

Total Number of Non-Natives _____ / Total Number of Species Found = % Non-Natives _____

Total Number of Natives _____ / Total Number of Species Found = % Natives _____

Adapted with permission from "Charting Exotics," by Jen Richards, Kelly Kearns, and Al Stenstrup. Wisconsin Department of Natural Resources.

Rare Bird Eggs for Sale

Objectives
Students will (1) identify reasons for and consequences of collecting wildlife and wildlife products, and (2) suggest and evaluate alternatives to collection to satisfy collection needs.

Method
Students participate in a debate.

Materials
Reference materials

Background
People seem to collect everything from rocks to stamps. Sometimes people collect wild and living creatures, both plants and animals. In some instances, those items are used for educational and research purposes. In other cases, they are simply mementos of travel and memorable events. In other cases, they are acquired for their decorative and non-native values. In Victorian times, many homes were decorated with collections of stuffed birds, mounted butterflies, bird eggs, and bird nests.

As people's attitudes regarding wildlife shift, so do their laws. In 1916, the Migratory Bird Treaty was signed between the United States and Great Britain (acting for Canada). Among other things, the treaty prohibited collecting the bird eggs and nests of migratory birds. Over time, similar treaties have been signed with other countries.

Whenever an object—living or not—is moved or removed from its natural environment, there is an effect on that environment, if not on the object or organism. Some of those effects are more obvious than others. Moving a rock under which wildlife lives may not seem as radical a move as taking eggs from a phoebe's nest, collecting dragonfly naiads from a pond, or capturing and mounting hundreds of species of butterflies.

Managers of protected wilderness and wildlife areas often admonish visitors to "take only pictures and leave only footprints." Unfortunately, many people feel that this applies only to protected areas. Not necessarily so. For example, the effects can be substantial on species and the environment when 30 student collectors pick their way through an area in search of things to take back to school. Collecting bird nests, as one example, can have several impacts—particularly in cases where the birds return to use the same nests year after year.

Grade Level: 5–8

Subject Areas: Environmental Education, Social Studies, Language Arts

Duration: minimum of two to three 45-minute sessions, depending upon extent of research and time for research

Group Size: any, working in two teams to prepare for and present debate

Setting: indoors

Conceptual Framework Topic Reference: ITIB3

Key Terms: collector

Appendices: Using Local Resources, Field Ethics, Animals in the Classroom, Agencies and Organizations

---

continued

The major purpose of this activity is for students to examine the reasons for and consequences of people's collecting tendencies, as well as to consider alternatives.

Procedure

OPTIONAL: Use this activity as an extension to a visit to a local natural history museum with taxonomic collections and models.

1. Ask students to brainstorm all of the kinds of collections they have seen or heard of that involve living or dead organisms, as well as any artifacts or rare objects made of living or once-living organisms. Examples could include butterflies, seashells, coral, bird eggs, ivory artifacts, pine cones, wild animals in zoos, and animals in research laboratories.

2. What are all the possible reasons for collecting? (Categorize the examples of collections according to the purposes they might serve. Some examples may fit into more than one category.) The idea is to think of a range of possible purposes—such as education, research, decoration, profit (as in selling the collectibles), memories, pets, or status.

3. Ask the students to divide into two working groups: one to present the reasons that collecting of such things should be allowed and one to present the reasons that collecting of such things should not be allowed. After dividing within each team to research aspects of the topic, each team should organize its information for presentation in a debate format.

   Each team can have a principal spokesperson or captain who makes opening, transition, and summary statements. The team captain can call on members of the team to provide specific information about pertinent topics as they arise during the debate. For example, a student on the "Reasons for Collecting" team might be an expert on the need for protecting genetic diversity by maintaining collections of wild animals in preserves and zoos. A student on the other team could be prepared to speak about the limitations of zoos and preserves that might outweigh the benefits. Both teams should consider consequences and alternatives, as well as include information about laws that already govern collecting and areas where violations are serious problems. NOTE: The U.S. Fish and Wildlife Service (USFWS) is the agency in the United States that has legal responsibility for transportation of species among states and among the United States and other nations, as well as preventing illegal import and export of wildlife and products. USFWS can be contacted at U.S. Fish and Wildlife Service, Interior Building, 1849 C Street NW, Room 3447, Washington, DC 20240; (202) 208-5634; or **www.fws.gov**. Also contact the regional USFWS office or state authorities for local regulations. The most local option provides for a greater chance of a timely response.

4. Following the debate, ask the students to discuss their feelings about the subject as they use the information and experience they now have. Was it difficult to debate "for" or "against," given their personal attitudes? Did students find their attitudes changing? If so, how? Ask the students to look again at their earlier list of possible purposes for collecting, adding any other purposes they may have identified as a result of their research. Discuss and evaluate whether they think each purpose is appropriate or inappropriate. If appropriate, identify under what circumstances.

   NOTE: Consensus is not necessary, except in areas where law prohibits collecting.

5. Finally, ask the students if they can come up with a list of alternatives for people who might want to "collect" things that seem to the students to be inappropriate. For example, the butterfly collector might try photography or the bird nest collector might try model-building of nests using raw materials just as birds do.

Extensions and Variations

1. If combining this activity with a trip to a local museum of natural history, do Steps 1 and 2 as part of pre-trip preparation. Next, go to the museum and do Steps 3, 4, and 5 after the trip.

2. After Step 2, ask students to copy the list they generated—and to work those items they feel they could accept as reasons to collect. Each student should keep his or her list until later. After the debate (in Step 4, above), ask the students to look at their lists reflecting the points of view they held before the debate. Are some purposes for collecting no longer acceptable that seemed so before, and vice versa?

3. Throughout time, native people have collected and used natural resources for ceremonial, religious, and cultural purposes. Should laws and guidelines for collecting living or dead organisms be different for native people? If yes, why? If no, why not?

Aquatic Extension

See the Project WILD Aquatic activity "Turtle Hurdles."

Evaluation

1. List three reasons why people collect wildlife and wildlife products. Identify and describe one situation in which you think that collection is inappropriate. Suggest and describe at least two alternatives a person might substitute.

2. Describe one way that collecting might contribute to the extinction of animal species. Describe one way that collecting might prevent a species from becoming extinct.

Pro and Con: Consumptive and Nonconsumptive Uses of Wildlife

Objectives

Students will (1) identify examples of consumptive and nonconsumptive uses of wildlife, (2) explain multiple points of view related to consumptive and nonconsumptive uses of wildlife, and (3) evaluate their personal views about consumptive and nonconsumptive uses of wildlife.

Method

Students research and debate the topic.

Materials

Research and writing materials

Grade Level: 5–8

Subject Areas: Language Arts, Social Studies, Environmental Education

Duration: minimum of two 45-minute sessions

Group Size: from two students to two teams of students

Setting: indoors

Conceptual Framework Topic Reference: ITIA, ITVA, ITVA1, ITVA2

Key Terms: consumptive, nonconsumptive, impact, value

Appendices: Using Local Resources, Agencies and Organizations

---

Background

Among many areas in which there are differences of opinion concerning wildlife and its habitat, one that gives rise to particularly heated discussion at times has to do with questions of "consumptive" and "nonconsumptive" uses of wildlife. Consumptive uses are generally considered to be those in which wildlife is killed, as in hunting, fishing, and trapping. Such activities may use wildlife as a food source, for sport, for recreation, as a source of products for personal use, as a source of products for commercial use and sale, as a means to control damage to private land and crops, and as a population management tool.

Nonconsumptive uses generally are considered to be those in which any wildlife is watched, studied, or recorded without being killed, such as in hiking, bird watching, sketching, and photography. Such uses may be for purposes of recreation, education, and research. Some nonconsumptive uses may actually be vicarious, such as movie, television, and gallery viewing of wildlife.

Just as consumptive uses of wildlife affect individuals and populations, so can nonconsumptive uses. There are times, for example, when nonconsumptive uses may actually be damaging to wildlife and its habitat, such as the too-close observation of wildlife during breeding seasons and high human use of areas where species may be negatively affected.

At first glance, it seems that distinguishing a consumptive from a nonconsumptive use of wildlife would be easy. When people directly kill an animal, it is clearly a consumptive act. Yet, direct killing is just one factor that affects wildlife mortality. The issue of wildlife consumption has some gray areas. One gray area is habitat and how people affect its quality and availability for wildlife. That gray area is defined by human impact on wildlife's basic needs for food, water, shelter, and space suitably arranged for survival.

How humans affect wildlife can take many forms. For example, the piping plover is a shore bird that feeds along the ocean's edge. At low tide, it runs behind receding waves and feeds on exposed marine worms and other invertebrates. When people approach a plover, it stops feeding and becomes defensive. A beach full of swimmers or a regular stream of joggers or sea shell hunters can keep plovers from feeding. Because of nearby human activity, many plovers starve to death. Loss of habitat and human disturbance are two of the plover's primary problems. The Great Lakes piping plover was listed as an endangered species in 1986 and the Northern Great Plains and Atlantic Coast populations were listed as threatened species the same year.

Are the beach goers, seashell hunters, and joggers consuming wildlife when they disrupt the piping plover's feeding? Without a doubt, they are having an impact on wildlife. The question is "Are they wildlife consumers?" Some could argue that wildlife consumption is a matter of degrees. The discussion is as much about indirect effects as it is about obvious direct wildlife consumption, and it easily expands into exploring what roles humans should play in natural systems.

The major purpose of this activity is for students to acquire information about different uses of wildlife, as well as about the reasons offered both for and against consumptive and nonconsumptive uses.

NOTE: There may seem to be a difference between "use" and "value." All wildlife has value in some sense of the word—from ecological to intrinsic. Consumptive and nonconsumptive uses of wildlife do not include all values of wildlife because use requires, in this sense, intentional human activity.

Procedure

1. Ask students to brainstorm a list of ways in which wildlife is used. Note that "uses" of wildlife do not necessarily represent all ways in which wildlife has value. Provide students with definitions of "consumptive use" and "nonconsumptive use," or see if they can provide the definitions.

2. Ask the students to volunteer to represent one side or another on the following debate topic: "Should wildlife be used consumptively and nonconsumptively?" One team of students should research and prepare arguments in favor of one position, and one team of students should research and prepare arguments against that position.

3. Provide the students with time to research and prepare for the debate.

4. On the day of the debate, arrange the classroom so that each team of students can face the others. Each team should appoint a captain to present the team's opening remarks, limited to 3 minutes. Each team captain should then call on one student from each team to face a person from the other team.

continued

First one person, then the other, is given 1 minute to present his or her point of view. Each person is then given 1 minute for a rebuttal. The remaining students on each team may serve as judges of which argument was presented most effectively and accurately. A point is given to the team represented by the person judged to be the most effective and accurate.

NOTE: The students should vote according to the effectiveness of the argument, irrespective of which team they personally represent. Such a process may prove difficult; if so, another classroom of students may be invited to serve as a team of judges. Or a speech and debate teacher, impartial adult, or such, could be invited to judge. After each team member has debated with a member of the other team, the team captains should give 3-minute closing statements. Five points should be awarded to the team judged to have given the most effective and accurate overall arguments.

5. Invite the students to summarize personally, plus as a group if they choose, their views about the uses of wildlife—consumptively, nonconsumptively, both, or neither.

Evaluation

1. Identify five examples of consumptive uses of wildlife and five examples of nonconsumptive uses of wildlife.

2. What facts, if any, are given by consumptive users to defend their position; what facts, if any, are given by nonconsumptive users to defend their position.

3. Describe differences, if any, in the ways and reasons that consumptive and nonconsumptive users may value wildlife. Describe similarities, if any.

4. Summarize your personal views about consumptive and nonconsumptive uses of wildlife and describe the reasoning behind your views.

Riparian Zone

Objectives

Students will (1) identify and describe factors frequently involved in land-use planning, and (2) evaluate possible consequences for wildlife and other elements of the environment—including people—where land-use planning does not take place.

Method

Students simulate a board of commissioners' hearing.

Materials

Poster-making materials, classroom available to be arranged as a "commission hearing room"

Grade Level: 5–8

Subject Areas: Environmental Education, Social Studies, Language Arts

Group Size: minimum of five students, with one serving as commissioner; easily serves large classroom of students

Duration: three 45-minute sessions

Setting: indoors

Conceptual Framework Topic Reference: ITIIA, ITIIB, ITIIIA2, ITIIIA3

Key Terms: planning, land-use, interest groups, riparian

Appendices: Using Local Resources, Simulations

Background

See the Project WILD activity "To Zone or Not to Zone" for another simulation activity about land-use planning. Other Project WILD activities include "Shrinking Habitat" and "Planning for People and Wildlife." This activity is most appropriate when students already have some background in land-use issues.

Worldwide, loss of habitat is generally considered to be the single most serious threat to wildlife. Development of land areas for varying purposes affects wildlife—whether for business and industry, housing, agriculture, or recreation. This is not to say that all development is "bad," nor that all development should cease. However, in the spirit of protection, wise use, and conservation of natural resources and the environment, it is important for people to recognize the effects of their actions and to learn to make decisions based on informed processes wherever possible.

The riparian zone is the area next to a waterway that is immediately affected by the presence of water. Typically, the vegetation in a riparian zone requires much more water than that of neighboring plants. Riparian zones are generally more lush and support a greater variety and number of wildlife species than surrounding uplands. Streams and rivers provide a natural seed dissemination route. Seeds may fall in a river upstream, be transported downstream, and eventually germinate and grow several miles from their origin. Because of their exposure to

continued

seeds from other areas and their ideal growing conditions, riparian areas often provide homes for new or introduced species of plants. These introduced plants often occupy a niche held by a native species. Occasionally, the newcomer is more competitive than the native species and replaces the native plant in the plant community. These introduced species are called non-natives.

The major purpose of this activity is for students to increase their understanding of effects of various kinds of development on wildlife and the environment, as well as to recognize the usefulness of land-use planning as a means by which to minimize negative impacts of some kinds of development.

Procedure

1. Provide students with the At Issue: Land-Use Planning scenario on page 344.

   OPTIONAL: Provide copies of site maps or photos that you find or develop that seem appropriate.

2. Ask the students to divide into interest groups, representing groups such as these and any others the students suggest:
   - State wildlife management agency, with responsibility for the animals involved.
   - State division of forestry, responsible for the vegetation on the state-owned lands.
   - U.S. Forest Service, responsible for the vegetation on the federally owned lands.
   - Private landowners in the area—including farmers, ranchers, people interested in developing their land as a subdivision, and people interested in no development but total preservation of the land they own.
   - Private interest groups—including people interested in recreation on and near the river, and preservationist groups who want all species of plants and animals in the area to be protected.

3. Ask each group to appoint an illustrator, spokesperson, and recorder.

4. Provide the groups time to research and prepare a presentation for the "commission hearing" in which they would convey their point of view on the topic.

5. About halfway through the preparation time, ask the students to appoint one individual from each group to serve on the board of commissioners. Ask these students to prepare criteria against which they will evaluate the land-use proposals and recommendations that will be given at the commission hearing by each of the interest groups.

6. Ask each interest group to prepare an illustration of its land-use proposals and recommendations on posters for visual aid as part of its presentation at the hearing.

7. When the groups are ready, ask the board of commissioners to convene the commission hearing. An impartial individual may be chosen to maintain order and keep time. Each group should, as called upon, present its position on the topic to the commissioners, making use of visual aids and speaking no more than 5 minutes. The commissioners may ask questions of the presenters.

8. After all the presentations have been made, the board of commissioners should decide how the land will be used, defending that decision with a short explanation.

9. What were the major issues in this situation? What were the major points made? Describe, discuss, and evaluate possible consequences—positive and negative—for wildlife, people, and the environment in the situation. What seem to be major factors to consider in such land-use issues? Summarize the importance of land-use decision making and planning.

Extensions

1. Research what land-use planning procedures are used in your community. What group or groups have authority to make binding decisions to ensure planning, if any?

2. Contact local agencies for information on woody species and other plants in a local riparian area. Determine which, if any, of these species are not native to the area. Hypothesize how these plants were introduced to the riparian area. List positive and negative effects of these species on other plants and animals. What can be done to reduce the impact of introduced plants in riparian areas?

Aquatic Extension

Conduct this activity in conjunction with other riparian activities from the *Project WILD Aquatic Curriculum & Activity Guide*. See "Blue-Ribbon Niche," "Riparian Retreat," and "To Dam or Not to Dam."

Evaluation

1. Identify three varying uses for which the same parcel of undeveloped land might be used.

2. Describe the possible negative consequences for people and wildlife if development occurs with no planning.

3. List, describe, and evaluate three different value positions that might be represented in a land-use controversy.

continued

At Issue: Land-Use Planning

Approximately 100 miles of what is called riparian zone—in this case riverbank property—is vegetated in mature trees and associated plants. The property includes both publicly and privately owned land. Many of the riparian zone's tree species are not native to the area. These plants are non-native species. For the past 90 years, non-natives have been introduced into this ecosystem. The non-native trees were both intentionally and accidentally introduced. Native trees still survive in the area but their numbers are declining. The non-native trees have crowded out some of the native trees, creating a different type of habitat. Many native wildlife species are not as well adapted to the new non-native tree-filled habitat.

Some ecologists have recommended that the non-native trees be eliminated from the riparian zone. These ecologists recommend that all of the riparian zone's properties be treated to eliminate the non-native trees. Any non-native trees left in the riparian zone would be potential seed sources for re-establishing non-native trees in areas where they have been removed. The ecologists propose that the cut logs could be sold as firewood or left on the ground.

Because the land has many owners, there are several different philosophies about how the land should be managed. The riparian zone public lands include both a wildlife refuge that has a policy against cutting trees for any reason and a state forest that permits tree removal but lacks the funding to complete such a project. The tree removal could occur on private lands only if the property owners choose to let that happen.

County ordinances would be necessary to prohibit any new introductions of non-native species. The ordinances could allow for exceptions for things like fruit trees, or could prohibit all non-native trees. These ordinances would particularly affect homeowners along the river who want to landscape or plant windbreaks. Many of the existing non-native trees are in established windbreaks and visual screens surrounding homes in this area.

The public agency responsible for management of wildlife in the area and a group dedicated to wildlife preservation strongly oppose the proposed plan to harvest trees. They argue that the impact on wildlife in the area will be extreme. Local wildlife will lose food and shelter that is provided by many of the non-native trees. They further argue that the project would cause many fish and other aquatic organisms to die. Logging would remove shade that keeps the water cool. Because the roots of the non-native trees hold the soil in the bank, their removal would lead to increased siltation in the river.

Other groups, including a local native plant association and a public agency responsible for endangered plants and animals, adamantly support the proposed plan to remove the non-native trees. They argue that native plants and animals are losing their position in the environment in favor of non-native plants and animals. Although they admit that short-term effects of siltation and habitat loss may present some problems, they argue that the long-term effects of re-establishing the native ecosystem will outweigh any short-term side effects.

All of the involved land is found in one county. The county Board of Commissioners will hold a hearing on the topic of removing the non-native trees. The proposal is called "The Vegetation Manipulation Plan for the Riparian Zone."

Changing the Land

Objectives
Students will (1) define fragmentation, (2) simulate and explain how fragmentation of biological communities can affect wildlife diversity and populations, (3) compare historical aerial photographs with current photographs and determine what factors influenced land-use decisions, (4) evaluate the impacts of different land uses, and (5) consider future land use changes to accommodate growth in a community.

Method
Students use worksheet maps to study fragmentation and use aerial photographs to examine changes in land use and how those changes affect ecosystems.

Materials
For each group of three to four students: copies of the Student Reference Sheets A and B on pages 349 and 350; copies of the Wood Thrush Creek Scenario (Present, A, and B) on pages 350 through 352; cut-out circles of adhesive paper, each 1 inch in diameter; transparency or plastic sheets; markers; copies of aerial photographs showing a local area in the past and in the present.

NOTE: To make this activity more relevant to students, use photos of the local community. Aerial photos can be purchased from most regional planning commission offices or from the Natural Resources Conservation Service.

Background
Humans affect biological communities in many ways. One way is through the process of fragmentation. Fragmentation is the breaking up of large and continuous ecosystems, communities, and habitats into smaller areas surrounded by human land use. Fragmentation eliminates corridors that connect natural ecosystems, leaving smaller islands of natural areas. As the size of a particular fragment becomes smaller and smaller, more and more species are affected. When humans develop a natural area for homes, business, agriculture, or recreation, they build roads, sewers, utility corridors, dams, buildings, parking lots, and other developments that affect wildlife populations. Areas that once were natural areas with diverse animal and plant life are now shopping malls, highways, golf courses, movie theaters, or farms. This process of scattered development leads to fragmentation.

Grade Level: 6–8

Subject Areas: Social Studies, Science, Environmental Education

Duration: two to three 45-minute sessions

Group Size: whole class, groups of three to four students for research and reporting

Setting: indoors

Conceptual Framework Topic References: ITIIA, ITIIIA, ITIIIA1, ITIIIA2, ITIIIA3, ITIIIB

Key Terms: land-use, transportation systems, fragmentation

Appendices: Observation and Inferences

---

continued

The prairie areas of the central United States are a good example of fragmentation. The native prairie contained more than 400 plant species and a multitude of animal species. As the prairies were broken up by human development, large ungulates, like the bison, quickly disappeared. As fragmentation continued, some plant species disappeared and many others became rare.

Aquatic ecosystems are also subject to fragmentation. Many rivers in the United States, both large and small, have been fragmented by dams and shorelines have been greatly altered.

People are changing the land. As the human population continues to grow, so does the need for food, shelter, and water. The demand for recreation and commerce is also increasing. Americans convert an estimated 2,000 to 2,800 acres of rural land each day to highways, housing, and other commercial development. Transportation systems are changing the face of our nation, our lifestyle, and the environment. The mobility and convenience provided by the automobile fuels this land-use change.

As a result of consumer demand and new technologies, agricultural production also has changed. Today, new products, irrigation, biogenetics, and increased production require new agricultural uses of the land. These changes can be observed by comparing current farm techniques to past farming practices.

Communities make land-use decisions every day. Given the impact that humans have on the land, a major challenge faces communities planning for continued growth. What are the best ways to accommodate growth and to minimize the impact on the existing community and the natural environment?

In this activity, students evaluate past land-use changes in a community and determine impacts on the land. In the first part of the activity, students determine the impact of new development in a large forested area occupied by neotropical migratory birds. What will the impact be of fragmentation? In the second phase of the activity, students look at past and present aerial photographs of their community. In looking at land-use changes, students consider what factors may have been involved in making the various land-use decisions. Students then determine what future land-use changes are required and discuss how the charges should be implemented to accommodate future growth. They consider the impact of land-use on wildlife habitat, water quality, and quality of life.

Procedure

Activity #1: Fragmentation

1. Divide the class into groups of three or four students.

2. Give each group a copy of Student Reference Sheets A and B. Ask students to read this background information.

3. Have students read Wood Thrush Creek Scenario: Present. To answer the question in this section, have the students cut out several 1-inch diameter circles (a quarter works well) from paper with an adhesive backing and place as many of those circles as possible on the map labeled Wood Thrush Creek, Present.

NOTE: If the map is copied as shown, 12 circles will fit on the map. If the map is enlarged, more circles may be required. The scale for the circles and the map is not indicated. This activity focuses on the *relative* change in area over time.

4. Ask students to read Wood Thrush Creek: Scenario A. Make sure all students can interpret the symbols that accompany the two Scenario A maps, Future: 10 Years and Future: 20 Years. Have the groups answer the questions and review the changes that occurred between the Present map and each Scenario A map. Use additional circles on the two Scenario A maps to determine changes in the number of Wood Thrush nesting territories for these time periods. The circles may touch the line representing the creek but may not touch lines representing human-made structures.

5. Ask the students to read Wood Thrush Creek: Scenario B. In Scenario B, the groups plan Wood Thrush Creek development. Have the groups answer the questions and review the changes that occurred between the Present map and each Scenario B map they develop.

6. Ask each group to share its plans for Wood Thrush Creek development with the class. Which plan from Scenario B does the class prefer? Ask each group to look 30 years into the future and decide which of the following additions the group would allow in the Wood Thrush Creek area:

   - Log another area,
   - Add five new homes, and/or
   - Develop an ATV/snowmobile trail.

7. Discuss fragmentation in the local community. What examples of fragmentation are evident? How can a region be managed to avoid fragmentation?

Activity #2: Land-Use Planning

1. Again, divide the class into groups of four to six students. Give each group the past and present aerial photos, a blank transparency or plastic sheet, and a marker.

2. Students place the transparency over the past photo and use a key to mark the buildings, roads, highways, railroads, buildings, houses, parks, etc.

3. Students then place the transparency from the past photo over the present photo, noting the changes in land use that have occurred over the years. Ask students the following questions:

   - What were the major changes in land use? What development occurred? (Students use their markers to note the changes.)
   - What types of land uses were lost? Forests? Agriculture? Parks? Why do you think these changes were made?
   - What changes occurred in the roadways or railways? Why?
   - Was there any commercial development? Parking lots? Shopping malls?
   - What are the effects, both positive and negative, that have occurred because of these changes? Are there effects on water quality? Quality of life?
   - How do you think these more recent changes have affected the wildlife in the area? Is there any evidence of fragmentation or possible fragmentation?

4. Have the students clean the transparencies or place a clean one over the present photo. Each group represents a land-use planning committee. Tell students the community is growing and in 10 years they are going to need two new elementary schools, 50 new houses, a new shopping center, two new fire stations, a larger hospital, and access (roads) to all of them. (For each area, add a variety of land uses.) Groups work together to plan where those new buildings, facilities, or recreation areas will go; what new roads, if any, will be needed; and how they will do this with as little impact as possible on the older community and the natural ecosystem. Discuss how and why groups targeted certain areas for development. What transportation systems will need to change? List the impacts of these developments on the community.

5. Discuss the different plans and ask students these questions: (1) Why do more roads lead to increased land use? (2) If you had a large area of land in your community that would be perfect for a large farm and you knew that there was a large demand for a crop you could grow, and thus a large sum of money available to be made, would you develop it? If so, how would you do so to decrease fragmentation and the loss of habitat?

continued

Extensions

1. **History:** Examine early photos of your community. What was Main Street like? What businesses were present? What was the common type of transportation?

2. **Local Planning:** Investigate the zoning ordinance in your community. Who is responsible for land-use planning? Who develops the zoning regulations? Invite a local planner to your classroom to talk about his or her role in community land-use planning.

3. **Natural Areas:** Identify an area on the aerial photo where no development has occurred. Complete an on-site inventory of the plant and animal life found there. Find out from the area's community development office if there are plans to develop the area and how. Have students design and submit a "Least Environmental Impact" plan to the office.

4. **Community Survey:** Develop a survey that could be used to interview elderly people in the community regarding the changes in wildlife they have seen during their lifetime. Analyze the findings to try to determine the cause of the changes.

5. **Schoolyard Habitat:** Evaluate school grounds to determine wildlife and habitat needs. Create and implement an action plan to meet the identified needs. Relate the findings to fragmentation and land-use planning.

Evaluation

1. Students compare the past and the present aerial photos to identify evidence of fragmentation. Students also research changes in the wildlife populations in their area and determine what has caused those changes. Have they been the result of fragmentation, loss of habitat, changes in food sources, or something else?

2. Procedure 4 of Activity #2 can be used as an evaluation. It could also be presented to the town's planning and zoning office.

Additional References

www.bts.gov/NTL/
(U.S. Department of Transportation–National Transportation Library)

www.farmland.org (American Farmland Trust)

www.planning.org
(American Planning Association)

www.sustainable.doe.gov/
(Center of Excellence for Sustainable Development)

natzoo.si.edu/smbc
(Smithsonian Migratory Bird Center)

www.usgs.gov (United States Geological Survey)

Adapted with permission from "Changing the Land" by Al Stenstrup, Wisconsin Department of Natural Resources and from *One Bird Two Habitats*, Wisconsin Department of Natural Resources. "Changing the Land" is a *Wild in the City* publication developed by the Wisconsin Department of Natural Resources and Project WILD with a grant from Phillips Petroleum Company and the National Fish and Wildlife Foundation.

Student Reference Sheet A

Neotropical Migratory Birds

Almost 70 percent of the world's bird species are declining in population. Many birds are on the endangered, threatened, or watch lists in different states and countries. The rapid decline in the species of birds worldwide signals that the ecology of the planet is changing. What are the major threats to birds worldwide? What are people doing to try to protect them?

You will complete a simulation that focuses on certain types of neotropical migratory birds. These birds breed and spend summers in the United States or Canada and then travel great distances to their wintering grounds in Central or South America. The majority of the approximately 200 species of neotropical migratory birds are songbirds.

The life cycles of these migratory birds are very complex. To understand the population changes of these birds, you must consider the breeding grounds in the north, the wintering areas in the south, and the migration path. Below are some of the major threats facing neotropical migratory birds:

- habitat fragmentation
- nest predation
- cowbird parasitism
- urbanization
- linear development (i.e., roads, pipelines, and high tower lines)
- loss of habitat—summer, winter, and stopover habitat

You will investigate how forest fragmentation might affect populations of interior forest migratory birds. Forest fragmentation is the reduction of extensive, contiguous forest into smaller, isolated parcels separated by roads, fields, houses, and other development.

Studies by the United States Fish and Wildlife Service have shown that many forest bird species are rare or absent from many small, isolated habitat blocks of forest. It is difficult to determine an exact size of territory needed in acres because minimum area estimates vary by species, regions, and habitat types. Despite these difficulties, general patterns of species of birds are emerging. Some bird species are not sensitive to habitat fragmentation and occur in habitat patches of all sizes, whereas others are moderately or highly sensitive and rarely occur in small forested areas. Listed below are samples of each:

Moderate or High Sensitivity

Ovenbird
Acadian flycatcher
Scarlet tanager
Wood thrush

Low Sensitivity

Red-headed woodpecker
Northern cardinal
Indigo bunting
Black-capped chickadee
Bluejay

Wildlife research now shows that many species of forest birds require large blocks of habitat. Moderate to high sensitivity species avoid habitat on the edge of built communities and do not nest successfully near edges. Populations of these species generally do poorly in areas where habitat is broken, or fragmented, into small, isolated blocks.

You will now look at two different scenarios for changes to a forested area and the effects of fragmentation on a wood thrush population.

continued

Student Reference Sheet B
Introduction to the Wood Thrush
(*Hylocichla mustelina*)

The wood thrush can be found in the moist and shady deciduous forests throughout the eastern United States. Because the population has been declining at a rate of 1 to 2 percent each year for nearly 30 years (1966–1994), it has been the subject of many ecological research projects. Research conducted on the breeding grounds has centered on the effects of forest fragmentation on nesting success.

Forest fragmentation is the name given to the reduction of extensive, contiguous forest into smaller, isolated parcels separated by roads, houses, agricultural fields, utility lines, logging, and other development. Carving up a forested area into smaller parcels creates more forest edge relative to forest interior. This process makes the wood thrush nests more susceptible to predators such as chipmunks, raccoons, blue jays, crows, and cowbirds. (The cowbird is a "brood parasite" that tends to select forest edges for reproduction and lays its eggs in other birds' nests. The "foster parents" usually raise the cowbird young at the expense of their own eggs and young.)

The Smithsonian Migratory Bird Center reports find that wood thrush nesting success is greatest in large forested areas. Success rates decline with smaller forest size as a result of increased predation on eggs and young.

Wood Thrush Creek Scenario: Present

The area around Wood Thrush Creek has been forested for many years. The area is privately owned, and Wood Thrush Creek is an excellent trout stream.

How many Wood Thrush nesting territories can be established in this wooded area?

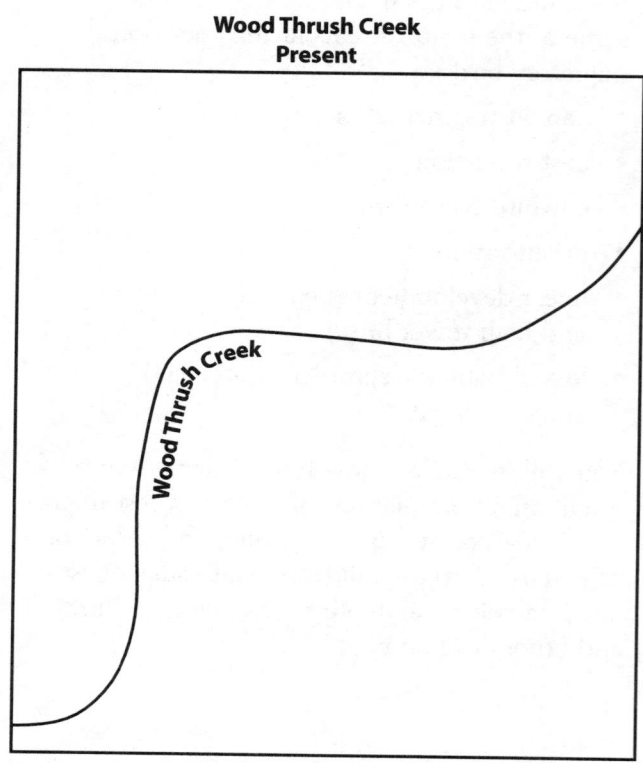

Wood Thrush Creek Present

Wood Thrush Creek Scenario: A

The owner has decided to sell some of the land. The owner also established a timber sale to provide some income and forest products, which are in demand. People are moving into the area and building homes.

- What are the changes in Scenario A during the first 10 years?
- What are the possible reasons those changes are occurring?
- How do the changes affect the wood thrush? How many circles will still fit in the forested areas if the circles cannot cover human structures represented on the map?
- What are the changes in Scenario A after 20 years? How many circles will still fit in the forested areas?

**Wood Thrush Creek
Future: 10 Years**

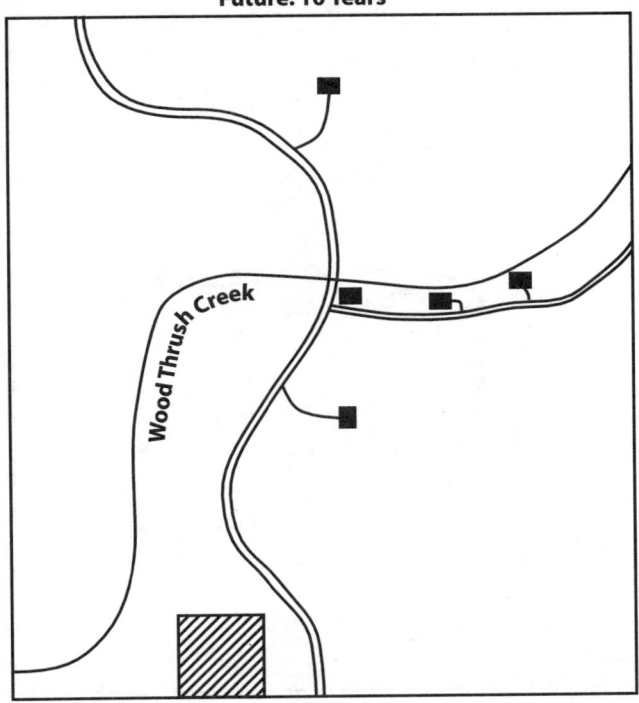

**Wood Thrush Creek
Future: 20 Years**

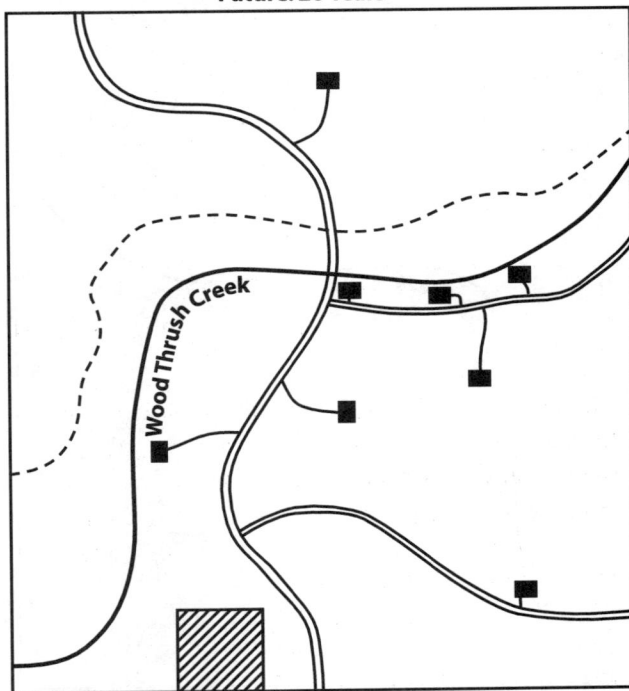

Paved Road　　House/Driveway　　Logged Area – Select Cut　　Snowmobile/ATV Trail

continued

Sustaining Fish and Wildlife Resources

Changing the Land

Wood Thrush Creek Scenario: B

Scenario B presents a different kind of change to the area. Your group will decide where to put the houses, roads, and other developments. Use the same number of homes and a logged area as in Scenario A. Fill in the areas with your plans. Try to provide for the maximum of forested areas large enough to support nesting areas for the wood thrush. Add a 4-inch long snowmobile/ATV trail on the Future: 20 Years map.

- What decisions did your team make when mapping the development?
- How would those changes affect the wood thrush? How many nest sites did you have in the first 10 years? Second 10 years?
- How do these changes compare to those in Scenario A?

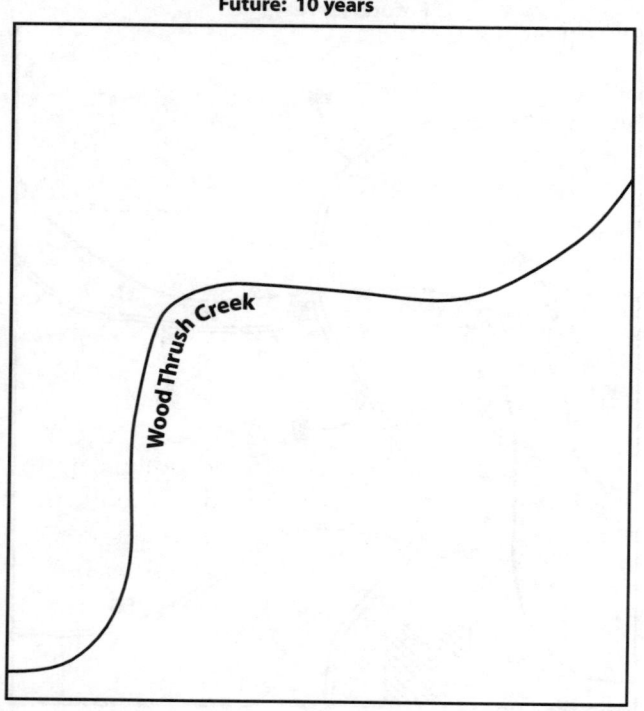

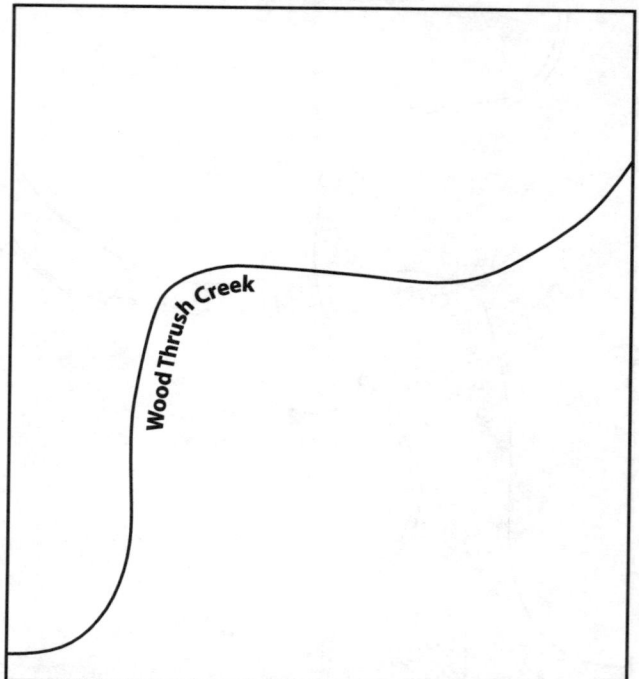

 Paved Road    House/Driveway   Logged Area – Select Cut    Snowmobile/ATV Trail

352   Project WILD K–12 Curriculum and Activity Guide

Cabin Conflict

Objectives
Students will (1) describe possible circumstances in which public and private interests may conflict in land-use issues, and (2) evaluate points of view that may arise under such circumstances.

Method
Students participate in a role-playing activity.

Materials
Classroom set up as courtroom, copies of Cabin Conflict background information on page 354

Background
Today, many conflicts arise concerning land use. It is recognized that large, continuous areas of land are necessary to provide some wildlife with suitable habitat. Sometimes individual, private landowners come into conflict with state or federal government mandates to provide adequate wildlife habitat.

Eminent domain (also called "condemnation") is the power of government agencies to acquire property for public use so long as the government pays the property owner just compensation. Recognized public uses for which the power of eminent domain may be used include—among other things—schools, parks, roads, highways, subways, fire and police stations, public buildings, and wildlife and natural resources management or refuge areas.

The major purpose of this activity is to provide students with the opportunity to look at various points of view in a land-use issue involving both public and private interests.

Procedure
1. Provide the students with the Cabin Conflict background information on page 354. Ask them to describe any similar situations they might know about. Allow them a few days to a week to look for similar land-use conflicts, examples of the use of condemnation for the public interest, or other conservation-related conflicts between public and private landowners being reported in local media. Encourage the students to bring in newspaper or magazine articles, discuss their findings, and use some of the information as background.

Grade Level: 9–12

Subject Areas: Social Studies, Environmental Education

Duration: two 45-minute sessions or longer

Group Size: large group

Setting: indoors

Conceptual Framework Topic Reference: ITIIIA2, ITIVA

Key Terms: land use, eminent domain, condemnation, deed

Appendices: Using Local Resources

---

continued

2. Set up a role-playing situation in which students become
   - cabin owners
   - state wildlife agency officials
   - jury (12 members)
   - judge
   - lawyers (two)
   - witnesses (as many as needed; identify characters and perspectives that would be useful)

3. Allow cabin owners and the wildlife agency people time to prepare testimony stating their arguments either for continuing private ownership or releasing that ownership. During this period, the judge and jury prepare to hear the case, plan procedure, and so on. Lawyers and witnesses also prepare.

4. After the testimony has been presented and opportunity for rebuttal has been provided, jury members should meet briefly to reach a decision. They should then return and report their decision to the entire class, explaining the reasons for their decision.

5. Ask the students to discuss the results. What were the issues involved? What arguments support each side? Which arguments, if any, seem most persuasive? Which do not, and why? What additional information, if any, would have been helpful in reaching a decision in this situation? Where and how could we get that information if we needed it?

Extension

Research the state or local area to find instances in which land was condemned for public use. What were the impacts of the condemnation for the landowners? The general public?

Evaluation

Pro or con: in some situations, is it appropriate for private land to be condemned for public use? Choose a position and support it.

Cabin Conflict

The following imaginary conflict is based on one family's real experience and similar cases.

A dispute has arisen between owners of three cabins situated on deeded land that has been designated as a state wildlife primitive, management, or refuge area by a legislative act and by the state wildlife agency. Under the act, all property owners would be required to sell their property to the state or their property would be condemned and taken by the state.

Two property owners use the property for weekend and summer homes while the other property owner uses the property as an environmental learning base for her elementary school students, as well as for a summer cabin. This property owner would like to keep the property to enhance the educational program and for its historical value.

Seventy-five years ago, the area was the site of a small mining community of about 500 people. Zinc and lead were mined. Part of the old smelter remains near the educational cabin. A black mountain of charcoal used in the smelting process and several old mine shafts still exist. The existing three cabins are located on originally deeded mining claims of about 3 acres each.

Back from the Brink

Objectives

Students will (1) explain the reasons for the decline of certain wildlife species and describe methods used in species recovery, (2) describe the effects of the decline and recovery of wildlife on people and the environment, (3) analyze issues surrounding the decline and recovery of wildlife species and examine strategies to resolve those issues, and (4) describe the importance of an environmentally literate citizen base to the success of the recovery project.

Method

Students are given background information on the recovery of wildlife species, and they are asked to analyze the issues and make recommendations for their resolution.

Materials

Paper; pencils; copies of the background information for the North American alligator, black-footed ferret, and the gray wolf on pages 358 through 361; Issue Analysis Sheet on pages 362 to 363; chalkboard or other large surface; access to research materials or state wildlife agency web sites, if possible

Background

The Endangered Species Act of 1973 requires the U.S. Fish and Wildlife Service to protect federally endangered and threatened species and to develop recovery plans for them. Some of these species are extirpated, or missing from their native range, although they are not extinct. In developing and implementing a recovery plan, you must consider many environmental and societal variables. If recovery of a species is successful, you must consider where reintroduction should occur and how it should be implemented. Biological considerations include researching the habitat (food, water, shelter, and space) needs of each species.

Biologists must take into account many factors. How will introduced species affect the other inhabitants in the ecosystem? Where will individuals of the species being introduced come from? Is there enough genetic diversity for long-term population sustainability? Why did the species decline in the first place? Have there been changes, events, or regulations that will now enable the species to recover?

Today, individuals involved in reintroduction plans consider a species' carrying capacity and society's tolerance for living with the species. How does the species affect people? Historically, how have people viewed and valued the species? If that species is an animal, are they afraid of it? Is the animal considered "cute" or "mean?" Do

---

Grade Level: 9–12

Subject Areas: Science, Language Arts, Social Studies, Environmental Education

Duration: three 45-minute sessions

Class Size: any

Setting: indoors

Conceptual Framework Topic Reference: ITIVA, ITIVB, ITIVC, ITVA, ITVB

Key Terms: reintroduction, recovery

Appendices: none

---

continued

people have an understanding of the natural history of the animal? Is there a perception that the recovery of the species will have an impact on the safety of people? Can the species affect their livelihood or limit resources for people on a local, state, or national level? For some species, few conflicts will occur. In other situations, the recovery of a species may raise many concerns and issues.

Recovery plans address different options. Recovery plans may, or may not, include strategies for the reintroduction of the species to native habitats. Important to the selection of a particular option is the classification of the species under the Endangered Species Act. Some species may be classified as an "experimental population." Experimental populations and their associated habitats are subject to fewer regulations and protections. Management of these populations is more flexible and can include a variety of options not permitted in populations designated as "endangered." Various possible scenarios are considered, as the plan examines the effects on the species, the ecosystem, other species, and people. Cost-effectiveness for the different options is examined as well. Before selecting the final option, individuals, groups, and organizations can voice their support or their concerns in public hearings.

The purpose of this activity is for students to analyze the complex human and environmental issues that are involved when a species is reintroduced to an area. It is important that the agencies and groups involved in developing the recovery plan acknowledge and address those concerns, because the long-term recovery of a wildlife species ultimately depends on the conservation measures developed and supported by people.

Procedure

1. Divide the class into groups. Assign each group one of the animals featured on pages 358 through 361, and provide them with the Issue Analysis Sheet on page 362 and 363.

2. Ask students to read the wildlife background information sheet for their animal and review the Issue Analysis Sheet. Have them conduct further research on their animal.

3. Ask the groups to discuss their species and their recovery. Then have the students complete the Issue Analysis Sheet. The sheet will ask students to address the species' preferred habitat; its food; what contributed to the loss or decline of the species; what has helped the recovery of the species; historical range; current range or status of the species (if available); existing or potential issues involved in the species' recovery; the interest groups, agencies, and people involved in the issue surrounding their species; and the steps that have been taken to help resolve these issues.

4. Have students discuss their responses and suggest additional options that might be considered to resolve these conflicts.

5. Ask students to prepare a media brief about their animal. It can be a short "infomercial," formal presentation, brochure, article, or web page. Have the students emphasize the issues and conflicts involved in the animal's recovery. Include the different options or steps they suggest be taken to help mitigate the conflict.

6. Have the groups poll the class for recommendations the students think would best resolve the issues.

7. Using the information provided in the background information sheet and presentations, ask students to construct a class chart summarizing the following: name of the animal, method of recovery, why recovery was able to occur, potential or existing issues or conflicts associated with recovery of the species, the people or groups involved in these conflicts, and the most common strategies selected for helping to resolve the issues or conflicts. Compare and contrast among the species using the following questions to help guide the discussion.

- What changes or events had to occur before species recovery projects could begin?
- How did the loss of the species affect people? The environment? Are the loss and/or recovery important? Why?
- What issues or potential conflicts are involved in the recovery of each animal? Who are the different "players" involved in these issues or conflicts? Are any of the issues or conflicts similar among the species?
- How has public perception of the species influenced decisions related to the issues?
- Are there reoccurring strategies in resolving conflicts associated with these species?
- How important is it that local individuals and groups understand the natural history of the species and its role in the ecosystem? Why?

8. After the class discussion, have the students return to their groups and finalize their recommendations or strategies to help resolve the issues surrounding their species.

9. Have students present the final strategies that will be used.

Extensions

1. Ask students to choose one of the species in this activity and to research what is being done to resolve issues and conflicts surrounding the recovery of the species.

2. Research rare or declining wildlife species found in your state. Develop a plan to bring about recovery for one of those species. How could it be determined if recovery might be feasible? What method could be used? What would justify the recovery of this species? How could local citizens be involved and help to resolve concerns?

3. In groups, have students construct a personnel chart that includes all job categories that might be needed in the recovery of their animal. Describe the role of each position and indicate possible employers.

Evaluation

1. Identify a wildlife species that is or has the potential to be involved in an issue or conflict on a local, state, or international level. Ask students to identify potential problems, conflicts, or issues. What strategies would they use to help prevent conflicts from arising in the first place? How would they resolve conflicts if they did occur? Ask the students to choose a wildlife species from the activity and to create a position statement portraying their views on the issues involved in that species' recovery.

2. Ask students to choose a wildlife species from the activity and to create a bumper sticker portraying their views on the issues involved in the species' recovery.

continued

North American Alligator *(Alligator mississippiensis)*

The North American alligator, a member of the crocodile family, can be found in marshes, swamps, shallow lakes, ponds, and waterways in the southeastern United States—from Texas to Florida and as far north as the Carolinas and southern Arkansas. As adults, these large reptiles can weigh more than 500 pounds and measure 8 to 13 feet or more in length.

North American alligators are predators and eat a wide variety of foods including fish, turtles, snakes, birds, and small mammals. The North American alligator has existed for more than 180 million years. It is well adapted to life in the wet areas of the south. Alligators are exothermic. They have no internal method to control body temperature and rely on water to keep their body temperatures lowered in the hot summers. The North American alligator helps retain water in its habitat by creating holes that retain water in times of drought. These "gator holes" help supply water for wetland plants and wildlife.

During the early colonization of the southeastern United States, alligator populations remained fairly stable throughout most of their range. However, at the end of the 19th century, it became fashionable to use alligator hide in boots, wallets, purses, belts, and other fashion items. Market hunters began to take alligators in large numbers to use their skins in the fashion industry. In the 1920s, 200,000 alligators were killed each year in Florida alone.

During the 1920s, thousands of acres of wetlands also were being drained to provide more land for agriculture and development, and to limit mosquito populations. With the combined pressures of habitat loss and market hunting, alligator populations began to plummet. By the 1950s, the American alligator was on the verge of extinction.

Between the 1940s and the 1960s, the southeastern states began protecting their remaining alligator populations. In 1967, the North American alligator was placed on the federal endangered species list, which provided it complete protection. It remained on the list under the Endangered Species Act of 1973. This act emphasizes protection and recovery of endangered species and helps provide funding for research and recovery projects. An amendment to the Lacey Act and CITES II (Convention on International Trade in Endangered Species of Wild Fauna and Flora) also protects the alligator by regulating interstate and international commerce in alligator products. (A South American alligator, not found in the wild in North America, is not endangered and never has been. Those alligators are sometimes sold in pet stores.) As a result of such efforts, the North American alligator has made a complete recovery. Effective management, habitat protection and restoration, law enforcement, and, in some states, reintroduction and restocking have enabled alligator populations to grow dramatically in recent years. In 1987, the American alligator was reclassified from "endangered" to "threatened."

While North American alligator populations continue to grow in the southeastern United States, the human population and associated development is also increasing. Because many people want to live along water, waterfront property has become a prime area for housing developments. People share these waterways with alligators while fishing, boating, swimming, and so forth. Greater contact has led to increased conflict between people and alligators, and most conflicts are due to alligators being in places where people do not want them. Although these reptiles typically stay away from people, people and alligator incidents can result when alligators lose their fear of people because someone has been feeding them. Alligators are large predators and have also been known to prey on household pets.

To help manage alligator populations, some states now allow closely monitored hunting and trapping. Alligator hide and meat are valued commodities. To help meet this need, alligator farming has become a thriving business. Some states have allowed the limited collection of eggs and hatchlings by licensed alligator farms and have allowed limited hunting by private individuals.

North American alligators remain protected on state, federal, and international levels to help ensure their continued survival.

Black-Footed Ferret (Mustela nigripes)

The black-footed ferret is the only ferret native to North America. These long, slender mammals were once found throughout the Great Plains, ranging from southwestern Canada to northern Mexico. Scientists do not think they were ever very abundant. The black-footed ferret is considered the rarest wild mammal in North America.

Black-footed ferrets are members of the mustelid family, along with weasels, otters, minks, badgers, and wolverines. Although they occasionally eat rabbits, mice, and other small mammals, black-footed ferrets feed almost exclusively on prairie dogs—in fact, prairie dogs make up more than 90 percent of a ferret's diet.

Prairie dogs are burrowing rodents that live in large groups often referred to as "towns." At one time, there may have been as many as 5 billion prairie dogs sharing the prairie with ferrets and other wildlife. It is no coincidence that the ranges of these two animal species overlap. Not only do black-footed ferrets rely on prairie dogs as their main food, but they also live and raise their young in the burrows of prairie dogs.

Prairie dog towns provide food and shelter for many other animals as well. Prairie dogs are the prey of other predators such as coyotes and red-tailed hawks. Burrowing owls use prairie dog holes for nest sites, and many species of snakes, lizards, and amphibians use the burrows for shelter and hibernation.

Prairie dog towns provide recreational opportunities for wildlife watchers, photographers, and hunters. Although valued or tolerated by many people, others consider prairie dogs as nuisances. Besides eating agricultural crops, they eat the prairie grasses that are also eaten by livestock. Most of the land that could be developed in some areas is inhabited by prairie dogs. In addition, prairie dogs can contact sylvatic plague, which, when transmitted to humans, is called bubonic plague.

Since the late 1880s, many methods have been used to control and eradicate prairie dog communities. At the same time, the majority of their habitat (more than 98 percent) has been lost to development. Poisoning, trapping, shooting, and other control measures; habitat loss; and disease have led to a decline in prairie dog populations. This loss of habitat and their major food supply, in conjunction with disease, caused black-footed ferret populations to plummet as well.

In 1967, the black-footed ferret was placed on the federal endangered species list. By 1980, black-footed ferrets were thought to be extinct. Then in 1981, a population of black-footed ferrets was discovered in a prairie dog colony in Wyoming. Biologists began to study these animals to determine what could be done to protect this colony. By 1985, the colony had expanded to 129 animals. Unfortunately, an outbreak of canine distemper almost wiped out the colony. By 1987, the 18 remaining black-footed ferrets were taken into captivity as a last ditch effort to save the species.

In 1988, the U.S. Fish and Wildlife Service adopted the Black-Footed Ferret Recovery Plan. State and federal wildlife agencies in cooperation with several zoos began a captive-breeding program to try to increase the number of black-footed ferrets. The goal of the program is to reintroduce these ferrets into the wild. Overall, the captive-breeding program has been a success. The first project to reintroduce black-footed ferrets into the wild took place in 1991 in a prairie dog colony in southern Wyoming. Since then, small numbers of ferrets have been reintroduced into Montana, Arizona, Utah, and South Dakota. On-site breeding programs have also begun in Arizona, Colorado, and Utah. In 1998, more than 100 black-footed ferrets were born in the wild, and more than 400 were born as part of the captive-breeding program.

Many challenges remain in this reintroduction effort. Little was known about black-footed ferrets, especially about how to raise them in captivity while maintaining their abilities to survive in the wild. Land-use conflicts among farmers, ranchers, and prairie dogs continue to exist, on public as well as private lands. Today, where some prairie dog species continue to be legally classified as "pests," poisoning and other measures are being used to control nuisance colonies. Urban development continues to affect the land used by both prairie dogs and black-footed ferrets. To help address some of the issues associated with the recovery project, the reintroduced black-ferret populations have been designated as "experimental nonessential" populations under the Endangered Species Act.

As land-use practices change and more prairie dog communities are eradicated, the final challenge may be to maintain enough suitable habitat and prairie dog communities for black-footed ferrets to survive in the wild.

continued

Gray Wolf *(Canis lupus)*

The gray wolf is a highly social animal, and lives in packs of two to more than a dozen animals. Within the pack there is a definite hierarchy of dominant and subordinate individuals. Typically, only the alpha (lead or highest ranking) male and female mate, which helps limit the size of the pack and the number of newborn pups. The alpha pair, along with its offspring, forms the pack. Wolves hunt in packs and will share their food with pups and other adults in their pack. This arrangement is rare in the animal world.

Gray wolves can survive in many habitats where food is plentiful. They usually live in isolated forested habitats interspersed with grassy areas where their prey—deer, elk, moose, and other ungulates—graze. Wolves are large animals and can weigh up to 175 pounds and measure up to 6½ feet in length, but most wolves are about half this size. Although named the "gray" wolf, the color of these mammals varies in shade from black to white to gray.

The gray wolf once was found throughout North America from Canada to central Mexico. When European colonists began to settle in North America, they relied on many species such as deer and elk for food and clothing and for trade. They had very little knowledge about predators. Wolves, like other predators, were viewed with fear or as competitors for important food sources. Settlers were also concerned that wolves would attack their livestock or themselves. Consequently, as early as 1630, large bounties were paid to people to kill wolves. The Massachusetts Bay Colony paid an average month's salary for the head of a wolf.

As more people settled the land, the pressure on wildlife drastically increased. Between hunting and loss of habitat, many wildlife species, including elk, bison, and deer, were almost eliminated from parts of the country. The wolf was being pushed into an ever-decreasing range with a greatly reduced food supply. Conflicts between wolves and people grew. Programs, including those subsidized by the government, were established to eradicate the wolf. By 1897, the eastern timber wolf (*Canis lupus lycaon*), a subspecies of the gray wolf, was eradicated from the northeastern United States.

Wolves remained fairly common in the wild lands of the northwest through the early 1900s. However, continued habitat loss and eradication programs persisted. By 1950, wolves had been eliminated throughout the contiguous United States except for some remote wild areas in northern Minnesota. In 1967, the eastern timber wolf was included on the federal endangered species list. In 1973, the northern Rocky Mountain subspecies (*Canis lupis irremotus*) was listed as endangered. With a relatively large eastern timber wolf population surviving in parts of Minnesota, there was some confusion as to the legal status of the wolf in the United States. To clarify the situation, the U.S. Fish and Wildlife Service (USFWS) reclassified the Minnesota wolf as "threatened," and all other gray wolves south of Canada were listed as "endangered."

The Endangered Species Act of 1973 provides protection for endangered species and requires that plans be prepared for the recovery of these species. Over many years, federal and state agencies, as well as interested organizations, conducted studies, held public hearings, and conducted opinion polls to help assess which recovery strategies would have the best chance of success. In 1987, the USFWS approved the Rocky Mountain Wolf Recovery Plan that designated three official recovery areas in the northern Rocky Mountains. These areas were in northwestern Montana (including Glacier National Park and the Bob Marshall Wilderness); central Idaho (the Selway-Bitterroot and Frank Church River of No Return Wilderness Area); and the Yellowstone ecosystem (including Yellowstone National Park and surrounding areas in Montana, Idaho, and Wyoming).

During the early 1980s, wolves naturally began to re-colonize in northwestern Montana, dispersing south from Canada. By 1994, approximately 64 wolves were in Montana, forming five packs. As a result, plans for wolf reintroduction centered on central Idaho and Yellowstone National Park. In 1994, final plans were made for the reintroduction. And between 1995 and 1996, 66 wolves were brought to the United States from Canada. Thirty-one were reintroduced into Yellowstone National Park, and 35 were reintroduced into central Idaho.

The reintroduction of wolves into the northwest has been very controversial. Wildlife biologists, environmental organizations, and many individuals applaud the return of wolves as a step in restoring the natural balance in the ecosystem. Chambers of Commerce, shopkeepers, and entrepreneurs view the wolves as a way to attract tourists to the areas and increase profits.

In contrast, agriculture and some hunting and outfitting interests feel the introduction of wolves will affect their ability to make a living. Some are concerned that there will be timber harvest restrictions where wolves have been reintroduced. Some hunters are worried that wolves will reduce opportunities for big game hunting. Sheep and cattle ranchers fear wolves will prey on livestock, thereby affecting their livelihoods. Wolves can and sometimes do prey on livestock. However, not all wolves do, even those near livestock. Wolves that do prey on livestock tend to continue to do so and may teach their pups to do so as well. Some people have expressed safety concerns as they enjoy outdoor recreation in areas where there are wolves even though there are no documented attacks on humans in North America.

Before reintroducing wolves, the USFWS examined several options or alternatives: (1) reintroduce wolves with the wolves classified as "experimental populations", (2) take no action—allow wolves to naturally expand into Idaho and Yellowstone, (3) change laws and prevent wolf recovery, (4) establish legislation for states to implement wolf recovery with no federal oversight, and (5) reintroduce with wolves classified as endangered.

In an effort to address the concerns of local citizens, the reintroduced wolves in Yellowstone and central Idaho were designated "nonessential experimental" populations under the Endangered Species Act. This classification allows more involvement on the state level, broader flexibility in managing individual wolves and the pack, and the use of management options that would not be permitted if the populations were classified as endangered. Should the wolves pose a threat to livestock, pets, or property, problem or nuisance wolves can be relocated or, if necessary, killed by designated personnel. In addition, when the wolf is classified as an "experimental" population, private landowners can injure or kill a wolf if it is caught in the act of wounding or killing livestock on private land.

Amid all of the publicity, issues, and controversies, wolves are returning to North America. The gray wolf populations in Montana, Yellowstone National Park, and central Idaho continue to grow and the eastern timber wolf populations in Minnesota continue to thrive. In the early 1990s, red wolves,* a smaller wolf species, were reintroduced into selected wild areas in North Carolina, Florida, and Tennessee. And in 1998, several family groups of the Mexican wolf, a subspecies of the gray wolf, were released in the wilds along the Arizona–New Mexico border. Now, there are some environmental groups examining the possibilities of restoring wolves to areas in the northeastern United States and southwestern Colorado.

* Most scientists classify the red wolf as a distinct species of wolf. Others describe it as another subspecies of the gray wolf.

continued

Sustaining Fish and Wildlife Resources

Back from the Brink

Issue Analysis Sheet

Species_____ Date_____

Team Members:_____

A. Natural History Information
Preferred habitat:

Food:

Historic range:

Current range:

Current status:

B. Decline and Recovery
Major reason(s) for the decline of this species:

Events, changes, or laws that occurred to enable recovery:

C. Issues/Conflicts
Identify and record existing or potential issues or conflicts associated with the recovery of this species. Then identify all potential interested groups, individuals, or organizations. Identify their views or opinions about the recovery of the species. Consider their reasons or motivations for these views.

Issue:

Interest GroupsView or OpinionReasons/Motivation

Issue:

Interest GroupsView or OpinionReasons/Motivation

Issue:

Interest GroupsView or OpinionReasons/Motivation

D. Issue or Conflict Resolution

1. What measures or strategies have been taken to resolve these issues? Do you agree with them? Why or why not?

*Strategy**Issue It Addresses**Agree Yes/No**Explain*

2. What are your recommendations to help resolve the issue or conflicts?

*Recommended Strategy**Issue It Addresses*

Philosophical Differences

Objectives
Students will (1) identify points of view of groups and organizations concerning wildlife, natural resources, and environmental issues; and (2) describe possible effects of various groups and organizations having differing points of view about wildlife, natural resources, and environmental issues.

Method
Students select a wildlife or other environment-related issue of concern to members of their community and correspond with representatives of a range of interest groups about their positions concerning the issue.

Materials
Newspapers, magazines, or other sources of news; writing materials; chalkboard

---

Grade Level: 9–12

Subject Areas: Environmental Education, Social Studies, Language Arts

Duration: two to three 45-minute sessions, over a 3-week period

Group Size: large group

Setting: indoors

Conceptual Framework Topic Reference: ITIA, ITIVA, ITIVB

Key Terms: issue, interest groups, philosophy, problem

Appendices: Using Local Resources, Agencies and Organizations

---

Background
One definition of the word "philosophy" describes it as a "system of principles for guidance in practical affairs." Private and public organizations and agencies frequently have an identifiable philosophy. Most organizations involved with natural resource and environmental issues support their actions and recommendations with statements of their philosophy. These statements may be made available in the form of speeches, newsletters, news releases, goal statements, and position and policy papers. The organizations and agencies may not clearly identify their underlying philosophies or perspectives, but they can be recognized after analysis of the groups' written and spoken statements and actions.

When discussing environmental concerns, many people use the words *issue* and *problem* interchangeably. But educators such as Harold Hungerford, professor of environmental education at Southern Illinois University, feel that it is important to distinguish between environmental problems and environmental issues. According to Hungerford, an environmental *problem* involves the interaction between people and the environment. He defines environmental *issues* as situations in which there is disagreement about solutions—often because of different values and beliefs. If we use this definition, soil erosion caused by hikers and horses in parks is an environmental problem. It becomes an environmental issue when people disagree about how to best address it.

The major purpose of this activity is for students (1) to recognize that organizations and groups may have differing perspectives with respect to wildlife, natural resources, and environmental concerns and (2) to describe possible effects of several different points of view.

Procedure

1. Lead a discussion on the differences between an issue and a problem. Ask the students for examples of each.

2. Ask the students to identify wildlife or other environmental issues in the news. They might read newspapers and magazines or watch television newscasts on a regular basis for 1 or 2 weeks to identify an issue and acquire some information about the issue. If the issue is related to wildlife, they could go directly to a range of interested organizations and groups such as their state wildlife agency; federal agencies involved with wildlife; representatives of private environmental, conservation, or animal welfare organizations; industry with land holdings involving wildlife; farmers; and people working in recreational or commercial activities involving wildlife. A range of organizations interested in wildlife that could be contacted include the American Humane Association, the Defenders of Wildlife, the Humane Society of the United States, the National Audubon Society, the National Rifle Association, the National Wildlife Federation, The Wildlife Society, Ducks Unlimited, Izaac Walton League of America, Sierra Club, The Nature Conservancy, and the Wildlife Management Institute. Representatives of such organizations, as well as other groups, can be of assistance in identifying an issue or providing background information. Ask all the students to bring in information about any issues they have identified. After reporting and discussing, ask the students to select one issue that seems most interesting to them and that involves various—if not clashing—philosophies on the parts of individuals, groups, and organizations with respect to the issue that is identified.

3. List pertinent information about the issue on the chalkboard. Identify the individuals, organizations, agencies, and other groups that seem most involved. Ask the students to select several of the groups, trying to identify those groups that seem to have strongly different points of view on the issue. Ask the students to divide themselves into working groups, with each group of students selecting one of the interest groups to investigate further. Ask each student group to try to predict and describe the philosophy that guides the interest group or organization they have selected to study.

4. Ask each group of students to draft a letter to be sent to the interest group. The letter should ask what the organization's point of view (policy or position statement) is with respect to the particular issue involved, the reasons the organization is taking that point of view, and a general statement of the goals of the organization, if available. Assist the students to make sure their letters are clear, concise, neat, grammatically correct, and free of spelling errors.

5. Mail the letters.

6. While waiting for a response, the student groups can write brief statements that predict the point of view they think they will receive from their organizations.

7. Once students receive responses, ask them to compare the responses to their predictions. Were there any differences between what the students predicted and the responses they received from the various groups? Were there any differences between past actions and statements from the groups

continued

and their present statements? If so, what were these differences and do they represent actual changes in guiding philosophy and policy changes in the groups or organizations? Do all or most members of an organization necessarily agree with its philosophy?

8. In summary, ask the students to identify and describe points of view, if any, that some or all of the groups share in common and points of view, if any, in which the groups strongly differ. In what way, if any, is it healthy for there to be groups with differing points of view? In what way, if any, might it be damaging? What possible effects are there from individuals, groups, and organizations having differing points of view with respect to wildlife, natural resources, and environmental issues?

Extensions and Variations

1. Instead of initiating a letter-writing phase, use the position statements from different groups on one issue.

2. Invite local members or representatives of the various groups to present their points of view in person.

3. Invite the students—as a group or as individuals—to decide (write, discuss, or present orally) their own position statement of the issue. How is it like and unlike others?

4. Emphasize the potential for communication skills, including analysis of points of view, in this activity. For example, analyze the stated positions of each group according to the following criteria:

   - Most of the scientific community accepts the position as accurate.
   - There is some scientific evidence to support it, but it is inconclusive.
   - It is rejected by the scientific community.

Establish other criteria (e.g., economic, social, ethical, historical, political, biological, ecological, philosophical).

To what degree are groups with opposing views similar and different when analyzed by these criteria? Are there areas where it is appropriate and feasible to work for compromise? Why or why not?

Evaluation

Not enough is known about the whooping crane, an endangered bird species. Some people feel that additional research must be conducted to learn more about the species. Some worry that direct human contact will accelerate the birds' population decline. Some feel that habitat loss is the real problem. Some think propagation in captivity is the best means of achieving a viable population. Some say that the species is going to become extinct anyway, and, therefore, any available funds should be spent on those species with a better chance for survival. Others are heartened by recent successful efforts to reintroduce some of the cranes to the wild. Predict and describe the points of view that five diverse groups could have concerning this issue. Describe and evaluate at least three possible effects of five diverse organizations having differing views.

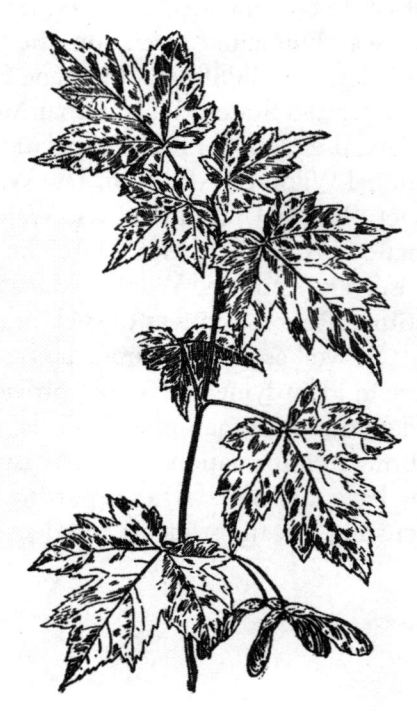

Turkey Trouble

Objectives
Students will (1) define and give examples of exponential and linear growth rates in wildlife populations, and (2) describe factors that affect and limit growth of wildlife populations.

Method
Students make computations and interpret results.

Materials
Paper, graph paper, pencils

Background
Growth rates can be characterized by two different growth curves: linear and exponential.

Linear growth occurs at a constant rate. Many increases or decreases occur at linear rates. An example of this would be having your salary increase by $1,000 per year.

Exponential growth occurs at an increasing rate through time. An example would be having your salary increase (or decrease) at a rate of 5 percent per year.

Since all populations have the reproductive potential to increase at an exponential rate, it is difficult to comprehend the gravity of problems associated with population growth. Population is limited by many factors, including availability and quality of water, food, shelter, and territory, as well as natural and human-made changes in habitat.

As an example, in 1935 Wyoming had no Merriam's turkeys within its borders. A decision was made to release 46 turkeys in a mountainous area of the state.

This activity will provide students with the opportunity to compute the possible growth of the turkey population during its first 5 years after the release. As background, students should recognize that in reality, these turkeys will be affected by many natural and human-caused limiting factors. For example, growth of bird populations is affected by factors such as the availability of food, water, shelter, and space; disease; predation; and climatic conditions; as well as broken or infertile eggs.

The major purpose of this activity is for students to acquire knowledge of factors affecting wildlife populations.

Grade Level: 9–12

Subject Areas: Environmental Education, Mathematics, Science

Duration: two 45-minute sessions, or one with homework

Group Size: any

Setting: indoors

Conceptual Framework Topic Reference: ITIIA

Key Terms: linear, exponential, limiting factors, population

Appendices: Using Local Resources

---

continued

Procedure

1. Compute the size of the population of Merriam's turkeys in Wyoming for 5 years, using the following assumptions. Complete the data table (see Chart A on page 370).

   Assumptions
   - None of the turkeys left the general area during the 5 years.
   - There was no disease or shortage of habitat that limited the population.
   - There were equal numbers of males and females in each hatch.
   - All sexually mature females successfully hatched a clutch of 10 eggs each year.
   - No turkeys reproduced until after they had completed more than 1 year of life.
   - All turkeys died during the winter after their fifth year of life (after hatching their fourth clutch).
   - All of the turkeys introduced were 1 year old and sexually mature.
   - There was an equal number of males and females in the original 46 released turkeys.

2. Plot the population for each of the 5 years on a graph as indicated by the diagram below.

3. Compute the size of the population of Merriam's turkeys in Wyoming using a linear growth model for 5 years using the following assumptions. Complete the data table (see Chart B on page 370).

   Assumptions
   - Each year, 250 offspring were produced by the turkey population.
   - None of the turkeys left the area.
   - There was no disease or shortage of habitat that limited the population.

4. Plot the data from step 3 on the same graph used in step 2.

5. Assign or discuss the following questions as related to the previous tasks:
   - In the examples given, which growth patterns appear to be increasing at a faster rate? Why?
   - The estimate of the true population of the Merriman's turkey by the Wyoming Game and Fish Department at the end of five 5 was 2,500. How can we account for the difference? Were any of the original assumptions incorrect? Which ones?
   - All populations have the potential to increase at an exponential rate. What factors limit this potential?

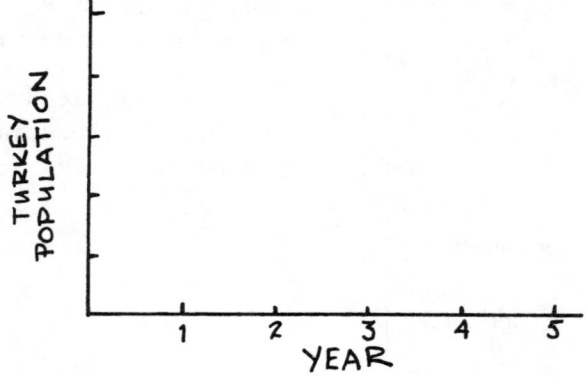

Extensions

1. Transfer this information to a similar situation in your state or province. Obtain background information and data from a local wildlife agency.

2. This activity does not address the consequences—potentially beneficial, harmful, or with no appreciable effect—of introducing or reintroducing species to an area. Introduction of non-native species, in particular, may have negative consequences for other wildlife and the environment. See related Project WILD activities "Planting Animals," and "Here Today, Gone Tomorrow."

Evaluation

1. On an island, a rabbit population doubles every year for 6 years. If you started with one pair (one male and one female), what would the population number after 6 years? This is an example of which kind of population growth?

2. A population of mountain lions is increasing by two members per year. If you started with two animals, what would the population size be after 6 years? This is an example of which kind of population growth?

3. List three natural limiting factors that could affect the growth of a rabbit population.

4. Use the Visual Vocabulary evaluation technique (see "Evaluating and Assessing Student Learning" in the Appendices) either to review or assess students on new concepts and terms introduced in this activity.

continued

Sustaining Fish and Wildlife Resources

Turkey Trouble

Chart A (Educator Copy) (Task 1)   EXPONENTIAL GROWTH DATA TABLE

	YEAR	1	2	3	4	5	6
1.	Beginning population	46	276	506	1,886	4,416	13,570
2.	– five year olds	0	0	0	0	46	230
3.	– last year's hatch (not yet breeding)	0	230	230	1,380	2,530	9,200
4.	= Breeding population	46	46	276	506	1,840	4,140
5.	Breeding pairs (#4 ÷ 2)	23	23	138	253	920	2,070
6.	Offspring (#5 x 10 eggs/clutch)	230	230	1,380	2,530	9,200	20,700
	+ breeding population (#4)	46	46	276	506	1,840	4,140
	+ last year's hatch (#3)	0	230	230	1,380	2,530	9,200
7.	= Total population	276	506	1,886	4,416	13,570	34,040

Chart A (Student Copy) (Step 1)   EXPONENTIAL GROWTH DATA TABLE

	YEAR	1	2	3	4	5	6
1.	Beginning population	46	276	506			
2.	– five year olds	0	0	0	0	46	230
3.	– last year's hatch (not yet breeding)	0	230	230			
4.	= Breeding population	46	46	276			
5.	Breeding pairs (#4 ÷ 2)	23	23				
6.	Offspring (#5 x 10 eggs/clutch)	230	230				
	+ breeding population (#4)	46	46				
	+ last year's hatch (#3)	0	230				
7.	= Total population	276	506				

Chart B (Educator Copy) (Step 3)   LINEAR GROWTH DATA TABLE

	YEAR	1	2	3	4	5	6
Population		46	276	506	736	966	1,196
+ increase		230	230	230	230	230	230
= total population		276	506	736	966	1,196	1,426

Chart B (Student Copy) (Step 3)   LINEAR GROWTH DATA TABLE

	YEAR	1	2	3	4	5	6
Population		46	276				
+ increase		230	230				
= total population		276	506	736			

Career Critters

Objectives

The students will (1) identify five examples of how wild animals and plants can be used to manage some environmental problems, and (2) describe and give examples of an organism and its niche.

Method

Students match organisms to environmental problems in a community and evaluate the potential of the organisms to help solve the problem.

Materials

For each small group: one Ecosystem Map, one set of Critter Cards, one set of Ecosystem Cards, and at least three of each different Critter Tokens

---

Grade Level: 5–6

Subject Areas: Environmental Education, Language Arts, Science, Social Studies

Duration: 30 to 45 minutes

Group Size: small groups of four to eight students

Setting: indoors

Conceptual Framework Topic Reference: WMIIA2

Key Terms: ecosystem, erosion, insecticide, manager, niche

Appendices: none

Background

Wild animals and plants can "manage" some environmental problems. Sometimes organisms can help solve or mitigate human-induced environmental problems simply by doing their "jobs." (An organism's ecological job is called its "niche.") Because this management approach is complex, the discussion questions should be emphasized to bring the activity into a more real-life perspective.

Procedure

Before the Activity

Make Critter Cards, Ecosystem Cards, Critter Tokens, and an Ecosystem Map before starting this activity:

1. To make the Critter Cards, copy the pictures on pages 375 through 378 onto heavy construction paper, and place the corresponding information on page 379 through 382 on the back of each card.

2. For the Ecosystem Cards, copy the information on page 373 and 374, cut out the cards, and place them on heavy construction paper.

3. Make three copies of the Critter Tokens on page 383 for each group, and cut them into individual squares.

4. Use a copy machine to expand the Ecosystem Map on page 384. Make one copy for each group of students.

The Activity

1. Introduce and define the key terms for this activity: ecosystem, erosion, insecticide, manager, and niche. These terms are found in the Glossary in the Appendices.

2. Divide the class into groups of four to eight students.

continued

3. Give each group a copy of the Ecosystem Map, a set of Ecosystem Cards, a set of Critter Cards, and a set of Critter Tokens. Have the group locate key areas on the map. Ask the students these questions:
   - Using the Ecosystem Cards, where are the ecosystems on the map?
   - Where does the stream begin and end on the map? Trace the course of the stream.
   - Where is the golf course in relationship to the stream?
   - Where are the parking lots in relationship to the stream?
   - Where is the park in relationship to other areas of town? Who do you think visits?
   - Where is the prairie ecosystem in relationship to houses?
   - What areas or neighborhoods on the map are similar to where we live?

4. Distribute the set of Critter Cards among the students in the group. Have the students read the back of the cards either silently or aloud and observe the illustrations on the cards. Tell the students to keep the cards they were given.

5. Arrange the Critter Tokens neatly around the edge of the Ecosystem Map in any order. There should be at least three of each different Critter Token.

6. Shuffle and stack the 12 Ecosystem Cards face down beside the Ecosystem Map. One student draws a card and reads it aloud to the group. Each student examines his or her own Critter Cards to determine if those animals or plants could help solve the ecosystem problem described. If so, the student explains how to the group. If the group agrees, a Critter Token of that plant or animal is placed on the Ecosystem Map. Remember, more than one plant or animal may be used to solve the problem. There may be unused Critter Tokens at the end of the activity. Continue drawing Ecosystem Cards until all are used.

7. When all the Ecosystem Cards have been drawn and all the ecosystem problems have been solved, have the groups compare their results.

8. Discuss and ask the students:
   - Could any of these solutions backfire? In other words, could the plants or animals used to help solve certain problems end up being a problem themselves?
   - Are there other wild plants or animals (not identified in this activity) that could have been used to help solve the ecosystem problems?
   - The gambusia fish is not native to many states. Is it okay to introduce "foreign species" to help with an ecosystem problem? What are the benefits? What are the risks?
   - How could the location of the 12 ecosystems on the map be redesigned to reduce some of the environmental problems?
   - Are there ways that animals, plants, and humans could work together to solve environmental problems?
   - In what ways is this activity realistic? Unrealistic?

Extensions

1. Students may research more information about the animals or plants on the Critter Cards.

2. Survey the neighborhood, or study the newspapers and news articles for local environmental problems. Could they be solved using wild animal or plant managers? Have students make their own maps of the community, highlighting environmental issues.

Evaluation

1. Have the students summarize five or more of the ecosystem problems described in this activity and explain how a wild animal or plant might be helpful in solving those problems.

2. Have the students define "niche." Give examples of the niches held by the animals and plants described in this activity.

3. Describe how wild plants and animals might be used to help solve one ecosystem problem not used in this activity.

Adapted with permission from "Career Critters" in *Ecosystem Matters* from the United States Department of Agriculture.

Answer Key to Ecosystems

1. Prairie Ecosystem — badgers
2. Farm Ecosystem A — bullsnakes
3. Golf Course Ecosystem — gambusia fish, bats
4. Urban Stream Ecosystem — beavers
5. Farm Ecosystem B — meadow larks
6. Stream Ecosystem A — willows
7. Pine Forest Ecosystem — woodpeckers
8. Garden Ecosystem — lady bug
9. Town Park Ecosystem — squirrels
10. Downtown Ecosystem A — trees
11. Foothills Ecosystem — plants
12. Downtown Ecosystem B — peregrine falcons

Ecosystem Cards

#1 Prairie Ecosystem

A prairie ecosystem is near a new housing development on the edge of town. Prairie dogs live in the grassy field. With all the new houses, lots of the prairie dogs' natural enemies—coyotes and eagles—have disappeared. Now the prairie dog population is growing. The prairie dogs are digging burrows and mounds in the lawns of the new homes. They are also eating vegetable gardens and underground telephone wires. Some people are worried that the prairie dogs might carry diseases, and they want to begin poisoning the prairie dogs. As a manager, how could you help solve this problem? What animal(s) or plant(s) in the cards provided could help with this problem?

#2 Farm Ecosystem A

You are a farmer. You store large amounts of grain and hay in your barn and storage bins. The problem is that field mice have discovered the grain, and now you are overrun with them. You could set numerous mouse traps, but this is time consuming. If you set out poison, you may poison birds and other animals by mistake. What animal(s) or plant(s) in the cards provided could help with this problem?

#3 Golf Course Ecosystem

You are the manager of a golf course. You are very proud of your golf course—especially the nearby stream, ponds, and water holes on the course. One problem: there are so many mosquitoes that the golfers are starting to complain. You could spray insecticide around the course to kill the mosquitoes, but it's expensive and probably would harm other animals. What animal(s) or plant(s) in the cards provided could help with this problem?

#4 Urban Stream Ecosystem

A stream ecosystem runs through town. Most of the time there is only a little water in your stream, but when a thunderstorm hits, lots of rain falls on paved streets and parking lots. The rain can't soak into the asphalt, so it runs downhill into the stream. The stream suddenly fills with fast-moving water. This water often carries the oil and gasoline that has dripped on the asphalt from cars. The stream banks erode so trees and shrubs along the edge of the stream sometimes fall, and soil washes away. When the storm is over, the stream gets low again. It is full of dirt, sand, and other pollutants. As a manager, your job is to stop the erosion of the stream bank and to keep the stream from having big changes in the level of water. What animal(s) or plant(s) in the cards provided could help with this problem?

continued

#5 Farm Ecosystem B
You are a farmer. Your crops are turning into a field of dreams for insect pests like grasshoppers. They are eating up your crops. You could spray with insecticides to kill the grasshoppers, but they are expensive. Your field is also close to homes. The homeowners do not want the spray to drift over into their yards. What animal(s) or plant(s) in the cards provided could help with this problem?

#6 Stream Ecosystem
A stream ecosystem runs near a farm. Along the edge of the stream is a nice, green area with lots of willows and tall trees. In the spring and summer, the farmer takes water out of the stream. The water goes from the stream down an irrigation ditch to water a field of crops. As a result, the water level in the stream may drop. Small fish can live in shallow water, but bigger fish need deep, cool pools of water. What animal(s) or plant(s) in the cards provided could help with this problem?

#7 Pine Forest Ecosystem
In your pine forest ecosystem, many of the trees are being damaged by bark beetles. Bark beetles bore through bark and eat the layers of wood inside. Your forest is infested with too many beetles, and a large number of trees have been infected. As a manager, your job is to maintain a healthy forest so that a variety of animals live there. You need to reduce the number of beetles. What animal(s) or plant(s) in the cards provided could help with this problem?

#8 Garden Ecosystem
Your town has a community garden where townspeople plant vegetables. However, this year small insects called aphids are eating the vegetables. People want vegetables to eat. You could spray insecticides to kill the aphids, but some people don't want to use insecticides. They are concerned about possible health effects. The community garden has another problem: the soil is too hard and packed so roots have a hard time growing. What animal(s) or plant(s) in the cards provided could help with this problem?

#9 Town Park Ecosystem
In the town park, some of the old oak trees are dying. They need to be replaced by young oak trees. Of course, that project would need funding. What animal(s) or plant(s) in the cards provided could help with this problem?

#10 Downtown Ecosystem A
Downtown becomes very hot in the summer. The sun shines on the sidewalks and asphalt streets and directly into the windows of buildings. People turn on air conditioning, which uses electricity and indirectly creates air pollution. The pollution makes being outside even more miserable. What animal(s) or plant(s) in the cards provided could help with this problem?

#11 Foothills Ecosystem
On the hills at the edge of town, many houses were going to be built. The bulldozers scraped the ground and plowed the dirt roads to get ready for the new construction. But the construction project was suddenly called off. The soil is now being blown away by the wind and washed downhill into the stream by rainstorms. What animal(s) or plant(s) in the cards provided could help with this problem?

#12 Downtown Ecosystem B
There are many pigeons downtown. They nest on the ledges of buildings. Some people like the pigeons, but others say there are just too many. Their droppings make certain areas really dirty, and the birds may carry diseases. What animal(s) or plant(s) in the cards provided could help with this problem?

Sustaining Fish and Wildlife Resources

Career Critters

Critter Cards

LADYBUGS

WILLOWS

BATS

BULLSNAKES

continued

Sustaining Fish and Wildlife Resources

Career Critters

Critter Cards

BEAVERS

WOODPECKERS

GRASSES

PEREGRINE FALCONS

Sustaining Fish and Wildlife Resources

Career Critters

Critter Cards

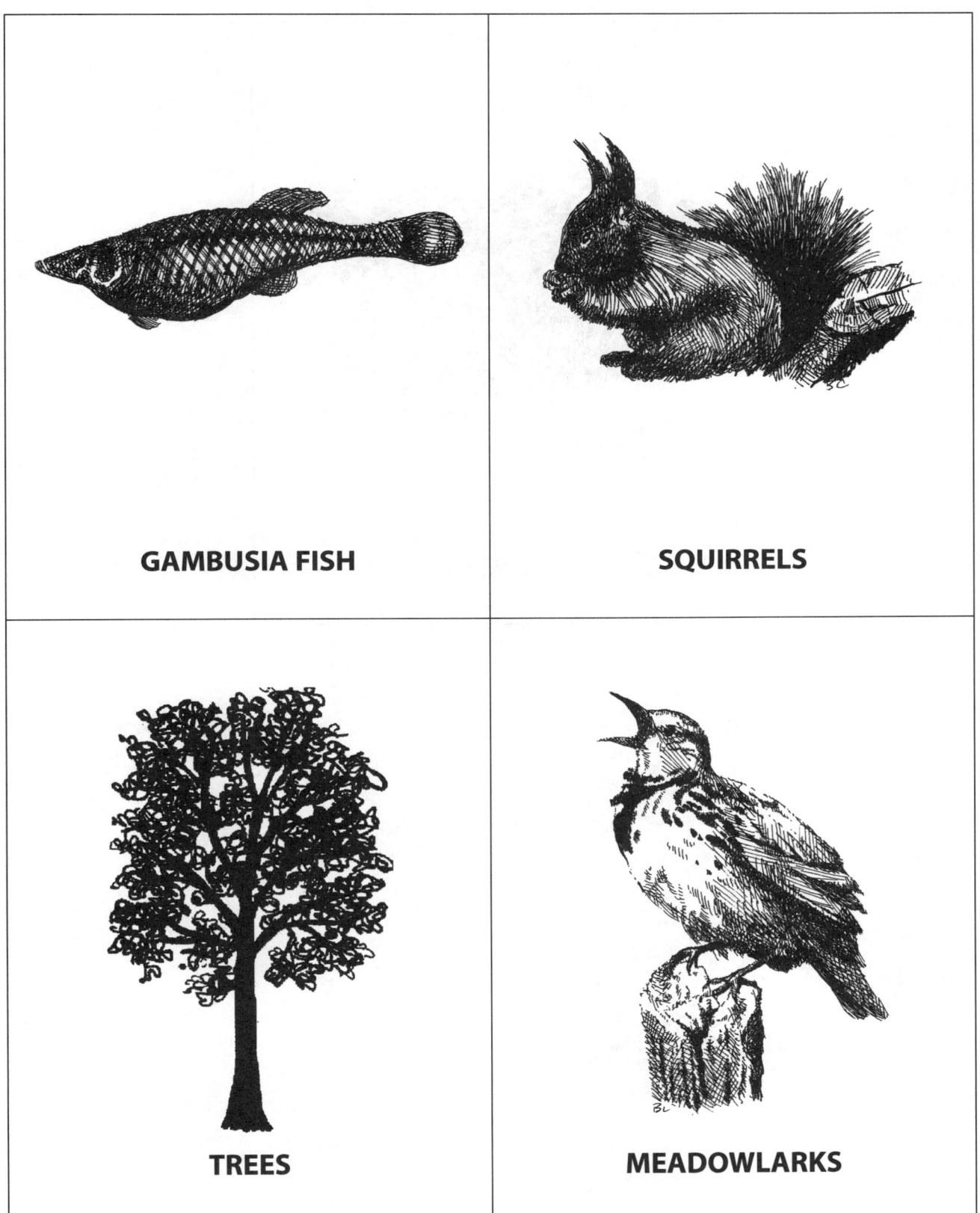

Critter Cards

BADGERS

Information for the Back of the Critter Cards

Willows
We are shrubs that grow along the edges of streams and beaver ponds. Our roots spread out and grow deep. They help hold the soil and keep it from getting washed away by floods.

Ladybugs
We are very small, and we eat other small tasty bugs such as aphids and scale insects.

Bullsnakes
We live in dry fields and around farms. We like to eat small mammals like prairie dogs and other rodents. Although we can grow to be very big (eight feet long and as thick as your leg), we are not venomous.

Bats
We are experts at eating flying insects. We swoop around and can eat thousands of flying insects in one night! Some people are scared of us, but we aren't really bad. Besides, we are active at night when most people are asleep.

continued

Information for the Back of the Critter Cards

Woodpeckers
We live in forests. We peck out the insects that live under the bark of sick or dead trees. We also use our beaks to chip deep holes into trees where we build our nests. Sometimes these holes are used by other birds, such as bluebirds and nuthatches, for their nests. Our holes help to bring new varieties of birds into the forest.

Beavers
Using our big front teeth, we cut down trees and shrubs, chew them into smaller sticks, and build small dams. These dams help to slow down the water in streams and make deep pools. Our dams help to slow small floods.

Peregrine Falcons
We are hawk-like birds that are built for speed. We live and nest near high cliffs, canyon walls, and even skyscrapers. We catch smaller birds to eat. Ecosystems with steep walls and plenty of birds can be good places for us.

Grasses
We grow fast, and our roots help keep soil from blowing away in the wind and washing away in the rain. We are often the first plants to grow where the soil has been disturbed, and we can tolerate long periods with little water.

Information for the Back of the Critter Cards

Squirrels
In the autumn, we collect acorns from oak trees and store them to eat in winter. Sometimes we hide our acorns underground. The only problem is we collect so many acorns that sometimes we forget where we've buried them! Some of these acorns sprout and grow into tall trees.

Gambusia Fish
We enjoy the nice warm waters of ponds and lakes. One reason is that mosquitoes do, too! A female adult mosquito lays her eggs in the water. The eggs hatch into wiggly worm-like animals that stay underwater. Eventually, they turn into flying mosquitoes. It's those underwater mosquito wigglers that we love to eat!

Meadowlarks
We are robin-sized birds that live in fields and on farms. We are known for our beautiful song and the black "V" on our chests. Many people don't know we like to eat many insects.

Trees
Trees do many good things for the environment. Our roots help to hold soil in place. We provide shade and keep areas cool. Our leaves help clear the air of some kinds of pollution.

continued

Information for the Back of the Critter Cards

Badgers

We live in underground burrows in dry fields. We are reclusive and avoid people. Although we are not much bigger than a small dog, we are tough and ready to defend ourselves. We dig underground to eat small, furry creatures like prairie dogs and other rodents.

Sustaining Fish and Wildlife Resources

Career Critters

Critter Tokens

Use open spaces to come up with your own critters.

continued

Sustaining Fish and Wildlife Resources
Career Critters

Ecosystem Map

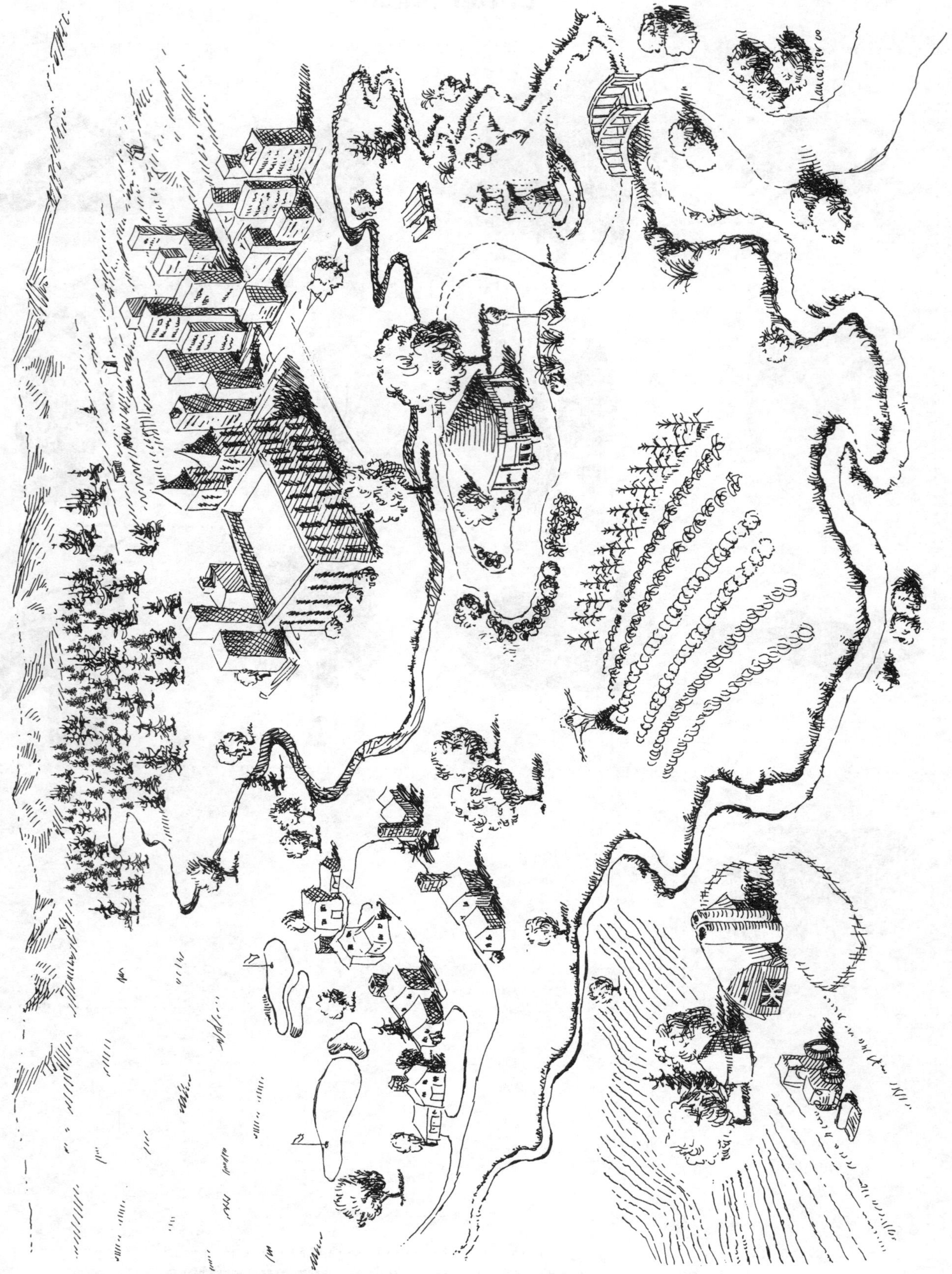

384 Project WILD K–12 Curriculum and Activity Guide

Wildwork

Objective
Students will identify and describe a variety of wildlife occupations.

Method
Students research wildlife-related careers and present their findings to the class.

Materials
Writing materials

Background
State and federal government agencies employ many specialists to help preserve and manage wildlife and wildlife habitats. Those employees do field work, conduct laboratory research, and oversee human interactions with wildlife. Universities and colleges, private and nonprofit wildlife-oriented agencies, zoos and museums, private industry, and others all employ people trained in the wildlife field. Some photograph, paint, draw, or write about wildlife for magazines, books, films, and television.

Grade Level: 5–8

Subject Areas: Social Studies, Language Arts

Duration: 10-minute introduction; one 40-minute session for presentations or longer depending on group size

Group Size: any

Setting: indoors

Conceptual Framework Reference: WMIIIC2

Key Terms: occupation, vocation, career

Appendices: Using Local Resources

The major purpose of this activity is for students to become familiar with career possibilities in wildlife-related fields.

Procedure

1. Ask students what careers they might be interested in pursuing. What kinds of jobs sound interesting? What about working with wildlife?

2. In a class discussion, find out what kinds of jobs students imagine exist in animal-related fields. Do any of their family or friends have animal-related occupations, involving wild animals, domesticated animals, or both?

3. Compile a list of possible wildlife-related occupations.

4. Ask each student or group of students to select one occupation to research. Find out what preparation (e.g., college) is needed for the job; what the responsibilities of the job entail; what special equipment, techniques, or, skills are needed, if any; and whether the demand for people in this occupation is growing, diminishing, or unchanged.

5. Have each student or group of students report on his or her wildlife-related occupation. This reporting can take a variety of forms, from skits about each job with props to help their portrayal, to a Wildlife Careers resource fair. The resource fair could have booths for each job, complete with visual aids, background information, and local contacts for additional information.

continued

Extensions

1. Contact someone in a wildlife-oriented job. Ask that person if he or she would be willing to contribute a class visit or letter describing the job. Have the students prepare questions in advance for the visitor. (Government wildlife agencies usually have a page of their website dedicated to jobs. They also print descriptive career leaflets. Write for a copy.) Compile a class letter to that individual, incorporating any questions the students might have. Here are some good questions to ask:

   - Why did you choose this career?
   - What education was necessary to prepare you for this job?
   - What do you do in a typical day's work?
   - How much do you actually work with wildlife? How much with people? How much with record keeping, reporting, and so on?
   - Do you work with people who have other wildlife-related careers?

   Share the letter of reply with the class, or have the professional visit the class to answer questions.

2. Investigate jobs related to a range of natural resources, from forestry to mining to litigation. Look at volunteer and private organizations as well as public and commercial, from attorneys for the National Wildlife Federation to public land coordinators for major oil companies.

3. Make a "wild web" showing the agencies, organizations, and occupations that typically could be involved in a wildlife management issue. Refer to the activity "History of Wildlife Management" to help explain each role in wildlife management.

Aquatic Extension

Focus specifically on the variety of aquatic-related careers that are available.

Evaluation

1. Identify and describe three jobs in which someone works with wildlife or other animals. Describe the training and qualifications required for each job.

2. Are there many jobs available in wildlife-related fields? Please explain your response.

3. Why, if at all, do you think careers in wildlife and other resource-related fields are important?

Checks
and Balances

Objectives
Students will (1) evaluate hypothetical wildlife management decisions, and (2) identify at least four factors that can affect the size of a wildlife population.

Method
Students become managers of a herd of animals in a conceptual and discussion-based activity.

Materials
Paper and pencils; paper to make condition cards; dice, one per student

Background
Wildlife managers attempt to maintain healthy populations of wild animals and preserve wildlife resources. Factors that may affect wildlife populations are loss of habitat, weather conditions, pollution of food and water sources, poaching, and pressure from recreation.

In the United States, it is the legal responsibility of state wildlife agencies to manage the wildlife populations within their respective states. It is the legal responsibility of the U.S. Fish and Wildlife Service, under the U.S. Department of the Interior, to govern policies and programs affecting migratory species of animals (principally birds), threatened or endangered species, illegal importation and exportation of animals and animal products, illegal interstate transportation of all species, and additional responsibilities related to the overall well-being of U.S. wildlife.

There are frequently differences of opinion about the most appropriate policies and programs affecting wildlife. Individual citizens, private conservation groups, private industry, community groups, and others all make important contributions to the overall conservation and protection of wildlife and its habitat.

Wildlife management is based on the best scientific and technical knowledge available. Such knowledge is continually affected by changes in the complex relationships among wildlife, human beings, and their shared environments.

The major purpose of this activity is for students hypothetically to assume the role of wildlife managers and thus to gain insight into some of the complex variables that influence stewardship of wildlife. This activity is not designed to provide a comprehensive understanding of all possible factors that can affect wildlife.

Grade Level: 5–8

Subject Areas: Mathematics, Science, Environmental Education

Duration: one to two 45-minute sessions

Group Size: any

Setting: indoors

Conceptual Framework Topic Reference: WMIIC2

Key Terms: management, population, herd

Appendices: Simulations

---

continued

Procedure

Before the Activity

Follow instructions for making Condition Cards found on page 390.

1. Each student is asked to be the manager of a moose (or other animal) population. The carrying capacity of the habitat is 100 animals. The point of the activity is to end up with a viable population after nine rounds, simulating 9 years. If at any time the student's population reaches fewer than 10 or more than 200 individual animals, that student no longer has a viable "herd" and watches the other students until the conclusion of the activity.

2. Each student has a beginning population of 100 animals. The cards are separated into three decks totaling 36 cards: a condition deck (18 cards), a reproduction deck (9 cards), and a management deck (9 cards). Shuffle the cards within each deck. Explain that cards will be drawn in the following sequence: condition card, reproduction card, condition card, management card. This sequence of draw will be repeated with each repetition representing an annual cycle (the students may think of each draw as representing a different season [e.g., autumn, winter, spring, summer]). As each card is drawn, it is read aloud to the entire class. Each student then rolls his or her die and follows the instructions on the card to determine his or her herd population's new size. Each card will require the student to calculate the increase or decrease of the population by a certain number. That number will be determined by multiplying the factor specified on the card by the roll of the die. Some computations will result in fractions; numbers may be rounded to the nearest whole.

NOTE: Students may object to the use of dice to determine the impact of decisions made for wildlife management purposes. Their concerns are appropriate; wildlife management is based on more than the chance elements reflected in the use of dice. However, chance has its impacts as well, as in the case of weather conditions in a given year. Encourage the students to discuss and consider what is realistic, and what is unrealistic, about the impact of dice in this activity. Encourage them to recognize that wildlife management is far more complex than can be represented through this activity.

3. Conclude the activity with a class discussion. Include topics such as identifying and describing what appeared to be the effects of the condition, reproduction, and management cards. What seemed to be the benefits and/or liabilities, if any, of management decisions made? Did populations "managed" under different strategies by different students show different trends? How do these compare? Would students "manage" differently if given a second chance? What aspects of this activity seemed realistic? Which didn't? What are examples of ways that habitat can be improved? Short term? Long term? Is human management of wildlife populations necessary? Beneficial? Why or why not? For people? For the animals?

Extension or Variation

Add a monetary aspect to the activity. Students allowing hunting might have more available revenue for projects like habitat enhancement because of income from the sale of hunting licenses. Other expenses might include salaries of wildlife managers, funds for research, feeding animals in severe conditions, relocation, and so forth.

Evaluation

1. Identify four factors that can affect the size of a wildlife population.
2. Some wildlife managers have said that wildlife management involves more management of people than of wildlife. Explain what they might mean by the comment.

Instructions for Making the Cards

Make the following cards, according to three categories: Reproduction Cards, Condition Cards, and Management Cards. There are a total of 36 cards. The number in parentheses indicates how many of each card are to be made. NOTE: The numbers of cards and the suggestions for numerical manipulations (e.g., three times the roll) are relatively arbitrary. They are designed for students to recognize that a number of diverse factors can affect wildlife; the numerical weights should not be interpreted literally. As the cards are read aloud, be certain to note differences in decreasing or increasing herd size by percentage or by number.

NOTE: The rate of reproduction is designed to vary with population density. The method for determining your population's rate of reproduction at a particular population size is derived from a number of assumptions. One of them is that the carrying capacity is 100 individuals. As your population drops below 100, the potential rate of reproduction increases reaching a peak at just above 50 individuals. This effect mimics the potential for rapid population growth many herbivore populations can exhibit when population levels are well below carrying capacity; in other words, food resources are readily available for reproductive effort, given that other environmental factors prove favorable. Below 10 individuals, reproduction is not allowed, reflecting severe reduction in reproductive activity observed at very low population levels because of, for example, unbalanced sex ratios, the inability to find suitable mates, or the disruption of social and mating systems. As the population grows above 100 individuals, the reproduction rate steadily decreases, reflecting the increasing activity of limiting factors as the population exceeds carrying capacity.

continued

Reproduction	**Reproduction Card—Average Year (6)** This has been an average reproduction year. Increase your herd by (100/your current population size) three times your roll, if your current population is over 50 individuals. If your population is between 50 and 10, increase your population by three times your roll. If your population is under 10, don't reproduce.	Reproduction	**Reproduction Card—Excellent Year (3)** This has been an excellent reproduction year. Increase your herd by (100/your current population size) five times your roll, if your current population is over 50 individuals. If your population is between 50 and 10, increase your population by the number equal to five times your roll. If your population is under 10, you may not reproduce.
Condition	**Weather Card (2)** _____ (Students need to specify what) has had a serious negative impact on the survival of the herd. Decrease your herd by the percentage equal to five times your roll.	Management	**Habitat Alteration Card (2)** _____ (Students need to specify what) has occurred, altering critical habitat. Increase or decrease (students choose which before rolling the die) the herd by the percentage equal to three times your roll.
Condition	**Weather Card (2)** _____ (Students need to specify what) has had a dramatic positive impact on the survival of the herd. Increase your herd by the percentage equal to five times your roll.	Management	**Habitat Improvement Card (1)** _____ (Students need to specify what) has occurred, improving critical habitat. Increase herd by the number equal to five times your roll.
Condition	**Habitat Destruction Card (2)** _____ (Students need to specify what) has occurred, destroying critical habitat. Decrease the herd size by the number equal to five times your roll.	Management	**Research Card (1)** _____ (Students need to specify what) research has been successfully accomplished. Increase or decrease (students choose which before rolling the die) the herd by two times your roll.
Condition	**Predator Card (1)** Predation has occurred, affecting the herd size. Decrease the herd size by the percentage equal to your roll.	Management	**Law Enforcement Card (1)** _____ (Students need to specify what) law enforcement activities have protected the herd against illegal actions like poaching. Increase the herd by the percentage equal to two times your roll.
Condition	**Habitat Degradation Card (4)** _____ (Students need to specify what) has occurred, damaging critical habitat. Decrease the herd by the number equal to three times your roll.	Management	**Education Card (1)** _____ (Students need to specify what) education activities have led to increased understanding of wildlife and habitat. Increase or decrease (students choose which before rolling the die) the herd by the percentage equal to two times your roll, or by two times your roll.
Condition	**Disease Card (1)** Disease has struck the herd. Decrease the herd by the percentage equal to your roll.		
Condition	**Habitat Loss Card (5)** _____ (Students need to specify what) has resulted in a loss of critical habitat for the herd. Decrease the herd by the number equal to five times your roll.	Management	**Habitat Acquisition Card (1)** Habitat acquisition has increased the area of available and suitable habitat. Increase the herd by five times your roll.
Condition	**Poaching Card (1)** Poaching—illegal killing of animals—has reduced the size of the herd. Decrease the herd by the number equal to two times your roll.	Management	**Hunting Card (1)** A request for a hunting season has been made. Do you wish to allow hunting in your area? If yes, decrease your herd by the percentage equal to five times your roll. If no, record no change in the size of your herd.
Management	**Habitat Restoration Card (1)** _____ (Students need to specify what) has occurred, restoring critical habitat. Increase the herd by the percentage equal to five times your roll.		

Sample Student Calculation Table

Year One Completed

Year	Starting Population	Condition				Reproduction				Condition				Management		
		Die Roll X	Card Factor =	Population Change	New Population	Die Roll X	Card Factor =	Population Change	New Population	Die Roll X	Card Factor =	Population Change	New Population	Die Roll X	Card Factor =	Population Change	New Population
1	100	2	-3	-6	94	1	+4	+4	98	5	-2	-10	88	3	+1	+3	91
2	91																
9																	

Student Calculation Table

Year	Starting Population	Condition				Reproduction				Condition				Management		
		Die Roll X	Card Factor =	Population Change	New Population	Die Roll X	Card Factor =	Population Change	New Population	Die Roll X	Card Factor =	Population Change	New Population	Die Roll X	Card Factor =	Population Change	New Population
1																	
2																	
3																	
4																	
5																	
6																	
7																	
8																	
9																	

Deer Crossing

Objectives

Students will (1) identify various factors involved in a wildlife management issue, and (2) evaluate alternatives in a complex issue involving wildlife.

Method

Students are given background information and asked to make recommendations.

Materials

Copies of the Deer Crossing Student Page on page 394

Background

The major purpose of this activity is to provide students with an opportunity to analyze and evaluate complex factors that frequently arise in wildlife management issues. Wildlife management decisions must consider political, social, economic, and biological concerns. The situation used to illustrate this activity is based on actual occurrences involving a herd of deer in the state of Idaho.

Grade Level: 9–12

Subject Areas: Social Studies, Environmental Education

Duration: two 45-minute sessions or longer

Group Size: large group

Setting: indoors

Conceptual Framework Topic Reference: WMIIC2

Key Terms: land use, condemnation, deed

Appendices: None

NOTE: To obtain more information on options and alternatives for control of deer populations, visit the Project WILD web site at **www.projectwild.org** or your state wildlife agency's web site.

Procedure

1. Provide groups of two to four students with the Deer Crossing Student Page, which is based on an actual situation in the state of Idaho. Ask the students, working in their groups, to read the information and to discuss and evaluate options they think are available to resolve the situation in the best possible manner. They should be prepared to share and explain the recommendations of their group.

2. Ask the student groups to present and explain their recommendations. If students do not already have background, they may need to do research to prepare for their presentations. If additional research is not possible, the students can identify areas where they think additional information is needed and why, before they feel they can make responsible recommendations. Where such points arise, ask for one or two students—if not more—to volunteer to obtain and verify this additional information. To formalize the reporting, each group could

   - describe the situation (or briefly review);
   - provide background information;
   - identify and describe factors involved in the issue;
   - identify and describe alternative solutions; and
   - state their recommended action, with their reasons for the recommendations.

392   Project WILD K–12 Curriculum and Activity Guide

Extension

See the Project WILD activity "Deer Dilemma," which further explores controversies related to the issue of deer population control.

Evaluation

1. What are the factors involved in this deer problem? What are the values that must be considered by the people trying to solve this problem? How might the problem have been avoided, or at least solved less expensively?

2. Consider this situation: A stream, dammed for flood control 5 years ago, has become an area for a number of wildlife and human problems. Because of the quantity of still and warm water available, the mosquito population is up and the number of fish species is being reduced. Soil and nutrients running off local farms have increased the growth of aquatic plants. The fishing, boating, swimming, and picnicking use of the area has declined from the early years. However, flooding concerns for the city downstream have been virtually eliminated. The residents in the town do not report being bothered too much by the mosquitoes.

List at least four factors that should be considered in this resource management issue. Identify, describe, and evaluate at least four possible actions that could be taken to resolve the resource problems that have developed, attending to the diverse values represented in the community as well as overall wildlife and human needs. Select what you think is the most reasonable and appropriate solution and explain your reasons.

continued

Deer Crossing Student Page

A major highway is being considered to replace an older, two-lane road. Building the new highway will make it possible for travelers to travel to a nearby town approximately 6 minutes faster than they could by the old road. The new highway would pose a major problem for a herd of deer in the area. Whereas the old road skirted a migration route used by the deer when moving between summer and winter feeding ranges, the new highway would lie directly in the path of the deer's migration.

The new highway was built, blocking the deer's migration. The deer tried to cross the highway, but many were killed in the process in collisions with autos and trucks. People also were injured, and some were killed. A large fence was built along both sides of this highway, in hopes of preventing the animals from trying to cross. Even so, some deer were able to cross, with collisions and fatalities still the result.

Most of the deer, however, were not able to jump the fence that was built. Instead, the majority of the herd bunched up on one side of the fence, without being able to cross. The problem was particularly critical each winter. The deer were trying to move out of the high mountains, where they spent the summer months, to get to lower feeding areas for the winter. There was not enough food for the deer if they could not get to their winter feeding area. They bunched up by the fence, ate any food in the area quickly, and began damaging the remaining vegetation and soil structure as they looked for food.

Every year since the highway was built, the state wildlife agency has brought in food for the hungry deer. Even so, some deer die from starvation each winter. Deer being fed under these crowded conditions in a central feeding area are more apt to contract and spread disease. They also become accustomed to being fed by humans. The wildlife agency has taken several approaches to relieve this situation. A 7 ½ mile-long fence was constructed to the north and east of the highway. This structure has helped to hold the deer farther north and helps to disperse the animals to minimize damage to the watershed in the vicinity of the feeding area. The U.S. Bureau of Land Management initiated a project to plant saltbush and bitterbrush on several hundred acres of land adjacent to this fence. An additional 1,500 acres has been seeded by plane. These bushes are now 3 to 4 feet high and provide natural winter range for the deer herd. Plans call for seeding another 3,000 to 4,000 acres, the acreage calculated as necessary to support a herd of 2,000 deer.

Consider the following possibilities—including costs and benefits of each—and any others that you might come up with that you think would be effective and appropriate:

- Issue hunting permits to reduce the size of the herd in the area,
- Live-capture and transplant deer to areas where there is sufficient room and food for them to live,
- Persuade the highway department to build underpasses or overpasses the deer can use to move from one feeding area to the other,
- Keep feeding the deer artificially,
- Let the deer starve, or
- Something else.

From Bison to Bread: The American Prairie

Objectives

Students will (1) describe the habitat needs of prairie plants and animals, (2) discriminate between plant and wildlife species that have benefited from changed prairie use and those that have not, (3) articulate reasons to develop or preserve prairies, and (4) describe how preservation and development might be balanced.

Method

Students will research plants and animals found in prairie ecosystems and debate the reasons for development or preservation of prairies.

Materials

Overhead of U.S. map showing range of prairies, copies of Prairie Questionnaire and Prairie Species Data Sheet on pages 402 and 403, flip chart or board for graphing responses to questionnaire; OPTIONAL: Copies of Readings from Lonesome Prairie

---

Grade Level: 9–12

Subject Areas: Science, Social Studies, Environmental Education, Language Arts

Duration: 15 minutes to prepare, one to three 40-minute sessions for activities

Group Size: individual and teams of three to four students

Setting: indoors and outdoors

Conceptual Framework Topic Reference: WMIC, WMIIA, WMIIC, WMIIC2, WMIIIB3, WMIIIB4, WMIIB5

Key Terms: exotic, forb, herbivore, humus, monoculture, pothole, playa, prairie, predator

Appendices: none

Background

When European explorers first came to North America, they used the word "prairie"— the French word for meadow—to describe the vast grasslands they encountered. Prairies are extensive grasslands with a diversity of forbs and few shrubs or trees.

The North American prairie originally extended from Canada into Texas and from Indiana to the Rocky Mountains. Less-extensive patches of prairie were also found in other states. Originally a vast, rich grassland, this region is now a mixture of cropland, pasture, development, and wild areas. Land that once supported lush grasses and grazing bison is now important in the production of corn, wheat, and livestock.

Today, little original prairie is left. As the demand for cultivated and grazing lands has increased, fewer prairies have remained in their original condition. While the conversion of prairie to cropland benefits people, natural prairies offer aesthetic and ecological benefits as rangeland, habitat for wildlife, a diverse pool of plant species, and a protective buffer to ground and surface water supplies.

Prairie Plant Life

Prairies are classified by the dominant grass species. The tallgrass prairie is found farthest east and contains grasses such as big and little bluestem, Indian grass, and switch grass. These grasses can grow 8 feet tall and extend roots more than 7 feet into the soil. Relatively heavy annual rainfall of 20 to 40 inches supports these grasses. Farther west, where rainfall is less plen-

continued

tiful (15–20 inches annually) and evaporation rates are higher, is the mixed-grass prairie. Typical species include little bluestem, needlegrass, and Junegrass, which grow 2 to 4 feet tall.

The shortgrass region receives less than 15 inches of annual precipitation. Side-oats grama, blue grama, western wheatgrass, and buffalograss are the dominant grasses in this area, rarely growing taller than 16 inches. Despite their small size, these grasses provide important forage all year.

Prairie grasses have dense mats of interlocking roots. This root network holds the soil, absorbs moisture, and helps the grass spread and renew itself. As grasses die, the roots decompose to form dark, humus-rich soil.

Grasses are not the only plants of the prairie. Among the forbs found are blazing star, sunflower, aster, prairie clover, and coneflower. Trees and shrubs provide occasional relief from the expanses of grass. Cottonwood, willow, bur oak, and American elm line prairie stream banks. Shrubs range from the hardy big sagebrush to the colorful prairie rose. Generally, though, tree and shrub growth is prevented by lack of moisture and periodic prairie fires. These fires, started by lightning or humans, remove trees, shrubs, and dead plants and release minerals into the soil, resulting in more vigorous plant growth.

Prairie Mammals

With the amount of grass found on the prairie, it is not surprising that grazing species are the dominant wildlife. In the past, bison, elk, and pronghorns were the most common grazing species. Mule deer and especially white-tailed deer were present where browse was plentiful. Although many of these larger mammals are no longer common, smaller animals, such as jackrabbits and prairie dogs, still inhabit the prairies.

The largest grazing animal of the prairies was the bison. A total population of 60 million bison may have existed in 1600. Because each animal requires approximately 30 pounds of forage per day, roaming bison had a significant impact on the vegetation of the prairie. By the late 19th century, however, the importance of bison as a prairie grazer and a major food source for the indigenous people had been reduced. Hunting and habitat alterations left only a few animals. Today bison populations are being maintained on federal, state, and private lands.

Pronghorn occupy drier portions of the prairies and depend on sharp eyesight and speed for protection in a habitat with little cover. Habitat loss, construction of fences, and a high susceptibility to disease resulted in the reduction of pronghorn numbers from former abundance to almost disastrous low populations.

A number of predators depend on these prairie herbivores. Native predators include the gray wolf, red wolf, coyote, kit fox, swift fox, mountain lion, badger, and bobcat. Of these, only the bobcat, coyote, and one fox (red fox) species have been able to adjust to changing land-use patterns. Wolf and mountain lion populations have been severely reduced.

Prairie Birds

The prairies provide a home to an amazing variety of birds. Waterfowl, prairie chickens, songbirds, and other species migrate, live, or nest in prairie grasses, rivers, and ponds. The prairie pothole region of North Dakota, South Dakota, Minnesota, and northwest Iowa is the backbone of duck production in the United States. The playa lakes region of Oklahoma, Kansas, Texas, Colorado, and New Mexico provides important habitat for waterfowl as well.

The most abundant species are the mallard, pintail, and blue-winged teal. Although comprising only 10 percent of the total waterfowl breeding area in the United States, prairie potholes produce 50 percent of the duck crop in an average year.

Prairie chickens and sharp-tailed grouse are major upland game birds of the prairies. Populations of these birds reached a peak in about 1900. Since then, their numbers have decreased because of habitat alterations brought about by agriculture and the drought of the 1930s.

A wide variety of other bird species are found on the prairies. Songbirds such as the meadowlark, bobolink, and yellow-headed blackbird are present; birds of prey include the red-tailed hawk, great horned owl, American kestrel, and Swainson's hawk. Shorebirds such as the long-billed curlew, the marbled godwit, and killdeer can be seen, as well as the sandhill crane, trumpeter swan, and the unique whooping crane, which is not generally considered a prairie species.

Agriculture on the Prairie

The North American prairie has some of the most productive agricultural soils in the world. However, the tall grasses, with their extensive matted root networks, deterred farmers in the eastern prairies for many years. As farmers gradually moved into the prairie regions of Illinois, they found their traditional plows no match for the dense roots of the prairie grass. It wasn't until 1843, when John Deere invented a new type of plow, that farming the tallgrass prairie became possible. Soon, the seemingly monotonous sea of grass provided rich soil for agriculture.

Encouraged by the Homestead Act of 1862, farmers began to settle on the eastern Great Plains in the mixed-grass prairie. At the same time, the number of ranches in the area increased as railroads provided better access to eastern markets and made long trail drives unnecessary.

By 1880, farming was well established on the prairies. In the tallgrass prairie of Iowa 69 percent was cultivated, largely in corn. Iowa now has lost more than 99 percent of its original prairies. The mixed-grass prairie had been found suitable for growing wheat. Those areas are now known as the "Cornbelt" and "Wheatland," respectively.

Challenges for the Prairie

In addition to conversion to farmland, prairies have been affected by other agricultural practices. Overgrazing results when too many cattle are placed on the range or when stock is grazed year-round. To support year-round grazing, landowners may plow the native vegetation and replace it with an exotic grass, which may provide better grazing but will produce a monoculture that is not as valuable to wildlife. A natural prairie supports a diverse plant and animal community that can survive periodic drought, fires, or other natural stresses.

Fire is an important component in maintaining the prairie ecosystem. Prairie plants and animals are adapted to periodic fire. Historically, Native Americans used fire to manage wildlife and early settlers followed this example. Eventually, the settlers stopped intentionally burning the prairie and put out fires that occurred naturally. Fire suppression allows species such as eastern red cedar to invade the prairie. This invasion changes the plant composition of the ecosystem and the prairie habitat is lost. While the lack of fire allows invasive woody plants to dominate the prairie, burning too often can also change the composition of plants and cause desirable prairie species to be lost.

Prairie potholes are important wetlands. To plant more crops, people often drained these potholes. (In Iowa, over 90 percent of the original wetlands, mostly prairie pothole marshes, were drained and converted to agricultural land.) Because this waterfowl breeding area is so productive, losing some of these wetlands can have a significant effect on waterfowl populations over all of North America.

continued

Another prairie issue focuses on water. The prairie vegetation permits water to be absorbed slowly rather than running off and causing erosion. As the water soaks in, it is filtered and cleaned. The Ogallala aquifer, a major water source in the Great Plains, underlies the prairie region. Extensive removal of native plants has increased runoff and reduced the infiltration of water. This change, combined with drilling wells for irrigation and development, has lowered the ground-water level in the aquifer. The increased rate of runoff, combined with exposed soils from agriculture and development, leads to increased soil erosion and fills in rivers, streams, and lakes with silt (fine soil). Formerly clear, meandered prairie streams that supported a diversity of animals now often are straightened, murky waterways with little biological diversity.

Planning for the Future

Many of the problems mentioned here can be avoided through planning. Protecting areas not suited for farming and avoiding overgrazing will maintain the grasses and plants. Farming around prairie potholes rather than draining them, provides continued waterfowl habitat and can even provide income to landowners through bird watching, photography, hunting, and trapping opportunities. Maintaining natural vegetation and avoiding complete conversion to croplands can protect the availability and quality of ground-water supplies and can reduce erosion that pollutes surface waters. Finally, while some frequency of fire is necessary for prairie maintenance, it should be used in moderation with rotational grazing to control shrub and tree growth without long-term damage to the grasses.

In addition, private groups and government agencies have purchased some remaining pieces of virgin prairie to preserve them. Scattered plots of natural prairies also are found along power lines and old railroad right-of-ways.

Acquisition, protection, improvement, and restoration of habitat are considered to be the most successful and cost-effective, long-range techniques for managing wildlife species. Prairies also can be restored, given the seed stock and enough time. Centuries are needed to produce the organic soils, but in 3 to 4 years, prairie plantings can attract wildlife and provide aesthetic pleasure. This restoration process is occurring today on a small scale in outdoor classrooms, in parks, on highway shoulders and median strips and in backyards. An expansive area of prairie is being restored using local eco-type seeds at the Neal Smith Wildlife Refuge east of Des Moines, Iowa.

The purpose of this activity is to highlight the importance of habitat in managing and conserving wildlife resources. Wildlife species are important components of a larger ecosystem and should be managed within the context of that ecosystem; and, therefore, wildlife management decisions must also consider political, social, and economic, as well as biological concerns.

Procedure

1. Have students complete the Prairie Questionnaire on page 402 to determine their present knowledge and attitudes toward prairies.

2. Have students individually tally their responses. Scores will range between 10 and 40. If a student strongly agrees with all statements, the rating total would be 10. If the student strongly disagrees with all statements, the rating would be 40.

3. Use the individual student totals to produce a graph of the class responses. The horizontal axis represents the possible point totals (10 through 40). The vertical axis represents the number of students having each score. Display the graph and have students plot their data.

4. Draw a "best-fit" line that indicates the class preference curve. For instance, if the class is neutral, the curve will be symmetrically arranged around a score of 25. If the class opinion leans toward preservation, the curve will be off-center to the right. If it leans toward development, the curve will be off-center to the left. See the sample graph on page 404.

5. Using the background information, lead an introductory discussion of prairies, prairie wildlife, and the natural history of prairies.

6. Using the map, show the class the original range of North American prairies. Ask your students how that land is now being used. List responses on the board.

7. Assign each student a prairie wildlife and plant species to research from the list on page 401. Have students research the habitat requirements of the species. What needs of this species are met by prairies? What is the range of this species? Have its habitats changed over time? What conservation regulations and management practices have been established to improve, protect, or enhance its habitats? Ask students to fill in the Prairie Species Data Sheet using their research.

8. If possible, visit a prairie. Check with your local state conservation agency, private conservation group, or local nature center for the location of a prairie. If it is not possible to visit a prairie, plan a simulated field trip instead. You can use the Readings from Lonesome Prairie on page 405 to show how people from different time periods viewed the prairie. Use photographs, movies, books, slides, and so on, to show the class the plants and wildlife of a prairie. Try to include as much diversity as possible (different types of prairies, rivers, streams, potholes, etc.).

9. Applying what they learned, students can make visual displays of the prairie site. Have students relate this information to the research done to complete the Prairie Species Data Sheet. Did the site provide suitable habitats for the wildlife they researched? Why or why not? At the site, what management practices to conserve habitat and wildlife are evident? How does plant diversity affect wildlife? How important is preservation or restoration of habitat to long-range management of wildlife species? Discuss students' answers, and note that change does not affect all species in the same way. Some animals are able to adapt to changes, and some are not.

Students' answers should reflect the following: prairie dogs dig burrows dangerous to grazing livestock and eat the same grasses as livestock; bison compete with cattle for grass and forage; mallards still migrate through and nest in prairie states, often feeding on cultivated crops; prairie chickens need thick grass to nest; plains pocket mice feed on seeds (either native or cultivated) and insects, and they live underground; ring-necked pheasants (introduced from China) make abundant use of fence rows and pastures; jackrabbits feed mostly on grasses, either native or cultivated; red-tailed hawks can adapt to many changes as long as food is available; black-footed ferrets use prairie dog burrows; and some species actually are more common because of their ability to adapt to land use changes.

The students' observations should show that a greater variety of plants in turn supports a greater variety of wildlife. This relationship is also seen in the reverse where an agricultural monoculture has a limited and less-diverse wildlife population. Habitat and wildlife are interrelated, with greater diversity of habitat resulting in greater diversity of wildlife.

continued

10. Randomly assign an equal number of students to each of the 10 Prairie Questionnaire statements. (If time is limited or the group is small, fewer statements can be used.) Each group should then develop an argument either for or against the assigned statement. Students should research information to support their reasoning and then present a short (5 minutes) description of their findings and conclusions to the class.

11. Allow time after the presentations for the class to debate each group's position. Ask the class to consider how the various positions on preservation and development might be balanced. What political, social, economic, and biological factors should be considered to reach a consensus? Why is it important to have a well-educated public in relationship to wildlife management issues?

12. After the debate, pass out a second set of Prairie Questionnaires, and have students repeat it and graph the results. Is the curve different this time? Did the research and debate change the group pattern? Did they change individual responses?

Extension

Make arrangements to take the group to a natural prairie site, a farm site, or both converted from a former prairie. The purpose of the field trips includes (1) providing a background for students' wildlife research, (2) exposing students to the components of the prairie habitat, and (3) demonstrating how prairies have been altered.

At the natural prairie site, students should look for ways the habitat meets the needs of the wildlife species researched to complete the Prairie Species Data Sheet. In addition, they should observe the diversity of the area. Working in groups, they should count the number of different species of plants, mammals, birds, insects, reptiles, and so forth, that are present.

For the farm site, select an area that was prairie in the past. A cultivated field is an excellent site, as it has natural features, is large enough and presents few safety hazards. Be sure to ask the landowner's permission and explain what the visit will entail. Caution students to take care not to harm crops. If possible, have the landowner present to explain what is being grown and how it is cultivated.

Evaluation

1. Describe the importance of the protection, improvement, and restoration of habitat for wildlife species conservation and management. Why should prairies be developed? Protected?

2. Describe factors to consider when balancing the preservation and development of prairie lands. Cite specific plant and animal relationships to support your answer.

Adapted with permission from: *Partners With Wildlife*, Kansas Department of Wildlife and Parks.

Wildlife Species

Red fox (*Vulpes fulva*)

Bison (*Bison bison*)

Pronghorn (*Antilocapra americana*)

White tail or black tail jack rabbit (*Lepus townsendi* or *Lepus californicus*)

Prairie dog (*Cynomys ludovicianus*)

Western meadowlark (*Sturnella neglecta*)

Dickcissel (*Spiza americana*)

Northern harrier (*Circus cyaneus*)

Burrowing owl (*Speotyto cunicularia*)

Greater prairie chicken (*Tympanuchus cupido*)

Sharp-tailed grouse (*Tympanuchus phasianellus*)

Plains spadefoot toad (*Scaphiopus bombifrons*)

Crayfish (*Orconectes virilis*)

Slender glass lizard (*Ophisaurus attenuatus*)

Western ornate box turtle (*Terrapene ornate*)

Western hognose snake (*Heterodon nasicus*)

Prairie rattlesnake (*Crotalus viridis*)

Dakota skipper (*Hesperia dacotae*)

Monarch butterfly (*Danaus plexippus*)

Goldenrod spider (*Misumena vatia*)

Two-striped grasshopper (*Mermiria bivittata*)

Plains pocket gopher (*Geomys bursarius*)

Tiger salamander (*Ambystoma tigrinum*)

Mallard duck (*Anas platyrhynchos*)

American bittern (*Botaurus lentiginosus*)

Northern pintail (*Anas acuta*)

Plains pocket mouse (*Perognathus flavescens*)

Ring-necked pheasant (*Phasianus colchicus*)

Red-tailed hawk (*Buteo jamaicensis*)

Prairie falcon (*Falco mexicanus*)

Black-footed ferret (*Mustela nigripes*)

Elk (*Cervus canadensis*)

Coyote (*Canis latrans*)

Thirteen-lined ground squirrel (*Citellus tridecemlineatus*)

Regal fritillary (*Speyeria idalia*)

Plant Species

Hackberry (*Celtis occidentalis*)

American plum (*Prunus americana*)

Bur oak (*Quercus macrocarpa*)

Eastern cottonwood (*Populus deltoides*)

Eastern red cedar (*Juniperus virginiana*)

Roughleaf dogwood (*Cornus drummondii*)

Persimmon (*Diospyros virginiana*)

Prickly pear (*Opuntia humifusa*)

Common mullein (*Verascum thapus*)

Compass plant (*Silphium laciniatum*)

Lead plant (*Amorpha canescens*)

Prairie blazing star (*Liatris pycnostachya*)

Purple prairie clover (*Petalostemum purpureum*)

Smooth sumac (*Rhus glabra*)

Common milkweed (*Asclepias syriaca*)

Prairie rose (*Rosa suffulta*)

Spotted Joe-Pye weed (*Eupatorium maculatum*)

Black-eyed Susan (*Rudbeckia hirta*)

Tall goldenrod (*Solidago altissima*)

Needle grass (*Stipa spartea*)

Prairie cordgrass (*Spartina pectinata*)

Hairy grama (*Bouteloua hirsuta*)

Buffalograss (*Buchloe dactyloides*)

Big bluestem (*Andropogon gerardi*)

Little bluestem (*Andropogon scoparius*)

Switch grass (*Panicum virgatum*)

Indian grass (*Sorghastrum nutans*)

Junegrass (*Koeleria macrantha*)

continued

Prairie Questionnaire

Name: _____

Here are 10 statements about how prairies might be used. Read each one, and then circle the number on the scale that best describes your feelings.

1. We need more cropland to feed the world's growing population.	1 strongly agree	2 agree	3 disagree	4 strongly disagree
2. The importance of prairies in U.S. history is a poor reason to preserve them.	1 strongly agree	2 agree	3 disagree	4 strongly disagree
3. Farmers should be allowed to drain and farm prairie potholes if they need the money instead of farming around them.	1 strongly agree	2 agree	3 disagree	4 strongly disagree
4. Wildlife species that depend on prairies are no longer important.	1 strongly agree	2 agree	3 disagree	4 strongly disagree
5. If a landowner can make more money by building houses on a prairie than by preserving it, then it is all right to build houses.	1 strongly agree	2 agree	3 disagree	4 strongly disagree
6. Prairies are not needed to prevent soil erosion and protect water quality.	1 strongly agree	2 agree	3 disagree	4 strongly disagree
7. Because Native Americans no longer depend on the prairie ecosystem and its wildlife, prairies do not need to be preserved.	1 strongly agree	2 agree	3 disagree	4 strongly disagree
8. The scenic beauty of the prairie should not be considered when deciding to develop or preserve a prairie.	1 strongly agree	2 agree	3 disagree	4 strongly disagree
9. Prairies make excellent sites for farming and development because they are generally flat and thus should be used for those purposes.	1 strongly agree	2 agree	3 disagree	4 strongly disagree
10. Prairies should be farmed even if they are rocky or steep.	1 strongly agree	2 agree	3 disagree	4 strongly disagree

Prairie Species Data Sheet

Add the name of the species you researched, and fill in the blanks using your findings.

Wildlife	Plant
Range:	Range:
Food:	Food:
Predators:	Predators:
Shelter:	Shelter:
Special adaptatons:	Special adaptatons:
Management practices:	Management practices:

continued

Sustaining Fish and Wildlife Resources
From Bison to Bread: The American Prairie

Sample Graph
Class Talley of Responses to the Prairie Questionnaire

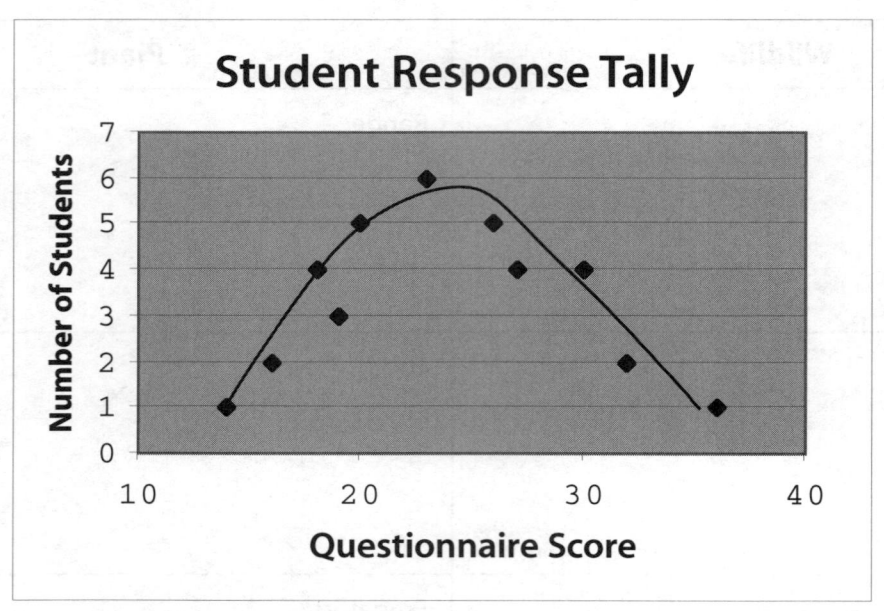

The Prairie Bioregion

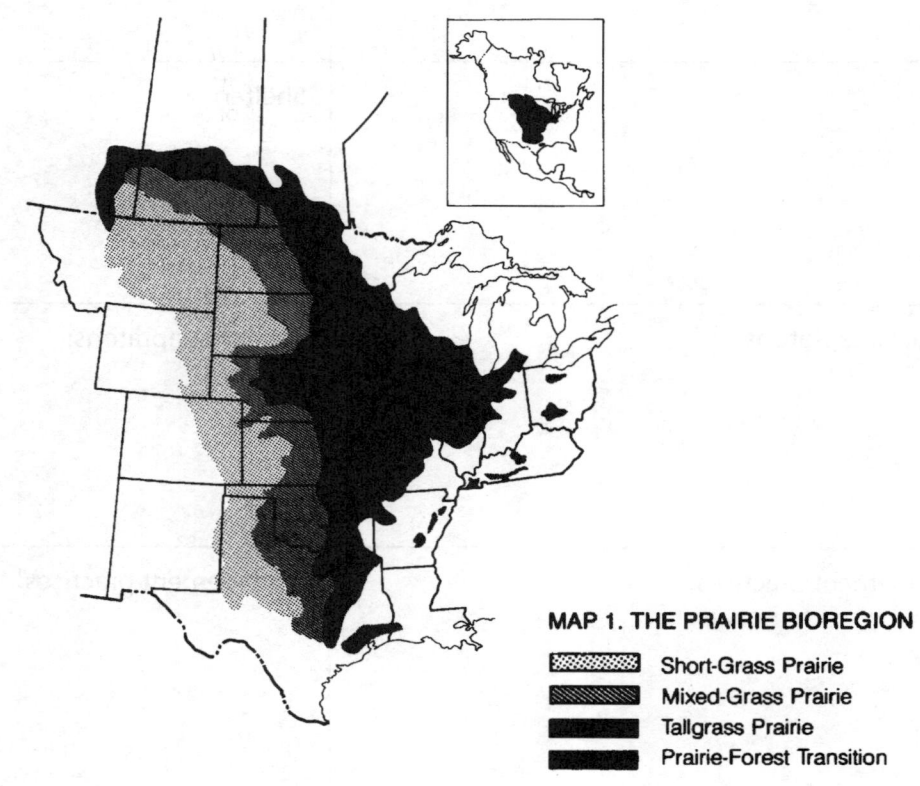

MAP 1. THE PRAIRIE BIOREGION
- Short-Grass Prairie
- Mixed-Grass Prairie
- Tallgrass Prairie
- Prairie-Forest Transition

Readings from Lonesome Prairie

Dear Diary:

The sun rose to a cloudless sky and what seemed to be an endless sea of waving grass. It has been 3 days since we left the secure and bustling city of Independence. The prairie goes on forever, as far as the eye can see.

Our journey would be simple if we could sail across the tops of the hills, but for every hilltop there is a valley. We travel the ridgetops as long as we can, but then we must travel down into the valley, only to have the oxen pull the wagon to the top of another hill.

I've found that it is much easier to walk than ride in the jolting wagon. Walking away from the wagon train, I can enjoy the songs of the birds—the sharp whistle of a partridge, the chirp of a lark, or the croaking of a raven in the distant woods. The birds' songs are mixed with the whirl of insect wings as they sail from one clump of grass to another.

I now recognize five different types of grasses, but the wildflowers will take much longer. The wildflowers make the prairie look like a floral tapestry, woven with threads of yellow, white, blue, lavender, and pink.

Along our path today, we encountered many streams, or perhaps it was the same one that kept crossing our path. Most have been shallow, not more than a foot deep. It is the 3 and 4 feet deep crossings that cause us to stop, unload the wagon, cross, and reload.

We did not stop today until after 2 o'clock. The prairie provided us with entertainment. Three very large black birds with red heads soared tirelessly for more than an hour. Not one flapped a wing the entire time.

The only shelter from the sun is under my bonnet, which has been hard to keep on because of the constant wind. The only other shade is from the occasional trees found along the streams. Cottonwood, elm, and sometimes a bur oak offer some relief.

We found little firewood for tonight's cook fire and will have to resort to a cold dinner. I hope we find firewood on tomorrow's journey. We made 12 miles today. I hope we can continue to make good progress.

—Nellie Morgan, June 6, 1855

Dear Diary:

I can't believe that when I agreed to marry Fred, I would have to leave my home at the corner of 6th and James and move to the farm. From my front steps, I could see the front doors of six of my best girlfriends, and the corner drug store was only two blocks away.

But not here—I am in the middle of the prairie. Our closest neighbors are the Humphreys, a half mile to the east, and the Floyds are just over a mile to the south. From my front steps, the only thing I can see is wave after wave of waist-high wheat. Out the back door is the barn and the corral full of Holsteins waiting for their 4 o'clock milking.

In the afternoons between chores, I've been reading Fred's family history. This farm has been in his family for more than 100 years. His great-grandmother, Nellie Morgan, was traveling west with her family when their wagon broke down. Having no materials to fix it or money to buy a new one, they decided to stake a claim here in Harvey County.

They first tried ranching but soon turned to growing wheat. Mennonite immigrants from Russia arrived in the area in the 1870s, bringing with them the drought resistant "Turkey Red" wheat. This plant forever changed the face of the prairie. Acres and acres of native prairie were plowed under to plant wheat, turning the "Great American Desert" into the nation's breadbasket.

Even though I've seen it many times before, I'm still impressed by the wheat harvest. Every year in June and early July, the harvest moves north across the state. Wheat fields, which were planted the previous fall, have reached a golden ripeness. Huge combines move through the fields, making short work of what previously was a labor-consuming job.

I need to get cleaned up and change clothes now. It's the Fourth of July, and there's a big celebration in town tonight. There'll be watermelon and hamburgers to eat, games, and a fireworks show. Maybe I'll see some of my high school friends.

—Linda Yoder, July 4, 1969

Bird Song Survey

Objective
Students will identify and describe the importance of bird counting as one means of inventorying wildlife populations.

Method
Students investigate an area and use bird-counting techniques.

Materials
Paper and pencil for note-taking, bird books as reference materials, drawing paper or magazine photos to illustrate final written project; OPTIONAL: binoculars, tapes of bird-call recordings, and battery-operated player

---

Grade Level: 9–12

Subject Areas: Environmental Education, Science

Duration: minimum of three 45-minute sessions, not including transportation to bird inventory site

Group Size: up to 30, with need to break into smaller groups for bird watching

Setting: outdoors

Conceptual Framework Topic Reference: WMIIIA, WMIIIB1

Key Terms: inventory, population, management, habitat

Appendices: Outdoors, Field Ethics, Animals in the Classroom

Background
People interested in wildlife and its habitat use many techniques to learn and assist in the management for conservation and protection of wildlife. Some techniques are used to acquire information and some to apply knowledge. Inventory is a technique that is used to acquire information about the number and kinds of wildlife in a given area.

This activity is designed to give students some experience in the use of inventory. Birds are the subject of study. The variety of species and the number of individual birds in an area are good indicators of the quality of that particular environment. Their presence indicates food, water, shelter, and space in an appropriate arrangement to suit their needs. Bird watching can be a valuable research tool, as well as an aesthetically pleasing activity that brings the student into touch with intangible values.

One means of identifying a bird species is by sight; another is by sound or song. Male birds of most species sing from conspicuous perches to mark territory, except during the nesting period. With practice, identification of many bird songs can be easily learned.

Procedure
NOTE: This can be an annual project or a one-time project during a single school year. Students who participate in a multiyear project can be contributing to a meaningful record of the natural history of their area.

1. Establish a suitable tract of land and an optimal season for conducting this activity. Check to find out in which time of year, in your area, there would be the greatest variety and number of birds. (Members of the National Audubon Society or the state nongame wildlife program may be able to assist with this information.) Find an area that is most likely to offer many habitats and thus is more likely to offer variety in birds as well. Transi-tion areas between differing ecosystems—like ponds, woods, and meadow areas—are apt to be good locations. Watering sites in desert areas and city sites with vegetation and water are other good locations. If the students are assisting in identifying the most suitable site, remind them of the basic habitat needs of animals, including birds: food, water, shelter, and space in an appropriate arrangement. They can use these components as working criteria.

2. Invite a member or members of a local bird club (e.g., affiliate chapter of the National Audubon Society) to instruct the class in field study techniques for bird watching. These people can help the class determine what bird species are common to the area, which are most easily identified or most difficult to spot, what precautions to take in order not to disturb the birds or other wildlife in the area to be studied, and so forth. As part of their preparation for their guests from the local bird club, ask students to bring in bird guides from home, school, local libraries, or natural history museums.

3. Try to obtain recordings of bird songs of selected species. Practice identifying the birds by their songs.

4. Now it is time to visit the site to apply the knowledge and skills the students have been working to acquire. Select a trail, path, or road to walk in the area that has an easily discernible starting and ending point. If possible, the students should walk the trail in the early morning, using techniques they were taught by the bird club members in making and recording their observations. Ideally, members of the bird club, parents, or other community members can come along to assist as well. OPTIONAL: Take along the recorded tapes of bird songs with a battery-operated recorder. This reference "in the field" is a big help in identification.

5. Repeat the inventory one or more times that morning to try to account for all breeding pairs. The number of singing males identified on each walk should be consistent.

6. Once back in class, have the students compile the results of their observations. Map the site and mark the locations of bird sightings (e.g., using colored dots for birds—with an explanatory key). Encourage the students to discuss their observations as well as the feelings they experienced in the process of watching the birds. Also talk about any difficulties they feel they might have experienced in getting an accurate count.

7. As an option—a small group of students might volunteer to compile all the findings in a written format, including magazine photos, sketches of the birds, or other items. This booklet could serve as the beginning of a year-to-year record of the inventory of birds in that location at that time of year, and it could be used by students conducting this project in subsequent years. As a new group of students repeats the inventory each year, the results could be graphed, showing year-to-year changes, if any. Trends could be analyzed, and so on. Additional information can be included in this report format, including a map of the area selected for the inventory with the trail and other notable landmarks identified.

continued

Extensions and Variations

1. In a single school year, conduct several counts throughout the migration period, checking to see what happens in the area selected. Take counts seasonally, noticing similarities and differences.

2. One or two singing male birds could be followed closely to determine the size of their respective territories. Be sure that students are following rather than chasing the bird. This variant could be a mapping and mathematics project, using geometry to calculate the area of the bird's territory. Map each location where the bird perches to sing his song, and try to determine where he comes into conflict with a neighboring, singing male.

3. Compare the class results with those of statistical count experts, if such research data are available.

4. Send for inventory techniques, counts, trends, and management implications for other species of animals from the state wildlife agency or other source. Make comparisons with class techniques and data.

CAUTION: Do not disturb the birds; make sure not to disrupt mating, nest-building, and nesting activities. Check with local authorities (e.g., the bird club members, state wildlife personnel) for precautions.

Evaluation

1. Summarize the findings from your study. Why is it important to be able to inventory wildlife populations?

2. Design a wildlife survey plan for conducting a butterfly inventory.

3. Use the Visual Vocabulary evaluation technique (see "Evaluating and Assessing Student Learning" in the Appendices) to either review or assess students on new concepts and terms introduced in this activity.

A Picture Is Worth a Thousand Words

Objectives

Students will (1) describe changes in public attitudes toward wildlife and its management, and (2) explain the importance to wildlife management of both scientific knowledge and skills as well as the importance of technological advancements.

Method

Students will compare photographs that represent changes in technology and practices in wildlife management.

Materials

Copies or transparencies of the 19 photographs included on pages 414 through 417, copies of the Photo Analysis Guide on page 413 for each student, notebook paper and writing materials

---

Grade Level: 9–12

Subject Areas: Social Studies, Science, Environmental Science

Duration: One 50-minute session

Group Size: any size

Setting: indoors

Conceptual Framework Topic References: WMIIIA, WMIIIB, WMIIIB2, WMIIIB3, WMIIIB4, WMIIIB5, WMIIIC, WMIIIC1, WMIIIC2

Key Terms: market hunting, poaching, fry (young fish), hatchery, funding, transplant, transportation

Appendices: none

Background

Wildlife management is the application of scientific knowledge and technical skills to protect, preserve, conserve, limit, or enhance wildlife and its habitat. Because management of one species of wildlife may have consequences for other species within the same ecosystem, wildlife managers must consider the entire ecosystem. If people are to accomplish management goals, an understanding of species biology, ecosystem structure, and ecosystem function must be combined with population and land-manipulation techniques. To develop wildlife management practices, managers have looked to an extensive body of ecosystem research. Technologies that allow for more science-based analysis also have been used.

The purpose of this activity is to emphasize that wildlife managers combine an understanding of species biology and ecosystem structure and function with population and land manipulation techniques to accomplish management goals. Because wildlife management is based on the natural sciences—such as biology, ecology, geography, and soil science, as well as on many other disciplines—wildlife agencies employ people with a variety of scientific training and vocational skills. Wildlife management practices involve population and habitat inventory and monitoring; direct management of wildlife species through manipulation of populations (e.g., artificial propagation, stocking, transplanting, predator and damage control, regulated harvest); indirect management of wildlife species through protection and manipulation of habitat; and public regulation and education. A public that is well educated about wildlife management issues is critical to the long-term success of wildlife management programs.

continued

Procedure

1. Introduce the lesson with this quote, "A picture is worth a thousand words." Ask students to explain why they think this quote is correct or incorrect.

2. Distribute the Photo Analysis Guide and explain each of the steps.

3. Once students are familiar with the Guide, use it to examine one of the photographs included with this activity.

4. Looking at Photo 1, have students individually answer the questions posed in the first three steps of the Guide. Have the students write their responses on a sheet of paper. Once the students have completed steps one through three for Photo 1, have them share their responses with the rest of the class.

5. Provide students with the background information about the photo and then briefly discuss student discoveries. Ask the students the following discussion questions:

   - What wildlife management techniques were depicted in the photograph? Does the photo show stocking, licensing, or population inventory programs?
   - How have the attitudes of people toward wildlife and its management changed over the past century?
   - Why is habitat protection and restoration so important to wildlife management?
   - How are biology, ecology, geography, and soil science important to wildlife management?
   - How have advances in technology helped make decisions related to wildlife and its management?

6. Ask the groups each to complete Step 4 of the Guide and then share their responses with the class.

7. Following the discussion, have students complete Step 5 of the Guide. This conclusion phase will allow students to examine the ways in which the background information has influenced their thinking about the photograph.

8. Divide the class into small groups and distribute one or more of the remaining photographs to each group. Repeat this process for each photograph to be analyzed.

Extension

Ask students to bring old photographs of wild animals or wildlife-related activities. Have the class analyze them using the Guide. The students who bring in the photos can provide the background information to the rest of the class.

Evaluation

1. Have students sort the pictures into categories and justify their choices.

   Examples:
   - Old attitudes versus recent attitudes
   - Low technology versus high technology
   - Consumptive use versus non-consumptive use

2. Have students choose one photograph that is most representative of the work of wildlife managers today and defend their choice.

Written by Chris Elnicki and Jeff Rucks, Colorado Division of Wildlife.

Background Text for Photos

Photo 1: Market Hunters

Market hunters exploited bison, antelope, deer and elk to meet the demands brought to the west by the mining boom. By the mid-1870s, market hunting had nearly wiped out the bison herds. By 1900, elk and deer populations were moving toward a similar fate.

Photo 2: Denver Market

This photograph was taken at the O. J. Munger and Company Wholesale Food Market at the corner of 16th and Market in downtown Denver, Colorado, in the late 1800s. Early Denver needed wild game to feed its expanding population. How have meat markets changed?

Photo 3: Moose Hunter

Moose populations were limited in the west between 1860 and 1978. However, conservation efforts between 1978 and 1986 proved more successful. This photo shows a scene from a moose hunt in 1985 when 500 people applied for licenses to take part in this opportunity. Compare this photo to Photo 1. What changes in policy and technology have occurred?

Photo 4: Modern Hunter

According to the Congressional Sportsman's Foundation, more people hunt and fish in the United States than attend National League Football, Major League Baseball, and National Hockey League games combined. Spending by hunters and anglers exceeds all U.S. exports of coal, corn, cigarettes, soybeans, meat, lumber, and metal ore combined. *Fortune* magazine estimates the economic impact of hunting is $10 billion annually. The funding for wildlife programs and services to support state parks and forests often does not come from state taxes. In Colorado, for example, more than 80 percent of the budget for wildlife programs and services is derived from selling hunting and fishing licenses, with the remainder coming from federal funding.

Photo 5: Confiscated Elk, 1930

By the early 1900s, state legislatures started to pass laws—including those establishing hunting and fishing license programs—to protect game animals. In this photo, the items on the wagon are hides of 441 illegally hunted elk. Regulations are a tool wildlife biologists use to conserve wildlife populations.

Photo 6: Confiscated Wildlife, 1989

Poaching continues to be a problem faced by state fish and wildlife agencies. This photo shows animals seized in 1989. This undercover operation was established to catch poachers and involved 275 wildlife officers from five states. Nearly 50 individuals were implicated by this operation.

Photo 7: First Fish Hatchery

In 1881, natural resource agencies were operating hatcheries like this one that stocked fish in streams. Compare this photograph with Photo 8.

Photo 8: Modern Fish Hatchery

The Rifle Falls Hatchery in Colorado became the largest state-owned hatchery in the world in 1955. Fish and wildlife management practices involve inventorying and monitoring populations and the propagation of species for stocking and reintroduction.

Photo 9: Fish Stocking

Horses carrying buckets and cream cans filled with fish were used to stock high mountain lakes at the turn of the 20th century. Compare this photo with Photos 10, 11, and 12.

Photo 10: Helicopter

Since the 1950s, airplanes, and more recently helicopters, have been used to stock fish into high mountain lakes. In this photo, a biologist stocks trout fry in a high mountain lake.

continued

Photo 11: Early Fish-Stocking Truck

This photo shows one of the earliest models of fish-stocking trucks.

Photo 12: Modern Fish Stocking Truck

This photo shows a modern-day fish stocking truck used by wildlife agencies for transporting and stocking fish. To keep the fish alive, each tank must have a constant flow of oxygen pumped into the water. Water temperature is regulated to reduce stress on fish.

Photo 13 and 14: Live Trapping Elk

Many techniques have been used to track migration patterns of elk and other big game. One of the most effective ways to study wildlife movement is to tag the animals. Handling wild animals is always a difficult, and sometimes dangerous, task. These photos demonstrate capture techniques from two very different eras. In the late 1800s, the capture was done rodeo style. In the more recent photo, a biologist jumps on a cow elk from a helicopter. The deep snow cushions both the person and the animal. Other techniques include the use of tranquilizer guns and large corral-type traps. Each technique has its positive and negative aspects. The safety of the animal and the safety of the biologist are always the most important issues when choosing a technique to study wild animals.

Photo 15: Early Fish Biologists

In the 1920s, fish eggs were collected from productive lakes and transported back to the hatchery. These men are preparing the eggs for transport.

Photo 16: Modern Fish Biologist

A researcher examines fish in the stress tunnel at a research lab. Technology changes influence environmental management decisions by allowing more sophisticated science-based analysis. Compare this photo to Photo 15.

Photo 17: Watching Wildlife

The Watchable Wildlife Program began during the 1980s. Wildlife agencies are making efforts to fund programs that focus more on viewing wildlife (nonconsumptive uses such as canoeing, hiking, bird watching, etc.) than harvesting (consumptive uses such as hunting, fishing, trapping).

Photo 18: Development

The biggest challenge facing most wildlife biologists today is the loss of wildlife habitat because of human population growth. Wildlife habitat is disappearing as habitat is converted into developments and agricultural production. Although regulations are a necessary tool, protection and restoration of habitat are considered to be the most successful and cost-effective long-term techniques for managing wildlife species.

Photo 19: Wildlife Education

Education became an important wildlife management tool in the 1990s. The more people know about the needs of wildlife, the more likely they will be willing to share their communities with wildlife.

Photo Analysis Guide

Step 1. First Impression

What is your first reaction to the photograph? What images or feelings does this photo bring to mind?

Step 2. Collecting Data

Make a list of things and people in the photograph. Classify and categorize the list. Look for details. Does the photo include written information? What clues exist concerning the date of the photograph?

Step 3. Inferences

What theories or educated guesses do you have about this photograph? What is happening outside of the photo? What are the people thinking or feeling? Is the picture staged or just a random moment in life?

Step 4. Perspectives

Why was the photo taken? Whose history is being told? What or who has been left out? Would anyone object to this photo?

Step 5. Conclusions

What insights about the past have you gained from analyzing and discussing this photograph? How did the background information change your understanding of the photograph? What changes in wildlife management techniques did you note through the history represented in the photos? What changes in the role of government in wildlife management did you discover?

NOTE: Project WILD recommends that students write their responses to the Guide. However, it may be redundant to do all steps with each photograph. Educators may want to cover some photos as a large group. With other photos, have students record their responses to every aspect of the Guide. Or have students verbally share each response with a partner or small group.

continued

Sustaining Fish and Wildlife Resources
A Picture Is Worth a Thousand Words

Photo 1

Photo 2

Photo 3

Photo 4

Photo 5

Photo 6

Photo 7

Photo 8

Photo 9

Photo 10

Photo 11

Sustaining Fish and Wildlife Resources
A Picture Is Worth a Thousand Words

Photo 12

Photo 13

Photo 14

Photo 15

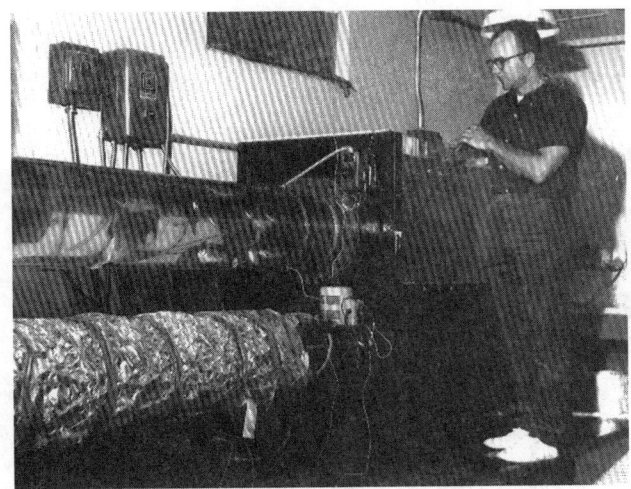

Photo 16

Photo 17

Photo 18

Photo 19

Wildlife Research

Objectives

Students will (1) identify reasons for research related to wildlife, (2) evaluate appropriate kinds of research related to wildlife, and (3) design and conduct a wildlife research project.

Method

Students evaluate types of research involving wildlife, apply their results to develop individual research proposals that meet criteria for appropriateness, and conduct research.

Materials

Writing materials; possible need for access to reference materials; observation tools such as video cameras, sketch books, and hand lenses

---

Grade Level: 9–12

Subject Areas: Environmental Education, Science

Duration: three to five 45-minute sessions, plus additional time for designing and writing

Group Size: any, whole class working individually or in small groups

Setting: indoors

Conceptual Framework Topic Reference: WMIII, WMIIIA, WMIIIA1

Key Terms: research, ethics

Appendices: Field Ethics, Outdoors, Using Local Resources, Animals in the Classroom

---

Background

Research, by definition, represents a quest for knowledge. It typically involves careful, systematic study and investigation. It does not necessarily involve intervention or experimentation; it may be entirely based on observation and other data-gathering techniques.

One area of scientific research involves the study of wildlife. Such research may be conducted in field or in laboratory settings. Research may involve wildlife directly, indirectly, or both. For example, it may focus directly on wildlife species, or indirectly on either habitats or societal factors such as attitudes, beliefs, and values.

Wildlife research may have a variety of purposes, including (1) to acquire knowledge specific to the animal under study (e.g., field research to identify food and cover needs, disease problems, and adaptability of transplanted bighorn sheep; and (2) to acquire knowledge specific to human activities that influence wildlife (e.g., potential impacts of a proposed land development on species of wildlife in an area).

Study of conditions affecting wildlife can be important to people as well as to the animals and for environments. However, there is controversy about what is ethical research involving animals. For example, questions of ethics may arise if research procedures involve activities that may harm or cause discomfort to individual animals in the process of acquiring information during the research.

The major purpose of this activity is for students to identify reasons for research related to wildlife and, through designing a possible research proposal, to consider what seem appropriate and inappropriate kinds of research and research practices.

Procedure

1. Brainstorm with your students a list of possible reasons to do research about or involving wildlife, directly or indirectly.

2. Discuss what seems to be reasonable, acceptable, and appropriate research and what does not.

3. Ask students to classify the kinds of research as acceptable or unacceptable, then to give their reasons for these classifications. Following this personal evaluation, ask them—as a group—to develop a set of criteria for acceptable and appropriate research.

OPTIONAL: Before they categorize and evaluate the various types of research, ask the students to do some library work to find additional information on the topic. A few students could be asked to place phone calls or write letters for additional information. For example, local agencies or organizations that might conduct research related to wildlife could be contacted to find out what kinds of research they conduct and what methods they use. Other agencies or organizations that oppose research involving wildlife could also be contacted for information. Review the questions the students will ask before they place their calls or send their letters to ensure the clarity of the request and to coordinate the inquiries, thus avoiding duplication of effort. If such contacts are made, ask the students to report back to the rest of the class.

4. Ask each student team to design and write a "Proposal to Conduct Research." The plan must follow good scientific methodology, take place on the school grounds or other approved site, and follow the class determined ethical guidelines developed in step 3. A proposal might be a behavioral study (e.g., students observe how house sparrows foraging for food respond to adjacent human activity). Their study might involve census work (e.g., how many ant colonies exist on the school site and what number of different species of ants is represented). The research project does not need to involve wildlife directly but, for example, could involve a survey of people's attitudes concerning wildlife. Such a research project could explore whether students think spiders serve any useful purpose on the school site. If the project directly involves wildlife, have the students become familiar with and incorporate the "Guidelines for Responsible Use of Animals in the Classroom" (see the Appendices) into their plan.

5. Evaluate each proposal to determine whether it follows good scientific procedures and to ensure that the plan is realistic. Students must be able to complete the research in the allotted time with the available resources.

6. After approval of the project, students conduct their research. They should compile their results and, if possible, draw conclusions. Their data may not support any conclusions; therefore, it is important for students to learn not to extend their conclusions beyond what their data support. Students can identify areas for further study and, if time permits, conduct some of those studies.

Evaluation

Suppose you are the director of a wildlife-research institute. You receive a letter from a fourth-grade student asking what your institute does and why it is important to the community. Write a letter in response.

Dropping in on Deer

Objectives

Students will (1) describe how habitat surveys provide important baseline information to guide management decisions; (2) apply field methodologies reflecting wildlife management practices developed through an understanding of species biology and ecosystem structure; and (3) explain the importance of scientific knowledge and technical skills in the conservation, limitation, preservation, and enhancement of wildlife and its habitat.

Method

Students estimate population density of deer in a given area by counting deer pellet groups.

Materials

Colored survey tape or wire survey flags, rope or string, stakes or dowel rods, measuring tape, compasses, clip boards and writing utensils, Pellet Group Counter Worksheets (one for each group of four students) on page 425; OPTIONAL: dry dog food nuggets

---

Grade Level: 9–12

Subject Areas: Environmental Education, Science, Mathematics

Duration: three sessions and one field trip

Group Size: groups of four students

Setting: outdoors

Conceptual Framework Topic References: WMIB, WMIII, WMIIIA, WMIIIA1, WMIIIB1

Key Terms: inventory, fecal pellets, scat, plot

Appendices: Field Ethics, Observations and Inferences

Background

One component of a wildlife biologist's job is to gather information about local animals and plants so that appropriate decisions can be made for their management. Deer populations are a concern in many areas where the numbers of deer are increasing. (For more information in issues related to deer populations, see the Project WILD activity "Deer Dilemma.") Assessing the size of the population is essential to any management strategy. How does a wildlife biologist know the size of the deer population in an area? Biologists use a variety of survey tools to gather information about the number of deer in a certain area at a certain time. This process is known as an inventory or census. "Density count" is another term biologists use to describe how many deer they find in a known area. One commonly used method of gathering these data is the aerial survey. A helicopter or airplane flies low over places where deer are known to reside, and the deer are counted and photographed. This technique is a "visual count," or direct accounting of what is seen on a given range.

Aerial surveys have limits in that deer may hide in the cover of trees and shrubs and may go uncounted. These surveys may be used for small areas, but they have limited application on a statewide scale. Consequently, other methods are also used to determine populations. Deer can be captured and released, a costly and time-consuming process. Deer killed through hunting can be monitored. Many states use computer models that estimate population size on the basis of known reproduction and mortality factors. One successful alternative is the strip census, or line transect, which provides a sample of what exists in a larger area. Pellet group (deer fecal material) counts are one example of a line transect.

Pellet group counts monitor population not by sighting the animal, but by tallying signs the deer leaves behind. This method gives an accurate accounting of animal use of an area of land. Because deer defecate frequently (approximately 12 times per day), pellet group counts are a useful way to evaluate the number of deer in a predetermined area—even if the deer themselves are not visible. How many deer are healthy for a given area depends on the quality of the habitat. If the habitat is over-browsed, then the number of deer that is indicated by the pellet count is too many. The biologist would keep records of pellet group counts for the overpopulated area over time to monitor the progress of management strategies. In "Dropping in on Deer," students will conduct a pellet group count, assessing deer activity on a measured plot. They will use similar methods to those used by wildlife biologists.

The purpose of this activity is to demonstrate that management practices use ecosystem research methodologies. Surveys of wildlife populations and their habitat provide important baseline information that guides management decisions.

Pre-Field Trip Preparation

NOTE: If a deer habitat is not available, this survey technique can also be simulated using small piles of dry dog food nuggets in place of the deer pellet groups.

1. It is important to scout the area to be used in advance. Finding places to successfully survey for deer activity requires previewing the area and is time well spent.

2. Because the students are simulating actions of wildlife biologists, they need to understand what the biologist does and why. Be prepared to discuss this subject.

3. Students should be familiar with deer physiology and functions so they appreciate the pellet count activity as a real learning tool. Be sure the students understand that each deer will leave behind approximately 12 pellet groups per day.

4. Tool preparation can be done with or without the students. Begin by tying the rope or string to a dowel or stake. After that is complete, measure 11' 9" of rope, and cut it. One rope and stake is needed for every four students.

NOTE: A circle with a radius of 11' 9" has an area of 1/100 (or 0.01) of an acre.

5. Consider enlisting some parents or adult volunteers to join the class on the field trip. An ideal ratio is one adult for every eight students.

6. Set up a "test plot" before the field trip. Search for litter, insects, or tiny hidden treasures in place of the deer pellets. This activity can be conducted in many habitat types to practice finding pellets in tall grass, brush, and so on. The class will work much more quickly having practiced the survey in advance.

Procedure

1. Explain to the students that wildlife biologists use many survey methods to assess the size and health of the deer population. One method is the pellet group count. The results of the survey help biologists decide how to improve habitat for deer or how many permits to issue for hunting. When doing a deer study, wildlife biologists first must establish an area to be studied. The site is inspected for deer droppings. In some cases, the pellet groups are removed from the survey plots so that only "fresh" use of the site will be recorded. The biologist then returns later and counts the new pellet groups that have been deposited. This technique eliminates the need to guess the "age" of each pellet group, and the information is more accurate. In most cases, however, the biologist saves time by simply estimating the age of the pellet groups during the survey. Students will use this latter approach. Pellets will be observed and recorded only. No animal droppings will be touched or contacted in any way.

2. Review the following ground rules before the students begin their surveys.

continued

- Do not touch or pick up any deer pellets or other animal droppings.
- Avoid wandering over the plot and trampling evidence before the survey begins.
- Be careful in your observations, and record information for each pellet group before moving on.

3. Divide the class into groups of four students. Each group will investigate several circular plots for deer pellets. Discuss exactly what the students will be doing before they begin their surveys. Find some recent and old deer droppings. Show them to the students, noting the characteristics that distinguish the two types.

4. Set up and examine the plots.

    a. Have the students disperse over the study area and randomly select the center point of their first plot. The more random the selection, the more accurate the information will be. (If students select just the sites with the most pellet groups, the estimate will be higher than the actual number of deer in the area.) Number the plots. At the site, have students note the condition of foliage near the ground and up to approximately 6 feet high. Is vegetation plentiful or sparse?

    b. One group member should push the stake into the ground until it can stand securely on its own. If the stake will not stand on its own or if the ground is too hard, then that student should stand with the stake to keep it in place during plot measurements. The stake should stay put from this point on, because it is the center of the area to be studied. The student holding the stake also can record data as it is collected.

    c. Have one student stretch the rope out its entire length and mark the outermost point with a rock or something similar. This is the starting point of the transect. (See Diagram A.)

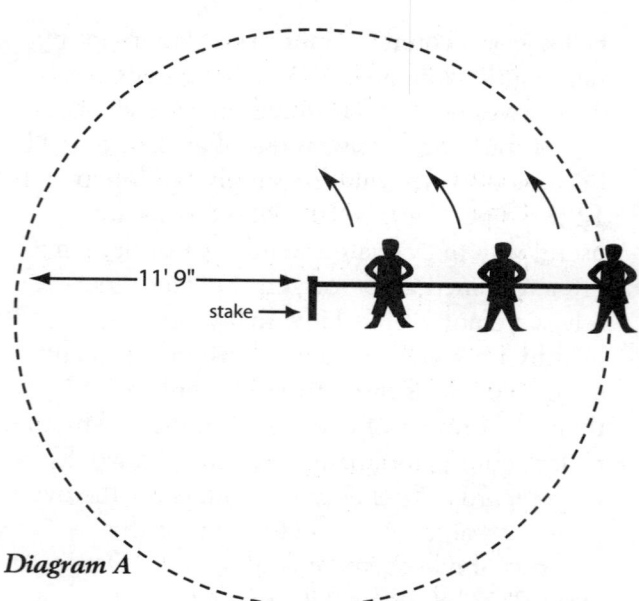

Diagram A

    d. Instruct the remaining students to position themselves evenly along the rope, all facing the same direction.

    e. Have the students walk slowly in a circle, keeping the rope taunt as they move the rope and search the ground for pellet groups.

    f. When a pellet group is encountered, have the students stop and examine it. As a rule, count a pellet group if at least half of the pellet group lies within the circle. If most of the pellets are beyond the end of the rope, the pellet group should not be counted as part of that plot. Determine if the pellets are recent (within a few months). If they are dry and cracked, they are not recent and should not be counted.

    g. On the Pellet Group Counter Worksheet, record each recent pellet group by placing a tally mark in the Number of Recent Pellet Groups per Plot column next to the plot number. The presence of old pellet groups should be noted in the right-most column of the worksheet. Also record in the far right column any evidence of other animals.

h. When the group completes the circle and students are back at the beginning marker, have the students total the number of recent pellet groups within the plot and record that number on the worksheet. Circle the total for each plot.

i. Move to a second randomly selected spot and repeat the process.

j. Depending on time, each group of students should attempt to complete 10 plots.

5. Calculate the findings. (This procedure can be done in the field or in the classroom.)

a. Have the students follow the procedures at the bottom of the Pellet Group Counter Worksheet to estimate the number of deer in the study area.

b. Compare the estimates from each group, and see how close their numbers are.

c. Total all the plots in the entire class, and determine a class estimate of the deer population.

6. Prepare to discuss the findings with the class as a whole.

- Did the students' estimate of the deer population make sense? If it didn't, discuss what might have affected the results.

- Would the results be different at a different time of year? Why or why not?

- Were there only groups of old pellets or only fresh ones? What does that mean?

- Were some plots or parts of plots filled with more pellet groups than others? What might that mean about the forage or terrain? The carrying capacity for deer in an area varies with the quality of the habitat. Keeping in mind the amount of near-ground vegetation, decide what the number of deer pellets tells you about the quality of the habitat at the site.

- Ask students how this information is useful in guiding wildlife management decisions.

continued

- What wildlife management decisions could they make based on the information they have?
- What additional information would they like to have? To determine if the number of deer is appropriate for the study area, students may want to conduct one or more of the extensions listed at the end of this activity.
- Why is it important for people who manage wildlife to have scientific knowledge and technical skills? What knowledge and skills do they need?

Extensions

1. Survey the same area over several years to build baseline data and monitor population trends.
2. Survey several types of habitats, and compare density of deer between areas.
3. Research statewide data from natural resource agencies, and compare findings to the data collected from this activity or from these extensions.

Evaluation

1. Have the students compile the findings from their groups and synthesize information in a report to the class. What are the wildlife management implications of the results?
2. Describe how habitat surveys provide important information to guide management decisions. Explain the importance of scientific knowledge and technical skills in the conservation, limitation, preservation, and enhancement of wildlife and its habitat.

Adapted from "Dropping in on Deer." Originally developed by Winston Dines for the Colorado Division of Wildlife.

What to Look for and What to Record

Recognizing deer droppings is not difficult in most settings. Deer defecate in clusters, usually all in one spot. Occasionally, the individual pellets get spread over a distance as the animal moves, but that is not common. Deer also leave droppings near places where they have been feeding. Unlike some animal species, they do not use their feces to mark their territory, nor do they always defecate in one location.

Students need to be aware that both fresh and older deer droppings may occur within their plot. Other types of scat (droppings) may be present as well. The only scat that can be confused with deer is that of elk and rabbit. Elk pellets resemble deer pellets in the clusters that occur, but the overall pellet size is larger. Rabbit droppings are found more randomly and widely scattered. Because rabbits produce one dropping at a time, clusters of pellets occur less often. The shape of rabbit pellets is spherical, and they are much lighter in color than deer pellets.

Condition of Droppings

RECENT (within 6 months) dark brown to brown in color; shiny or smooth in texture; some speckles of plant fibers may be visible

OLD (more than 6 months) exterior very dry and cracked; light brown to yellow in color; many plant fibers visible

Pellet Group Counter Worksheet

Directions: On each of your circle plots, look carefully at the ground for groups of deer pellets. Each time you notice one, inspect it and estimate its age. Record the number of recent pellet groups in each plot below. Then use the equations to estimate the population. Record other observations in the right-hand column, including old pellet groups and evidence of other animals.

Pellet Group Plot Number	Number of Recent Pellets Groups per Plot	Other Observations (other animal signs)
1		
2		
3		
4		
5		
6		
7		
8		
9		
10		
Total		

Calculations:

A. $\dfrac{\text{total \# pellet groups}}{\text{\# total plots}} \times \dfrac{100 \text{ plots}}{\text{acre}} = $ # pellet groups per acre

B. $\dfrac{\text{\# pellet groups per acre}}{12 \text{ pellet groups per deer per day}} = $ # deer days/acre

C. # deer days/acre × # acres in study area = # of deer days in study area

D. # deer days ÷ 180 days = **number of deer living in the study area.**

NOTE: Because only recent (within 6 months) pellet groups are counted, 180 days or 6 months is used (in calculation D). Please be aware that pellets decompose much faster in areas of high humidity. In order to determine a decomposition rate specific to your area for use in calculations, please contact your state wildlife agency. If you find pellets last three months (approximately 90 days), replace "180" with "90" in calculation D.

Deer Dilemma

Objectives

Students will (1) define wildlife management as the application of scientific knowledge and technical skills to protect, preserve, conserve, limit, or enhance wildlife and its habitat; (2) describe how wildlife resources can be managed and conserved; (3) demonstrate their understanding that wildlife species are important components of a larger ecosystem that should be managed within the context of that ecosystem; (4) distinguish between consumptive and nonconsumptive resource uses; (5) consider the needs of people as well as wildlife in the sustainability of the resource; and (6) distinguish between game, nongame, endangered, and threatened species of wildlife.

Method

Students conduct a board of commissioners meeting to hear the concerns of constituents regarding the ever-increasing deer population in and around a local park and make a decision concerning this issue.

Materials

Copy or copies of the Crystal Lake Park scenario on page 430, role cards on page 431, a timer with a bell

Background

For management purposes, wildlife often has been divided into categories, including game, nongame, endangered, and threatened. Game species are those that currently are hunted, fished, or trapped by humans for recreational or economic purposes. Nongame species are those that traditionally are not hunted, fished, or trapped for either recreational or economic purposes by humans. Endangered species are those in danger of extinction throughout all or a significant portion of their range. Threatened species are those likely to become endangered.

Wildlife management applies scientific knowledge and technical skills to protect, preserve, conserve, limit, or enhance wildlife and its habitat. Conservation is the use of natural resources in a way that ensures their continuing availability to future generations through wise use or protection. Wildlife management considers the needs and desires of people, as well as the viability of wildlife. In the context of an ecosystem, management of one species of wildlife may have consequences—positive or negative—for other species within the same ecosystem.

Grade Level: 9–12

Subject Areas: Social Studies, Language Arts, Science, Environmental Education

Duration: minimum two 45-minute sessions

Group Size: 15 to 30 students

Setting: indoors

Conceptual Framework Topic References:
WMIA, WMIA1, WMIA2, WMIA3, WMIA4, WMIB, WMIC, WMIIA, WMIIB, WMIIB1, WMIIC, WMIIC1, WMIIC3, WMIID, WMIIE

Key Terms: wildlife management, conservation, game animal, non-game animal, endangered, threatened, consumptive, nonconsumptive

Appendices: none

The white-tailed deer (*Odocoileus virginianus*) is the most common and easily recognized large herbivorous game mammal in the United States. Deer populations are currently at record levels throughout most of their range and deer densities are greater than when the early colonists arrived in the New World.

By the early 1900s, deer had vanished from much of their historical range because of extensive forest clearing and unregulated hunting for food and profit. Deer populations began to rebound with the advent of modern wildlife management and the passage of the Federal Aid in Wildlife Restoration Act. Although many states had passed laws to protect deer, very few had the financial capabilities to hire enough game wardens to enforce these laws. This act helped states by dedicating a portion of a federal excise tax on sporting goods and firearms to wildlife management work.

White-tailed deer have the same basic needs as all other animals: food, water, shelter, and space. A deer eats herbaceous and woody plant material. However, the types of plants and the extent to which deer will eat different plants can vary greatly across the deer's range. Deer in areas of high deer populations generally are less picky eaters. Deer in low-density deer herds can be more selective in their food choices. Deer obtain water both by drinking and through eating succulent, herbaceous vegetation.

Deer live in farmland and timberland. They also may live in forests, but areas of early successional forest stages and agriculture fields are considered to be better deer habitat and are capable of supporting higher deer densities. Subdivisions with manicured lawns and ample herbaceous plantings are better deer habitat than many of our large, undisturbed forestlands.

Deer are a prey species with a high reproductive rate allowing for rapid population growth in the appropriate situations. One male, or buck, deer will breed with many different female, or doe, deer during a given mating season. Mature does (those at least 2 years old) generally have two fawns annually. If the deer herd is in excellent physical condition, many does may have triplets. In fact, deer populations in excellent physical condition often have yearling does producing two fawns, and the female fawns even can have fawns themselves in their first year of life. In the absence of predators, deer populations can grow to very high densities in a short time.

There are natural limits to the number of deer a particular habitat can support. This concept is known as the biological carrying capacity. A parcel of land will support only so many deer. Once that number is reached, the general health of the deer population will begin to decline. Mature does will produce only one fawn, and yearlings and fawns no longer breed. At this level of population density, the deer begin to greatly affect the species composition of the land they live on. Deer will eat any plant material within their reach. The result is a forest completely devoid of any understory habitat and the disappearance of all the woodland creatures that depend on the understory as their habitat. Plants once found in that area become virtually nonexistent and the once-balanced ecosystem becomes skewed to one species, deer. Regeneration of tree species is often halted because the deer almost immediately browse the young saplings.

Overabundant deer herds, therefore, are potentially devastating for forest ecosystems as a whole. Since societal changes and economic concerns have virtually eliminated natural predators of deer, such as wolves and cougars, throughout much of their range, humans are left as the last remaining predator of deer. Wildlife managers are able to manage deer populations using regulated hunting to ensure a viable deer herd as well as a healthy forest ecosystem. Wildlife managers use season lengths, bag limits, and sex permits (where hunters can hunt either does or bucks) to regulate the number of deer taken by hunters each year. Annual monitoring ensures that deer populations remain at a level that is compatible with local community tolerance for deer and with the forest ecosystem.

continued

As additional areas are closed to hunting for a many reasons, deer herds in these areas have begun to expand. Although most areas have not yet reached the biological carrying capacity, many are approaching a new threshold defined as the "cultural carrying capacity." The cultural carrying capacity is a function of the human population. As developments expand into what was once rural habitat, the deer populations become protected and grow uncontrolled. For a period of time, this growth has no noticeable impact for the humans or the deer. At some point, however, the deer population exceeds a level acceptable to the local human population. This threshold varies more by the tolerance of the human population than the actual density of the deer population. Deer begin eating ornamental plants, and the number of vehicle-deer collisions increase.

Biologists and researchers continue to study methods to control deer and human conflicts in those areas. Lethal measures are currently the most effective method; however, much research has been conducted on birth control and other nonlethal methods.

Procedure

1. Present information on wildlife management to students, and discuss key concepts using the white-tailed deer as an example. Have students distinguish between game and nongame animals.

2. Present the Crystal Lake Park scenario to students. Make copies of the scenario for each of the students.

3. Select five to seven students to serve as members of the Board of Commissioners, and appoint one of them as chairperson.

4. Select one student to portray each of the individuals described in the student pages at the end of the activity. Depending on class size, educators may or may not use all of the roles. (Names may be adjusted to match the gender of the students.)

5. Allow students time to develop a position on the role they have been given.

6. Have the rest of the students participate as townspeople. Instruct them that they will develop their own personal positions on the issue, which they may change after listening to the positions of the speakers.

7. Have each student with a role give a brief (3 to 4 minutes) presentation to the Board of Commissioners from the perspective of the person he or she represents, stating his or her opinions on the issues and offering suggestions as to how to resolve the issue. This session should be conducted in the same manner as a normal public meeting. (Students may be encouraged to attend a local board or commission meeting to learn how these meetings function.)

8. The Board of Commissioners then takes a brief recess to make a decision. While the Commissioners are meeting, the student constituents involved in the role-play and the students in the audience will cast their own written votes. Tally the student votes.

9. Have the Board of Commissioners report its decision to the group.

10. The decision of the Board is compared to the votes cast by the constituents.

11. Discuss with students how they feel about the decision of the Board of Commissioners. Did it reflect the prevailing perspective of the constituents? Did everyone vote the same? How did the viewpoint of each board member and group representative influence those votes? Which groups will be supportive of the board's decision and which will be opposed? How did the interplay of ideas and perspectives strengthen the ability of the group to fully address this issue?

12. Have the students discuss the main concepts of the activity:
    - What is the purpose of conservation? What is wildlife management? How can wildlife resources, such as deer, be managed for conservation purposes? How is scientific knowledge (of biology, ecology, etc.) important in understanding the complexities of wildlife management?
    - Should deer be managed to consider other plants and animals or just humans? What are the positive and negative consequences for each of these components in our ecosystem?
    - Each constituent group had different views. How could the consideration for all of these concerns affect the scope and effectiveness of those responsible for wildlife management?
    - How should the deer be managed on privately owned land that is not directly controlled by state or federal wildlife management agencies?

Extensions

1. Encourage students to contact local wildlife professionals, foresters, park managers, and local interest groups to develop an understanding of how those situations are handled in their state or community.

2. Have students research management issues related to deer or other wildlife in their community and discuss how wildlife management concepts apply to the issue.

Evaluation

1. Use the students' presentations and discussions of how and why wildlife could be managed from Steps 3 through 11 in the Procedure section as an evaluation tool.

2. Have the students write their responses to the questions posed in Step 12 of the Procedure section.

continued

Student Pages

Crystal Lake Park's Deer Dilemma

Crystal Lake Park is an 850-acre multiple use park in Suburbanville, USA. The park has several soccer fields, a baseball complex, and a 6-acre lake used for fishing and canoeing. There is a nice picnic area adjacent to the lake. Nature trails exist around the lake, and the upper end of the lake is composed of a small wetland renowned for its excellent bird watching. Several nature trails exist in the forested portion of the park, but approximately 600 acres of the park land is seldom, if ever, entered by park visitors. The park is bordered on the southern and eastern sides by subdivisions. To the west lies the last remaining farm in this portion of the county. The Wolfpack River bounds the northern portion of the area.

Residents of the subdivisions, along with Charlie Fields, the neighboring farmer, have petitioned the local Board of Commissioners to do something about the ever-increasing deer population in the park. Mr. Fields currently allows hunting on his property but complains that the deer simply move to the park when the hunting starts and that very few are taken by the hunters on his property during the hunting season. Incidentally, he has resorted to using out-of-season nuisance animal permits to shoot the deer at night while they are eating his crops. Mr. Fields does not like this option but feels he must shoot the deer in order to keep his farm profitable. The residents of the local communities have tried everything from fencing and repellants to feeding the deer in hopes of keeping the deer away from their flowers and out of the roads. Many residents are ready to use lethal control in this area. However, the issue has divided the community, and arguments about what to do with the deer are common. Some residents don't mind the deer and are willing to tolerate their presence. Many park visitors do not want the deer harmed in any way because they enjoy seeing the herds of deer grazing on the soccer fields in the evenings as they drive through the park.

The Board of Commissioners has called a public meeting to listen to the concerns of their constituents and ultimately to make a decision concerning this issue. State laws do not prohibit hunting in this park, so the decision will need to be made at the local level. The board has made no decision as to what option or options (more than one might be appropriate) to approve and has convened this meeting to hear ideas from their constituents.

Role Cards

Charlie Fields
Mr. Fields is a local farmer. His family has farmed this land for three generations, and he plans to pass the farm along to his children. He grows mostly grain crops on his farm. For the past 5 years, he has experienced considerable loss from deer eating his crops. Mr. Fields leases the hunting rights on his farm to a local group of hunters. The hunters have told Mr. Fields that they see very few deer during the hunting season because they all appear to move into the park. Mr. Fields is frustrated and would like the county to open the park to hunting in order to reduce the density of deer.

Dorothy Right
Mrs. Right is a local attorney who lives in one of the adjacent subdivisions. Mrs. Right enjoys hiking in the park during the evening hours with her two children. She is very concerned about the idea of hunting occur-ring adjacent to their subdivision and doesn't want any harm to come to her children. Mrs. Right does not oppose the lethal removal of deer from the park; she just wants to be sure things are done safely and in the least conspicuous way possible.

Michael Green
Mr. Green is a resident of the local subdivision and is an avid gardener. His roses were once award-winning and the envy of his friends and neighbors. Now his roses are food for the local deer herd. He is very upset and has tried several forms of repellants and fences to no avail. Mr. Green hates the deer and sees no value in their presence. He is supportive of removing all deer from the park.

Bob Stats
Dr. Stats teaches environmental biology at the local university, where he also does research on wildlife populations and factors that affect population changes. He prefers monitoring the deer herd size annually and using a combination of management techniques tailored to the population size each year.

Betty Bumper
Ms. Bumper lives at the end of county road in an area that is quickly becoming developed with new housing. Her work schedule demands that she be on the road at sunrise and at dusk when the deer appear to be most active. Therefore, she has hit several deer, and her auto insurance has increased. She is supportive of whatever means can be taken to diminish the number of deer in the area.

Don Dearlove
Mr. Dearlove is a member of an animal rights organization that believes that hunting of animals for any reason is cruel and unnecessary. He enjoys seeing deer in the area but is concerned about the potential for accidents and about the health of the deer herd. He feels local residents should use other methods of control.

Lynn Ranger
Ms. Ranger is a park naturalist who can testify about the reduction in the understory plant diversity of the park and how the population of deer has affected it. She has documented evidence that some rare plants are declining in number and some animal species are being affected by the declining plant diversity.

John Dodds
Mr. Dodds's son contracted Lyme disease last year, and he blames the deer. He is in favor of any means of removing the deer to diminish the threat of contracting this disease.

Brad Arms
Mr. Arms is one of the people who hunt on Charlie Fields's land. He believes that the best way to manage the deer herd is to allow regulated hunting in the park. He also sees this as an opportunity to provide hunter education to the community and to dispel some of the misconceptions about hunting and deer management. He is willing to pay for the opportunity to hunt in the park and to donate a portion of the harvested meat to food shelters in the community.

Playing Lightly on the Earth

Objectives

Students will (1) distinguish between games that are damaging and not damaging to the environment, and (2) invent games with a benign effect on the environment.

Method

Students look for evidence of games that harm the environment and then invent and play games with a benign effect on the environment.

Materials

None

Background

Personal choices of all kinds can have an effect on the environment. Students can look at the games they play outside and can choose those that have little or no damaging effect on the environment, rather than those that leave scars—aesthetically and ecologically.

The major purpose of this activity is for students to become aware of the choices they make each time they play a game outside and to consciously experience games that have a benign effect on the environment. The activity is designed for students to experience success at a personal and immediate level in maintaining and improving the quality of their own environments.

Procedure

1. Ask the students to think of examples of ways to play outside that do not cause serious or permanent damage to the environment and of ways that are damaging. The damage might affect nonliving things such as putting graffiti on cement walls. It might be damaging to plants and animals such as carving initials on tree trunks. Are there any games that do no damage? There may not be, but we can think about how much damage is done, how permanent it is, and what it affects.

2. Go outside and look for evidence of games that have damaged the environment. Ask students what could have caused the damage and how it might have been prevented.

3. Introduce the concept of playing games that do not seriously harm the environment.

Grade Level: Pre-K, K–4

Subject Areas: Environmental Education, Science, Expressive Arts

Duration: one 30- to 45-minute session

Group Size: any

Setting: outdoors

Conceptual Framework Topic Reference: RAIC1, RA1C2

Key Terms: game, harm

Appendices: Outdoors

---

432 Project WILD K–12 Curriculum and Activity Guide

4. Ask the students to work together in small groups—from two to seven or eight—to invent a game that does no serious harm to the environment, including plants and animals. The students could also try to invent games that could make this a better environment in some ways. Give the students about 15 minutes to invent their games.

5. Ask each group to present its game to the other students. Play each of the games. Ask the students to talk about their feelings about the importance of playing games that do little if any damage to the environment.

Extensions

Analyze various kinds of recreation for their impact on wildlife, vegetation, or other natural resources.

Evaluation

1. Keep a record of the games played outside for 1 week. Identify which, if any, are harmful to the environment. For 1 week or longer, play only games that do no harm to the environment.

2. Invent a game for younger children that does not harm the environment. Teach it to a younger child or group of children. Explain what the younger child or children learned about care for the environment.

Litter We Know

Objectives
Students will (1) identify and evaluate ways that litter pollution can endanger wildlife, and (2) propose ways to help eliminate these dangers to humans and wildlife.

Method
Students collect and evaluate litter, making collages.

Materials
Large sheets of poster board for mounting collages, glue, different types of litter collected, work gloves, trash bags

Background
Litter can be very harmful to wildlife that comes in contact with it. Discarded fishing line can trap the legs, wings, or beaks of waterfowl such as geese and herons. When the fishing line wraps around its beak, a bird cannot feed itself. If the bird's wings become tangled, then it cannot fly or swim.

Fish, birds, and other animals may also get trapped into the loop portions of plastic six-pack can holders. Many times animals will become trapped in the loops and then cannot feed themselves. If the animals get the loops tangled around their feet, they will not be able to escape from predators.

Broken glass from bottles and other glass objects can injure people, pets, and wildlife. Half-open cans also can be a problem for some animals. Smaller animals in search of food often get their heads stuck inside such cans and jars. Plastic items and bottle caps may be eaten by wildlife, including fish, thus injuring or killing them. Cigarette butts, cellophane wrappers, and polyurethane cups, when eaten by deer and other wildlife, can cause internal problems.

In some cases, animals have learned to take advantage of litter. Animals will come into urban areas or areas with discarded food to feed on the litter and garbage. This intrusion puts the animals and humans in danger.

Much of the waste that is thrown away can be reused or recycled. Improvements in product packaging can help reduce unnecessary waste, and proper disposal methods can help eliminate potential dangers to wildlife.

Contact your state wildlife agency, or other state agencies, for additional information about problems resulting from litter. Local cleanup campaigns, recycling organizations, and animal welfare organizations may also be able to assist you in considering alternatives for reducing litter problems.

Grade Level: 5–8

Subject Areas: Social Studies, Expressive Arts, Environmental Education

Duration: minimum of one 45-minute session

Group Size: small teams of three to five students

Setting: indoors and outdoors

Conceptual Framework Topic Reference: RAIC1, RAIC2

Key Terms: litter, pollution

Appendices: Outdoors, Using Local Resources, Early Childhood

Procedure

1. Divide the class into three or four groups.

2. Ask each group to bring a collection of litter to class in a paper bag. Suggest the students look in parks, camping areas, school grounds, or any other area where they will have permission to collect trash. Advise students to wear work gloves. Caution them about hazards such as broken glass and medical wastes.

NOTE: They should not take things out of garbage cans.

3. Have the groups make and display collages of these items.

4. Discuss the effects of litter. OPTIONAL: Ask a wildlife specialist to join the class for the discussion. If available, show a film or read brochures on the subject.

5. Ask the students to assign a numerical value to each kind of litter. The item potentially most harmful to wildlife has the highest score; the least harmful has the lowest score.

6. Have each group figure a total score for the collage using the numerical values of each piece of litter.

7. Propose and evaluate ways that people can eliminate litter pollution. For example, can manufacturers devise another method of packaging six-packs? Could companies produce plastic six-pack holders that would deteriorate? How could people fishing have more control over losing their fishing line? How can individuals be instructed about the dangers as well as the unsightliness of littering? What progress has been made in recent years? What actions still are needed? What can students do personally—as individuals, as groups, and as family units—to eliminate or reduce their own litter?

Extensions

1. Research local and state laws regarding recycling. Determine how those laws affect wildlife.

2. Is there a litter cleanup program in your community? If yes, learn more about it. If not, find out why not.

Aquatic Extensions

1. Focus specifically on litter that can be potentially harmful to aquatic wildlife.

2. Consider what happens to garbage that is dumped into the ocean. Where off the coast of the United States is this done? What towns and cities contribute to this ocean dumping? Where does the garbage go? How are coastal towns affected by this? How is wildlife affected by this? When considering the impact on wildlife, think about any possible effects on the wildlife's food, water, shelter, and space. Are there regulations affecting the dumping of garbage into the seas? If so, are they enforced?

3. Plan a "Volunteers for Wildlife" cleanup program.

Evaluation

1. Identify four ways that litter can harm wildlife.

2. Identify three things people can do to lessen the effects of litter on wildlife.

3. Propose what you consider to be one of the most effective ways to eliminate or reduce litter. Explain why you think this proposal would be effective.

Planning for People and Wildlife

Objectives
Students will (1) describe considerations that are important in land-use planning for cities and other communities of people, (2) identify means by which negative effects on wildlife and other elements of the natural environment can be reduced in developing cities, and (3) describe actions that can be taken to enhance some contemporary cities as places in which both people and some wildlife can live.

Method
Students imagine and research what the area where they currently live was like before humans developed the community, design planned communities, and build and evaluate models of their community designs.

Grade Level: 5–8

Subject Areas: Social Studies, Science, Environmental Education

Duration: minimum of five 45-minute sessions

Group Size: any

Setting: indoors

Conceptual Framework Topic Reference: RAIC

Key Terms: land-use planning, community, city

Appendices: Using Local Resources, Ecosystem, Taking Action, Simulated Field Trips

---

Materials
Heavy cardboard or masonite; salt, flour, and water to make salt clay for a model-building material; glue; toothpicks; natural materials such as dried grass and construction paper for making buildings, roads, people, wildlife, and other components of a community; tempera paint, brushes; and any other materials available and useful in building models

Background
NOTE: This activity is most effectively used to culminate a unit on land-use planning, as well as to focus on issues affecting people, wildlife, and the environment.

Cities have developed as people have clustered together for purposes of meeting their needs—from shelter to food to physical safety. Cities typically have developed as hubs of transportation and commerce, again serving as a means by which people meet their day-to-day survival needs. The development of cities, however, has been a mixed blessing. The large concentration of people in a given area has displaced plants and animals that previously lived there and has given rise to problems unique to such crowded conditions. For example, varying forms of pollution accumulate in such centers, frequently with inadequate means for handling them—from products of industry to human waste.

Most cities are not the result of careful planning. Most have developed haphazardly, with attention to problems taking place only when crises emerge. Crime, unemployment, poor housing, air pollution, depletion of water supplies, contamination of water supplies by industrial and domestic waste disposal, energy consumption, transportation costs, and land use are all among the serious problems facing cities today.

People are faced with many important choices concerning how and where they will live. Many people in the United States are leaving the cities for suburban and rural life, bringing some of the same problems with them that encouraged them to leave the cities in the first place. New communities—large and small—are being developed. Some are the result of individual families moving into previously undeveloped areas; some are the result of business interests organizing to develop resources in an area and creating entirely new cities in the process. This change is happening in areas all over the planet. Areas of some large and old cities are decaying as they are abandoned. In some cities, redevelopment projects are taking place to try to improve the habitability of the older neighborhoods.

Ethical questions arise as people make decisions about where and how they will live. Any development or redevelopment of an area has an impact on the plants and animals that do and can live there, as well as on any people who might live there. Sometimes the development can be of benefit, and sometimes it can cause long-term harm. When such decisions are made, it seems prudent to plan for the effects of our actions as carefully and thoughtfully as possible.

The purpose of this activity is for students to consider the importance of land-use planning in community maintenance, improvement, and development. The concepts can be applied when considering redevelopment of old cities, as well as when building new cities and alternative communities in which people can live and work.

Procedure

1. Ask the students to close their eyes and picture the community where they live. If they live in a city, or if there is a city nearby, ask them to picture how the city looks. Next ask them to try to picture what that area might have looked like before the city or community was built in that spot. What plants were common to the area? What animals? Was there water in the area? What was the topography of the land?

2. Ask for a committee of volunteers to find out more precisely what the land, vegetation, wildlife, water, and so on was like before their community was built. If the students live in a rural area, have them find out how the area has changed since the first settlers came there. Ask the committee to report back to the rest of the students with this information in approximately one week. Sources could include state, city, or county historical societies, libraries, and such. City, regional, and state or province land-use planning offices may also have such information.

3. Ask the committee to report to the rest of the students both visually and verbally. For example, the report could list the descriptive characteristics of the vegetation in the area and could identify the kinds of wildlife along with the food and water sources upon which that wildlife depended. Ask the committee to describe its findings thoroughly enough that the rest of the students can clearly picture what the area looked like before a community was developed there. Also ask the committee to leave a visual record of the major information that they found so the rest of the students can use it as a reference.

continued

4. Next, ask all of the students, including the committee members who did the research, to divide into working groups of two to four students. Tell the groups it is their task to develop a community in this natural area, given the background information the committee has provided. In designing their communities, the students need to examine how a community develops where people will live and work with the least possible negative effect on the existing vegetation, air quality, water, soil, and wildlife, while still meeting the needs of the people. To do this, the students need to consider the following, as well as other factors they identify:

   - water sources, transportation, and treatment;
   - economic base (e.g., industry, small business);
   - kinds of housing, school, shopping areas, and job sites;
   - economical and recreational features (e.g., open space, green belts, parks);
   - sewage and waste disposal and treatment;
   - aesthetics;
   - environmental safeguards; and
   - means to expand effectively the number of people who can live in the community, if necessary, while retaining minimum effect on the quality of the environment.

5. Once each group has come up with a community development plan, review and discuss those plans.

6. Once the plans have been approved, provide the students with the necessary materials to build a model of their community. (See the Materials section.)

7. After all groups have developed their models of the communities they have designed, have a "Model Community Design Show," with each group explaining the design features of its community.

8. Discuss in detail the advantages and disadvantages of each community design. For example, include "What if?" questions, such as, "What if a new school had to be built?" and "What if there is a drought or severe winter, would it be necessary to take special measures to assist the wildlife?"

9. Return to the models after 2 weeks to a month, and ask the students to reflect on whether they would make any changes in their community designs—as if they'd had the opportunity to "live" in their communities for a while and might now see the need to do some things differently.

10. Ask a local architect, city planner, wildlife biologist, or other resource manager to visit the class to review and discuss the various model communities with the students who designed them.

Extensions and Variations

1. Show the students photos of actual cities. Look for advantages and disadvantages of city life under a variety of circumstances.

2. Obtain a map showing a community 15, 25, 50, 75, or 150 years ago. Evaluate the planning—or lack of—that seems to have taken place and the results.

3. Using one of the commercially available software programs that simulate land-use planning and community design, have students develop their community plans on the computer.

Aquatic Extensions

Review and discuss the following scenario: Ten years have passed since the city was established. In the meantime, the population of the community has doubled. What measures, if any, have been taken to protect the availability and quality of water in the community? What effects, if any, have there been on wildlife in the area as a result of this increase in population? What changes, if any, need to be made to protect the availability and quality of the water resources in this community for the next 25 years—for both people and wildlife?

Evaluation

1. Identify five important land uses to be considered in a community.

2. For each of the previously mentioned considerations, list two ways to reduce effects on the environment and wildlife.

3. In most major cities, land-use planning has been non-existent, minimal, or recent. Describe five methods that might be used to enhance the existence of a city's people and wildlife, with explanations for the methods you choose.

4. Make a plan to re-establish a wildlife species that once thrived in your community. Choose an animal that is not extinct. Show how that plan will fit with the existing plan you already created for your community. Take into account both the habitat needs of the wildlife species and the needs of the community of people. Older students can consider relevant state and federal wildlife laws.

Improving Wildlife Habitat in the Community

Objectives

Students will (1) apply their knowledge of wildlife by describing essential components of habitat in an arrangement appropriate for the wildlife, and (2) evaluate compatible and incompatible uses of an area by people and specified kinds of wildlife.

Method

Students design and accomplish a project to improve wildlife habitat in their community.

Materials

Writing and drawing materials; poster or butcher paper; or model making materials, such as plaster, clay, small replicas of animals, and so forth

---

Grade Level: 5–8

Subject Areas: Social Studies, Environmental Education

Duration: one or two 45-minute sessions, if hypothetical; much more time, if project is to be implemented

Group Size: any

Setting: indoors (and outdoors, optional)

Conceptual Framework Topic Reference: RAIC3

Key Terms: habitat, improvement

Appendices: Taking Action, Using Local Resources

Background

This activity provides an opportunity for students to evaluate and apply much of what they have learned about wildlife and its needs.

The major purpose of this activity is to provide students with experience in looking at their own communities, applying knowledge and skills they have acquired, and evaluating and experiencing the possibilities of enhancing their communities as places within which both people and wildlife can live suitably.

See the "Taking Action" Appendix beginning on page 487 for additional tips on involving students in environmental action projects.

Procedure

1. Ask the students whether their community could benefit from improved areas for wildlife habitat. If yes, this activity provides a process for helping to make such improvements. If a need is identified, the scope of such a project is a major decision. Habitat improvement projects can be large or small. If a project from this activity actually will be implemented, remember these points:

   - It needs to be within the scope and means of the students to experience success with it.
   - It clearly should be of benefit to wildlife and the community.

440   Project WILD K–12 Curriculum and Activity Guide

2. After general discussion, ask the group to divide into teams of four or five. Give each team the task of beginning a design for a habitat improvement project. The project could involve native plants and animals and could make a contribution to the community. Provide time for the students to discuss and make decisions about the following:

- What is the purpose of the project?
- Whom will it serve? Will people be able to visit? Will it be for plants and animals only? What plants and what animals? If people can visit, what will they be allowed to do? What won't they be allowed to do?
- What positive contributions might this improved wildlife habitat area make to the community? What possible problems could arise, if any?
- What will you need to accomplish the project? Where will you get the materials or services? What will it cost? How will it be paid for?
- Where will the area be? How large will it be?
- What are the habitat needs of any animals who will live there? What species of animals can live in the area that is available? (Some animals need more room than others. If you are to have a self-sustaining system, you will need a population in an area large enough for successful breeding over time.)
- What herbivores and carnivores might be needed? Predators? Prey? What specific kinds of plants (herbs, shrubs, trees, grasses, etc.) are needed and in what arrangement?
- What will be the water sources? How will air and water quality be maintained?
- What kinds of programs, if any, will be necessary to maintain the area once it has been improved?
- Who must be contacted so this project can be undertaken? What permissions will be needed? From whom?
- In balance, is the project a good idea—for the wildlife, the environment, and the people who live in this community?

OPTIONAL: Make a site visit.

3. Ask the groups to prepare the following: (a) a written description of their habitat improvement project, including its location, characteristics, inhabitants, and purposes; and (b) a map or scale model of the area. The map or model can include

- habitat components for various species;
- wildlife living in the area, in their appropriate locations;
- bodies of water, natural or made by people;
- major areas of vegetation and a key as to type;
- major landmarks (e.g., rock outcropping, roosts for birds, bare ground, meadows, brush, low trees, high trees);
- major food sources and types (e.g., berry patch for birds, rodents for coyotes or birds of prey); and
- areas developed for human access.

4. Ask each team to display its plans. After all the students have had an opportunity to read the background information and see the map or model of each habitat improvement project, ask the students to talk about what they learned in the process of creating these designs. They can include discussion of problems they encountered, what seemed realistic, what did not, and so forth. In discussion—and using their observations of the various proposed projects—ask the students to summarize what seemed to be the most important things to remember about designing such an area (e.g., size appropriate to wildlife, diversity, native elements, appropriateness to community wants and needs).

continued

Extensions

1. Consider the feasibility of designing and implementing one or more of these projects for your community. Have a local wildlife specialist and appropriate local officials (landowners, zoning authorities) critique and cooperate with you on any proposed project before you get under way with it. Make sure the project is worthy, feasible, and legal—and then proceed!

2. Tie your habitat improvement project into an existing network of habitat improvement projects. Contact your local wildlife or State Project WILD Coordinator and find out if any adopt-a-stream, backyard habitat, or school site habitat improvement programs are taking place in your area. If there are none, the Project WILD Coordinator may be able to refer you to a national program that could provide you and your students with ideas and assistance.

Aquatic Extension

Choose a habitat improvement project directly related to aquatic wildlife and aquatic habitats.

Evaluation

1. Rate the following uses of an area as either compatible or incompatible for people and wildlife:
   - houses being built 200 feet from a heron rookery,
   - picnic tables set up in an area heavily populated by squirrels,
   - snowmobile trails through a deciduous forest, and
   - swimming beach at a local lake.

   Think of your own examples. What could be done to make each of these uses more compatible for both people and wildlife?

2. Draw a picture or a blueprint of a community in which people have taken actions to improve the environment for both people and wildlife. Explain some of the features of the plan. Compare similarities and differences between the plan and the characteristics of your own community.

Enviro-Ethics

Objectives
Students will (1) distinguish between actions that are harmful and beneficial to the environment, and (2) evaluate the appropriateness and feasibility of making changes in their own behaviors related to the environment.

Method
Students develop and use a "Personal Code of Environmental Ethics."

Materials
None

Background
Ethics are derived from our guiding moral principles. They are influenced by age, gender, culture, family, and religion. Between the ages of 10 and 18, many people go through profound moral growth. During that time, they typically not only develop the mental reasoning abilities to grapple with moral issues, but also find themselves in more and more situations in which they have to make their own decisions. Ethics extend into many areas, including how people treat wildlife and the rest of the environment.

As students become more informed about wildlife and topics associated with the environment, as well as with the range of viewpoints surrounding them, they may experience shifts in their environmental ethics. Superficial understandings probably will lead to superficial ethical decisions. Having accurate information about wildlife and human effects on the environment will tend to help students reach more responsible decisions concerning wildlife and the environment upon which all life depends.

Class discussions related to ethics need to be designed to respect the student's right to privacy and nonparticipation. Educators could review and follow any policies related to teaching about ethics. Many educators have incorporated environmental ethics into drug prevention and other health programs. Developing ethical standards in one area can serve as a bridge to developing them in others.

The major purpose of this activity is to provide students with the encouragement and opportunity to examine personal lifestyles in light of their effects on wildlife and the environment.

Grade Level: 5–8

Subject Areas: Language Arts, Social Studies, Environmental Education

Duration: one or two 30- to 45-minute sessions

Group Size: any

Setting: indoors or outdoors

Conceptual Framework Topic Reference: RAIC2

Key Terms: ethics, responsibility, lifestyle

Appendices: Field Ethics, Animals in the Classroom

Procedure
1. Involve the students in discussion about the effects each of us has on aspects of the environment—from using electricity to make breakfast, to putting on clothes that were derived from some natural resources and transported to us by some means, to use

continued

of the varied products we choose and use each day, to our choices of recreation and entertainment.

2. Have each student identify someone who has done something that benefited wildlife and the environment. It could be someone famous like Theodore Roosevelt or Rachel Carson, or someone who might not be known by very many people at all. Ask about the beliefs or values that selected person holds (or has held) about the environment.

3. Next, ask each student to identify something they have done to help wildlife and the environment that they did not have to do. Ask why they chose to perform that task voluntarily. Talk about what "ethic" or "ethical standard" guided their decision. Explain that complex issues, like most wildlife and other environmental issues, contain a wide range of valid ethical positions.

4. Have the students brainstorm a list of the daily effects each of us has on the environment. This discussion can include our use of water, electricity, and fossil fuels; the effects caused by the production and manufacture of our food and clothing; and the environmental consequences of our recreation and entertainment choices.

5. Discuss how all living things affect the environment. Ask how some human environmental impact is different from the impact caused by other living things. Discuss how ethics can influence human effects on wildlife and the environment. Ask how a personal code of environmental ethics might have guided the people who were identified as having done something for wildlife and the rest of the environment. Now ask the students how they think a personal code of environmental ethics might guide them as they make decisions about the daily effects they just listed.

6. Ask each student to work alone to devise a "Personal Code of Environmental Ethics." This code may be written or not. Emphasize the importance of the code's being for the person who creates it. The code may consider daily actions that are harmful to the environment and those that are beneficial. The students could consciously create their code on the basis of actions they believe are beneficial, or at least not harmful, to elements of the environment.

7. Ask for volunteers to share their "Personal Code of Environmental Ethics." They might share the entire code or a segment of it. They might describe the thinking that went into the decisions they made in constructing their code. Students might illustrate a part of their code—if they chose not to write it—to convey a major idea. Encourage the students to ask each other questions about the codes—in the spirit of learning more about each person's priorities, but not in a judgmental approach. The purpose is for each student to evaluate his or her own priorities in a responsible consideration of day-to-day actions that affect the environment without being actively critical of another student's approach to the same problem. In this way, each student simply is encouraged to take responsibility for his or her own actions.

8. Encourage the students to try using their codes, keeping track of how easy or difficult it is for them to live by them. "Progress reports" are appropriate—again in the spirit of each person's paying attention to his or her own actions and bearing responsibility for them.

Extensions and Variations

1. Reflect for a few minutes on your daily life. In fact, close your eyes and follow yourself through a typical day. What natural resources do you use? What choices do you make that affect the environment? What choices do you make that affect wildlife and its habitat? What choices do you make that affect other people, here and elsewhere on the planet? If you could, what things—if any—would you change about your daily life in order to have a more beneficial, or less harmful, effect on the environment? What things—if any— do you already do that you think are helpful, or at least not harmful, to the environment? Brainstorm 10 words that come to mind when you think of actions and behaviors you value. Create a sentence, paragraph, or poem that might capture the essence of your own "Personal Code of Environmental Ethics."

2. Develop a "life map." It could include where you want to live; whether you want a family; what kind of home, transportation, food sources, job, or recreation you want; and so forth. Look at the costs and benefits of your choices—for you personally, other people in your community, wildlife, other natural resources, and such.

3. Revisit this activity several times throughout the year. It can serve as a starting point for numerous classroom activities.

NOTE: Students can establish their own or class ethical guidelines for a variety of experiences. For example, students can establish guidelines related to having animals in the classroom, going on field trips, or using electricity and paper in the classroom.

4. Locate and study ethical codes issued by various environmental organizations.

Evaluation

1. Develop a list of five environmental issues.

2. Develop a list of ways that you directly or indirectly contribute to an environmental problem.

3. Identify, describe, and evaluate one way you could lessen your role in contributing to an environmental problem.

4. What changes can you make in your lifestyle that will reduce your role in contributing to an environmental problem?

Can Do!

Objectives

Students will (1) identify a problem involving wildlife in their community, (2) suggest and evaluate alternative means by which to either solve the problem or at least improve the situation, (3) successfully undertake the project, and (4) analyze and describe the process by which they successfully solved the problem or improved the situation.

Method

Students select an environmental project, conduct research, make plans, and follow procedures to accomplish the project.

Materials

Writing materials

Background

Each of us can make constructive contributions to improving the environment in which we live. Sometimes our actions can improve the environment for people, sometimes for wildlife, and sometimes for both. Sometimes our effectiveness can be improved if we work with other people—sharing ideas, information, and skills.

A working knowledge of the following terms will be useful to students in this activity:

environmental problem: a difficult situation involving the interaction between people and the environment

environmental issue: a situation in which there is a disagreement about solutions to an environmental problem, often because of differing values and beliefs

authority: an individual or group of people with the power to make changes

compromise: a way to settle a problem in which both "sides" usually give a little

consensus: when a group of people reach a general agreement on a solution (It may not be exactly what every member wants, but what they can agree to.)

Given that it is important for young people to learn that they "can do" for people, wildlife, and the environment—use your judgment in the course of this activity to assist students in selecting a project that is realistic, constructive, and possible. If not, the students may experience an activity that contributes to their thinking that they "can't do."

Grade Level: 9–12

Subject Areas: Environmental Education, Social Studies

Duration: minimum of three 45-minute sessions

Group Size: any

Setting: outdoors and indoors

Conceptual Framework Topic Reference: RAIC1

Key Terms: problem, authority, compromise, constructive, realistic, effective, alternatives

Appendices: Taking Action, Outdoors

The major purpose of this activity is to provide students an opportunity to experience success in taking constructive actions to improve the environment for people and wildlife.

NOTE: See "Taking Action" beginning on page 487 for additional tips on involving students in environmental action projects.

Procedure

1. Ask the students to think of ways in which they could improve areas of the community as a home for wildlife. They might generate a list of activities that have a negative effect on wildlife. The list might include litter that poses a hazard for some kinds of wildlife; a muddy area that birds use for water but that has been recommended for paving to minimize dust and mud; a proposed pesticide spraying that will not only kill the "pest" but also perhaps affect other plants and animals; removal of a tree that presently helps contribute to cleaning the air, produces oxygen, and serves as a food and shelter source for varying kinds of wildlife, and so forth.

2. Looking at the list of possible issues and suggestions for ways to improve wildlife habitat at school, ask the students to select one they think they realistically could handle and do something constructive about. If they have difficulty in deciding which one and if reasonable support has been offered for each, the students might vote to decide. In hopes of swaying the class vote, students could also make speeches in support of the project they want to tackle.

3. Once the project has been selected, ask the students to work alone or in small groups to begin to generate ideas for possible solutions to the problems or the issue and to find ways to implement the project. Each individual or small group could come up with a plan, including a written description plus illustrations or sketches of how it will work and how it can be accomplished.

4. Ask the groups to present their plans to the rest of the students. Students may ask questions for clarification. Once all the plans have been presented, ask the students to select the plan that seems most (a) constructive, (b) realistic, (c) helpful to wildlife, and (d) apt to make a lasting contribution. Students might also develop a new plan that is based on the ideas presented.

5. Also ask the students to select one or more alternative plans, in case their first choices are not acceptable to authorities.

6. Once a plan and alternatives have been selected, ask the students to select a delegation to present their proposal to the authorities or whoever the appropriate authority is. Remember janitors, grounds-keepers, school board, and so on—anyone who would be physical or officially involved. A practice session before the students and any interested parents or other students would be helpful. At the practice session, the student delegation would make its presentation, responding to any questions from the audience.

7. Have the students make an appointment to present their proposal, make the presentation, and report back to their group. If their plan is accepted, they need to make sure they know whom to contact next to complete their project successfully. Making sure they have all necessary permissions secured, the students should proceed to accomplish their project successfully. If their plan, including alternatives, is not accepted, have the students identify why not. Have them find out exactly what people objected to in their original plan. The students can then respond to those objections with alternative proposals. Creating an alternative plan may require further research, careful interviews, and time.

continued

8. Once the project is accomplished, ask students to analyze their results. Did things work out as they wanted them to? Were there any surprises? Any unforeseen problems? How might they have been any more effective?

Aquatic Extension

Choose an issue to solve that involves water as a component of habitat.

Evaluation

Staff members at a nature center report they have noticed a smaller bluebird population in recent years. People are taking bluebird nest boxes down from trees and breaking them. The nature center director says there is no money to pay for security guards or to make repairs. Make a plan for helping the bluebirds.

Sustainability: Then, Now, Later

Objectives

Students will (1) define the different components of a sustainable community, (2) relate the effects of individual actions on the long-term health of the environment, and (3) explain how communities can become sustainable.

Method

Students analyze two articles on sustainability in which they investigate community life in the present and 100 years ago and then predict community life 100 years in the future.

Materials

Copies of articles on sustainability on pages 453 and 454, access to reference materials

Background

Sustainability refers to long-term strategies to restore and maintain environmental quality. It seeks to maintain the quality of human life while living within the carrying capacity of supporting ecosystems. Renewable resources must be used sustainably, that is, using those resources at rates that do not exceed their capacity for renewal.

Achieving this goal requires cooperation among the various components of society: individuals, businesses, and government.

> "Our vision is of a life-sustaining Earth. A sustainable United States will have a growing economy that provides equitable opportunities for satisfying livelihoods and a safe, healthy, high quality of life for current and future generations. Our nation will protect its environment, its natural resource base, and the function and viability of natural systems on which all life depends."
>
> —*The President's Council on Sustainable Development, 1996*

Grade Level: 9–12

Subject Areas: Language Arts, Expressive Arts, Science, Social Studies, Environmental Education

Duration: four 45-minute sessions with additional time to research, develop, and present skits

Setting: indoors

Conceptual Framework Topic References: RAI, RAIA, RAIB, RAIC

Key Term: sustainability

Appendices: none

> The goal of sustainability is "to meet the needs of the present without compromising the ability of future generations to meet their own needs."
>
> —*United Nations World Commission on Environment and Development (The Brundtland Commission), Our Common Future, 1987*

continued

The purpose of this activity is to focus on the role of the individual and on how daily decisions can affect the economy and governmental policies. Because communities must live within the limits of their natural resources, people need to learn to live sustainably by understanding the effects of their actions on the long-term health of the environment. It is the responsibility of citizens, government, and industry to avoid waste and destructive exploitation of natural resources, including wildlife.

Procedure

1. Have students read the first sustainability article on page 453. Ask the class to identify the main topic of the article. What would they title the selection? Have different students read each of the three paragraphs aloud to the class, and ask the class to identify the main point of each. Do they agree with the ideas in each paragraph? Why or why not? Challenge the students to suggest an example that supports the main idea of each paragraph and an opposing example.

2. Lead a discussion on individual needs and wants. Have students list three products or services they believe they "need" and list the reasons they need them. Have them also list three products or services they "want" and list the reason they want them. Share the lists among the class.

3. Have the students read the second sustainability article on page 454. What title would they suggest for this selection? Have the students compare the two articles for content, style, and philosophy. Could the same person have written them? Make sure the students support their answers with examples from the text of the two selections. Do the students agree with the five categories presented? How would they categorize ecosystem management types? Next, let the students know that both articles were written in Canada. How applicable are the themes in the United States? In which other countries might the articles be applicable? Not applicable? Why?

4. Divide the class into three groups: "1900," "2000," and "2100." The first group represents the community about 100 years ago, the second group is today's community, and the last group represents the community about 100 years into the future. Divide these three groups into subgroups representing government, agriculture, business and industry, or other perspectives. Tell students that they will portray people living during their assigned time period. As a person living at that time, what do they think would be their "wants" and "needs?" Have each subgroup research and list three wants and three needs for their assigned perspective. Then ask each subgroup to share the lists with the class and explain the rationale for the choices.

5. Ask students to develop a list of resources that might be consumed to meet the needs and wants on their lists. Have them list any waste materials that might be generated and share the list with the class.

6. Have the "1900" and "2000" groups investigate the sources of energy, water, food, shelter, and means of transportation and waste disposal for their communities during that period. They should research the wildlife present, too. They may use library research, Internet searches, newspaper articles, and interviews. Ask the "2100" group to predict the sources of energy, water, food, shelter and means of transportation and waste disposal for a community of people living during the year 2100. They should base their predictions on projections from current rates of use and growth. This information can be obtained from a county or district planning commission.

7. Have each group perform a skit to demonstrate the lifestyle of its period. Group members should work into the skit information they learned from their research on the available resources, goods, and services at the time. They also could suggest which of these items are considered a necessity or

a luxury by the characters in the skit. Cite a particular day, such as Thanksgiving, so that all three skits relate to similar activities. Students should describe their communities on that day, incorporating answers to the following questions into their skits:

- What does it look like outdoors and indoors?
- What did you eat, and where did the food come from?
- What is your source of water, and how did you obtain it?
- Where are your sources of energy to heat or cool your home, cook the food, and provide light?
- How did you dispose of wastes?
- Where did you go, and how did you get there?
- What did you do after you ate?
- What technology is available to you, and how does it affect your day?
- What type of wildlife exists in the community?

8. After each skit, ask the rest of the class to identify the products or services in the skit. How do they relate to the environment? Which products and services were environmentally friendly or beneficial? Which are harmful? How do the wants and needs from each time period affect the choices for the time period that follows?

9. Discuss global interdependence today and in the future versus the local sustainability of the past. How has technology allowed us to sustain our populations beyond what would have been the carrying capacity of a community without technology? What resources, products, or services readily were available within the home or community in the past that now are obtained from sources outside the community?

10. Ask the students to consider how the actions of the following members of the community might influence the environment:

- the owner of a business;
- a worker for a business or the government;
- a consumer buying products or services;
- an investor putting funds to use for buildings, transportation, and technology;
- a policymaker setting regulations for a government; and
- a voter deciding who will govern.

11. Discuss what can be done today to ensure the sustainability of the community for the future.

Extensions

1. Review the list of Inventions and Innovations found on page 455. Have students choose several inventions or innovations that have had a negative effect and several that have had a positive effect on the wildlife and the environment and then explain how. Have the students research several environmental disasters that occurred as a result of production activity and several technological breakthroughs that led to dramatic changes in the environment.

2. Ask students to identify several products or services provided by the government (either federal, state, or local) intended to achieve a positive influence on wildlife and the environment. Ask students to assess the success of those products or services.

3. Ask students to identify an environmental problem in their community. Have them research governmental regulations intended to mitigate this problem. Ask them to assess the success of these regulations.

continued

4. Have students create a mural that depicts their community of the past, present, and the future.

5. Have students design a web page that features what they learned about the sustainability of their community.

6. Have students research the various agencies and organizations that deal with sustainability. What policies are currently in place? What situations are leading to pending policies? What do the local and state legislators think about these issues?

7. Have students consider how they might reduce the size of their "ecological footprint" by examining their "needs" versus their "wants."

Evaluation

1. Have students demonstrate concepts of sustainability through their skit and the question and answer session that follows.

2. Ask students to write an essay describing how individual choices have an effect on the environment. How can individuals improve the environment? How can individuals influence business decisions and governmental policy to achieve a more positive influence on the environment?

3. Have students present examples of communities that have been negatively affected because they did not live in a sustainable manner.

4. Have students find examples of sustainable communities in the United States, abroad, or both.

5. Use the National Environmental Education and Training Foundation (NEETF) "Report Card on Environmental Knowledge, Attitudes, and Behaviors" survey as pre- and post-tests for student knowledge of natural resources. A copy of this survey can be found at NEETF's website: **www.neeft.org**.

Sustainability Article #1

How do we bring about changes in human behavior that result in actively protecting and preserving our natural world? How can we repair damage to habitats and reduce damage in the future? Whatever methods are used, most likely everyone will pay the costs. The questions that society must decide involve balancing the value of material wealth and the value of environmental health. Until recently, that balance has favored production and consumption at the expense of natural resources because society has not understood nor put a price on the value of a healthy environment. Placing a value on actions necessary to achieve and maintain a healthy environment is important, because achieving it will cost money. Producing goods in a way that does not damage the environment may initially result in higher prices and fewer material goods, but we may be willing to pay that price for a healthy world. Others argue that new technologies will be developed that will help increase production without damaging habitats. But such developments take time and money, too, and may be short-sighted.

If we are willing to pay for a healthy environment, it is the individual who will probably lead the fight. Although business and government are crucial decision-making components driving the economy, politicians tend to act only when they're convinced that the voters want them to, and businesses produce goods and services that the public demands and will pay for. Sustainable change must be supported at the ultimate grassroots level because it is our cumulative individual material needs and wants that generate the production and economic activity that leads to the use of our resources.

For us to use limited resources most effectively and wisely, it will be important to distinguish "needs" from "wants." Needs are necessities, or things we must have. Wants are luxuries, or non-essential things that we would like to have for enjoyment or convenience. The distinction between the two may vary between individuals and even countries. What satisfies as a basic need for shelter in one country, for example, may be totally unacceptable in another. Perhaps because our economy does so well in meeting our basic needs, we are now able to focus on the environmental implications of our economic activity. We have tended to measure progress in terms of the quantity of goods and services, but now we are challenged to consider the quality of life as well, and to value things that have not historically had a price tag: a wilderness, a sparkling stream, clean air, and so on. Do we need more goods and services? How much do we need?

Adapted with permission from Jackson, Judith (Ed.), Environomics, Canadian Foundation for Economic Education: Toronto, Ontario, 1996.

continued

Sustainability Article #2

Over the past century, we have managed ecosystems in at least five different ways. Until the middle of this century, the industrialized world tended to see the environment as an infinite supply of resources and a bottomless sink for wastes. This first approach, often referred to as "frontier economics," prevails even today in some developing nations and some sectors of industrialized countries. The economy was seen to exist in almost complete isolation, separate from the environment. Resources were seen as being abundant. So, for example, an increased demand for forest products could be met simply by building a new mill. The more pressing problem with frontier economics was the scarcity of workers, not of resources. Consequently, the destruction of the environment made little difference, because fresh territory and fresh resources always were within reach. It also can be argued that a further consequence of the frontier economics approach was the development of separate sciences. Forests or crops, for example, never were considered in relation to the soil that held them in place, to the rivers that ran through them, or to the animals that lived within them. Government programs, university faculties, and economic theories all perpetuated this rather unconnected and restrictive outlook on the world.

By the late 1960s and 1970s, many people in industrialized nations began to recognize the interdependence of man and the environment, and they became increasingly concerned about pollution. Although the environment continued to be less important than economics, the need to conserve and maintain resource stocks became a consideration for the first time. During this period policies were introduced to make polluters more accountable for the damage they caused and the relationship among land, soil, water, air, and animal life was made a factor within the traditional sciences. Under this second approach, known as "resource management," the environmental implications of resource removal was evaluated. These assessments, however, often were made as an afterthought, following the planning stages of a given development project. Consequently, business decision-making processes continued largely as before, with environmental consequences considered after the basic decisions were made.

Resource management remains, to a large extent, the dominant mode of thinking about the environment and economic development. Nevertheless, environmental awareness is growing at an increasingly rapid pace. "Selective environmentalism," a third approach, reflects a contrasting style of thinking. It can best be described as a "doing my part" approach, where consumers and agencies express their concerns about environmental degradation by making selected efforts to stop it. This desire to do something for the environment has led to many "environmentally friendly" products and initiatives, such as municipal recycling programs. However, selective environmentalism places little, if any, emphasis on cost-effectiveness. Moreover, it makes the assumption that the economy will simply take care of itself.

"Deep environmentalism," the fourth approach, disavows economics to the furthest degree. Here, the human race is seen as no more than one of many species that share this planet. Clearly, deep environmentalism is the antithesis of frontier economics. Where frontier economics gave little attention to the environment, deep ecology gives little attention to the economy.

The most balanced approach considers "sustainable communities." This fifth outlook supports the view that a healthy environment is essential for a sound and prosperous economy. Society, economics, and the environment are, therefore, seen as elements of a mutually supporting ecosystem and are automatically taken into account before decisions are made. A sustainable community approach holds that resources must be treated on the basis of their future, as well as their present, value. With today's unprecedented threats of global change and worldwide degradation of environmental resources, the need to integrate environmental, social, and economic goals in the broader ecological context has never been greater.

Adapted from "Ecosphere," Environment Canada: The State of Canada's Environment-1991. Ottawa: Supply and Services Canada, 1991, pp. 1–5, 1–7, 1–8. Adapted with the permission of the Minister of Public Works and Government Services Canada, 2000.

Inventions and Innovations

Plastics

Electric car

Snowblower

Steam engine

Aircraft de-icer

Gasoline-powered engine

Submarine telegraph cable

Newsprint

Braille

Panoramic camera

Helium substituted for hydrogen in airships

Telephone

Radio

Snowmobile

Football

Zipper

Self-cleaning ovens

Velcro

Polyester

Light bulb

Cardiac pacemaker

Jet engine

X-ray machine

Pizza

E-mail delivery services

Ear piercer

CDs

Remote control unit for television

Microwave ovens

Cellular telephones

Antibiotics

High-yield corn

Pesticides

Rubber tires

Hair coloring

Flush toilets

Air conditioning

Washing machine

Hair dryer

Contact lenses

Refrigerator

Double-paned windows

Insulation foam

Automobile

Personal computers

Computer modems

Toothpaste

Table hockey

Notes

Appendices

Conceptual Framework

This framework serves as the conceptual basis for activities in the *Project WILD* and *Project WILD Aquatic K–12 Curriculum and Activity Guides*. Every concept statement in a topic area is directly addressed by the activities listed for that topic. Activities under other topics may also support the concepts directly or indirectly.

Ecological Knowledge

Wildlife Populations (WP)

I. Characteristics

  A. Wildlife comprises all nonhuman and nondomesticated animals. Wildlife includes but is not limited to insects, spiders, birds, reptiles, fish, amphibians, and mammals.

   1. Wildlife is all around, although it may not be seen or heard or its presence otherwise sensed.

   2. Wildlife varies from forms that are microscopic to those more than 100 feet in length, and it occurs in a variety of forms, colors, and shapes.

  B. All living things go through a series of orderly changes in life cycles. Some species have distinct changes; the young of other species resemble their parents.

  C. Living things all need food, water, shelter, and a suitable place to live.

  D. Animals can be classified according to life needs, behavior, and physical characteristics, including body appearance, movement, habitat type, and relationship to humans (wild/domesticated).

II. Population Dynamics

  A. Wildlife numbers and species compositions are not static but are constantly changing.

   1. Systematic inventory of wildlife populations did not become a common practice until the 1930s, although journals of early explorers reflect considerable variation in historic population levels.

   2. Some wildlife populations exhibit cyclic patterns over time.

    a. Living things tend to reproduce in numbers greater than their habitat can support.

     (1) Carrying capacity is the dynamic equilibrium expressed by the availability of habitat components and the number of animals the habitat can support.

     (2) Each area of land or water, and ultimately the planet, has a carrying capacity of plants and animals.

      (a) Carrying capacity is determined by climatic, geological, biological, or behavioral factors, along with human activities.

      (b) Carrying capacity may fluctuate from season to season and year to year.

      (c) Carrying capacity affects and is affected by wildlife behavior.

i. The numbers, health, and distribution of wildlife are related to carrying capacity.

ii. Carrying capacity limitations can result in competition between and among domestic animals, wildlife, and humans.

b. A population tends to increase in size until limited by one or more factors.

(1) When one or more limiting factors exceed the tolerance range for an animal, population, or species, it directly affects the well-being of the animal(s) and may result in death or extinction.

(2) Limiting factors include life history parameters such as food, water, shelter, space, disease, predation, and climatic conditions, as well as human activities such as development, pollution, and hunting.

B. Natural laws are ultimately as binding on human populations as on wildlife.

Habitats, Ecosystems, and Niches (HN)

I. Distribution

A. Wildlife is present in nearly all areas of the Earth.

B. Each environment has characteristic life forms.

1. The environment—created and shaped by natural forces or modified by humans—shapes life forms that occupy it.

2. Each species occupies a niche within the range of environments in which it is found.

II. Importance

A. Good habitat is the key to the survival of humans and wildlife.

1. Habitat is composed of many integrated components including food, water, shelter or cover, space, and the suitable arrangement of these in relation to each other.

2. In addition to supporting wildlife, ecosystems must furnish the products humans need to survive.

B. Wildlife may be used as an indicator of the environmental health of an ecosystem.

Interdependence (ID)

I. Commonalities

A. All living elements of an ecological system are interdependent.

1. All forms of life depend on food, water, shelter, and space in a suitable arrangement.

2. Humans and wildlife have similar basic needs.

a. Humans and wildlife share environments and are subject to essentially the same environmental conditions.

b. The health and well-being of humans and wildlife depend on the quality of the natural environment.

B. Plants and animals in ecological systems live in a web of interdependence, in which each species contributes to the functioning of the overall system.

continued

II. Interactions
   A. All living things are affected by and interact with their environments.
   B. In a naturally functioning ecosystem, life forms and environmental factors interact to keep wildlife populations in long-term dynamic equilibrium with each other and with their habitats.
      1. Many interactions result in a flow of energy and matter throughout the system.
         a. Energy takes a one-way course through an ecosystem and dissipates at every trophic level.
         b. Material substances, such as water, nitrogen, carbon, and phosphorus, cycle through ecosystems.
      2. Food webs illustrate the interrelationships of all living things.
         a. Either directly or indirectly, plants support nearly all forms of animal life, including humans.
            (1) Energy from the sun and organic matter enters the animal world through herbivores, those animals that eat plants.
            (2) A relatively large quantity of plant material is required to support herbivores (primary consumers), and herbivores can support only a smaller number of carnivores (secondary consumers).
            (3) Decomposers complete the cycle by breaking down organic matter formed by photosynthesis.
         b. Trophic relationships in an ecosystem may be complex and may vary depending on environmental conditions.
   C. Wildlife interacts with other wildlife and thereby affects the functioning of the ecological system.
      1. Interactions exist between different populations.
         a. Competition is a major determinant of community structure.
         b. Predation can be beneficial or harmful to a population as a whole.
         c. Symbiotic relationships may benefit or harm one or both of the partners.
      2. Interactions exist among members within a population, including competition and cooperation.

Changes and Adaptations (CA)

I. Environmental Changes
   A. Variation and change occur in all ecological systems.
   B. Succession is an orderly, gradual, and continuous replacement of one natural community of life by another.
      1. Succession influences what kinds of plants and animals live in an area.
         a. New communities arise when ecosystems change through succession.
         b. Newer communities may have less diversity.
         c. Species present in new communities will have traits that allow them to survive in the new environment.
         d. Over time, species diversity may increase in a new community.
      2. Natural events and human activities affect the rate and direction of succession.
   C. All forms of life are affected by changes in the quality, quantity, and distribution of their habitats.

II. Organism Adaptations
   A. All life forms exhibit adaptations to the environments in which they live.
      1. Fish and wildlife are adapted to their environment in ways that enable them to survive and maintain their populations.
         a. Many physical and behavioral adaptations, such as body coverings, hibernation, and migration, are associated with climatic conditions.
         b. Adaptations to predator and prey relationships may include behavioral (e.g., signaling, flight, freezing) as well as physical (e.g., camouflage, mimicry) variations.
         c. Reproductive strategies are adaptations that maximize species survival.
      2. Fish and wildlife species differ in their ability to adapt to changes in their habitats.
   B. Each habitat is suitable only to those life forms that are adapted to its ecological conditions.
   C. Isolated ecosystems are more vulnerable to environmental change.

Biodiversity (BD)

I. Types

Biodiversity can refer to a variety of natural systems, a variety of species in an area, or a genetic diversity within a species.

   A. Ecosystem Diversity
      1. Ecosystem diversity is affected by many influences, such as climate and level of disturbance.
      2. Ecosystems undergo successional changes that are usually gradual.
      3. Species that are not able to adapt to ecosystem change may become extinct.
      4. A biologically healthy ecosystem is diverse over the range of the ecosystem, not necessarily within each community.
   B. Species Diversity
      1. Climate and habitats influence species diversity.
      2. Organisms that are not able to adjust to ecosystem changes will die.
      3. New ecosystems and ecosystems that are harsh tend to have relatively few species.
      4. Species diversity tends to be higher in the transition zone between ecosystems.
   C. Genetic Diversity
      1. Genetic variability is important to health within a species.
      2. Diversity facilitates adaptation to change and provides sources of new genetic material.

II. Human Influence
   A. Some wildlife species are not native but have been introduced to the area they presently occupy. Such introductions can be beneficial, harmful, or both to other species in the ecosystem.
   B. Adding or subtracting members from a community affects other members of the community.
   C. Human activities can affect the rate at which wildlife becomes threatened, endangered, or extinct.

continued

III. The Importance of Habitat
   A. Habitat is the key to wildlife survival.
   B. Improving habitat improves wildlife populations.
   C. Reintroduction of wildlife into its former range may be possible if suitable habitat and suitable wild stock are available, and if such other conditions as weather and predator levels do not substantially interfere.
   D. Management of one species will affect other species in a community.
   E. For a wildlife population to sustain itself, there must be suitable habitat to support a viable breeding population, not just a few individuals.

Social and Political Knowledge

Cultural Perspectives (CP)

I. Cultural Development
   A. Human cultures and societies, past and present, affect and are affected by wildlife and its habitat.
   B. Values, ethics, and historical traditions of cultures and societies are reflected in their treatment of wildlife and other resources.
      1. Human and wildlife relationships are expressed through legends, myths, religious teachings and writings, symbols, protocols, ceremonies, and other cultural and societal activities.
      2. Appreciation of wildlife is often portrayed through creative expression of human relationships with wildlife in historic and contemporary times.

II. Appreciation

Societies and cultures within societies may have different attitudes toward wildlife and its uses, formed and transmitted by family, community, and other social groups in a variety of ways.

   A. The aesthetic and spiritual values that humans place on wildlife vary from person to person and culture to culture.
   B. Different cultures may disagree over certain uses of and rights to wildlife and its habitat.
   C. Wildlife and its habitat are interpreted and treated differently by people viewing them from various cultural perspectives and frames of reference.
      1. Increasing separation of people from direct contact with the natural world has influenced human actions and attitudes toward wildlife. Therefore, actions and attitudes toward wildlife may be positive, negative, naïve, or misguided.
      2. Formal and nonformal education and the media shape the attitude of people toward wildlife and its habitat.

Economic, Commercial, and Recreational Considerations (EC)

I. Economic Considerations
   A. Natural resources include water, air, minerals, soil, fossil fuels, and plant life, as well as aquatic and terrestrial wildlife.
      1. Nonrenewable natural resources are those available on a finite basis.
      2. Renewable natural resources, including wildlife, can replenish themselves independently or with human assistance.

B. The distribution and abundance of wildlife can affect the economy of an area.
  1. Some wildlife provides products of commercial value or subsistence needs to humans.
  2. Members of some cultures still depend on wildlife to supply a portion of their requirements for food, shelter, and clothing.
  3. Human use of wildlife directly and indirectly creates job opportunities for people.
C. Economic trends, in addition to increased human population and mobility, have important influences on wildlife and its habitat.
D. The human culture and economic condition of an area affect and are affected by the available resources, including wildlife and its habitat.

II. Commercial, Recreational, and Other Economic Considerations
A. Historically, when conflict between recreational and commercial harvest of a wildlife species became severe, the commercial use had been eliminated.
B. Recreational trends affect wildlife and its habitat.
  1. Wildlife-based recreation is of major importance to many millions of North Americans.
    a. Consumptive wildlife-based activities, such as hunting and fishing, provide U.S. and Canadian citizens with millions of days of outdoor recreation each year.
    b. Nonconsumptive activities, such as wildlife photography, painting, feeding, and observation, also provide millions of days of recreation annually.
  2. More leisure time and the growing popularity of outdoor activities are increasing the pressures on wildlife and habitat.
C. Funds provided by consumptive users, not general tax dollars, historically have been the primary source of income for most state wildlife management programs and some federal programs.
  1. Charging an access fee to hunt, fish, camp, play, or trap on private land is common.
  2. Reductions in income from direct consumptive uses of wildlife (hunting, fishing, etc.) and nonconsumptive uses (camping, bird watching, etc.) have resulted in a loss of revenue for natural resource agencies.

Historical and Geographic Development (HG)

I. Development of Society

Historically, wildlife affected the development, movement, and size of human societies.

A. Human societies and cultures developed in various ways, partly because environmental factors produced different types of plants and animals in different places.
B. Wildlife has played a significant role in the development of human culture through its influence on art, religion, and commerce.
C. Wildlife questions and issues have influenced alliances and conflicts between and within communities, societies, states, and nations.

continued

II. Development of Commerce

Throughout history humans have used wildlife for food, shelter, clothing, and other products.

A. All livestock and pet animals were domesticated and developed from wildlife species as humans sought to provide themselves with food, shelter, medicines, and companionship, and to satisfy other needs or wants.

B. The ways in which humans value wildlife and natural resources have changed over time.

C. As human populations have grown and pressures on wildlife populations have increased, people have developed systems to study wildlife and to regulate human impact on wildlife and habitats.

Political and Legislative Frameworks (PL)

I. United States

A. Political trends affect wildlife and other natural resources.

B. In the United States, wildlife is considered to be a public resource. Ownership of land or water alone does not secure ownership of wildlife on that land or in that water as it does in some other countries.

1. Public decisions that affect wildlife and the environment are made through social and political processes designed to represent the wishes of the society.

2. Primary responsibility for most wildlife conservation programs in the United States is delegated to governmental agencies.

    a. States are considered to have a greater responsibility for wildlife conservation programs than does the federal government. State wildlife agencies are legally responsible for managing most wildlife on public and private lands within their geographic jurisdictions.

    b. Federal agencies, in cooperation with state agencies, are legally responsible for managing wildlife affecting national interest, such as most threatened and endangered species and migratory wildlife.

3. Nongovernmental institutions play significant roles in influencing environmental policy and direction.

    a. Wildlife interest groups use judicial, legislative, and regulatory systems in reaching their objectives.

    b. Private organizations, industrial interests, and individual citizens also conduct wildlife conservation activities.

C. Societies develop programs and policies relating to wildlife and its habitat through a variety of social mechanisms.

II. International

A. Other nations and governments have different policies and philosophies relating to wildlife ownership and protection and to habitat management.

B. Many wildlife species regularly move across national boundaries, necessitating the adoption of international agreements and the formation of international agencies and organizations to ensure protection and management of these species.

Sustaining Fish and Wildlife Resources

Attitudes and Awareness (AA)

I. Awareness

    A. Humans may find peace and inspiration through study and observation of wildlife, or simply through knowledge of its existence.

    B. Citizens benefit from experiencing and enjoying their natural resources.

II. Values

    A. Wildlife has intrinsic value, although humans often recognize only values based upon human wants and needs.

        1. The value placed on wildlife is commonly an issue in resource management decisions because value is often intangible and varies from person to person.

        2. Various groups interested in wildlife represent a wide range of philosophies and ethics concerning wildlife and how best to ensure its long range health and viability.

    B. Ecosystems have a finite capacity to provide for wildlife and human needs and wants. Sustainable living requires humans to live within the limits of the ecosystem capacity.

Human Impacts (HI)

I. The Importance of Impacts

    A. Human effects on fish and wildlife and their habitats are a driving force affecting environmental quality worldwide.

    B. The presence of people affects wildlife in positive and negative ways.

II. Impacts

    A. Humans have the capacity to sustain themselves and wildlife.

        1. Although all organisms affect their environment, only humans have the capacity to consider the effects of their actions and to develop a community that is sustainable into the future.

        2. A sustainable community is one that is in balance with a healthy environment and perpetuates a healthy environment for future generations.

        3. The development and adoption of sustainable human lifestyles and social decisions can change the negative effects of human activity on wildlife.

            a. Individual lifestyle decisions including recreational choices, transportation options, housing selections, vocation, food, clothing, and energy use affect wildlife directly and indirectly.

            b. Community conservation practices, plus social, cultural, and economic values affect environmental programs and activities.

    B. Human populations and technologies often require space and activities that are detrimental to wildlife and its habitat.

        1. Human development encroaches on wildlife habitat, decreasing the amount of available habitat.

        2. Wildlife habitats are being fragmented by urban sprawl, resulting in restricted wildlife movement.

        3. Some habitats are being altered by human development activities such as water storage and landscaping.

continued

4. Contaminants and their bio-accumulative risks to both wildlife and humans threaten sustainable environments.

5. Pollutants fall into a number of categories including acid rain, terrestrial runoff, biological (exotics, disease, waste), industrial waste and spills, post-consumer petroleum products, sewage, silt or sediment, thermal pollution, and radioactive and solid waste. Each of these pollutants creates particular effects on habitats and, if severe enough, may cause habitat loss.

C. Loss and degradation of habitat are considered the greatest problems facing wildlife today.

1. Wildlife habitat loss because of natural trends or human activities is a condition common in nearly all nations.

2. One specific cause of habitat degradation is pollutants, which can negatively affect environmental quality.

3. Many critical habitats have been, and are, under pressure from historic and current development. Many have been damaged or lost.

4. Remaining critical habitats can be, and in some cases are being, protected and maintained; damaged habitats can be, and in some cases are being, rehabilitated.

Issues and Trends (IT)

I. Global Perspectives

A. Current wildlife issues and trends are complex, involve alternatives, and affect the environment.

B. Many problems, issues, and trends involving wildlife in other parts of the world are similar to those in this country.

1. Wildlife issues can affect global and international as well as national, regional, and local political activities—particularly regarding human harvesting practices, transmission of pollutants and their secondary impacts, migratory species, and aquatic habitats.

2. Consumptive uses of wildlife have been excessive in some settings and continue as a persistent problems in other parts of the world.

3. Commercial sale of wildlife and wildlife products is controversial and has worldwide implications.

II. Wildlife Populations

A. Human activities increasingly determine which species of plants and animals will flourish and which will decline or disappear.

1. Most species that are endangered or threatened became so from natural or human-caused changes in their habitat and their inability to adapt or adjust to such changes.

2. Exotic species introduced into a community can change the functioning of that system.

a. Evaluation of the impact of non-native plants and animals on ecosystems is important to the management and conservation of those ecosystems.

b. Citizens must be aware of their potential role in the dispersal of non-native species and the transmission of disease, and must take steps to avoid contributing to these problems.

B. Private landowners play an important role in sustaining and improving wildlife habitat.

III. Land Use
- A. As human populations increase and become significantly urban, land usage is altered dramatically.
    1. Individual transportation systems that allow increased accessibility spearhead development and drive land-use changes.
    2. Natural areas are being converted to agricultural, recreational, residential, and commercial purposes.
    3. Fragmentation of biological communities, caused by human activities, affects wildlife diversity and populations.
- B. Consumer changes lead to agricultural production changes.

IV. Human Perspectives
- A. Wildlife issues involve conflicts between different interest groups.
- B. Issues involving wildlife and its habitat are often products of cultural differences and priorities.
- C. Well-informed individuals can assist resource management through increased involvement.

V. Consumptive and Nonconsumptive Uses
- A. Conflicts exist within and between consumptive and nonconsumptive resource users. Any resolution must consider the needs of all groups and the sustainability of the resource.
    1. Whether uses of wildlife should be consumptive or nonconsumptive is of concern to many people.
    2. Among consumptive groups, conflicts often involve how, when, and how much wildlife populations are used.
- B. Nongame species have begun to receive greater and more specific management attention.

Wildlife Management (WM)

I. Basic Concepts
- A. For management purposes, wildlife often has been divided into categories, including game, nongame, endangered, and threatened.
    1. Game species are those that are hunted, fished, or trapped for recreational or economic purposes by humans.
    2. Nongame species are those that are not hunted, fished, or trapped for either recreational or economic purposes by humans.
    3. Endangered species are those in danger of extinction throughout all or a significant portion of their ranges.
    4. Threatened species are those likely to become endangered.
- B. Wildlife management is the application of scientific knowledge and technical skills to the protection, preservation, conservation, limitation, or enhancement of wildlife and its habitat.
- C. Conservation is the use of natural resources in a way that assumes their continuing availability to future generations through the wise use or protection of natural resources.

continued

II. Management Considerations
   A. Wildlife resources can be managed and conserved.
   B. Wildlife species are important components of a larger ecosystem and should be managed within the context of that ecosystem..
      1. Management of one species of wildlife may have positive or negative consequences for other species within the same ecosystem.
      2. Management of aquatic wildlife and its habitat is directly influenced by land-based activities in the surrounding watershed.
   C. Wildlife management considers the needs and desires of people as well as wildlife.
      1. Humans differ in how they value wildlife and its habitat, and the total demand on each may exceed the supply.
      2. Wildlife management decisions must consider political, social, economic, and biological concerns; such decisions should involve all interested or potentially affected constituencies.
      3. These same factors may limit the scope and effectiveness of wildlife management activities.
   D. Philosophies and practices in wildlife management have been both supported and criticized by individuals, as well as by public and private organizations.
   E. Most wildlife exists on land or in waters that are not directly controlled by state or federal wildlife management agencies.

III. Management Practices

Wildlife managers combine an understanding of species biology and of ecosystem structure and function with population- and land-manipulation techniques to accomplish management goals.

   A. Wildlife management is based on natural sciences such as biology, ecology, geography, and soil science, as well as on many other disciplines.
      1. Wildlife management practices have been developed through extensive research on ecosystems, through both observation and experimentation.
      2. Habitat management practices are often intended to mimic the effects of natural ecosystem processes, especially disturbance.
   B. Wildlife management practices involve population and habitat inventory and monitoring, direct management of wildlife species through manipulation of populations, indirect management of wildlife species through protection and manipulation of habitat, and public regulation and education.
      1. Surveys of wildlife populations and their habitat provide important baseline information to guide management decisions.
      2. Wildlife populations are manipulated through practices such as artificial propagation, stocking, transplanting, predator and damage control, and regulated harvest.
      3. Acquisition, protection, improvement, and restoration of habitat are considered to be the most successful and cost-effective long-range techniques for managing wildlife species.

4. Regulations are necessary for wildlife conservation, but they cannot substitute for the availability of suitable habitat, nor can they maintain the population of a species whose habitat has been depleted or destroyed.

5. A public that is well educated about wildlife management issues is critical to the long-term success of wildlife management programs.

C. Scientific knowledge of all aspects of wildlife, including biological and social, is growing.

1. Technology changes affect environmental management decisions by allowing more sophisticated science-based analysis.

2. Wildlife agencies employ persons with a variety of scientific training and vocational skills.

Responsible Action (RA)

I. All plants and animals (human and wildlife) must live within the limits of their natural resources.

A. Both consumptive and nonconsumptive resource uses by people can strengthen their sense of responsibility toward the environment and encourage ethical actions.

B. It is the responsibility of citizens, government, and industry to avoid waste and destructive exploitation of natural resources, including wildlife.

C. Communities can learn to live in a sustainable manner by understanding the effects of their actions on the long-term health of the environment.

1. Citizens must understand their rights, privileges, and responsibilities, plus the consequences of their actions. That is, they should be aware of methods to help protect and improve the resource and should have the opportunity to practice and apply them.

2. Private decisions that affect wildlife and the environment are made through personal judgments. Each person makes such decisions each day, including use of time and energy, consumer choices, and vocational and leisure time activities.

3. Citizens can become involved in the management of wildlife, habitat, and the environment by direct participation in the political process or through local, state, national, or international organizations.

4. Individuals can influence public processes by voting, demonstrating, lobbying, seeking office, and supporting compatible interest groups.

5. All users of wildlife must respect the rights and property of others, consider effects on the habitat, and observe rules and regulations relating to wildlife.

6. Communities can learn to live in a sustainable manner by understanding the effects of their actions on the long-term health of the environment.

7. Education can help landowners so that they can prosper while maintaining environmental quality and integrity into the future.

D. Each individual has a responsibility to act in ways that can directly or indirectly reduce the impact of the pollutants on the environment.

II. Conservation, restoration, and enhancement of natural resource habitats benefit humans.

Early Childhood Extensions

Adaptation Artistry

1. Read a children's book with color photographs to help the students see and understand an animal's adaptations. Discuss adaptations that are easy to see, such as color or camouflage, beaks, feet, size, and animal locomotion. Discuss with the students what it would feel like to have the special animal features talked about in the story and activity.

2. Watch nature videos to show the students the differences in animal locomotion. Have students try to copy the animal's movements. Discuss why these special features may help the animals to survive.

3. Have the students use clay to sculpt animals with adaptations. Have the students describe the special features their animal has and how those features help their animal to survive.

And The Wolf Wore Shoes

Have the students create a classroom poster on chart paper. Using bears as an example, draw a line down the middle and label each side: Things Story Bears Do / Things Real Bears Do. Have students come up with characteristics for each. Have them decorate the poster border with bear drawings.

Animal Charades

Design *Animal Charade* cards using laminated drawings or photos that students can pull out of a hat. Ask the students: If this animal walked across the room, how would this animal move? If this animal swam across a pond, how would it move in the water? Can you make your face look like the face of this animal? What does this animal look like when it is eating?

Ants on a Twig

1. Have students draw or finger paint their ant observations.

2. Demonstrate ant behavior by playing *Follow the Leader*, using one single line, rather than two opposing lines.

Bearly Growing

Teachers can make a life-sized wall mural of the life stages of both humans and bears. Have students compare their own sizes to the drawings on the wall mural.

Beautiful Basics

1. Display a variety of photos or drawings of humans, domesticated animals, and wild animals in their habitats. Show the first photo, for example, of a grassy field. Ask the students, if they were going to live in this field, what would they as humans need? Then ask the same for pets and wildlife. Compare.

2. Group photos or drawings by basic needs: food, water, shelter, space.

Classroom Carrying Capacity

1. Read a nonfiction story about an animal. Have the students sit on the floor, taking up as much room as they would like. About every other page, have the students move closer together. Tell students that the classroom is beginning to shrink. By the end of the story, the students should have moved in so far that they are elbow-to-elbow with no room to spare. Discuss how the students felt about being so close together. Have them tell how they felt at the beginning of the story compared to now.

2. Ask the students how much space an animal needs. List responses. Discuss the needs of the animal from the nonfiction story. Did the animal in the story need space? Discuss a variety of animals (e.g., ants, bears, lizards, and birds). Why do these animals need different amounts of space?

Color Crazy

Begin this activity with an introduction to bright colors. Have students identify, compare, and sort the colors in their classroom and school yard.

Ethi-Thinking

Have the students give a "thumbs up" or a "thumbs down" after showing pictures of both negative and positive activities to wildlife and the environment. Ask students "why" or "why not" for each.

Everybody Needs a Home

1. Read stories about animal shelters and provide pictures.

2. Create a matching game with pictures that match animals to their shelters.

3. Look for signs of animal shelters outside.

First Impressions

Create three large circles on the floor of the room with rope, masking tape, or hula-hoops. Within each circle draw a face: one with a smile, one with a frown, and one with a straight line. Have the students stand around the outside of the three faces, and explain to them the names of each face: Smiley, Frowny, and Undecided. Hold up a photo of an animal, and ask students to walk into the face that best describes how they feel about the animal. Write the name of the animal on a chart, and make a tally list for each face. Ask the students what they already know about the animal. Read more about the animal, and then discuss whether anyone changed their mind about the animal and why they did.

Good Buddies

1. Discuss the animal relationships described by using face symbols ("smiley," "no expression," and "frowny" faces). Categorize the animal relationships on a wall chart using the face symbols in association with the vocabulary words: Mutualism = smiley/smiley, Commensalism = smiley/no expression, or Parasitism = smiley/frowny.

2. Create a matching game using cards for each pair of animal buddies. Cut the cards in half using different types of cuts—like a puzzle—where each pair has its own special cut. Give a card to each student. Ask the students to find their match by comparing the cut side of the card to the cut side of other students, cards. Once all students find their match, they sit with their matching buddy. Students should take turns showing the class their animal buddies while the educator tells the group about the animals.

Grasshopper Gravity

Have the students use snails for this activity and compare themselves with grasshoppers.

Interview a Spider

1. Have an adult represent an animal. Let students ask questions about the animal. Draw the animal, and write the answers on chart paper.

2. The animal can be a "secret." Let students guess which animal is being represented.

Litter We Know

Have the students save their trash from lunch. Prepare two bar graphs that read: *How many pieces of litter came from my lunch?* (0, 1, 2, 3, 4, or more) and *What is my litter made of?* (glass, metal, paper, plastic, food). Students can use stickers or post-it notes for graphing. Brainstorm ways that the students' lunch litter could harm or help wildlife. Discuss ways that students can make a positive difference with lunch trash.

continued

Oh, Deer!

Provide big name cards or pictures that the students can wear as necklaces to represent food, water, shelter, and space rather than having them hold their arms to represent what component of habitat they represent. The name cards can be laid out on the ground. When they turn around to face away, the students can choose one and put it on.

Seed Need

Students can make mini-collages or mini-pictures with what they find on their socks.

Stormy Weather

After the "field trip," have the students sculpt, finger paint, make a collage, or draw their response. When the students are finished, have the group share about its art work.

Surprise Terrarium

Distribute squares of wallpaper or some kind of patterned paper for a real or imaginary background scene. Tell the students that each square is habitat for a special animal. Distribute the paper, and let them draw and create collage animals that might live there. When they are finished, let students share what kind of animal it is and how it blends into its habitat.

Tracks!

1. Show the students pictures of animal tracks. Discuss what tracks are and what makes one animal's tracks different from another. Discuss obvious differences in foot sizes and shapes.

2. Help students to make tracks of their own feet by using water-based paints. Let students compare their own tracks to an animal's tracks.

What Bear Goes Where?

Build a bear den in the classroom, specific to each species, using a large cardboard box. Paint, color, or collage the outside of the box to look like the bears' habitat. Create a bear habitat in the classroom, and eat things the bear might eat (e.g., fruit, gummy insects, and berries for the black bear).

What's Wild?

1. Read stories to the students about both wild animals and domesticated (pets and farm) animals. Discuss similarities and differences.

2. Show the students photos of animals. Allow the students to classify the photos into two groups: Wild and Not Wild/Domesticated. Discuss why each animal is classified into the group.

Wildlife Is Everywhere!

1. Discuss with students how to become a wildlife explorer by observing nature or looking for animal tracks and signs. Students should find a partner. Give each pair of students a special place in the school yard where they can look for signs of wildlife. Have students spend up to 10 minutes observing their place. Afterwards, the pairs can draw a picture of what each saw to show to the rest of the class.

2. Have the students create a wildlife explorer journal. Students can color a new page for each new place and each new day they look for wildlife.

3. Conduct this activity in each season to see what changes take place from fall, winter, summer, and spring. Try this activity before and after a rain shower. What were the differences?

Source: Early Childhood Extensions contributed by Audrey Walker, Utah Division of Wildlife.

Using the Outdoor Classroom

Education places many demands on educators and students alike. In the urgency for educators to teach more and faster, there is a growing assumption that the classroom building is the only place where legitimate learning can take place. The result of this tendency is increasingly to abandon the outdoor world. The *Project WILD K–12 Curriculum and Activity Guide* and the *Project WILD Aquatic K–12 Curriculum and Activity Guide* both have numerous activities that are enhanced when conducted outside. Effective learning is often heightened in natural settings. The most fundamental reason for teaching outdoors whenever possible when using Project WILD, is that nature itself is the subject. The natural context—the living world and people's interactions with it—is the subject for most Project WILD activities.

The school ground, a nearby park, a pond, a small stream, a vacant lot, and sites visited on extended field trips all may enhance learning when incorporated within instructional experiences. In this urbanized age in which much information comes to us vicariously and abstractly, it is increasingly important to make sure that students have meaningful, first-hand experiences with the living world. Another benefit gained from outdoor experiences is that they provide a foundation for lifelong learning and leisure pursuits. More and more leisure activities take advantage of outdoor settings. Bird watching, hiking, camping, photography, and drawing and sketching, plus sports such as skiing, snorkeling, and running are all popular. Students who are grounded in outdoor studies are more apt to continue outdoor active learning beyond their school years.

Getting outside does not require the capacity to drive distances to undeveloped forests and open spaces. Using the outdoors as a natural classroom can take many forms. It may be as simple as using the windows and windowsills of the classroom to observe what's outside or using the school grounds as legitimate and appropriate places for study of concepts. Urban settings, such as city parks, can offer a variety of opportunities. Such natural explorations lead students to understand and remember important concepts. With confidence gained first hand in relatively small scale field experiences, students can more effectively embrace ideas that involve wildlife in the global ecosystem.

Field Ethics

The question of whether to collect some objects from natural settings—either temporarily or permanently—is difficult to answer. Such decisions are left to individual educators and their students and are based on thoughtful decision making, caution, and respect for the living environment. In most cases, Project WILD urges no collecting at all—and recommends instead simply leaving the natural environment as it is found, with as little impact from students in the process of learning as possible.

There are times, however, when it may seem appropriate and so instructionally powerful that some limited forms of collecting are desired. Such collecting for instructional purposes can take a variety of forms. Sometimes it involves going outside and picking up fallen leaves on an autumn day. Sometimes it involves collecting litter from a park. Sometimes it involves using a net and examining organisms found in pond water.

If any collecting is to be done, it should begin with a respect for the environment. Educators should determine in advance what laws may apply. Then, involve students in deciding what, if anything, to collect and how much collecting is appropriate. By involving students in the process of deciding whether and what to collect, they are more likely to develop an ethic that considers the impact on ecosystems. This kind of thoughtful decision making about the consequences of our actions is an important, lifelong skill.

The following ethic was developed by a class of sixth graders in Illinois:

1. We should obey all laws protecting plants and animals.
2. We should ask the owner before we take anything.
3. We should collect an animal only if we know we can keep it alive long enough to learn from it.
4. We should not collect things that will hurt us.
5. We should collect something only if there are a lot of them in that place.
6. We should collect something only if we can learn something very important about it.

Obviously, any collecting for instructional purposes should alter the environment as little as possible and should not significantly damage wildlife or its habitat. Where possible, anything collected from the environment for instructional purposes should be returned to its original location at the conclusion of the activity.

Beyond the collecting issue, students must understand that humans can affect living things in other ways. For example, just by walking over fragile areas outdoors or observing animals under certain conditions, we can destroy or disturb organisms. Leaving a trail can injure or kill small plants and animals, just as walking along the banks of a stream can affect vegetation. Even walking on rocks can remove new soil and crush mosses and lichens if they are present. Students must pay attention to the consequences of their actions. Thoughtful decision making and responsible behavior are not just an outcome or goal of Project WILD, but a path to take in the process of learning.

Observations and Inferences

Learning how to be observant and learning how to make inferences are two important skills. They are two skills that students can develop when participating in some of the Project WILD instructional activities. Because many students seem to confuse observations and inferences, this section is intended to help distinguish between the two.

Observations are descriptions of characteristics or attributes—for example, of objects, processes, or events. Inferences are judgments or interpretations about things such as objects, processes, or events.

If a student sees a fish in the water and describes the fish's coloration, length, width, thickness, mobility, fin pattern, scale configuration, and eye characteristics, that student is making an observation. A student who sees a fish darting about near some fish eggs in the water and says it is a female fish protecting a nest has made an inference.

Observations are objective in the sense that what is said about objects, processes, or events can usually be agreed upon by any observer. Descriptions of characteristics such as measurements, weights, color, fin patterns, and such, may usually be the same for any observer, while inferences—derived from judgments or interpretations—go beyond descriptions.

For many students, the act of labeling something becomes an end in itself. For example, a student may observe a fish and identify it as a trout. Observationally, the student may be seeing an animal of about 10 inches in length with a body 2 inches thick and 3 inches deep that lives in an aquatic environment. Inferentially, the student may decide that the fish is protecting a nest. Inferences go beyond objective information of the kind obtained by observation and involve efforts to determine cause-and-effect relationships with other elements. Inference requires students to use observations in combination with information they may be missing in order to establish what are intended to be informed cognitive leaps, or inferences.

In scientific study, observations typically are gathered. Later, when patterns begin to emerge, the process of inference begins. The distinction between these two modes of inquiry becomes especially important when we consider how willingly some people tend to come to conclusions on the basis of inferences with no grounding in observational experience. At best, such inferences reflect guessing and, at worst, superstition and prejudice. Learning the skills of observation adds richness to the database from which inferences are made. As students learn these skills of observation, mature inferences tend to emerge, which, in turn, lead to hypothesis and theory in science.

Guidelines for Interviewing People

To some extent, everyone in a community is an expert on something. Perhaps students will want to know what something in the community looked like 20 or 40 years ago. They may want to speak with some long-term residents of the area. An interview can provide a powerful piece of oral history, or it can be an intrusion into the life and privacy of a person. If students are encouraged to interview people, some guidelines are useful.

Recommendation: Send an introductory letter on school stationery explaining the project and asking for cooperation and assistance—with thanks in advance.

Plan interviews in advance, at least in terms of outlining major questions to be asked. Students need to be reminded to conduct themselves in a professional manner and to keep the interview focused on the purposes of the research. For example, have students listen and record their subject's responses. Rather than the students using the time of the interview to expound their own views on the topic, their task is to learn the subject's views. Treat the subject with dignity and respect at all times. If any form of recording is desired, ask the people in advance for their permission, and advise them how the information will be used. If a student wants to quote the person being interviewed by name, give the person the opportunity to see the written proceedings of the interview, review any excerpts to be used, or review the recording before any class or public use of the information takes place.

If any public opinion surveys or other forms of interviews in public places are planned, students should be supervised by adults. People who might be concerned (businessowners, mall managers, etc.) need to be asked in advance and informed about the project and its purposes. If people do not want to be interviewed, thank them politely for their time and allow them to proceed with their business. As a general principle, recommend that any interviews conducted by students be arranged in advance with the involvement of their teacher. An in-class trial run or practice session using role-playing techniques can be an effective preparation for actually conducting interviews. Students act the parts of interviewers and subjects while other students serve as constructive critics of their performances.

Guidelines for Responsible Use of Animals in the Classroom

The National Science Teachers Association (NSTA) Position Statement

These guidelines are recommended by the National Science Teachers Association (NSTA) for use by science educators and students. They apply in particular to the use of nonhuman animals in instructional activities planned or supervised by teachers of science at the pre-college level.

Observation and experimentation with living organisms give students special perspectives of life processes that are not provided by other modes of instruction. Studying animals in the classroom enables students to develop skills of observation and comparison; a sense of stewardship; and an appreciation for the unity, interrelationships, and complexity of life. This study, however, requires appropriate, humane care of the organism. Teachers are expected to be knowledgeable about the proper care of organisms under study and the safety of their students.

These are the guidelines recommended by NSTA concerning the responsible use of animals in a school classroom laboratory:

- Acquisition and care of animals must be appropriate to the species.
- Student class work and science projects involving animals must be under the supervision of a science teacher or other trained professional.
- Teachers sponsoring or supervising the use of animals in instructional activities—including acquisition, care, and disposition—will adhere to local, state, and national laws, policies, and regulations regarding the organisms.
- Teachers must instruct students on safety precautions for handling live animals or animal specimens.
- Plans for the future care or disposition of animals at the conclusion of the study must be developed and implemented.
- Laboratory and dissection activities must be conducted with consideration and appreciation for the organism.
- Laboratory and dissection activities must be conducted in a clean and organized work space with care and laboratory precision.
- Laboratory and dissection activities must be based on carefully planned objectives.
- Laboratory and dissection objectives must be appropriate to the maturity level of the student.
- Student views or beliefs sensitive to dissection must be considered; the teacher will respond appropriately.

—Adopted by the NSTA Board of Directors in July 1991

Source: Published by the National Science Teachers Association, 1842 Wilson Boulevard, Arlington, VA 22201.

Using Local Resources

In the course of conducting activities in Project WILD, educators may find that local resource people would be of great assistance. Some of the topics covered in Project WILD activities address areas in which many educators may not have extensive background experience. Various resource people in the community may be invited to share with students their special knowledge of wildlife, environmental, or natural resource topics. However, involving such resource people should be done in a manner that uses each expert's time effectively. Preparing in advance before inviting experts to speak to classes, sending students to interview them, or taking field trips to special facilities is important. Here are a few basic suggestions that may help you with this process.

Have students explore the question of who might have special knowledge to contribute to a particular activity or topic.

One of the important skills that students can learn is "How can we find out?" Part of this process may involve asking someone who knows more than we do. Students can go on a "treasure hunt" for potential experts. Where could they find someone who knows about local water quality—in the local city health department? In the state water commission? In the Office of the Environment? Are any citizen groups interested in the topic? Do they publish any resource materials? Do local colleges and universities have people on their faculties with expertise in this area? Develop a list of "leads," possible avenues to explore in order to identify the experts on a topic in your area.

Develop a plan for approaching the agencies or organizations where "experts" may be found.

Once the students have decided where experts might be found, they will need to decide how to approach those institutions in order to actually acquire the names of some people who might be speakers, lead field trips, or be interviewed. Some governmental agencies, for example, have public affairs departments, and those departments might be the best place to start. Some public libraries have information librarians who specialize in that sort of task and may know whom to approach. Some universities and colleges publish speaker lists that include topics that faculty members are willing to speak about. Local businesses may also have people who are experts. Again, the public affairs departments may be good places to start. Sometimes you may be referred directly to the resource person. In case this happens, consider the next suggestion, found below, before you undertake this part of the search.

Once you have identified potential resource people, develop a strategy for determining whether they would be willing to act as experts for your class and, if so, how they would like to work.

As a teacher, you may want to speak with resource people before you actually have them come to your class (usually a good idea). Sometimes, when you explain the questions in which your class has an interest, or the topic of your study, the experts may suggest that they themselves are not the best choice to address the topic. They may suggest someone else. Some experts are not comfortable speaking to large groups of people, especially young students. They may want to talk to a small group, or even one student, who can take the information back to the rest of the class. Some may not be able to get away from their work to visit your school during the day. In that case, you may want to consider whether a field visit would be possible for the class. The expert may suggest other sources of information, such as books, magazines, or films.

If the resource person is willing to work directly with students, find out what advance preparation is needed and in what type of setting the expert would like to work. Would he or she like written questions from the class beforehand? Would he or she be willing to be recorded or videotaped or written up in the school or local newspaper? If the expert is coming to your school, what sort of special equipment will be needed (slide projector, overhead, etc.)? If the class will take a field trip to visit the resource person at his or her office, laboratory, business, or home, what should the class know in advance? Are any special clothes required? How long will the visit be? Where should the group report to start the visit? Attention to this kind of detail can make the trip more productive, effective, and appropriate.

Decide who will act as interviewers, recorders, moderators, and hosts. Brief the class about the roles each of these students will serve, and the responsibilities and expectations for behavior of all students.

Resource people coming to a school for the first time may be quite uncertain about simple things, beginning with how to find the school. A letter to the resource person in advance will help to verify the details of the arrangements to which you have agreed, and you might include a map to the school. When a guest arrives at the school, a student can meet and escort the visitor to the classroom, asking if he or she wants assistance with any materials, and so forth. If student interviewers will visit the resource person, they should have a letter of introduction, they should be briefed about how to interview the person, and they should operate in pairs or with adult supervision for personal safety. Students who leave the school grounds to interview people should see themselves as representing the school and your class in particular. They will want to leave a good impression. Whether guests come to school or students visit resource people in the community, the importance of courteous, considerate, and responsible behavior should be stressed.

Do advance work on the topic.

Resource people usually do not mind giving their time to people they think can use it well. If you and the class have done some homework on the subject, you are more likely to ask intelligent questions and be able to understand what the expert has to offer. This advanced preparation is strongly recommended in any circumstance. It is especially important to make the best use of a field trip to a complex facility, such as, a community sewage treatment plant or a fish hatchery.

Remember that a little consideration and hospitality go a long way.

Resource people can become lifelong supporters of your school and its programs, or lifelong critics. Which will happen depends not only on things such as the suggestions offered here, but also on small but important things such as thanking them at the time of their visit (or your visit) and following up with a letter. If the class uses the information from the resource person in some special way, send a picture or samples of the work to the resource person to show what was accomplished. If the local media produce an article, send along a copy to your expert. Do not expect or demand large amounts of additional time from the experts, but do let them know that their expertise was appreciated as well as how it was used.

Hints for Using Simulated Field Trips

A simulated field trip is a powerful way for students to create vivid experiences in their minds. Many older people remember when the major form of entertainment was radio. With its absence of visual images, radio required its listeners to create mental pictures of the way various characters looked and acted. It was common for listeners to imagine landscapes, cities, and any number of exotic settings, thereby stretching their creativity.

Research has shown that with their eyes closed, people activate parts of their brain-mind systems that are not often stimulated. When we picture things in our minds, we call these parts of our brains into activity. Studies show skill in picturing things in our minds enhances our ability to enrich reading and to increase skill and imagination in writing. The capacity to remember concepts, words, names, and ideas is enhanced.

The following guidelines provide a basic, useful approach to simulated field trips as a teaching tool:

1. Ask the students to lay aside all pens, pencils, books, and such.

2. Instruct the students to sit in a comfortable and relaxed position with their eyes closed.

3. Wait until you see a general state of relaxation before beginning.

4. Using a steady and paced reading or speaking style, begin offering the students the narrative. Remember to speak slowly and steadily. If you want the students to create rich mental pictures, you must allow them time to do so. It takes about as much time to observe mental images as it does to carefully review actual physical settings.

5. Once the narrative is finished, invite the students to review all of the images they saw in their minds. Again, try to allow enough time for an adequate visual review—and remember, the review takes time.

6. After an adequate time for mental review (at least 1 minute and possibly 2 minutes), ask the students to open their eyes.

7. Begin discussing the simulated field trip in terms of the instructional purpose for its use.

In some cases, the process serves simply to provide a visual review of some of the students' past experiences. At other times, you are providing stimuli for the students to create original images. In any case, it is important to realize that there are no mistakes in mental images. The images are data. If students create images that are consistent with what you expected, consider the images to represent differing perspectives rather than wrong answers. Try to honor and nourish variety as a means to add richness to the topics being explored. In addition to being a powerful and effective way to explore and remember concepts, regular use of simulated field trips also tends to relax students. When relaxed, they frequently will be more productive in all academic areas.

Using Simulations for Instructional Purposes

An educational simulation is an instructional activity that models aspects of the real world to teach one or more concepts. Simulations—especially those that involve students in kinesthetic learning experiences—are used frequently in Project WILD.

In the *Project WILD K–12 Aquatic Curriculum and Activity Guide*, "Hooks and Ladders," a salmon simulation, and "Migration Headache," an activity about limiting factors affecting populations of migrating water birds, are examples. In conducting simulations for instructional purposes, you must remember that the activity can take on a life of its own. The students can become so involved in the role they are playing that they forget to relate the objects, events, and processes to what they represent in nature.

Students of all ages may tend to become competitive when they are responsible for capturing or escaping the animals depicted in an activity. Antic and energetic physical behavior often results. During such activity, the students identify subjectively with the role they are playing. This identification is important and should be encouraged as part of the powerful learning that is possible through simulations. Yet it also is important to link the subjective experience with the objective concepts that are central to each activity.

Distinguish between what is realistic and what is not realistic about the simulation. Simulations, by definition, are simple representations of more complex natural interactions. Teachers should point this out to students and help them understand how the simulation is like and unlike the real situation.

Simulations always leave out some elements that exist in nature. They simplify to make a point. Make sure that the students are clear about the point and the limitations of the activity in demonstrating the complexities of real-world situations.

A Guide to the Ecosystem Concept

Many hundreds of books and many thousands of research articles have been written in the field of ecology. There are also many fine textbooks. This short description of a complex and sophisticated field cannot, by its brief nature, do anything more than provide a summary of a few major concepts. However, the *Project WILD* and *Project WILD Aquatic K–12 Curriculum and Activity Guides* contain a number of activities that are designed to invite students of all ages to ask questions about how ecosystems work. To address these questions, educators need not be professional ecologists nor have extensive backgrounds in biology or wildlife management. This appendix is designed as a reference to help educators develop a few simple and powerful ecological concepts with students.

The Ecosystem

The word ecosystem combines two words: ecology and system. It connects the idea of "eco," the household of nature, with that of "system," a set of interactions over time among living and nonliving elements of the household. Ecologists have offered a number of definitions of this concept. One of the problems that many educators encounter with the term is the question of size of an ecosystem. Some have seen photos of Earth from space and have heard the entire planet referred to as an ecosystem. This ecosystem is called the "global ecosystem," or "biosphere."

The term ecosystem is a convenience. We can draw an imaginary line around a section of the larger world, decide to treat its elements separately from the rest, and call it an ecosystem. When we describe how the organisms in the system behave; how they interact, grow, adapt; what they eat; how long they live; what happens to them when they die; and what they require to stay healthy or to reproduce, we are dealing with the way in which the household system operates—and we are thinking SYSTEM-atically. We are finding connections.

Often the connections between elements of a system are subtle and hard to see or understand. Quite frequently, this is because they take a long time to happen. The life cycle of some organisms in an ecosystem in the forests of the west coast of North America is 300 to 500 years. In an average human life span, we might see little change in those forests. But the life cycle of an ecosystem in a pond that dries up during the summer and is frozen in the winter might be 12 months. Life cycles in a jar of microbes might be measured in hours.

Ecosystem is really a term that represents an idea more than a place or set of things. When children set up a wide-mouth jar in the classroom with pond water, a few small animals, and some plants in it, and then cap the bottle tightly, they have established an ecosystem. The jar contains biotic and abiotic elements. The biotic elements are all the living things in the jar: plants, snails, microbes, and so forth. The abiotic elements are the nonliving elements: air, water, rocks, and bottom debris. Even here it is often difficult to distinguish between living (biotic) and nonliving (abiotic) things. Some biologists would define the abiotic components as those elements in the system that are not of biological origin.

Appendices

A Guide to the Ecosystem Concept

Problems arise when one considers that some of the carbon dioxide gas was produced by animals and some of the oxygen, if not all of it, by plants. This little ecosystem in a jar will quickly turn into a gooey mess unless the children place the bottle in the light—but not in direct sunlight. The system in the bottle is not going to operate without a source of energy, namely light energy. If there are not too many animals and other nongreen organisms in the jar, the bottle can be tightly sealed, even "air tight," and may operate as a self-contained environment for many years. It will slowly change over time. Some organisms will die and be decomposed. Slow hatching eggs or spores may develop and germinate. The acidity of the water may change. The color of the water may change and absorb more heat and light. The system will undergo a life cycle of its own, slowly aging and changing.

When the term ecosystem is used in Project WILD, it describes a system in which there are living organisms, nonliving components, and a primary source of energy interacting over time within a defined locale. In most systems, the primary source of energy is the sun. We could establish organisms in various environments, but unless there was an appropriate balance or set of relations among them, the system would quickly or slowly go into crisis and die. Many students and teachers have seen examples of changed systems when they have cleaned out refrigerators or discovered last month's uneaten lunch in the bottom of their lockers.

One ecosystem that is often studied in school is the pond. Pond is not a word that is typically used with a precise definition. It is like the word ecosystem in many ways. In some parts of the world, a pond is a small body of fresh water, usually a very small body of water. In other places, a pond can be a lake quite reasonable in size and depth. In some countries, ponds can be small bays with narrow entrances to the ocean. Here we use the term to refer to small, shallow, fresh-water bodies of water.

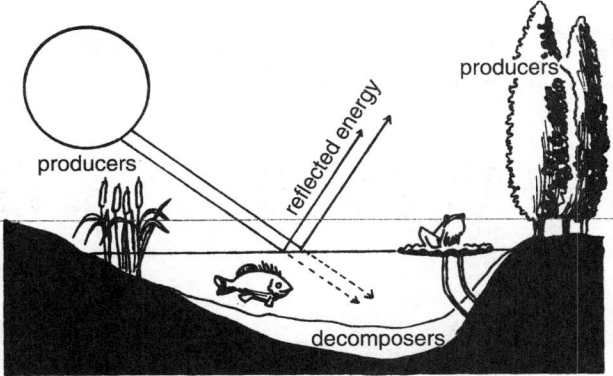

Diagram A

Diagram A shows a "typical" pond. While it is greatly oversimplified, it shows the basic elements of any ecosystem. There is the sun—the energy source. The sun is the "engine" driving the rest of the system. There are the green plants and animals. The green plants are direct "sun catchers." The wonderful process of capturing some of the sun's energy is known as photosynthesis—photo (light) and synthesis (assembly, connection, manufacture). The energy of the sun is stored in the form of chemical bonds in molecules. Photosynthesis magically stores solar energy by assembling complex molecules with six carbon atoms from building blocks of carbon dioxide (CO_2) and water. Animals cannot do this trick. They rely on the green plants to catch solar energy and to use it to assemble food materials. The green plants are the food factories in natural systems. They are called producers. The plants also provide oxygen as a byproduct of this process.

Not all animals eat plants directly. Those that eat plants and only plants are known as primary consumers, or herbivores. They are one step away from being sun catchers. Animals that eat other animals are two steps away from the sun, so they are often called secondary consumers, or carnivores (meat eaters). The sequence becomes more complex if we add animals that prey on other meat eaters: tertiary consumers (three steps away from the sun). Diagram B on the following page illustrates some of those relationships.

continued

483

© Council for Environmental Education 2001

Appendices

A Guide to the Ecosystem Concept

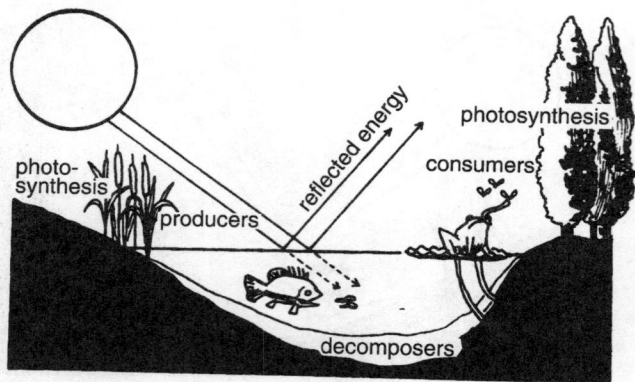

Diagram B

A diagram linking some of these organisms as producers and consumers is illustrated as a food chain. Diagram C shows a very simple food chain that might be associated with a pond. In this diagram, the eagle eats the fish that eats the frog. In turn, the frog eats spiders and the spiders eat insects.

Diagram C

But this food chain is not an ecosystem. Some things are missing. There are no direct sun catchers (producers)—no green plants capable of photosynthesis. The eagle cannot capture energy from the sun directly. It is at least three steps away from the sun's input of energy. In its tadpole stage, the frog eats plant material. The insect might feed on plant nectar, or its larval stage might eat leaves. The food chain describes only a portion of the connections in the pond ecosystem. If the diagram were more complex, then a food web would be produced. It would include all the producers and consumers in the pond, or as many as we can identify. It would introduce a new set of special consumers, the decomposers. They are the garbage collectors of nature. They do not trap solar energy directly, because they are not green and, therefore, cannot perform photosynthesis. They break down a variety of materials into simpler compounds. They produce CO_2 and release needed elements into the system. Without these recyclers, the entire ecosystem gradually would run down. Imagine a forest in which none of the fallen trees, branches, dead animals, and leaves ever rotted. Soon it would be impossible to move through the debris and nothing new could grow. Decomposition is a creative activity. Without some decomposition in ponds, the accumulation of materials falling to the bottom would result in the pond's rapidly becoming so shallow that it would no longer be a pond.

As a general principle, students need to understand that both energy and materials constantly circulate in all ecosystems. Plants, through the process of photosynthesis, are the major point of entry of the sun's energy into the natural system. However, that energy does work in ecosystems in other ways as well. Solar heating of the atmosphere and oceans produces the flow of winds and the great patterns of air circulation in the atmosphere. The absorption of solar energy in the oceans is expressed in the flow of ocean currents. In a way, the entire planet is a great solar-powered engine. All materials cycle—some slowly, some quickly.

Carbon dioxide, for example, is a byproduct of respiration in plant and animal cells. The carbon of CO_2 is used by green plants in photosynthesis and becomes the building block of many biological molecules, including sugars, proteins, and fats. Once assembled into these materials, the carbon may be taken in by animals when they eat food materials—whether from plant or animal sources. Food is both a source of energy and a source of raw materials for biological construction.

The carbon cycle is one of the great cycles in natural systems. Nitrogen, water, and elements such as phosphorus are also involved in cycles. The passage of materials along food chains and through cycles is responsible for the concentration of chemicals such as pesticides. Small amounts of pesticide molecules passed along a food chain may accumulate when they reach the top consumer, whether that be an eagle or a human. Sometimes animals like the humpback whale may "shorten" the steps between the input of solar energy and themselves by feeding directly on millions of small animals and plants that are closer to the source of solar energy. (See Diagram D.)

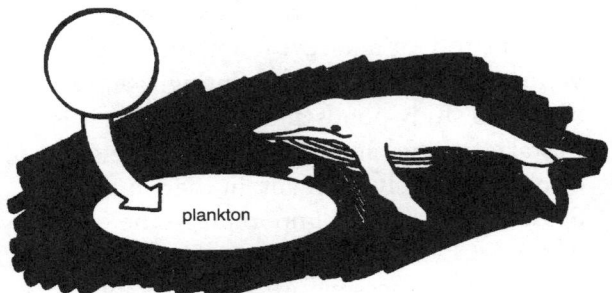

Diagram D

An ecosystem, therefore, may be viewed as a set of elements, living and nonliving, interacting over time within a defined locale. Ecologists attempt to define ecosystems in terms of sets of elements that normally interact with each other. At a global level, all the elements on the planet interact. The rain that falls today on the plains may have evaporated yesterday from the leaf of a tree in the coastal forest. But in practical terms, for studying and understanding the interactions among organisms in the environment, you will find it useful to draw boundaries around certain groups of organisms that are normally interacting in a relatively direct way, as a community or neighborhood grouping. This grouping may be considered an ecosystem.

Within these biological neighborhoods, it is possible to assign organisms both an "address," describing their typical location in space, and an "occupation," or role, that they play in the system. An organism's address is its "habitat."

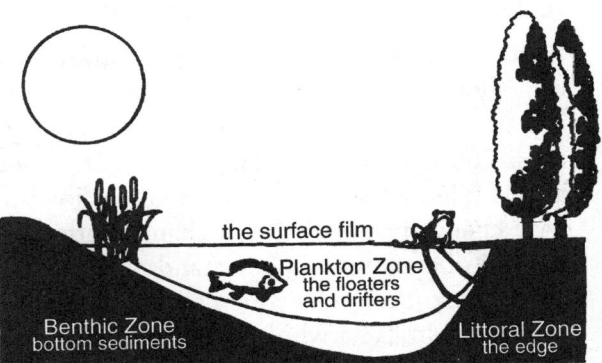

Diagram E

The occupation of an organism in an ecosystem is called its "niche." For many people, the term niche seems to describe a location, a type of space, but as the term is used by ecologists, it applies to the organism's roles or activities in the system. This has frequently been a source of confusion.

There are many different aquatic ecosystems. Within those systems are a variety of zones. Diagram E illustrates some of the zones that can be found in a typical pond ecosystem. There are organisms occupying the edge or margins of the pond. These are said to be in the littoral zone. There are others that float and drift in the water itself. These are planktonic organisms and may be plants or animals. There are still others that live on the bottom and in the sediments. And there are those, like water-striders, that inhabit the narrow zone composed of the actual water surface film. Sometimes organisms inhabit different zones at different stages in their lives.

It is important to explore a variety of zones in different habitats because students will encounter quite different sets of organisms in different zones. Often, people tend to overlook some zones—possibly because they do not seem very interesting or attractive. Who wants to spend time sifting through the muck on a pond bottom when the dip nets are filled with interesting things found in the water or on the rushes at the shore line? But, to develop an understanding of the diversity of life forms that inhabit an ecosystem, we need to explore the whole range of addresses where they might be found.

continued

Tips on Studying Ecosystems

A major purpose in having students study ecology is for them to develop an awareness and understanding of relationships. This process entails developing the ability to see systems, or sets of interactions, and to think about how they have changed and still might change with time. It entails beginning to understand living systems as complex mosaics in which all the parts fit together to make a whole. The removal of one small, apparently unimportant component can often have major consequences.

It is convenient for teachers to start small with students. Making miniature ecosystems in jars and plastic bags can start students thinking about what elements are needed to keep an ecosystem healthy. Asking students to create drawings connecting things from nature to as many other things (themselves included) as they will promote thinking about interactions. A dead leaf floating on the surface of a pond might be seen as simple litter until—by drawing connections in as many directions and dimensions as possible—the student starts to see it as food, as a habitat, and as a former trap for the sun's energy. The student thus begins to appreciate the role of apparently inert and dead material.

At times, individual organisms can be strange, beautiful, or even humorous. The next step in developing ecosystemic thinking is to try to appreciate the role played by the organism in the community of which it is a part. Is this a predator, or is it prey? Ultimately, all organisms are "food," even if for microbes. Does one organism provide a home for other organisms? Is it a sun catcher, a trapper of solar energy? An important part of the debriefing of many of the activities in Project WILD is to ask students to think about these connections, and ultimately to connect themselves to the system as well.

Naming is often both an asset and an obstacle to the study of natural systems. When students go to a community, they want to know the names of the organisms they encounter. This is a good time to learn to recognize some plants and animals. But often it is enough to appreciate differences and similarities, and even for students to assign names of their own making to the things they see. Do not let a lack of detailed knowledge of names discourage study. Instead, use this opportunity to pose the "How can we find out?" questions. Emphasize the characteristics of plants and animals and their interactions, rather than losing sight of those attributes in a quest to label the parts.

Finally, it is often a powerful experience for students to visit and revisit a natural setting at various seasons of the year. Spring is an ideal season to study ponds and streams. But it is a mistake for students to think of nature as dead, or even as largely dormant, in the winter. Seasonal changes are important to the economy of nature. Ecosystems change over time. The changes of the seasons are an important expression of continuing natural change in natural systems. So, if the opportunity presents itself, have students follow an ecosystem—perhaps a pond, stream, lake, or river—through the seasons from late summer to fall, through winter and into spring and summer. School grounds can also provide useful opportunities of this kind. Some schools have adopted a local pond or stream and have made it the focus of studies by classes over many years. If the past data are saved, students can appreciate what is happening to their local ecosystems.

Taking Action
Involving Students in Environmental Action Projects

The following excerpt has been adapted from Project WILD's *Taking Action: An Educator's Guide to Involving Students in Environmental Action Projects*, published by the Council for Environmental Education in cooperation with World Wildlife Fund. For more information or to order this guide, please contact Project WILD, 5555 Morningside Drive, Suite 212, Houston, TX 77005, phone: (713) 520-1936, E-mail **info@projectwild.org**, or visit the Project WILD web site at **www.projectwild.org**.

What Is an Action Project?

Project WILD has defined environmental action projects as any activities that get students involved in tackling an environmental issue or problem, or that aim at improving an environmental setting. Activities are often most successful when they're focused on the local community, such as the enhancement of outdoor habitats or the development of natural sites within a neighborhood or on the school grounds. Projects can also work on a much broader scope—raising money to adopt sea turtles, for example.

An action project can be simple or complex—as straightforward as putting up a community bulletin board of environmental current events, or as involved as developing and implementing a community plan for oil collection and recycling. However complex, most action projects will fit into a variety of educational settings. Many educators find that action education blends well with their regular teaching duties, while others choose to make it the basis for after-school sessions. Action learning is effective in nonformal settings too, involving young people through nature centers, zoos, aquaria, and scouting programs.

Who Can Do Action Projects?

Students of all ages can take part in environmental action projects, matching the complexity of the tasks to the abilities of students. Older students can get involved in issues that require research, issue analysis, in-depth discussion, careful planning, and follow-up. Students might establish river monitoring activities or conduct community education initiatives. Younger students can begin with projects that don't involve heated controversy, long-term commitments, or complex solutions. Picking up litter, writing a letter about an environmental concern, or planting a butterfly garden are excellent starting points for younger students.

Some Tips to Keep in Mind

Encourage student ownership and initiative.

The more students are involved in the project, the more they'll get out of it. To the extent possible, allow the students to make their own decisions on which problem to focus, how to conduct the project, and how to share results. Help the students chart their own course, evaluate the pros and cons of each choice, and then gauge how much direction is needed.

Encourage parents and other community members to support the project.

Conflict sometimes can surface when students interact with community members who don't agree with a specific activity or who don't feel that action projects are an appropriate educational approach. In many cases, you can diffuse this response by discussing projects with parents and community members beforehand and by explaining how environmental action projects enhance educational goals.

continued

Keep your opinions in perspective.

Allow the students to research material, discuss the issues, and form their own perspectives on issues. Allow everyone the chance to openly express his or her opinions, no matter how different they may be. It is also critical to keep students on track and focused on the facts. Emotionally charged debate and hotly contested points of view can obscure the real facts and divert students' attention from the issue under scrutiny.

Encourage student cooperation, compromise, and understanding.

Have the students work in small groups as much as possible. Besides the well-documented educational benefits of cooperative learning, group work offers a taste of real-life problem-solving. Teams of scientists, politicians, business people, and concerned citizens often arrive at a plan of action together. Ideally, each person brings his or her own perspectives and talents to the process, and the results reflect the strengths of those human resources. Multiple perspectives encourage thoughtful debate, boost critical thinking skills, and allow students to make informed choices—especially if opinions are accompanied by reliable information.

Help students evaluate their methods and change their plans if necessary.

From time to time over the course of a project, have the students assess the overall scheme and evaluate their methods. Ask if they think things are running as smoothly as expected. If they think there's room for improvement, ask what might be done to adjust the situation. In some cases, problem-solving teams can brainstorm ways to deal with the snags and setbacks encountered along the way.

Help students appreciate the value of their work.

It's important for students to know that their project, no matter how small, is significant. Assure students that every action counts. Even if the students' actions don't seem to have much effect right away, the long-term results can be very important.

Approaches to Environmental Action

Teach It!—
The Educate and Inform Approach

Projects that focus on teaching others about environmental issues (These might include older students mentoring younger students, conducting community education programs, writing and performing songs and poems, or conducting workshops with school or community groups.)

Make the Case—
The Persuasive Approach

Projects designed to convince people to support a certain course of action or point of view (Activities include creating posters or brochures, conducting debates, writing letters to the editor, giving speeches, and distributing public service announcements.)

Be on the Money—
The Economic Approach

Strategies that encourage consumers to shop with the environment in mind, as well as projects that raise money to support specific organizations, programs, or individuals working on environmental issues (Activities might include promoting environmentally friendly products, asking for cash or in-kind donations of time and materials from businesses and community groups, or applying for grants.)

Get Physical—
The "Ecomanagement" Approach

Projects that physically improve the environment, such as planting trees, landscaping school grounds, cleaning up neighborhood parks or streams, or building bird and bat houses

Make Decisions—
The Political Action Approach

Projects focusing on political action that could include speaking at a public hearing, meeting with an elected representative to discuss specific legislation, testifying before lawmakers, circulating petitions and fliers, writing letters to the editor, or campaigning for candidates

Become Legal Eagles—
The Courtroom Approach

Projects that attempt to create change through legislation, or that take legal action against an individual, corporation, community, or government agency (Although most projects that involve primary and secondary students will not involve actual legal action, many projects can educate youngsters about existing laws and the workings of the legal system.)

Sources: "Approaches" adapted with permission from *Investigating and Evaluating Environmental Issues and Actions* by Harold R. Hungerford et al. (Champaign, IL: Stipes Publishing Co., 10–12 Chester St., 1992).

Seven Steps to Action

Here are some basic steps that will help students get action projects off the ground. While the steps are listed in order, it's important to note that planning and implementing a project is not always a clear-cut, linear process. In some cases, students will investigate an issue, discuss it, begin to work on it, and then change their strategy as they use new information. They might decide to narrow their focus or switch projects after realizing that the potential solutions are beyond their capabilities. Such adjustments are a normal part of the learning process.

1. Get Informed

Before students decide which environmental projects to pursue, they need to become informed about the possibilities. Students may collect a pool of information from newspapers and magazines, interview community members and parents, or contact organizations and government agencies that focus on environmental issues.

Another important step in this initial process, if it can be arranged, is for students to get out and see local environmental problems firsthand. A field trip to a stream in need of cleanup is much more powerful than reading about water pollution. Even if the students eventually select a problem that's occurring thousands of miles from their community, the exposure to concerns in their own backyard will be an important learning experience.

2. Create a List of Possibilities

Once the students' search has highlighted a number of potential topics, have them work in groups to develop a list of the most interesting or worthwhile ones. Then have the students draft a list of projects to address all or part of each topic.

Environmental topics can be very broad and there are almost always several project possibilities for each topic. For example, water quality in the community might encompass pollution in a local river, lead in the city water system, or leaks in a landfill. Projects might include monitoring the pollution levels in the river over time and presenting data to the city council, conducting an education campaign about lead in the city's drinking supply, or developing a recycling plan to reduce the pressure on a landfill. Have students list the topic they most want to tackle. Then they can brainstorm specific projects that might help the situation, listing any additional information they'll need to evaluate each project.

3. Narrow the Choices

Once the groups have selected the issues and projects they are most interested in, they need to evaluate and narrow their choices. For each project listed, the groups need to realistically address what they might accomplish and what problems the project might solve.

Encourage students to discuss the feasibility of each possibility by asking specific questions that help them think about the details of accomplishing certain tasks. Students may want to develop criteria to help them first select a project and then decide how they will determine the most appropriate solution. How much time will the project take? How complex is it? What resources are needed? Whom will they need to talk to?

continued

Sometimes it's difficult for students to decide among local, national, and global projects. Although each will provide learning opportunities, an advantage of a local project is that students will learn more about how their own community works. They'll also be more likely to see real results.

4. Select a Project

By this point, students should have narrowed the list to the top three to five projects. Give them adequate time to research. Then encourage the use of libraries, interviews with experts, surveys, newspaper articles, local TV news, and so on. Invite experts or resource people in to discuss problems, find potential solutions, and help evaluate students' ideas. The more your students know about specific possibilities, the better equipped they'll be to develop a realistic action plan.

As students approach their final decision, have each group present a case for one or more of the projects that the group feels strongly about. Then hold a group vote or have a large group discussion to reach consensus. The important thing is to let students have as much say in the decision-making process as possible, choosing a project that they think is both interesting and achievable.

5. Create an Action Plan

Once students have done their research and selected a project, help them get started on their action plan by asking, "What do you hope you'll be able to accomplish by doing this project?" After students share their answers, guide them in developing a goal for the project and specific, concrete objectives that need to be accomplished along the way.

Remind students to keep the goal and objectives in mind as they work to complete a planning sheet that includes the following:

1. What environmental problem or issue will the project address?

2. How would you briefly describe the goal of the project and the strategy to accomplish this goal?

3. What are the specific objectives that will help the group reach its overall goal?

4. What are the approximate starting and ending dates of the project?

5. Did you list the tasks to accomplish to meet each objective? Include a tentative completion date for each task, the names of people responsible, the supplies and equipment needed, any funding needed, and ideas of where to get materials and funding.

6. Did you write down the names of people and organizations that may be able to provide useful information, specific skills, or expertise, or other help?

7. Did you list ideas on how to publicize and generate support for the project?

8. Did you describe how your success will be measured?

A large-format task and time line chart may help the groups keep track of responsibilities and deadlines. As the students work on their action plan, guide them toward realistic objectives. One of the most common problems for students is thinking too big. Help them focus and simplify the project by discussing the responses to the questions on their planning sheet and by asking them to really consider hard questions. How will the funds be raised? Can the problem be tackled on a smaller scale?

6. Put the Plan into Action

Students' projects will work best if they keep careful records of what they've done, when they did it, whom they've contacted, and so on. They'll also need to keep track of who's doing what to make sure crucial tasks are being completed and to avoid duplicating efforts. It's important that students take stock of the project periodically to see if they're on target and to make modifications, if necessary. Remind them that it's acceptable to rethink their goals and objectives and to revise their plan of action in light of new information or unexpected obstacles.

To build support for action projects, publicize any successes and showcase the ways that action learning promotes educational goals and addresses community priorities. There are many ways to let others know what students have done—holding a community awards event, getting a reporter from the local newspaper or television station to cover a project, or sending out public service announcements (PSAs). Have the students brainstorm ways to publicize their work.

7. Assess, Generalize, and Apply

Taking time to reflect upon and evaluate an action project helps students understand what they've accomplished and allows them to recognize how their project has facilitated their personal growth. As a project nears completion, guide students in assessing the project itself, as well as their feelings about the experience. It's important for students to evaluate the success of each project and to think about improvements for the next time. It's also important that they look beyond the immediate impact to more long-term, broad-scale gains—skills, knowledge, and attitudes that they can apply to other aspects of their lives.

Ideas for Measuring Success

Assessing Student Knowledge

- Keep a video or photo log of project highlights. After the project is completed, use the video or photo scrapbook as a springboard for discussions in which students share what they learned and their feelings about the experience.

- Collect memorabilia (articles about the project, newspaper photos, students' own photos, planning schedules, and so on) to create an action project scrapbook that students can sign and write comments in.

- Ask the students whether they've changed their thinking or behaviors as a result of the project. Have the students write essays describing what those changes are and what students think prompted them.

- Have the students keep a journal to record feelings about the project, its progress, and its setbacks, and to keep notes about working with others. After the project, students share parts of their journals with the group and discuss their perceptions.

- Have the students evaluate other members of their group, as well as themselves. Before they do, give students pointers on positive, constructive feedback. Focus the session on specific points, such as contribution to the project, effort, conflict resolution approach, and so on.

- Have the community members who were involved in the project assess student performances. Educators can develop an assessment form or have students conduct short interviews.

Assessing Project Success

- Have the students describe how well they think their project accomplished the objectives they outlined at the start.

- Have the students conduct surveys, field studies, or interviews to assess the success of their completed project. What worked? What didn't? Why?

- Evaluate how the students planned for ongoing maintenance and sustainability of the project.

- Have the community members and others who were involved in the project assess project outcomes.

Evaluating and Assessing Student Learning

As the nation moves toward educational reform and literacy in all subject areas, standards in assessment become vital. The National Research Council suggests that the following assessment standards be used with students:

- Assessment Standard A: Assessments must be consistent with the decisions they are designed to inform.
- Assessment Standard B: Achievement and opportunity to learn science (or other subject areas) must be assessed.
- Assessment Standard C: The technical quality of the data (or other information) collected is well matched to the decisions and actions taken on the basis of their interpretation.
- Assessment Standard D: Assessment practices must be fair.
- Assessment Standard E: The inferences made from assessments about student achievement and opportunity to learn must be sound.

Source: *National Science Education Standards* (Washington, DC: National Research Council, National Academy Press, 1996).

Project WILD is designed to assist teachers as they assess student learning. Each activity has an evaluation section that suggests at least one way to evaluate students' work, accomplishments, or performance. This section correlates directly with the stated objectives. Some of the suggested evaluations assess student understanding of factual information. Many of them ask students to demonstrate a theoretical or applied conceptual understanding.

Exemplary practice outlines the following strategies when assessing students' learning. Project WILD encourages educators to incorporate some of these methods when using this guide.

Educator-Generated Tests

Unlike commercially produced tests, educator-generated tests are created by the instructor. They can be multiple choice, fill-in-the-blank, true/false, or essay type tests. Project WILD recommends that this type of evaluation be used on a regular basis for ongoing evaluation rather than as a cumulative tool.

Portfolios

A portfolio is a collection of class or project work chosen to specifically address a student's progress. Portfolios usually include examples of student work, reflections, self-evaluations, and goal-setting items. The purpose of a portfolio is to document what has been taught and the national standards that have been met. It also allows subject area assessments to be integrated and student growth to be charted.

Performance Tasks

A performance task is an assessment tool (generally chosen by the student) that demonstrates an understanding of concepts and processes as they apply to everyday life. The task is usually meant for a larger audience rather than for the educator alone. It is carefully planned and evaluated with detailed scoring. Performance tasks can range from solving a real-life problem to preparing a speech or project, demonstrating a specific skill, or writing a paper or report.

Journals and Learning Logs

Journals and logs are tools for students to use to record their own learning in a less-formal manner. Journals are usually a subjective account of a student's perspective on what has been learned. Logs are more detailed and give a direct account that follows a given format.

Visual Vocabulary

An alternative method of assessment for the expression of learned concepts is through pantomime and creative movement. Students review vocabulary they have researched and then select specific terms that demonstrate their understanding of the activity's concepts.

Observation Checklists

Educators may use observation checklists to monitor whether a student has mastered a specific skill. This type of checklist is a useful tool to address specific skills.

Graphic Organizers

Web diagrams, charts, and other forms of graphics can be generated by students to demonstrate what they have learned and how it has been organized into their thought process.

Interviews and Conferences

Educators can assess learning by interviewing and conferencing with students using a systematic approach. When discussing a topic, students can clarify their thinking and educators can gather information on how students are processing what they have learned.

Rubrics

Rubrics are used for any of the assessment strategies outlined above. Rubrics are a way of scoring students in a detailed manner. Rubrics are usually judged by a set of criteria that will evaluate all aspects of the student learning, breaking the tasks down into smaller attainable pieces. The use of rubrics allows students and educators to know specifically what is expected and how each student has measured up to those expectations. Rubrics can be used in self-evaluation, by peers, or by educators. Sometimes a single rubric is used in all three ways to provide a more accurate evaluation.

Skills Index

Below is an alphabetical listing of all activities found in the *Project WILD K–12 Curriculum and Activity Guide*. Also listed are the page numbers, suggested grade levels, settings (indoor or outdoor), and skills addressed for both cross-discipline and subject-specific areas. Under Grade Level, an **E** indicates that the activity correlates to national learning standards for grades K–4, an **M** for grades 5–8, and an **H** for grades 9–12. A **P** indicates that the activity is also suitable for early childhood (pre-K). The specific skills for each subject area can be found on the Project WILD website at **www.projectwild.org**.

SYMBOL NOTE: The dot and triangle symbols are of equal value. They were used to help distinguish between the Cross-Discipline Skills and the Subject Area Skills.

Activity Name	Page Number	Grade Level/National Learning Standards Correlation	Indoors (I) or Outdoors (O)	Analysis	Application	Classification	Comparison	Construction	Description	Evaluation	Generalization	Observation	Problem-solving	Research	Synthesis	Science	Math	Social Studies	Language Arts	Environmental Education	Expressive Arts
A Picture Is Worth a Thousand Words	409	H	O	•	•				•	•		•				▲				▲	
Adaptation Artistry	128	M	I	•	•		•	•	•	•	•	•			•	▲			▲	▲	▲
And the Wolf Wore Shoes	180	E	I	•	•	•	•					•				▲			▲	▲	
Animal Charades	280	E	I,O	•	•							•				▲			▲		▲
Animal Poetry	282	M	I,O						•						•				▲		
Ants on a Twig	88	M	O	•		•	•		•		•					▲				▲	▲
Arctic Survival	234	H	I	•	•					•	•		•	•		▲		▲		▲	
Back from the Brink	355	H	I	•			•	•	•						•	▲		▲	▲	▲	
Bearly Growing	19	M	I				•	•			•					▲	▲			▲	
Beautiful Basics	58	E	I	•			•	•								▲			▲	▲	
Bird Song Survey	406	H	O		•			•	•			•				▲				▲	
Birds of Prey	111	H	I	•			•		•	•	•	•				▲	▲			▲	
Bottleneck Genes	172	H	I	•	•				•	•	•				•	▲				▲	
Cabin Conflict	353	H	I						•	•								▲		▲	
Can Do!	446	H	I,O	•	•				•	•			•		•			▲		▲	
Career Critters	371	M	I	•	•		•		•	•			•		•	▲		▲	▲	▲	
Carrying Capacity	46	H	I	•			•			•						▲				▲	
Cartoons and Bumper Stickers	192	M	I,O	•					•		•							▲	▲	▲	▲
Changing Attitudes	255	M	I	•			•			•			•					▲		▲	

494 Project WILD K–12 Curriculum and Activity Guide

Skills Index

Activity Name	Page Number	Grade Level/National Learning Standards Correlation	Indoors (I) or Outdoors (O)	Analysis	Application	Classification	Comparison	Construction	Description	Evaluation	Generalization	Observation	Problem-solving	Research	Synthesis	Science	Math	Social Studies	Language Arts	Environmental Education	Expressive Arts
Changing Societies	258	M	I	●			●		●	●	●		●	●	●	▲		▲		▲	
Changing the Land	345	M	I	●	●		●		●	●	●		●		●	▲		▲		▲	
Checks and Balances	387	M	I	●						●						▲	▲			▲	
Classroom Carrying Capacity	9	E	I	●	●		●			●	●		●			▲				▲	
Color Crazy	2	E	I					●	●		●	●				▲			▲	▲	▲
Deer Crossing	392	H	I	●	●		●			●			●		●			▲	▲	▲	
Deer Dilemma	426	H	I	●	●		●		●			●	●		●	▲		▲	▲	▲	
Does Wildlife Sell?	213	M	I	●		●				●		●						▲	▲		
Drawing on Nature	285	M	O		●			●			●	●			●				▲	▲	▲
Dropping in on Deer	420	H	O	●	●	●				●			●		●	▲	▲			▲	
Eco-Enrichers	102	M	I	●	●	●	●		●		●	●	●			▲				▲	
Ecosystem Facelift	166	M	I	●	●			●					●	●	●	▲		▲	▲	▲	
Energy Pipeline	105	M	I	●		●	●				●				●	▲	▲			▲	
Enviro-Ethics	443	M	I,O	●	●		●		●	●			●		●			▲	▲	▲	
Environmental Barometer	77	E,P	O	●			●	●		●		●				▲				▲	
Ethi-Reasoning	203	M	I	●	●					●			●		●			▲		▲	
Ethi-Thinking	303	E	I	●	●			●	●	●			●		●				▲	▲	
Everybody Needs a Home	59	E	I	●			●				●					▲			▲	▲	
Fire Ecologies	140	H	I,O	●					●	●	●		●	●	●	▲				▲	
First Impressions	178	E	I	●			●		●	●		●							▲	▲	
Flip the Switch for Wildlife	319	M	I	●	●		●	●		●			●	●	●	▲			▲	▲	
For Your Eyes Only	197	M	I,O	●						●									▲	▲	
Forest in a Jar	137	H	I	●	●		●		●	●				●		▲			▲	▲	
From Bison to Bread: The American Prairie	395	H	I,O	●	●					●			●		●	▲		▲		▲	
Good Buddies	91	M	I		●	●							●			▲				▲	
Graphananimal	49	E,P	I,O	●		●		●				●				▲	▲			▲	
Grasshopper Gravity	4	E	I,O	●		●	●		●			●	●			▲			▲	▲	
Habitat Lap Sit	61	M	I,O									●				▲				▲	▲
Habitat Rummy	14	M	I	●	●	●	●									▲				▲	
Habitracks	53	E	I,O	●		●	●					●			●	▲				▲	
Habitrekking	79	E	I,O	●	●		●		●	●	●		●		●	▲			▲	▲	▲
Hazardous Links, Possible Solutions	326	M	O	●			●		●	●	●				●	▲				▲	▲
Here Today, Gone Tomorrow	154	M	I	●		●									●	▲				▲	
History of Wildlife Management	267	M	I	●						●				●	●			▲		▲	
How Many Bears Can Live in This Forest?	23	M	O	●						●	●	●				▲	▲			▲	

continued

Appendices

Skills Index

Activity Name	Page Number	Grade Level/National Learning Standards Correlation	Indoors (I) or Outdoors (O)	Analysis	Application	Classification	Comparison	Construction	Description	Evaluation	Generalization	Observation	Problem-solving	Research	Synthesis	Science	Math	Social Studies	Language Arts	Environmental Education	Expressive Arts
I'm Thirsty	134	M	I	●						●	●					▲	▲			▲	
Improving Wildlife Habitat in the Community	440	M	I	●	●			●	●	●			●		●			▲		▲	
Interview a Spider	12	M	I						●		●	●		●		▲			▲	▲	
Know Your Legislation: What's in It for Wildlife?	272	H	I	●	●		●		●									▲	▲	▲	
Learning to Look, Looking to See	278	E,P	I,O						●	●		●							▲	▲	
Let's Talk Turkey	248	M	I	●			●	●	●					●		▲		▲		▲	
Litter We Know	434	M	I,O	●		●		●		●		●	●	●				▲		▲	▲
Lobster in Your Lunch Box	245	M	I	●		●		●						●		▲	▲			▲	
Make a Coat!	243	E	I	●		●		●	●		●				●			▲		▲	▲
Microtrek Treasure Hunt	82	M	O	●	●	●			●		●	●	●			▲			▲	▲	
Migration Barriers	308	M	I	●			●		●						●	▲		▲		▲	
Move Over Rover	144	M	I,O	●		●		●	●		●		●	●	●	▲				▲	▲
Museum Search for Wildlife	182	M	I	●	●					●	●							▲	▲		▲
Muskox Maneuvers	130	M	O	●				●	●	●	●					▲				▲	▲
My Kingdom for a Shelter	28	M	I,O		●			●	●		●					▲				▲	▲
No Water Off a Duck's Back	305	M	I	●						●	●					▲	▲			▲	
Noisy Neighbors	317	M	I,O							●				●		▲		▲		▲	
Oh Deer!	36	M	O		●		●		●		●					▲	▲			▲	▲
Owl Pellets	100	M	I	●		●	●		●							▲				▲	
Pay to Play	216	M	I	●	●					●					●	▲		▲		▲	
Philosophical Differences	364	H	I	●		●	●		●					●				▲	▲	▲	
Planning For People and Wildlife	436	M	I	●			●	●				●		●		▲		▲		▲	
Planting Animals	152	M	I	●				●				●				▲			▲	▲	
Playing Lightly on the Earth	432	E,P	O	●			●				●		●		●	▲				▲	▲
Polar Bears in Phoenix?	125	M	I	●	●		●	●		●		●		●		▲				▲	▲
Power of a Song	194	M	I							●											▲
Prairie Memoirs	188	M	I	●			●		●				●	●		▲		▲	▲		
Pro and Con: Consumptive and Nonconsumptive Uses of Wildlife	338	M	I	●			●						●	●				▲	▲	▲	
Quick-Frozen Critters	122	M	O	●				●	●	●						▲				▲	
Rainfall and the Forest	73	M	I	●			●			●				●		▲		▲		▲	
Rare Bird Eggs for Sale	335	M	I	●	●				●				●					▲	▲	▲	
Riparian Zone	341	M	I	●					●	●			●	●		▲	▲	▲			
Saturday Morning Wildlife Watching	184	E	I	●		●	●		●		●			●		▲		▲	▲	▲	

496

Skills Index

Activity Name	Page Number	Grade Level/National Learning Standards Correlation	Indoors (I) or Outdoors (O)	Analysis	Application	Classification	Comparison	Construction	Description	Evaluation	Generalization	Observation	Problem-solving	Research	Synthesis	Science	Math	Social Studies	Language Arts	Environmental Education	Expressive Arts
Seed Need	98	M	I,O	•		•	•		•			•				▲	▲			▲	
Seeing Is Believing	116	E	I	•	•	•	•	•	•		•	•			•	▲				▲	
Shrinking Habitat	310	M	I,O		•			•	•	•					•	▲		▲		▲	▲
Smokey Bear Said What?	314	M	I	•		•	•	•	•				•	•	▲		▲		▲		
Spider Web Geometry	34	M	I,O	•				•	•			•		•		▲	▲		▲	▲	▲
Stormy Weather	85	M	I,O				•		•		•					▲			▲		
Surprise Terrarium	120	E	I		•					•	•					▲				▲	
Sustainability: Then, Now, Later	449	H	I	•		•	•	•	•			•		•	•	▲		▲	▲	▲	▲
The Hunter	287	M	I	•			•	•										▲	▲		
Thicket Game	114	E,P	O	•	•				•		•	•				▲				▲	▲
Time Lapse	158	M	I	•	•	•	•	•	•						•	▲				▲	▲
To Zone or Not to Zone	321	M	I	•	•		•		•	•			•	•				▲		▲	
Too Close for Comfort	300	E	I	•						•						▲				▲	
Tracks!	30	M	O	•	•							•			•	▲				▲	▲
Turkey Trouble	367	H	I	•							•					▲	▲			▲	
Urban Nature Search	70	M	O	•		•	•		•		•	•				▲			▲	▲	
We're in This Together	44	H	I	•	•	•			•		•			•	•	▲		▲	▲	▲	
What Bear Goes Where?	118	E	I	•	•	•	•	•				•			•	▲				▲	▲
What Did Your Lunch Cost Wildlife?	68	M	I	•	•	•	•			•			•		•	▲		▲	▲		
What You Wear Is What They Were	210	M	I				•	•			•		•		•	▲				▲	
What's for Dinner?	96	M	I	•		•		•								▲			▲	▲	
What's That, Habitat?	56	E	I	•			•				•					▲				▲	▲
What's Wild?	7	E	I			•		•				•				▲			▲	▲	▲
Which Niche?	66	M	I	•	•	•	•		•		•			•	•	▲		▲	▲	▲	
Who Fits Here?	64	M	I			•		•						•		▲				▲	
Wild Bill's Fate	270	H	I	•						•				•				▲	▲	▲	
Wild Words	41	M	O		•			•	•		•					▲			▲		
Wildlife on Coins and Stamps	208	H	I	•		•	•				•	•		•				▲	▲	▲	▲
Wildlife Bibliography	253	M	I	•		•	•							•	•			▲	▲	▲	
Wildlife in National Symbols	186	M	I	•			•	•		•				•	•			▲	▲	▲	▲
Wildlife Is Everywhere!	51	E	O	•							•	•				▲				▲	▲
Wildlife Issues: Community Attitude Survey	297	H	I	•	•	•				•				•	•	▲			▲	▲	▲
Wildlife Research	418	H	I	•	•		•		•	•			•	•		▲				▲	
Wildwork	385	M	I	•					•					•	•			▲	▲		
World Travelers	330	M	I,O	•	•	•	•		•							▲	▲			▲	

Topic Index

Below is an alphabetical listing of all of the activities found in the *Project WILD K–12 Curriculum and Activity Guide*. Also listed are the page numbers, the grade level, the approximate duration of the activity, and the broad topic categories for each activity.

GRADE LEVEL NOTE: An **E** indicates that the activity correlates to national learning standards for grades K–4, an **M** for grades 5–8, and an **H** for grades 9–12. A **P** indicates that the activity is also suitable for early childhood (pre-K).

DURATION NOTE: The length of the activity is listed by a letter code: **A** = up to 45 minutes, **B** = 45 to 60 minutes, **C** = 60 to 90 minutes, **D** = 90 minutes to 3 hours, **E** = over 3 hours, and **V** = variable length.

TOPIC NOTE: Many of the topics listed incorporate important subtopics. For instance, *Biodiversity* includes *Endangered, Invasive,* and *Exotic Species; Change* includes *Succession; Environmental Quality* includes *Pollution, Acid Rain, Erosion,* and *Eutrophication; Population Dynamics* includes *Predator and Prey Relationships* and *Limiting Factors; Sustainability* includes *Conservation;* and *Food Chains* includes *Food Webs, Energy Transfer,* and *Trophic Relationships.*

Additional topics are listed in the Expanded Topic Index on on pages 503–512.

SYMBOL NOTE: The dot and triangle symbols are of equal value. They are placed in alternating columns for ease of tracking down the column.

Activity Name	Page Number	Grade Level/National Learning Standards Correlation	Duration (A,B,C,D,E,V)	Adaptations	Biodiversity	Change	Consumptive Use	Culture	Economics/Commerce	Environmental Quality	Food Chains	Habitats	Interdependence	Issues	Land Use	Ocean/Marine	Political Processes	Population Dynamics	Resource Management	Responsible Action	Sustainability	Urban	Values
A Picture Is Worth a Thousand Words	409	H	B			●	▲	●	▲			●	▲			●	▲		▲	●			▲
Adaptation Artistry	128	M	C	●																			
And the Wolf Wore Shoes	180	E	B					●															
Animal Charades	280	E	A																					▲
Animal Poetry	282	M	B																					▲
Ants on a Twig	88	M	B										●	▲										
Arctic Survival	234	H	C				▲		▲						●	▲					▲			
Back from the Brink	355	H	D		▲															▲				
Bearly Growing	19	M	B			●										▲								
Beautiful Basics	58	E	A								●					▲								
Bird Song Survey	406	H	D								●								▲			●	▲
Birds of Prey	111	H	C	●		●					▲	●			●	▲	●		●				

DURATION: A = up to 45 minutes, B = 45 to 60 minutes, C = 60 to 90 minutes, D= 90 minutes to 3 hours, E = over 3 hours, V = variable length

Appendices

Topic Index

Activity Name	Page Number	Grade Level/National Learning Standards Correlation	Duration (A,B,C,D,E,V)	Adaptations	Biodiversity	Change	Consumptive Use	Culture	Economics/Commerce	Environmental Quality	Food Chains	Habitats	Interdependence	Issues	Land Use	Ocean/Marine	Political Processes	Population Dynamics	Resource Management	Responsible Action	Sustainability	Urban	Values
Bottleneck Genes	172	H	A		▲							●									▲		
Cabin Conflict	353	H	D				●		●			●	▲			●	▲		▲	●	▲		▲
Can Do!	446	H	D				●					●		●		●	▲		▲	▲	▲	●	▲
Career Critters	371	M	A							●									▲		▲		
Carrying Capacity	46	H	B			●						●			▲			●						
Cartoons and Bumper Stickers	192	M	B					●					▲								▲		▲
Changing Attitudes	255	M	D					●					▲										▲
Changing Societies	258	M	C			●	▲	●	▲				▲	●	▲								▲
Changing the Land	345	M	D			●				▲		●	▲			●		●	▲	●	▲		
Checks and Balances	387	M	C			●	▲		▲	●		●			●	▲		●	▲	●	▲		
Classroom Carrying Capacity	9	E	A			●	▲					●			▲			●						
Color Crazy	2	E	B											●									
Deer Crossing	392	H	D			●	▲	●		●		●		●	▲	●	▲	●	▲	●	▲	●	
Deer Dilemma	426	H	C	●			▲	●	▲	●		●				●	▲	●	▲	●	▲		▲
Does Wildlife Sell?	213	M	C					●	▲											●	▲		▲
Drawing on Nature	285	M	A																				▲
Dropping in on Deer	420	H	V									●						▲					
Eco-Enrichers	102	M	D									●										●	
Ecosystem Facelift	166	M	D		▲	●				▲			●	▲	●				▲	●	▲	●	
Energy Pipeline	105	M	C							▲		●											
Enviro-Ethics	443	M	S					●				●								●	▲	●	▲
Environmental Barometer	77	E,P	C							●		●								▲	●		
Ethi-Reasoning	203	M	C			●	▲	●															▲
Ethi-Thinking	303	E	B					●				●									▲	●	▲
Everybody Needs a Home	59	E	A									●			▲								
Fire Ecologies	140	H	E			●	▲				●	●							▲	●	▲		▲
First Impressions	178	E	A			●	▲					▲							▲	●			▲
Flip the Switch for Wildlife	319	M	V			●		●	▲			●			●	▲	●	▲	●	▲	●	▲	●	▲
For Your Eyes Only	197	M	A					●											▲	●			▲
Forest in a Jar	137	H	D			●						●											
From Bison to Bread: The American Prairie	395	H	E						▲			●				●	▲		▲	●	▲		▲
Good Buddies	91	M	B										●										

DURATION: A = up to 45 minutes, B = 45 to 60 minutes, C = 60 to 90 minutes, D = 90 minutes to 3 hours, E = over 3 hours, V = variable length

continued

Appendices

Topic Index

Activity Name	Page Number	Grade Level/National Learning Standards Correlation	Duration (A,B,C,D,E,V)	Adaptations	Biodiversity	Change	Consumptive Use	Culture	Economics/Commerce	Environmental Quality	Food Chains	Habitats	Interdependence	Issues	Land Use	Ocean/Marine	Political Processes	Population Dynamics	Resource Management	Responsible Action	Sustainability	Urban	Values
Graphananimal	49	E,P	B									●											
Grasshopper Gravity	4	E	B	●								●											▲
Habitat Lap Sit	61	M	A									●			▲								
Habitat Rummy	14	M	C									●			▲								
Habitracks	53	E	B									●			▲								●	
Habitrekking	79	E	D					●							●	▲							●	
Hazardous Links, Possible Solutions	326	M	A	▲			●	●			●	▲	●		●	▲				●	▲		▲
Here Today, Gone Tomorrow	154	M	C		▲							●	▲		▲				●	▲	●	▲		▲
History of Wildlife Management	267	M	D	▲	●	▲	●					●	▲			▲			▲	●		▲		▲
How Many Bears Live in This Forest?	23	M	A			●						●		●	▲				●					
I'm Thirsty	134	M	B	●															●		▲			
Improving Wildlife Habitat in the Community	440	M	V		●		●	▲				●		●	▲	●	▲	●	▲	●	▲	●	▲
Interview a Spider	12	M	D	●								●			▲									
Know Your Legislation: What's in It for Wildlife?	272	H	E					●		●							▲		▲	●	▲		▲
Learning to Look, Looking to See	278	E,P	A																					▲
Let's Talk Turkey	248	M	B			●	▲		●				▲											
Litter We Know	434	M	B					●											▲	●		●		
Lobster in Your Lunch Box	245	M	C				●	▲		▲		▲			▲						▲			
Make a Coat!	243	E	B					▲				▲												▲
Microtrek Treasure Hunt	82	M	V									●											●	
Migration Barriers	308	M	B					▲				●	▲	●	▲	●						▲	●	▲
Move Over Rover	144	M	C	●	▲							●		●										
Museum Search for Wildlife	182	M	V					●					▲											▲
Muskox Maneuvers	130	M	A	●															●					
My Kingdom for a Shelter	28	M	D									●			▲								●	
No Water Off a Duck's Back	305	M	C			●	▲	●				●								▲	●	▲		
Noisy Neighbors	317	M	D							●					▲				▲	●		●		
Oh Deer!	36	M	A			●						●		●	▲				●					
Owl Pellets	100	M	A	●							▲			●	▲				●					

DURATION: A = up to 45 minutes, B = 45 to 60 minutes, C = 60 to 90 minutes, D = 90 minutes to 3 hours, E = over 3 hours, V = variable length

500   Project WILD K–12 Curriculum and Activity Guide

Appendices

Topic Index

Activity Name	Page Number	Grade Level/National Learning Standards Correlation	Duration (A,B,C,D,E,V)	Adaptations	Biodiversity	Change	Consumptive Use	Culture	Economics/Commerce	Environmental Quality	Food Chains	Habitats	Interdependence	Issues	Land Use	Ocean/Marine	Political Processes	Population Dynamics	Resource Management	Responsible Action	Sustainability	Urban	Values
Pay to Play	216	M	V				▲	●	▲				▲			●	▲		▲	●	▲		▲
Philosophical Differences	364	H	D					●		●							▲		▲	●			▲
Planning for People and Wildlife	436	M	E			●		●	▲			●	▲	●		●	▲		▲	●	▲	●	▲
Planting Animals	152	M	C		▲	●						●		●				●			▲		
Playing Lightly on the Earth	432	E,P	A					●								●			▲	●	▲	●	
Polar Bears in Phoenix?	125	M	B	●	▲			●				●	▲	●	▲					▲				
Power of a Song	194	M	A					●	▲				▲											▲
Prairie Memoirs	188	M	D			●	▲	●	▲		▲	●	▲	●								▲		▲
Pro and Con: Consumptive and Nonconsumptive Use of Wildlife	338	M	D				▲	●	▲				▲						▲			●	▲	
Quick-Frozen Critters	122	M	A	▲											●	▲		●						
Rainfall and the Forest	73	M	V	●							●				●	▲		●						
Rare Bird Eggs for Sale	335	M	D		▲			▲	▲	●				●			▲		▲	●	▲		▲
Riparian Zone	341	M	D					●		●		●		●		●	▲				▲		▲
Saturday Morning Wildlife Watching	184	E	B					●								●								
Seed Need	98	M	A													●								
Seeing Is Believing!	116	E	C	●																				
Shrinking Habitat	310	M	B			●			▲		▲	●	▲	●	▲	●		●	▲	●	▲	●	▲
Smokey Bear Said What?	314	M	B			●						●		●						▲	●	▲		
Spider Web Geometry	34	M	D														▲		●				●	
Stormy Weather	85	M	A													●	▲							
Surprise Terrarium	120	E	A	●																				
Sustainability: Then, Now, Later	449	H	E				●	▲	●	▲	●			▲	●	▲	●			▲	●	▲		▲
The Hunter	287	M	B					▲											●	▲	●	▲		▲
Thicket Game	114	E,P	A	●									●					●						
Time Lapse	158	M	D	●	▲	●						●	▲	●										
To Zone or Not to Zone	321	M	D			●		●	▲			●	▲			●	▲			●	▲	●	▲
Too Close for Comfort	300	E	A		▲					●		●	▲	●	▲			●	▲	●		▲
Tracks!	30	M	D	●												●	▲			▲				
Turkey Trouble	367	H	C				●					●			▲			●		●			

DURATION: A = up to 45 minutes, B = 45 to 60 minutes, C = 60 to 90 minutes, D = 90 minutes to 3 hours, E = over 3 hours, V = variable length

continued

Appendices

Topic Index

Activity Name	Page Number	Grade Level/National Learning Standards Correlation	Duration (A,B,C,D,E,V)	Adaptations	Biodiversity	Change	Consumptive Use	Culture	Economics/Commerce	Environmental Quality	Food Chains	Habitats	Interdependence	Issues	Land Use	Ocean/Marine	Political Processes	Population Dynamics	Resource Management	Responsible Action	Sustainability	Urban	Values
Urban Nature Search	70	M	V												●				▲			●	
We're in This Together	44	H	D					●		●					▲							●	▲
What Bear Goes Where?	118	E	A	●											▲								
What Did Your Lunch Cost Wildlife?	68	M	V						▲	●	▲	●		●		●					▲		▲
What You Wear Is What They Were	210	M	C					●	▲				▲		▲						▲		▲
What's for Dinner?	96	M	A						▲		▲			●	▲								
What's That, Habitat?	56	E	A									●	▲										
What's Wild?	7	E	B	●																			▲
Which Niche?	66	M	V	●								●		●								●	
Who Fits Here?	64	M	C	●																			
Wild Bill's Fate	270	H	E					●															▲
Wild Words	41	M	A														▲						▲
Wildlife on Coins and Stamps	208	H	B					●					▲										▲
Wildlife Bibliography	253	M	D					●	▲				▲				▲						▲
Wildlife in National Symbols	186	M	C					●	▲				▲										▲
Wildlife Is Everywhere!	51	E	A																			●	
Wildlife Issues: Community Attitude Survey	297	H	E					●															▲
Wildlife Research	418	H	E					●											▲	●			▲
Wildwork	385	M	A					●	▲														
World Travelers	330	M	D	●	▲	●						●									▲	●	

DURATION: A = up to 45 minutes, B = 45 to 60 minutes, C = 60 to 90 minutes, D = 90 minutes to 3 hours, E = over 3 hours, V = variable length

Expanded Topic Index

The following is an alphabetical listing of topics included in Project WILD activities. This is not a comprehensive listing; that is, it does not list every possible topic. It does however include topics that might be included in an elementary course of study in a variety of subject areas. Activities are listed in alphabetical order, not according to the degree to which they emphasize the topic. We hope this serves to assist in your curriculum planning as you integrate Project WILD activities into existing courses of study and other instructional programs.

Adaptation

Adaptation Artistry; Birds of Prey; Bottleneck Genes; Deer Dilemma; I'm Thirsty; Move Over Rover; Muskox Maneuvers; Owl Pellets; Polar Bears In Phoenix?; Quick-Frozen Critters; Rainfall and the Forest; Seeing Is Believing; Surprise Terrarium; Thicket Game; Tracks!; What Bear Goes Where?; Which Niche?; Who Fits Here?; World Travelers

Advertising

Does Wildlife Sell?; Power of a Song

Aesthetic Values of Wildlife

Animal Poetry; Bird Song Survey; Cabin Conflict; Cartoons and Bumper Stickers; Does Wildlife Sell?; Drawing on Nature; Fire Ecologies; First Impressions; Here Today, Gone Tomorrow; Migration Barriers; Museum Search for Wildlife; Planning for People and Wildlife; Power of a Song; Pro and Con: Consumptive and Nonconsumptive Uses of Wildlife; Rare Bird Eggs for Sale; Shrinking Habitat; To Zone or Not to Zone; Too Close for Comfort; Wildlife as Seen on Coins and Stamps; Wildlife in National Symbols; Wild Words: A Journal-Making Activity

Aestivation

Birds of Prey

Agriculture

Fire Ecologies; Hazardous Links: Possible Solutions; What Did Your Lunch Cost Wildlife?; What You Wear is What They Were

Basic Survival Needs

Ants on a Twig; Bearly Growing; Beautiful Basics; Birds of Prey; Bottleneck Genes; Carrying Capacity; Changing the Land; Checks and Balances; Classroom Carrying Capacity; Deer Crossing; Ecosystem Facelift; Everybody Needs a Home; Flip the Switch for Wildlife!; Habitat Rummy; Habitat Lap Sit; Habitracks; Habitrekking; Hazardous Links: Possible Solutions; Here Today, Gone Tomorrow; How Many Bears Can Live in This Forest?; Improving Wildlife Habitat in the Community; Interview a Spider; Lobster in Your Lunch Box; Migration Barriers; My Kingdom for a Shelter; Noisy Neighbors; Oh Deer!; Owl Pellets; Polar Bears in Phoenix?; Quick-Frozen Critters; Rainfall and the Forest; Shrinking Habitat; Spider Web Geometry; Stormy Weather; Too Close for Comfort; Tracks!; Turkey Trouble; We're in This Together!; What Bear Goes Where?; What You Wear is What They Were; What's for Dinner?; What's That, Habitat?

Camouflage

Color Crazy; Quick-Frozen Critters; Surprise Terrarium; Thicket Game

Career Education

History of Wildlife Management; Which Niche?; Wildwork

continued

Carrying Capacity

Carrying Capacity; Checks and Balances; Classroom Carrying Capacity; Deer Dilemma; Flip the Switch for Wildlife!; How Many Bears Can Live in This Forest?; Improving Wildlife Habitat in the Community; Oh Deer!; Planting Animals; Rainfall and the Forest; Shrinking Habitat; Too Close for Comfort

Change

A Picture Is Worth a Thousand Words; Birds of Prey; Bottleneck Genes; Carrying Capacity; Changing Societies; Changing the Land; Checks and Balances; Classroom Carrying Capacity; Deer Crossing; Eco-Enrichers; Ecosystem Facelift; Fire Ecologies; Flip the Switch for Wildlife!; Forest in a Jar; From Bison to Bread: The American Prairie; Hazardous Links: Possible Solutions; History of Wildlife Management; How Many Bears Can Live In This Forest?; Improving Wildlife Habitat in the Community; Let's Talk Turkey; Oh Deer!; Prairie Memoirs; Planning for People and Wildlife; Planting Animals; Shrinking Habitat; Smokey Bear Said What?; Sustainability: Then, Now, Later; To Zone or Not to Zone; Turkey Trouble; World Travelers

Commensalism

Good Buddies

Commercial Values of Wildlife

Does Wildlife Sell?; Fire Ecologies; First Impressions; Lobster in Your Lunch Box; Make a Coat!; Power of a Song; Pro and Con: Consumptive and Nonconsumptive Uses of Wildlife; Rare Bird Eggs for Sale; What You Wear is What They Were; Wildlife Bibliography; Wildlife in National Symbols

Communications

And the Wolf Wore Shoes; Cabin Conflict; Can Do!; Cartoons and Bumper Stickers; Changing Attitudes; Checks and Balances; Does Wildlife Sell?; Enviro-Ethics; Ethi-Reasoning; First Impressions; History of Wildlife Management; Improving Wildlife Habitat in the Community; Know Your Legislation; Migration Barriers; Philosophical Differences; Planning for People and Wildlife; Power of a Song; Riparian Zone; Saturday Morning Wildlife Watching; To Zone or Not to Zone; What Did Your Lunch Cost Wildlife?; Wild Bill's Fate; Wildlife as Seen on Coins and Stamps; Wildlife in National Symbols; Wildlife Issues: Community Attitude Survey

Community Attitudes

Cabin Conflict; Can Do! Changing Attitudes; Enviro-Ethics; Ethi-Reasoning; Ethi-Thinking; Fire Ecologies; Flip the Switch for Wildlife; History of Wildlife Management; Improving Wildlife Habitat in the Community; Know Your Legislation; Philosophical Differences; Pro and Con: Consumptive and Nonconsumptive Uses of Wildlife; Rare Bird Eggs for Sale; Riparian Zone; Shrinking Habitat; The Hunter; To Zone or Not to Zone; We're in This Together!; What Did Your Lunch Cost Wildlife?; Wildlife Issues: Community Attitude Survey

Components of Habitat

Ants on a Twig; Beautiful Basics; Bird Song Survey; Everybody Needs a Home; Habitat Lap Sit; Habitat Rummy; Habitracks; Habitrekking; Improving Wildlife Habitat in the Community; Oh Deer!; Owl Pellets; Polar Bears in Phoenix?; Rainfall and the Forest; Shrinking Habitat; Spider Web Geometry; We're in this Together!; What Bear Goes Where?; What's That, Habitat?

Concept Review

Ecosystem Facelift

Conflicting Points of View Regarding Natural Resource Issues

Cabin Conflict; Cartoons and Bumper Stickers; Changing Attitudes; Checks and Balances; Deer Crossing; Deer Dilemma; Does Wildlife Sell?; Ethi-Reasoning; Fire Ecologies; For Your Eyes Only; History of Wildlife Management; Improving Wildlife Habitat in the Community; Know Your Legislation; Migration Barriers; No Water Off a Duck's Back; Philosophical Differences; Power of a Song; Pro and Con: Consumptive and Nonconsumptive Uses of Wildlife; Rare Bird Eggs for Sale; Riparian Zone; Saturday Morning Wildlife Watching; Shrinking Habitat; Smokey Bear Said What?; The Hunter; To Zone or Not to Zone; What Did Your Lunch Cost Wildlife?; Wild Bill's Fate; Wildlife Issues: Community Attitude Survey

Conservation

Cabin Conflict; Can Do!; Cartoons and Bumper Stickers; Checks and Balances; Deer Crossing; Does Wildlife Sell?; Enviro-Ethics; Ethi-Reasoning; Ethi-Thinking; Fire Ecologies; Flip the Switch for Wildlife!; Hazardous Links: Possible Solutions; Here Today, Gone Tomorrow; History of Wildlife Management; I'm Thirsty!; Improving Wildlife Habitat in the Community; Know Your Legislation; Lobster in Your Lunch Box; Migration Barriers; No Water Off a Duck's Back; Planning for People and Wildlife; Planting Animals; Playing Lightly on the Earth; Rare Bird Eggs for Sale; Riparian Zone; Shrinking Habitat; Smokey Bear Said What?; The Hunter; To Zone or Not to Zone; Too Close for Comfort; What Did Your Lunch Cost Wildlife?; What You Wear is What They Were

Consumptive/Nonconsumptive

A Picture Is Worth a Thousand Words; Arctic Survival; Changing Societies; Deer Dilemma; Let's Talk Turkey; Pay To Play; Prairie Memoirs; Pro and Con: Consumptive and Nonconsumptive Uses of Wildlife; Sustainability: Then, Now, Later; The Hunter

Crowding

Changing the Land; Deer Crossing; Deer Dilemma; Planning for People and Wildlife; Shrinking Habitat; Too Close for Comfort

Cycles

Birds of Prey; Checks and Balances; Deer Crossing; Energy Pipeline; Fire Ecologies; Forest in a Jar; Hazardous Links: Possible Solutions; Oh Deer!; Rainfall and the Forest; Smokey Bear Said What?

Culture

A Picture Is Worth a Thousand Words; Cabin Conflict; Can Do!; Cartoons and Bumper Stickers; Changing Attitudes; Changing Societies; Deer Crossing; Deer Dilemma; Does Wildlife Sell?; Enviro-Ethics; Ethi-Reasoning; Ethi-Thinking; Fire Ecologies; Flip the Switch for Wildlife!; For Your Eyes Only; Hazardous Links: Possible Solutions; History of Wildlife Management; Improving Wildlife Habitat in the Community; Know Your Legislation; Lobster in Your Lunch Box; No Water Off a Duck's Back; Pay To Play; Philosophical Differences; Planning for People and Wildlife; Playing Lightly on the Earth; Polar Bears in Phoenix?; Power of a Song; Prairie Memoirs; Pro and Con; Consumptive and Nonconsumptive Uses of Wildlife; Rare Bird Eggs for Sale; Riparian Zone; Sustainability: Then, Now, Later; To Zone or Not to Zone; We're in this Together!; What You Wear is What They Were; Wild Bill's Fate; Wildlife as Seen on Coins and Stamps; Wildlife Bibliography; Wildlife Issues: Community Attitude Survey; Wildlife Research; Wildwork

Definitions of Wild and Domesticated Animals

Animal Charades; Interview a Spider; Lobster in Your Lunch Box; What's Wild?

continued

Dependence on Plants

Checks and Balances; Deer Crossing; Eco-Enrichers; Fire Ecologies; Habitrekking; Hazardous Links: Possible Solutions; Improving Wildlife Habitat in the Community; Lobster in Your Lunch Box; Oh Deer!; Rainfall and the Forest; Riparian Zone; Shrinking Habitat; Smokey Bear Said What?; What Did Your Lunch Cost Wildlife?; What You Wear is What They Were; What's for Dinner?; Who Fits Here?

Ecological Values of Wildlife

Cabin Conflict; Eco-Enrichers; Environmental Barometer; Fire Ecologies; First Impressions; Good Buddies; Here Today, Gone Tomorrow; History of Wildlife Management; Lobster in Your Lunch Box; Migration Barriers; Owl Pellets; Planning for People and Wildlife; Planting Animals; Rare Bird Eggs for Sale; Seed Need; Shrinking Habitat; Spider Web Geometry; To Zone or Not to Zone; Too Close for Comfort; Which Niche?

Economics

A Picture Is Worth a Thousand Words; Arctic Survival; Changing Societies; Changing the Land; Checks and Balances; Deer Dilemma; Does Wildlife Sell?; Ecosystem Facelift; Flip the Switch for Wildlife!; From Bison to Bread: The American Prairie; Improving Wildlife Habitat in the Community; Make a Coat!; Migration Barriers; No Water Off a Duck's Back; Pay To Play; Planning for People and Wildlife; Power of a Song; Prairie Memoirs; Shrinking Habitat; Sustainability: Then, Now, Later; To Zone or Not to Zone; What Did Your Lunch Cost Wildlife?; What's For Dinner?; Wildwork

Ecosystems

Birds of Prey; Carrying Capacity; Fire Ecologies; Rainfall and the Forest; Riparian Zone; Who Fits Here?

Endangered (Rare, Threatened and Extinct) Species

Hazardous Links: Possible Solutions; Here Today, Gone Tomorrow; History of Wildlife Management; Planting Animals; Polar Bears in Phoenix; Rare Bird Eggs for Sale; Too Close For Comfort; Who Fits Here?

Energy

Energy Pipeline; Flip the Switch for Wildlife!; Lobster in Your Lunch Box; Migration Barriers; Planning for People and Wildlife; What Did Your Lunch Cost Wildlife?

Environmental Impact Statement

Migration Barriers

Environmental Problems

Cabin Conflict; Deer Crossing; Habitrekking; Hazardous Links: Possible Solutions; Know Your Legislation; Noisy Neighbors; Philosophical Differences; Rare Bird Eggs for Sale; Riparian Zone; We're in This Together!

Environmental Quality

Career Critters; Deer Dilemma; Habitrekking; Hazardous Links: Possible Solutions; Noisy Neighbors; Sustainability: Then, Now, Later; We're in This Together!

Evidence of Wildlife

Bird Song Survey; Environmental Barometer; Graphananimal; Habitrekking; Owl Pellets; Spider Web Geometry; Surprise Terrarium; Too Close for Comfort; Tracks!; Urban Nature Search

Fire

Fire Ecologies; Smokey Bear Said What?

Food Chain

Birds of Prey; Energy Pipeline; Hazardous Links: Possible Solutions; Owl Pellets; Prairie Memoirs; Shrinking Habitat; What Did Your Lunch Cost Wildlife?

Game/Nongame

Deer Dilemma; History of Wildlife Management; Pro and Con: Consumptive and Nonconsumptive Uses of Wildlife; Rare Bird Eggs for Sale

Habitat (application; see Components of Habitat for Introduction)

Bird Song Survey; Birds of Prey; Cabin Conflict; Can Do!; Carrying Capacity; Checks and Balances; Classroom Carrying Capacity; Ecosystem Facelift; Ethi-Thinking; Flip the Switch for Wildlife!; Hazardous Links: Possible Solutions; Here Today, Gone Tomorrow; History of Wildlife Management; How Many Bears Can Live in This Forest?; Improving Wildlife Habitat in the Community; Migration Barriers; Move Over Rover; Oh Deer!; Planning for People and Wildlife; Planting Animals; Polar Bears in Phoenix?; Prairie Memoirs; Rainfall and the Forest; Shrinking Habitat; Time Lapse; To Zone or Not to Zone; Turkey Trouble; What Did Your Lunch Cost Wildlife?

Habitat Improvement

Cabin Conflict; Can Do!; Checks and Balances; Ecosystem Facelift; Environmental Barometer; Fire Ecologies; Flip the Switch for Wildlife!; History of Wildlife Management; Improving Wildlife Habitat in the Community; Planning for People and Wildlife; Shrinking Habitat; Smokey Bear Said What?

Habitat Loss

Cabin Conflict; Carrying Capacity; Changing the Land; Checks and Balances; Classroom Carrying Capacity; Deer Crossing; Fire Ecologies; Flip the Switch for Wildlife!; From Bison to Bread: The American Prairie; History of Wildlife Management; How Many Bears Can Live in This Forest?; Improving Wildlife Habitat in the Community; Migration Barriers; My Kingdom For a Shelter; No Water Off a Duck's Back; Oh Deer!; Planning for People and Wildlife; Planting Animals; Riparian Zone; Shrinking Habitat; Smokey Bear Said What?; To Zone or Not to Zone; Too Close for Comfort

Herbivores, Carnivores, Omnivores

Energy Pipeline; Hazardous Links: Possible Solutions; Owl Pellets; Shrinking Habitat

Historical Values of Wildlife

A Picture Is Worth a Thousand Words; Cabin Conflict; Cartoons and Bumper Stickers; Changing Attitudes; Changing Societies; Changing the Land; First Impressions; From Bison to Bread: The American Prairie; Here Today, Gone Tomorrow; History of Wildlife Management; Let's Talk Turkey; Lobster in Your Lunch Box; Make a Coat!; Migration Barriers; Museum Search for Wildlife; Pay To Play; Planning for People and Wildlife; Polar Bears in Phoenix?; Power of a Song; Prairie Memoirs; Pro and Con: Consumptive and Nonconsumptive Uses of Wildlife; Shrinking Habitat;Sustainability: Then, Now, Later; The Hunter; Time Lapse; To Zone or Not to Zone; Too Close for Comfort; What You Wear is What They Were; Wildlife as Seen on Coins and Stamps; Wildlife Bibliography; Wildlife in National Symbols

continued

Human Responsibilities and Wildlife

Cabin Conflict; Can Do!; Cartoons and Bumper Stickers; Changing Attitudes; Checks and Balances; Deer Crossing; Does Wildlife Sell?; Enviro-Ethics; Ethi-Reasoning; Ethi-Thinking; Fire Ecologies; First Impressions; Flip the Switch for Wildlife!; Grasshopper Gravity; Hazardous Links: Possible Solutions; History of Wildlife Management; Improving Wildlife Habitat in the Community; Know Your Legislation; Litter We Know; Lobster in Your Lunch Box; Migration Barriers; No Water Off a Duck's Back; Noisy Neighbors; Pay To Play; Planning for People and Wildlife; Planting Animals; Playing Lightly on the Earth; Polar Bears in Phoenix?; Power of a Song; Rare Bird Eggs for Sale; Riparian Zone; Saturday Morning Wildlife Watching; Shrinking Habitat; Smokey Bear Said What?; The Hunter; To Zone or Not to Zone; Too Close for Comfort; What Did Your Lunch Cost Wildlife?; What You Wear Is What They Were; Wild Bill's Fate; Wildlife Research

Humor

Cartoons and Bumper Stickers; Saturday Morning Wildlife Watching

Hunting

Changing Attitudes; Checks and Balances; Classroom Carrying Capacity; Deer Crossing; Ethi-Reasoning; History of Wildlife Management; Philosophical Differences; Pro and Con: Consumptive and Nonconsumptive Uses of Wildlife; The Hunter

Interdependence

Birds of Prey; Bottleneck Genes; Can Do!; Changing Societies; Checks and Balances; Deer Crossing; Ecosystem Facelift; Energy Pipeline; Enviro-Ethics; Fire Ecologies; Flip the Switch for Wildlife!; Forest in a Jar; Good Buddies; Hazardous Links: Possible Solutions; How Many Bears Can Live in This Forest?; Improving Wildlife Habitat in the Community; Migration Barriers; Move Over Rover; No Water Off a Duck's Back; Oh Deer!; Owl Pellets; Planning for People and Wildlife; Planting Animals; Polar Bears in Phoenix?; Prairie Memoirs; Quick-Frozen Critters; Rainfall and the Forest; Rare Bird Eggs for Sale; Riparian Zone; Shrinking Habitat; Smokey Bear Said What?; Sustainability: Then, Now, Later; Thicket Game; Time Lapse; To Zone or Not to Zone; Too Close for Comfort; Tracks!; Urban Nature Search; What Did Your Lunch Cost Wildlife?; Which Niche?; World Travelers

International Alliances

Rare Bird Eggs for Sale; Wildlife Bibliography

Intrinsic Value

Arctic Survival; Ecosystem Facelift; Changing Societies; Grasshopper Gravity; Here Today, Gone Tomorrow; Make a Coat!; Pro and Con: Consumptive and Nonconsumptive Uses of Wildlife; Rare Bird Eggs for Sale; The Hunter; What You Wear is What They Were; Wild Bill's Fate; Wild Words; Wildlife Research

Introduced Species

Lobster in Your Lunch Box; Planting Animals; Time Lapse; Turkey Trouble; World Travelers

Inventory

Bird Song Survey

Land Development

Deer Crossing; Flip the Switch for Wildlife!; Migration Barriers; Planning for People and Wildlife; Riparian Zone; Shrinking Habitat; To Zone or Not to Zone

Land Use

A Picture Is Worth a Thousand Words; Birds of Prey; Cabin Conflict; Can Do!; Changing the Land; Deer Crossing; Deer Dilemma; Ecosystem Facelift; Flip the Switch for Wildlife!; From Bison to Bread: The American Prairie; Improving Wildlife Habitat in the Community; Migration

Barriers; Pay To Play; Planning for People and Wildlife; Playing Lightly on the Earth; Riparian Zone; Shrinking Habitat; Sustainability: Then, Now, Later; To Zone or Not to Zone; Too Close for Comfort; What Did Your Lunch Cost Wildlife?

Land Use Planning

Birds of Prey; Cabin Conflict; Can Do!; Deer Crossing; Improving Wildlife Habitat in the Community; Migration Barriers; Planning for People and Wildlife; Riparian Zone; Shrinking Habitat; To Zone or Not to Zone

Legislation

Know Your Legislation; Wild Bill's Fate

Limiting Factors

Checks and Balances; Hazardous Links: Possible Solutions; Here Today, Gone Tomorrow; How Many Bears Can Live in This Forest?; Improving Wildlife Habitat in the Community; Muskox Maneuvers; Oh Deer!; Planting Animals; Quick-Frozen Critters; Rainfall and the Forest; Shrinking Habitat; The Hunter; Too Close for Comfort; Turkey Trouble

Literature

And the Wolf Wore Shoes; Animal Poetry; The Hunter; Wild Words

Management of Habitat

A Picture Is Worth a Thousand Words; Cabin Conflict; Can Do!; Carrying Capacity; Cartoons and Bumper Stickers; Checks and Balances; Classroom Carrying Capacity; Deer Crossing; Dropping in on Deer; Ecosystem Facelift; Fire Ecologies; Flip the Switch for Wildlife!; From Bison to Bread: The American Prairie; Hazardous Links: Possible Solutions; Here Today, Gone Tomorrow; History of Wildlife Management; Improving Wildlife Habitat in the Community; Migration Barriers; No Water Off a Duck's Back; Planning for People and Wildlife; Planting Animals; Polar Bears in Phoenix?; Shrinking Habitat; Smokey Bear Said What?; Sustainability: Then, Now, Later; The Hunter; To Zone or Not to Zone; Too Close for Comfort; What Did Your Lunch Cost Wildlife?

Management Techniques

A Picture Is Worth a Thousand Words; Back from the Brink; Bird Song Survey; Cabin Conflict; Can Do!; Career Critters; Cartoons and Bumper Stickers; Checks and Balances; Deer Crossing; Deer Dilemma; Dropping in on Deer; Fire Ecologies; From Bison to Bread: The American Prairie; Hazardous Links: Possible Solutions; History of Wildlife Management; Improving Wildlife Habitat in the Community; Migration Barriers; No Water Off a Duck's Back; Pay To Play; Planning for People and Wildlife; Planting Animals; Pro and Con: Consumptive and Nonconsumptive Uses of Wildlife; Shrinking Habitat; Smokey Bear Said What?; The Hunter; To Zone or Not to Zone; Too Close for Comfort; Turkey Trouble

Migration

Bird Song Survey; Deer Crossing; Migration Barriers

Music

Power of a Song

Mutualism

Good Buddies

National Symbols

Wildlife as Seen on Coins and Stamps; Wildlife in National Symbols

Native American Indians

Philosophical Differences; The Hunter

Native/Non-Native Species

Ecosystem Facelift; Here Today, Gone Tomorrow; Lobster in Your Lunch Box; Planting Animals; World Travelers

continued

Newspaper

Cabin Conflict; Cartoons and Bumper Stickers; Does Wildlife Sell?; Interview a Spider; Wildlife Issues: Community Attitude Survey

Niche

Career Critters; Ecosystem Facelift; Which Niche?

Occupation/Vocation

Checks and Balances; History of Wildlife Management; Smokey Bear Said What?; Which Niche?; Wild Bill's Fate; Wildlife Research; Wildwork

Parasitism

Good Buddies

People and Wildlife Sharing Environments

Cabin Conflict; Can Do!; Changing the Land; Checks and Balances; Deer Crossing; Enviro-Ethics; Ethi-Reasoning; Ethi-Thinking; Habitrekking; Hazardous Links: Possible Solutions; History of Wildlife Management; I'm Thirsty!; Improving Wildlife Habitat in the Community; Litter We Know; Microtrek Treasure Hunt; Migration Barriers; No Water Off a Duck's Back; Noisy Neighbors; Philosophical Differences; Planning for People and Wildlife; Planting Animals; Playing Lightly on the Earth; Pro and Con: Consumptive and Nonconsumptive Uses of Wildlife; Riparian Zone; Shrinking Habitat; Spider Web Geometry; Stormy Weather; Sustainability: Then, Now, Later; The Hunter; To Zone or Not to Zone; Too Close for Comfort; We're in This Together!; What Did Your Lunch Cost Wildlife?; Wildlife is Everywhere

Pesticides

Hazardous Links: Possible Solutions; What Did Your Lunch Cost Wildlife?

Philosophy

Cabin Conflict; For Your Eyes Only; History of Wildlife Management; Know Your Legislation; Philosophical Differences; Pro and Con: Consumptive and Nonconsumptive Uses of Wildlife; The Hunter

Plants

Fire Ecologies; Habitrekking; Rainfall and the Forest; Riparian Zone; What You Wear is What They Were; Who Fits Here?

Politics

A Picture Is Worth a Thousand Words; Cabin Conflict; Can Do!; Deer Crossing; Deer Dilemma; Flip the Switch for Wildlife!; From Bison to Bread: The American Prairie; History of Wildlife Management; Improving Wildlife Habitat in the Community; Know Your Legislation; Philosophical Differences; Pay To Play; Planning for People and Wildlife; Rare Bird Eggs for Sale; Riparian Zone; To Zone or Not to Zone; Wild Bill's Fate; Wildlife Bibliography

Pollution

Checks and Balances; Habitrekking; Hazardous Links: Possible Solutions; Litter We Know; No Water Off a Duck's Back; Noisy Neighbors; Too Close for Comfort; We're in This Together!; What Did Your Lunch Cost Wildlife?

Populations

Birds of Prey; Bottleneck Genes; Carrying Capacity; Changing the Land; Deer Crossing; Deer Dilemma; Dropping in on Deer; Ecosystem Facelift; I'm Thirsty!; Turkey Trouble

Predator/Prey Relationships

Birds of Prey; Muskox Maneuvers; Owl Pellets; Quick-Frozen Critters; Spider Web Geometry; The Hunter; Thicket Game

Appendices
Expanded Topic Index

Private Conservation Groups
Bird Song Survey; History of Wildlife Management; Know Your Legislation; Philosophical Differences; Riparian Zone; To Zone or Not to Zone

"Real" and "Make-Believe"
And the Wolf Wore Shoes; Saturday Morning Wildlife Watching; Wildlife in National Symbols

Recreational Value of Wildlife
Cabin Conflict; First Impressions; History of Wildlife Management; Pay To Play; Planning for People and Wildlife; Playing Lightly on the Earth; Pro and Con: Consumptive and Nonconsumptive Uses of Wildlife; Rare Bird Eggs for Sale; Shrinking Habitat; The Hunter; To Zone or Not to Zone; Too Close for Comfort; Wildlife Bibliography

Refuges
Cabin Conflict; History of Wildlife Management; Riparian Zone

Renewable and Nonrenewable Natural Resources
Arctic Survival; Make a Coat!; Sustainability: Then, Now, Later; The Hunter; What Did Your Lunch Cost Wildlife?; What You Wear is What They Were

Resource Agencies and Organizations
A Picture Is Worth a Thousand Words; Bird Song Survey; Birds of Prey; Cabin Conflict; Changing the Land; Checks and Balances; Deer Crossing; Deer Dilemma; Does Wildlife Sell?; Ecosystem Facelift; Flip the Switch for Wildlife!; For Your Eyes Only; From Bison to Bread: The American Prairie; History of Wildlife Management; Know Your Legislation; Migration Barriers; Pay To Play; Philosophical Differences; Planting Animals; Rare Bird Eggs for Sale; Riparian Zone; Smokey Bear Said What?; The Hunter; To Zone or Not to Zone

Responsible Human Actions
Cabin Conflict; Can Do!; Checks and Balances; Deer Crossing; Does Wildlife Sell?; Enviro-Ethics; Ethi-Reasoning; Ethi-Thinking; Fire Ecologies; First Impressions; Flip the Switch for Wildlife!; Here Today, Gone Tomorrow; History of Wildlife Management; Improving Wildlife Habitat in the Community; Know Your Legislation; Litter We Know; No Water Off a Duck's Back; Noisy Neighbors; Philosophical Differences; Planning for People and Wildlife; Playing Lightly on the Earth; Polar Bears in Phoenix?; Power of a Song; Pro and Con: Consumptive and Nonconsumptive Uses of Wildlife; Rare Bird Eggs for Sale; Riparian Zone; Saturday Morning Wildlife Watching; Shrinking Habitat; Smokey Bear Said What?; The Hunter; Too Close for Comfort; What Did Your Lunch Cost Wildlife?; What You Wear is What They Were; Wild Bill's Fate; Wildlife Research

Seasons
Deer Crossing

Seed Dispersal
Seed Need

Similarities and Differences Between People, Wildlife and Domesticated Animals
And the Wolf Wore Shoes; Ants on a Twig; Bearly Growing; Beautiful Basics; Carrying Capacity; Everybody Needs a Home; Habitat Lap Sit; Habitracks; Habitrekking; Hazardous Links: Possible Solutions; How May Bears Can Live in this Forest?; I'm Thirsty!; Noisy Neighbors; Saturday Morning Wildlife Watching; Shrinking Habitat; Stormy Weather; Too Close for Comfort; We're in This Together!; What's For Dinner?; What's That, Habitat?; Which Niche?

Soil
Eco-Enrichers; Fire Ecologies

continued

Stereotypes

And the Wolf Wore Shoes; Does Wildlife Sell?; First Impressions; Saturday Morning Wildlife Watching; Wildlife in National Symbols

Stocking

History of Wildlife Management

Succession

Fire Ecologies; Forest in a Jar; Time Lapse

Symbiosis

Good Buddies

Symbols

Wildlife as Seen on Coins and Stamps; Wildlife in National Symbols

Television

Does Wildlife Sell?; Saturday Morning Wildlife Watching; Wildlife Issues: Community Attitude Survey

Territory

Bird Song Survey

Toxic Substances

Hazardous Links: Possible Solutions; No Water Off a Duck's Back; What Did Your Lunch Cost Wildlife?

Urban

Bird Song Survey; Can Do!; Deer Crossing; Deer Dilemma; Eco-Enrichers; Ecosystem Facelift; Enviro-Ethics; Environmental Barometer; Ethi-Thinking; Flip the Switch for Wildlife!; Habitracks; Habitrekking; Improving Wildlife Habitat in the Community; Litter We Know; Microtrek Treasure Hunt; Migration Barriers; My Kingdom for a Shelter; Noisy Neighbors; Planning for People and Wildlife; Playing Lightly on the Earth; Pro and Con: Consumptive and Nonconsumptive Uses of Wildlife; Shrinking Habitat; Spider Web Geometry; To Zone or Not to Zone; Urban Nature Search; We're in This Together!; Which Niche?; Wildlife is Everywhere!; World Travelers

Variety of Wildlife

Adaptation Artistry; And the Wolf Wore Shoes; Animal Poetry; Ants on a Twig; Back from the Brink; Bearly Growing; Bird Song Survey; Birds of Prey; Changing the Land; Color Crazy; Eco-Enrichers; Environmental Barometer; Fire Ecologies; Graphananimal; Habitrekking; Here Today, Gone Tomorrow; How Many Bears Can Live in This Forest?; I'm Thirsty!; Improving Wildlife Habitat in the Community; Interview a Spider; Lobster in Your Lunch Box; Museum Search for Wildlife; Muskox Maneuvers; My Kingdom for a Shelter; Owl Pellets; Polar Bears in Phoenix?; Rainfall and the Forest; Seeing Is Believing; Spider Web Geometry; Surprise Terrarium; Time Lapse; Tracks!; What Bear Goes Where?; Which Niche?; Who Fits Here?; Wildlife as Seen on Coins and Stamps; Wildlife in National Symbols; World Travelers

Water

I'm Thirsty!; No Water Off a Duck's Back; Rainfall and the Forest; Riparian Zone

Wildlife as an Indicator of Environmental Quality

Deer Crossing; Environmental Barometer; Habitrekking; Hazardous Links: Possible Solutions; Litter We Know; No Water Off a Duck's Back; Noisy Neighbors; Owl Pellets; Shrinking Habitat; Too Close for Comfort; Tracks; Wildlife Research

Zoos

Polar Bears in Phoenix?; Rare Bird Eggs for Sale

Metric Conversion Chart

Symbol	When You Know	Multiply By	To Find	Symbol
		Length		
in	inches	2.5	centimeters	cm
ft	feet	30.0	centimeters	cm
yd	yards	0.9	meters	m
mi	miles	1.6	kilometers	km
cm	centimeters	0.4	inches	in
m	meters	3.3	feet	ft
m	meters	1.09	yards	yd
km	kilometers	0.6	miles	mi
		Area		
in^2	square inches	6.5	square centimeters	cm^2
ft^2	square feet	0.09	square meters	m^2
yd^2	square yards	0.84	square meters	m^2
mi^2	square miles (640 acres)	2.6	square kilometers	km^2
acre	acre (43,560 ft^2)	0.4	hectares	ha
cm^2	square centimeter	0.16	square inches	in^2
m^2	square meter	10.8	square feet	ft^2
m^2	square meter	1.2	square yards	yd^2
km^2	square kilometer	0.4	square miles	mi^2
ha	hectare	2.5	acres	acre
		Mass		
oz	ounces (avoirdupois)	28.0	grams	g
lb	pound	0.45	kilograms	kg
t	short tons (2,000 lb)	0.9	tonnes (metric ton)	t
g	grams	0.035	ounces (avoirdupois)	oz
kg	kilograms	2.2	pounds	lb
t	tonnes (metric tons)	1.1	short tons (2,000 lb)	t
		Volume		
tsp	teaspoons	5.0	milliliters	ml
Tbs	tablespoons	15.0	milliliters	ml
fl oz	fluid ounces	30.0	milliliters	ml
c	cups (liquid)	0.24	liters	l
pt	pints (liquid)	0.47	liters	l
qt	quarts (liquid)	0.95	liters	l
gal	gallons	3.8	liters	l
ft^3	cubic feet	0.03	cubic meters	m^3
yd^3	cubic yards	0.76	cubic meters	m^3
ml	milliliters	0.2	teaspoons	tsp
ml	milliliters	0.07	tablespoons	Tbs
ml	milliliters	0.03	fluid ounces	fl oz
l	liters	4.2	cups (liquid)	c
l	liters	2.1	pints (liquid)	pt
l	liters	1.06	quarts (liquid)	qt
l	liters	0.26	gallons	gal
m^3	cubic meters	35.0	cubic feet	ft^3
m^3	cubic meters	1.3	cubic yards	yd^3
		Temperature		
°F	degrees Fahrenheit	(9/5 x °C) + 32	decrees Celsius	°C
°C	degrees Celsius	5/9 x (°F-32)	degrees Fahrenheit	°F

© Council for Environmental Education 2001

Glossary

abiotic: a nonliving factor in an environment (e.g., light, water, temperature)

adaptation: an alteration or adjustment in structure or habits by which a species or individual improves its condition in relationship to its environment

aerate: to supply with air or oxygen; to supply the blood with oxygen as in the function of lungs; to supply running water with additional oxygen as when a stream runs over falls or rapids or when wind creates waves on a lake

aesthetic: relating to or dealing with the beautiful (An aesthetic value relates to the value placed on beauty.)

aestivation: dormancy, typically seasonal

amphibian: an animal that typically lives in an aquatic habitat breathing by gills as young, and primarily in a terrestrial habitat breathing by lungs and through moist glandular skin as adult (e.g., frog)

anadromous: species of fish that live their lives in the ocean and migrate to fresh water to spawn

animal community: animals of various species living within a certain habitat, each occupying a specific position in this particular environment; directly parallel and related to plant communities

annual turnover: the rate of replacement of individual animals in a population from the beginning of 1 year until the end of the following year (The reproductive capability of a species will match the mortality, or turnover, rate.)

annual: a plant that completes its life cycle from seedling to mature seed-bearing plant during a single growing season

anthropocentric: valuing the environment and its resources for personal needs and interests

anthropomorphism: the attribution of human characteristics to nonhumans, especially animals

aquatic: growing, living in, or frequenting water

arboreal: inhabiting trees

attitude: one's opinion or state of mind

bag limit: the maximum number of animals allowed to be taken by an individual in regulated fishing or hunting

behavior: the actions and reactions of humans or animals in response to stimuli

biennial: a plant that lives for two growing seasons, producing leaves during the first season, flowers and seeds during the second

big game: a term for large species of wild animals, birds, or fish hunted for food or sport (e.g. deer, elk, moose, bear)

bioaccumulation: the storage of chemicals in an organism in higher concentrations than are normally found in the environment

biocentric: a person whose attitude toward the environment considers all of the plants and animals

biodegradable: capable of being decomposed by biological agents, especially bacteria

biodiversity: a term used to represent the variety of life forms in a given area

biologist: a person who studies living organisms and their relationship to one another

biomagnification: the accumulation of chemicals in organisms in increasingly higher concentration at successive trophic levels

biome: a large geographic area with somewhat uniform climatic conditions; a complex of communities characterized by a distinctive type of vegetation and maintained under the climatic conditions of the region

biosphere: part of the Earth's crust; water and atmosphere where living organisms can subsist

biota: the animal and plant life of a region

biotic: the living organisms in a given community, including all plant and animal life within the community

biotic potential: the capacity of a population of animals or plants to increase in numbers under optimum environmental conditions

blind: a hiding place for observing

bounty: a reward or payment for removing certain species of animals felt to be harmful

breeding: a series of complex behavioral interactive patterns from courtship to rearing of young that are necessary for the continuation of a species

broadleaf: the term describing a plant with wide, broad leaves rather than needlelike leaves

brood: the offspring of a bird or mammal

browse: to feed on the twigs, leaves, and shoots of woody plants and other vegetation

burrowing: to dig a hole or tunnel for habitation or refuge

canopy: layer formed by the leaves, and branches of the forest's tallest trees

carnivore: a meat eater

carrion: the bodies of dead animals, usually found in nature in the process of decay

carrying capacity: the maximum number of individuals or inhabitants that a given environment can support without detrimental effects

cast: to regurgitate indigestible prey remains

chaparral: a biome characterized by hot, dry summers and cool, moist winters and dominated by a dense growth of mostly small-leafed evergreen shrubs, as that found in the foothills of California

climatic: the average condition of the weather as defined by temperature, precipitation, and wind velocities; the environmental conditions relating to weather

climax: the final stage of plant or animal succession; when environmental conditions have been stable long enough for an area to develop a semi-permanent biome

climax community: a stage in ecological development in which a community of organisms, especially plants, is stable and capable of perpetuating itself

coloration: a genetically controlled pattern or markings that protects an individual organism

community: a group of plants and animals living and interacting with one another in a specific region under relatively similar environmental conditions.

competition: the simultaneous demand by two or more organisms for limited environmental resources, such as nutrients, living space, or light

conifer: a plant that bears its seeds in cones; mostly needle-leafed or scale-leafed; mainly evergreen

coniferous: refers to cone-bearing (A coniferous forest is one composed of pines, firs, spruces, or a combination of these.)

consensus: when a group of people reach a general agreement on a solution

conservation: the use of natural resources in a way that ensures their continuing availability to future generations; the wise and intelligent use or protection of natural resources

conservation easement: purchased development right to a property (The owner continues to own the property and can continue to use it for agriculture, but can never develop it or change it to a higher density zoning.)

consumer: the first part of an ecosystem is the nonliving substance; the second part consists of those organisms that are called "producers," or food makers; the third part of this system is called the "consumer" because it uses the producer for its food; it may in turn be used as food by a secondary consumer

consumptive use: in general terms related to wildlife, any use that involves activity resulting in the harvesting of wildlife

courtship: a behavior pattern that ensures mating with a suitable partner of the correct species at the correct time

cover: the vegetation, debris, and irregularities of the land that provide concealment, sleeping, feeding, and breeding areas for wildlife

continued

covey: a small flock or group, often a family group, of birds such as quail

crepuscular: active at dawn and dusk

cultural carrying capacity: the largest number of humans, a certain standard of living, that a piece of land can support

dabbling ducks: ducks that frequent shallow marshes, ponds, and rivers and "tip up" to feed (They feed with body above water and take off vertically when startled; also called "puddle ducks" [see "diving ducks"]).

deciduous: trees that shed or lose foliage at the end of the growing season

decomposer: those organisms (e.g. bacteria, fungi) that convert dead organic materials into inorganic materials

depredation: the act of preying upon, usually in relation to wildlife damage to crops or animals

desert scrub: arid environments with irregular winter rainfall, summer rainfall, or biseasonal rainfall; highly varied plant life, with leafless, drought deciduous, or evergreen species of trees, shrubs, herbs and grasses, yuccas, agaves, and cacti

display: an observable behavioral pattern that is used to communicate visually, such as the presentation of colors or plumage by male birds as part of courtship or intimidation

diurnal: active by daylight; the opposite of nocturnal

diversity: variety

diving ducks: ducks that prefer deep water as in lakes and bays (They feed by diving below the surface and take wing from a running start.)

domesticated: to train or adapt an animal or a plant to live in a human environment and be of use to human beings

dominant species: plant or animal species that exerts a major controlling influence on the community

ecological niche: the role played by an organism in a biological community; its food preferences, requirements for shelter, special behaviors, and the timing of its activities (e.g., nocturnal or diurnal)

ecologist: a scientist who studies the interrelations of living things to one another and to their environment

ecology: the study of the relation of organisms or groups of organisms to their environment; the science of the interrelations between living organisms and their environment

ecosystem: a natural unit that includes living and nonliving parts interacting to produce a stable system in which the exchange of materials between the living and nonliving parts follows closed paths

edge community: the area that borders two habitats; a transition zone

edge effect: the tendency of wildlife to use the areas where two vegetative types come together forming an edge

endangered: a species that is in danger of extinction throughout all or a significant portion of its range

energy: the capacity to do work; source of usable power

environment: the circumstances and conditions surrounding an organism that influences its existence, including physical, biological, and all other factors

environmental issue: a situation in which there is disagreement about solutions to an environmental problem, often because of differing values and beliefs

environmental problem: a difficult situation involving the interaction between people and the environment

erosion: to wear away or corrode

ethics: a personal or social moral code

eutrophication: enrichment of soils and water resulting from fertilization, sewage, effluent, or other waters that carry a high plant-nutrient component

evergreen: a plant having foliage that remains green throughout the year

exotic: a plant or animal that is not native to a habitat (e.g., the ring-necked pheasant is introduced from China)

extinction: the condition of having been removed from existence

extirpated: missing from native range but not extinct

feral: referring to domesticated animals that are now wild

finite: having bounds or limits; capable of being counted or measured

flyway: fly routes established by migratory birds

food chain: the transfer of food energy from one organism to another as each consumes a lower member and in turn is preyed upon by a higher member

food web: an interlocking pattern of food chains

forage: refers to vegetation taken naturally by herbivorous animals

forb: a broad-leaved flowering plant such as sunflower and prairie clover; does not include grasses, sedges, trees, shrubs

forest floor: the layer of decomposing material that covers the soil in a forest

forest management: the practical application of scientific, economic, and social principles to the administration of a forest for specified objectives

fragmentation: an area that is not continuous or isolated

fry: small, young fish that have recently hatched

funding: a source for money; to furnish a fund for

game animal: legal designation for animals that may be managed and hunted only under regulation

gene pool: the availability of genes within a species

genetic diversity: the chromosomal diversity available within a species

grassland: a vegetative community where grasses are the most conspicuous members

grazer: a herbaceous organism that consumes primarily grasses

habitat: the arrangement of food, water, shelter or cover, and space suitable to animals' needs

hardwood: a deciduous or broadleaf tree

harvest: the intentional gathering of plants, animals, and other natural resources for use

hatchery: a place where fish eggs are hatched and raised

herb: any flowering plant or fern that has a soft, rather than woody, stem

herb layer: the layer of soft-stemmed plants growing close to the forest floor

herbivore: a plant eater

hibernation: the act of passing the winter, or a portion of it, in a state of sleep; a torpid or resting state

home range: the area where an animal travels in the scope of normal activities

humus: organic material resulting from decaying plant and animal matter

hunter: a person or animal who is in search of wildlife

hunting: the act of a person or animal who hunts

hunting pressure: the numbers, amount, or concentration of hunters in a specific area and upon a specific animal

indigenous: a naturally occurring species

inorganic: involving neither organic life nor products of organic life

insecticide: a chemical used to kill insects

insectivorous: refers to insect eaters

interaction: the relationship of one organism to another; the action of one population affecting the growth or death rate of another population

interdependency: when different species within an ecosystem rely upon one another for survival

introduced species: a non-native species that is intentionally or accidentally brought into an ecosystem

invade: to enter or permeate an area; to overrun

invasive species: a plant or animal species that has the ability to significantly displace desirable species or to reduce the yield of growing crops

inventory: a detailed, itemized list used in the process of identifying and counting animals

irrigation ditch: a man made waterway used to supply water

key plant species: those plant species that are used to indicate the general condition of a habitat

continued

land use: usually refers to how the land is used by people

license: in wildlife terms, a legal permit for hunting, fishing, trapping, and so forth

lichen: algae and fungus growing together in a symbiotic relationship

life cycle: the continuous sequence of changes undergone by an organism from one primary form to the development of the same form again

limiting factors: influences in the life history of any animal, population of animals, or species (e.g., food, water, shelter, space, disease, predation, climatic conditions, pollution, hunting, poaching, and accidents)

litter: carelessly discarded garbage; the number of young born per birthing to a mammal

management: in general terms related to wildlife, the intentional manipulation or nonmanipulation of habitat or the organisms within the habitat

market hunting: where hunting is done on a commercial level for the sale of hides, pelts, or meat

microclimates: the climates of small specific areas as contrasted to the general climate of the area

microhabitat: a small habitat within a larger one in which environmental conditions differ from those in the surrounding area

microorganism: an organism microscopic in size, observable only through a microscope

migratory: birds or other animals that make annual moves from one region or country to another to settle

mitigate: to make up for; to substitute some benefit for losses incurred

mixed forest: a forest that includes both coniferous and deciduous trees

monoculture: the raising of a crop of a single species, generally even-aged (Parts of the Midwest are a monoculture of corn or soybeans.)

mortality rate: the death rate; usually expressed in deaths per thousand

mulching: to add materials to soil to protect from cold, to reduce evaporation, to control weeds, or to enrich the soil

multiple use: a term referring to a system of management in which lands and waters are used for a variety of purposes

multiple-use forestry: any practice of forestry fulfilling two or more objectives of management

mutualism: a close association between two different species whereby each species derives some benefit

natal: related to birth or being born

native: a plant or animal species that was produced, grew, or originated in a certain region

natural selection: a process in nature resulting in the survival and perpetuation of only those forms of plants and animals having certain favorable characteristics that enable them to adapt best to a specific environment

needleleaf: bearing needlelike leaves

niche: the function or position of an organism or a population within an ecological community

nitrogen fixation: the conversion of atmospheric nitrogen into organic compounds or to forms readily utilizable in biological processes

nocturnal: active by night; the opposite of diurnal

nonconsumptive use: in general terms related to wildlife, any use that does not directly kill wildlife

nongame: all wildlife species that are not commonly hunted, killed, or consumed by humans, such as songbirds and raptors

non-native: in conservation terms, an organism that has been introduced into a new area

nonrenewable resource: nonliving resources such as rocks and minerals that do not regenerate themselves and cannot be replaced in this geological age

omnivore: an animal that eats both plant and animal materials

organic matter: chemical compounds of carbon combined with other chemical elements and generally manufactured in the life processes of plants and animals

organism: a living thing; a form of life composed of parts that work together to carry on the various processes of life

parasite: an organism that lives by deriving benefit from another organism, usually doing harm to the organism from which it derives benefit

pelage: body covering on a mammal

perennial: a plant that lives for several years and usually produces seeds each year

pesticide: any chemical preparation used to control populations of organisms

philosophical attitude: values the balanced system of living and nonliving things

photon: a discrete particle of energy

pinch period: that period of an annual cycle when the factors necessary for life are least favorable

plankton: microscopic organisms that are suspended in an aquatic habitat and that serve as food for fish and other large organisms

plant communities: an association of plants, each occupying a certain position or ecological niche, inhabiting a common environment and interacting with each other

playa: shallow, circular depressions in the land that collect water to form wetlands, ranging in size from less than an acre to several hundred acres; commonly found on the high plains of the southwestern United States

plot: an area of land

poaching: hunting illegally, not complying with regulations regarding areas, sex, seasons, or limits

pollution: contamination of soil, water, or atmosphere by the discharge of harmful substances

population: the number of a particular species in a defined area

population inventory: a measure of the current density of a species of animal or plant

pothole: depressions in the land—usually caused by glaciers—that fill in with water and form small lakes and ponds

prairie: a grassland habitat, characterized by precipitation from 12 to 40 inches, high evaporation rates and periodic fires

predaceous: living by seizing or taking prey

predation: the act of preying upon

predator: an animal that kills and eats other animals

prescribed burning: the planned application of fire to natural fuels with the intent to confine the burning to a predetermined area

preservation: protection that emphasizes nonconsumptive values and uses; to keep in a perfect or unaltered condition

prey: animals that are killed and eaten by other animals

primary producers: organisms that are able to manufacture food from simple organic substances

private lands: lands owned by particular people who can determine, within the law, how those lands will be used or managed

producer: a green plant or bacterium that uses photosynthesis or chemosynthesis; constitutes first trophic level in food chain

public lands: lands managed and used by the public

rain shadow: an area on the leeward side of a mountain barrier that receives little rainfall

range: the geographic region where a plant or animal normally lives and grows; an area grazed by livestock, wildlife, or both

rangeland: an expanse of land suitable for livestock to wander and graze on

raptor: birds that are predatory and prey on other animals (e.g. eagles, hawks, owls)

rare: referring to wildlife species not presently in danger but of concern because of low numbers

recovery: as related to conservation, when a plant or animal population has been removed from the endangered or threatened species lists, meaning their population is large enough to sustain itself in the wild

recreation: entertainment that refreshes one's mind or body, frequently implying activity in the out-of-doors

reintroduction: as related to conservation, when a plant or animal species is introduced back into their natural habitat

continued

renewable resource: a commodity or resource—such as plants and animals—that is replaceable by new growth and that has the capacity to renew itself when conditions for survival are favorable

resident wildlife: animals that are residents of a specific area on a year-round basis as opposed to being migratory

resource: a portion of an environment that people have placed or assigned value or see as being available for use

revenue: money generated

rodent: mammals with large incisors adapted for gnawing or nibbling (e.g., rabbits, rats, mice)

savanna: a flat grassland with scattered trees or clumps of trees of tropical and subtropical regions

scat: fecal material

scavenger: an organism that habitually feeds on refuse or carrion

scrub: low, woody vegetation composed principally of shrubs

season: a period of time, usually when something specific occurs (e.g., season characterized by climatic conditions or time when hunting, fishing, or trapping is permitted for a particular species)

sere: the sequence of an ecological community successively occupying an area from initial stage to climax (e.g., the change from a bare field to a mature forest)

shelter: cover for natal activity or bedding and protection from weather

skink: any of a family of smooth, shiny lizards having a cylindrical body and small or rudimentary legs and living chiefly in temperate and tropical regions

slough: a hollow filled with mud and water (e.g., an inlet from a river, backwater, or tidal flat)

small game: a term for smaller species of wild animals, birds, or fish hunted for food or sport (e.g., rabbits, squirrels, quail) or nongame (e.g., songbirds and birds of prey)

snag: a standing dead tree that has no branches or leaves

social limits: the saturation point of a species in an environment; how much crowding an individual will accept

softwood: a coniferous tree

spawning: the act of producing or depositing eggs; usually referring to fish

species: a population of individuals that are more or less alike and that are able to breed and produce fertile offspring under natural conditions; a category of biological classification immediately below the genus or subgenus

state wildlife agency: the state agency that has the legal responsibility for management of some or all wildlife, including habitat protection, restoration, and alteration; planning; land acquisition; research; education; information; endangered species; consumptive uses; nonconsumptive programs; and regulations and usually law enforcement

static: showing little change, usually used in reference to a population or to a condition of habitat

stewardship: related to the environment, the concept of responsible caretaking; uses the premise that we do not own resources but are managers of resources and are responsible to future generations for their condition

stream bank: the slope of land adjoining a stream

stress: usually thought of as a physical factor that applies to detrimental pressure to an organism or population (e.g., a drought period would be a stress to a plant community)

subsistence: the act or means to exist; to find ones supply of food from hunting and fishing

succession: the orderly, gradual, and continuous replacement of one plant or animal by another

sustainability: maintaining resources in such a way to be able to renew themselves over time or to keep in existence and supply with necessities

symbiosis: a close living relationship between organisms

terrestrial: living or growing on land

territorial imperative: the instinctive compulsion to gain and defend a territory

territory: dominance over a unit of habitat; an area defended by an animal against others of the same species

threatened: in wildlife terms, a species present in its range but in danger because of a decline in numbers

topography: the technique of representing surface areas of land on maps

transplant: to transfer from one area to another

transportation systems: the ways in which people move from place to place

tree: a woody plant 12 or more feet (4 or more meters) tall with a single main stem (trunk) and a more or less distinct crown of leaves

trophic level: a group of living things that share the same level in the food chain

understory: the layer of plants growing under another higher layer of plants (e.g., grass, weeds, and brush under forest trees)

vegetation: the mass of plants that covers a given area

veldt: South African grassland, with scattered trees

viable: capable of living, growing, and developing

waterfowl: water birds, usually ducks or geese

wild: not tamed or domesticated, living in a basically free condition (A wild animal provides for its own food, shelter, and other needs in an environment that serves as a suitable habitat.)

wildlife: animals that are not tamed or domesticated and includes, but is not limited to, insects, spiders, birds, reptiles, fish, amphibians, and mammals, if nondomesticated

wildlife management: the application of scientific knowledge and technical skills to protect, preserve, conserve, limit, enhance, or extend the value of wildlife and its habitat

wildlife manager: a person who manages wildlife habitat, other related human activities, or both

woodland: land having a cover of trees and shrubs

yard up: to gather in a sheltered area in winter; used typically in reference to deer, moose, and so forth

zero population growth: sustaining population numbers at a fixed level so as to prevent increase

This glossary is designed primarily for reference and background information. Occasionally, terms are defined within an activity and are not repeated here. Key vocabulary for activities is usually defined here, especially if it is specific to wildlife and the understanding of natural systems. This glossary is compiled from four principal sources. The majority of the terms and definitions are reprinted with few changes from *Multidisciplinary Wildlife Teaching Activities*, developed and edited by William R. Hernbrode (Columbus, OH: ERIC Clearinghouse for Science, Mathematics, and Environmental Education, 1978). The next largest group of entries is derived from the glossary that appears in the Project Learning Tree Environmental Education PreK–8 Activity Guide (Washington DC: American Forest Foundation, 1993). A number of entries are adapted or reprinted from Wildlife Aid No. 2 (Portland, OR: U.S. Forest Service, R-6, June 1965). Additional entries are based on the contributions of our Committee, members, staff, and reviewers. All glossary materials derived from previously published sources are adapted or reprinted with the permission of the copyright holder.

continued

Agencies and Organizations

The following federal agencies have responsibilities involving wildlife and are referenced in Project WILD activities. State wildlife agencies may be contacted directly in each state. Project WILD encourages educators and students to contact a range of organizations so they can make informed decisions. We recommend that requests be as specific as possible; mailed on behalf of a class rather than each individual student; and sent with a stamped, self-addressed envelope for return of requested materials.

Federal Agencies

Bureau of Land Management
Interior Building
1849 C Street, NW, Mail Stop LS406
Washington, DC 20240
(202) 452-5125
www.blm.gov

Cooperative Extension Service
U.S. Department of Agriculture
800 Ninth Street, SW
Washington, DC 20024
(202) 720-3029
www.reeusda.gov

National Marine Fisheries Service
U.S. Department of Commerce, NOAA
1315 East-West Highway
Silver Spring, MD 20910
(301) 713-2370
www.nefsc.nmfs.gov

National Park Service
Interior Building
PO Box 37127
Washington, DC 20013-7127
(202) 208-6843
www.nps.gov

Natural Resources Conservation Service
U. S. Department of Agriculture
PO Box 2890
Washington, DC 20013
(202) 720-4525
www.nrcs.usda.gov

U.S. Army Corps of Engineers
Public Affairs
441 G Street, NW
Washington, DC 20314
(202) 761-0011
www.hq.usace.army.mil/cepa/cepa.htm

U.S. Department of Agriculture
1400 Independence Avenue, SW
Washington, DC 20250
(202) 720-4623
www.fsis.usda.gov

U.S. Environmental Protection Agency
Environmental Education Division
401 M Street, SW
Washington, DC 20460
(202) 260-2090
www.epa.gov

U.S. Fish and Wildlife Service
Department of Interior
1849 C Street, NW, Rm 3012
Washington, DC 20240
(202) 208-5634
www.fws.gov

U.S. Fish and Wildlife Service
Reference Center
5430 Grosvenor Lane, Suite 110
Bethesda, MD 20814
(301) 492-6403
fa.r9.fws.gov/r9fwrs

USDA Forest Service, CF
Natural Resource Conservation Education
PO Box 96090
Washington, DC 20090-6090
(202) 205-1545
www.fs.fed.us

Regional Offices
U.S. Environmental Protection Agency

U.S. EPA Region 1
Environmental Education Program
1 Congress Street, Suite 1100
Boston, MA 02114-2023
(800) 438-2474
www.epa.gov/region01/

U.S. EPA Region 2
Environmental Education Program
290 Broadway, 26th Floor
New York, NY 10007
(212) 637-3671
www.epa.gov/region02/

U.S. EPA Region 3
Environmental Education Program
1650 Arch Street (3CG00)
Philadelphia, PA 19103-2029
(800) 438-2474
www.epa.gov/region03/

U.S. EPA Region 4
Environmental Education Program
61 Forsyth Street, SW
Atlanta, GA 30303
(404) 562-9900
www.epa.gov/region04/

U.S. EPA Region 5
Environmental Education Program
77 West Jackson Boulevard (PI-19J)
Chicago, IL 60604
(312) 353-2000
www.epa.gov/region05/

U.S. EPA Region 6
Environmental Education Program
1445 Ross Avenue (6XA)
Dallas, TX 75202-2733
(214) 665-6444
www.epa.gov/region06/

U.S. EPA Region 7
Environmental Education Program
901 North Fifth Street
Kansas City, KS 66101
(913) 551-7000
www.epa.gov/region07/

U.S. EPA Region 8
Environmental Education Program
999 18th Street, Suite 500
Denver, CO 80202-2405
(303) 312-6605
www.epa.gov/region08/

U.S. EPA Region 9
Environmental Education Program
75 Hawthorne Street (CGR-3)
San Francisco, CA 94105
(415) 744-1161
www.epa.gov/region09/

U.S. EPA Region 10
Environmental Education Program
1200 Sixth Avenue (EXA-142)
Seattle, WA 98101
(800) 424-4372
www.epa.gov/region10/

U.S. Forest Service

U.S. Forest Service
Northern Region (R-1)
200 East Broadway
Missoula, MT 59807-7669
(406) 329-3316
www.fs.fed.us/r1/

U.S. Forest Service
Rocky Mountain Region (R-2)
PO Box 25127
Lakewood, CO 80225
(303) 275-5350
www.fs.fed.us/r2/

U.S. Forest Service
Southwestern Region (R-3)
517 Gold Avenue, SW
Albuquerque, NM 87102
(505) 476-3300
www.fs.fed.us/r3/

U.S. Forest Service
Intermountain Region (R-4)
Federal Building
324 25th Street
Ogden, UT 84401-2310
(801) 625-5605
www.fs.fed.us/r4/

U.S. Forest Service
Pacific Southwest Region (R-5)
1323 Club Drive
Vallejo, CA 94592
(707) 562-8737
www.fs.fed.us/r5/

U.S. Forest Service
Pacific Northwest Region (R-6)
PO Box 3623
Portland, OR 97208-3623
(503) 808-2592
www.fs.fed.us/r6/

continued

U.S. Forest Service
Southern Region (R-8)
1720 Peachtree Road, NW
Atlanta, GA 30309
(404) 347-4177
www.fs.fed.us/r8/

U.S. Forest Service
Eastern Region (R-9)
310 West Wisconsin Avenue, Room 500
Milwaukee, WI 53203
(414) 297-3600
www.fs.fed.us/r9

U.S. Forest Service
Alaska Region (R-10)
709 West 9th Street
PO Box 21628
Juneau, AK 99802-1628
(907) 586-8863
www.fs.fed.us/r10

U.S. Forest Service
Northeastern Area-State & Private Forestry
11 Campus Drive
Newtown Square, PA 19023
(610) 557-4160
www.fs.fed.us/na/

Organizations

American Cetacean Society
National Headquarters
PO Box 1391
San Pedro, CA 90731-0943
(310) 548-6279
www.acsonline.org

American Fisheries Society
5410 Grosvenor Lane
Bethesda, MD 20814-2199
(301) 897-8616
www.fisheries.org

American Humane Association
63 Inverness Drive East
Englewood, CO 80112
(303) 792-9900
www.americanhumane.org

American Sport Fishing Association &
    Future Fisherman Foundation
225 Reinekers Lane, Suite 420
Alexandria, VA 22314
(703) 519-9691
www.asafishing.org

Animal Protection Institute
1122 S Street
Sacramento, CA 95814
(916) 447-3085
www.api4animals.org

Animal Welfare Institute
PO Box 3650
Washington, DC 20007
(202) 337-2332
www.awionline.org

Center for Coastal Studies
59 Commercial Street, Box 1036
Provincetown, MA 02657
(508) 487-3622
www.coastalstudies.org

Center for Marine Conservation
1725 DeSales Street, NW, Suite 600
Washington, DC 20036
(202) 429-5609
www.cmc-ocean.org

Cetacean Society International
PO Box 953
Georgetowne, CT 06829
(203) 431-1606
csiwhalesalive.org

Cousteau Society
870 Greenbriar Circle, Suite 402
Chesapeake, VA 23320
(800) 441-4395
www.cousteausociety.org

Defenders of Wildlife
1101 14th Street, NW, Suite 1400
Washington, DC 20005
(202) 682-9400
www.defenders.org

Ducks Unlimited
1 Waterfowl Way
Memphis, TN 38120
(901) 758-3825
www.ducks.org

Fund for Animals
200 W. 57th Street, Suite 508
New York, NY 10019
(212) 246-2096
www.fund4animals.org

Greenpeace
702 H Street, NW
Washington, DC 20001
(800) 326-0959
www.greenpeaceusa.org

International Association of Fish
   and Wildlife Agencies
444 North Capitol Street, NW, Suite 544
Washington, DC 20001
(202) 624-7890
www.iafwa.org

International Whaling Commission
The Red House
135 Station Road
Impington, Cambridge UK CB4 9NP
England

Izaak Walton League of America
707 Conservation Lane
Gaithersburg, MD 20878-2983
(301) 548-0150
www.iwla.org

National Association for Humane and
   Environmental Education
Humane Society of the United States
2100 L Street, NW
Washington, DC 20037
(202) 452-1100
www.hsus.org

National Association of Conservation Districts
PO Box 855
League City, TX 77574-0855
(281) 332-3402
www.nacdnet.org

National Audubon Society
700 Broadway
New York, NY 10003
(212) 979-3000
www.audubon.org

National Rifle Association
Wildlife Management Division
11250 Waples Mills Road
Fairfax, VA 22030
(703) 267-1000
www.nra.org

National Wildlife Federation
11100 Wildlife Center Drive
Reston, VA 20190-5362
(703) 438-6000
www.nwf.org

National Wild Turkey Federation
770 Augusta Road
Edgefield, SC 29824
(803) 637-3106
www.nwtf.com

New England Aquarium
Central Wharf
Boston, MA 02110
(617) 973-5200
www.neaq.org

Rocky Mountain Elk Foundation
2291 W. Broadway
PO Box 8249
Missoula, MT 59807
1-800-CALL-ELK
www.rmef.org

Safari Club International
4800 West Gates Pass Road
Tucson, AZ 85745
(520) 620-1220
www.safariclub.org

Sierra Club
85 Second Street, 2nd Floor
San Francisco, CA 94105
(415) 977-5500
www.sierraclub.org

The Nature Conservancy
4245 North Fairfax Drive, Suite 100
Arlington, VA 22203
(800) 628-6860
www.tnc.org

The Wilderness Society
900 17th Street, NW
Washington, DC 20006-2596
(202) 833-2300
www.wilderness.org

The Wildlife Society
5410 Grosvenor Lane, Suite 200
Bethesda, MD 20814
(301) 897-9770
www.wildlife.org

Whale Center of New England
Box 159
Gloucester, MA 01930
(978) 281-6351
www.whalecenter.org

Wildlife Management Institute
1101 14th Street, NW, Suite 801
Washington, DC 20005
(202) 371-1808
www.wildlifemgt.org/wmi

World Wildlife Fund
1250 24th Street, NW
Washington, DC 20037
1-800-CALL-WWF
www.worldwildlife.org

Evaluation of Project WILD Materials

Project WILD meets the international criteria for environmental education and provides educators with materials that support national, state, and district standards in science, mathematics, language arts, social studies, and expressive arts. Project WILD curriculum materials undergo a thorough review, testing, and evaluation process. The purpose is to develop well-conceived, tested, current, and effective instructional resources of the highest quality that meet the needs of educators and students.

Expert Review

All of the instructional activities in Project WILD, as well as the conceptual framework, have been reviewed for educational soundness, balance, and content accuracy. Primarily classroom teachers, often in cooperation with nonformal educators and wildlife specialists, wrote the initial instructional activities. Reviewers throughout each stage of Project WILD's development have included classroom teachers, university faculty, resource agency personnel, wildlife biologists, representatives of private conservation groups, public wildlife and natural resource agency personnel, representatives of animal welfare organizations, spokespersons for environmental organizations, school administrators, curriculum developers, environmental education specialists, representatives of private industry, citizen volunteers, and others. Results of this review process have been used in editing and improving the Project WILD instructional materials throughout the history of the program.

Pilot Test

This entire pilot testing and revision process was developed and implemented by a respected team of independent researchers for the initial version of the *Project WILD Elementary and Secondary Activity Guide*, first introduced in 1983. Each of the instructional activities that appear in the Project WILD materials was tested by educators to ensure its quality and appropriateness. Revisions—from major to minor—were made in each of the activities tested, and a few activities were discarded entirely following the testing process.

Field Test

Following the year of the pilot test of the *Project WILD Elementary and Secondary Activity Guides*, a major field test was designed and conducted to determine the effectiveness of the materials when used by teachers with their students. Again, this study was developed and implemented by a knowledgeable and esteemed team of independent researchers. The field test was conducted in three states, in three demographic areas (urban, suburban, and rural), and across all elementary and secondary grade levels during a full school year. Two hundred fifty-nine teachers and more than 6,000 students were involved.

The results indicate that Project WILD has a definite impact on teachers and students. Students showed significant gains in learning, and developed attitudes toward wildlife that are consistent with the goals of Project WILD. Educators generally found the activities stimulating and worthwhile in their classes and were able to integrate the activities into their curricula. A direct relationship was evidenced between the number of Project WILD instructional activities used by teachers and the students' gains in knowledge and attitudes. Statistical significance was found where teachers used seven or more Project WILD instructional activities. Project WILD was shown to be effective in urban, suburban, and rural areas.

Continuing Evaluation

Project WILD continues to be monitored and evaluated on an ongoing and long-term basis to ensure its quality and effectiveness, as well as to make revisions and additions to the program as needed. Those involved with Project WILD welcome additional independent studies. Funding is not typically available to assist; however, Project WILD can provide other assistance.

Additional Studies

A study similar to the major field test of Project WILD was conducted in Lee County, Florida, with comparable results. Several master's theses and doctoral dissertations, both quantitative and qualitative, have focused on or included Project WILD throughout the United States. Various surveys were conducted to determine actual use of the Project WILD materials following Project WILD workshops.

In 1996, a study in Taiwan focused on the impact of the Project WILD curriculum on student learning, attitudes, and behavior. Project WILD was shown to be most effective on positive, long-term behaviors related to the environment. Preliminary results from the 1999–2000 study in South Dakota support these findings.

Additional studies related specifically to the Project WILD K–12 materials are anticipated and encouraged.

For Additional Information

Please contact the Project WILD National Office for any additional information about evaluation of Project WILD.

Acknowledgements

Project WILD has been made available as the result of the concerned and dedicated efforts of literally hundreds of thousands of people.

It is not possible to individually thank and credit all of those who have assisted—including the thousands of students in kindergarten through high school classrooms who participated in the pilot and field test stages of the project's development.

Project WILD would like to make special mention of the contributions of the American Forest Foundation, cosponsor of Project Learning Tree with the Council for Environmental Education. Project Learning Tree's record of quality and success led directly to the development and subsequent availability of Project WILD.

Project WILD would also like to acknowledge the generous support made possible through the contributions of the International Association of Fish and Wildlife Agencies, as well as the other associate sponsors and contributors to the project.

2001–2002 Council for Environmental Education Board Members
Bill Andrews, Bill Futrell, Josetta Hawthorne (*ex-officio*), Dean Hildebrand, Rudy Schafer, Teresa Spurling, Sharon Walker, Jim Wilson

2001–2002 Project WILD Program Committee Members
Tuss Erickson, John Gahl, Suzie Gilley, Josetta Hawthorne (*ex-officio*), Gary Heath, John Kimball, Max Peterson, Margaret Tudor

Third Edition: 2001 Reprint

Project Oversight
Josetta Hawthorne

Project Supervisor
Suzy Sanders

Editorial Coordinator
Barb Pitman

Copy Editing
Barbara Hart, Publications Professionals, LLC

Graphic Design and Layout
Pam Cullen, Page Productions

New Artwork
- Rob Flemming, Staff Artist, Texas Parks and Wildlife Department: line drawing on p. 423.
- Conrad Field for Alaska Department of Fish and Game 2001: line drawing on p. 133.
- Council for Environmental Education: photograph on p. 442.
- A. P. Graphics: modifications to the Ecosystem Map on p. 384.
- American Sheep Industry Association: photograph on p. 212.

We also would like to express our appreciation to the Project WILD State Coordinators, who provided feedback and suggestions during the process of updating the guide for reprint.

Third Edition: 2000 Update

Project Oversight
Donna Asbury, Kelly Schaefer

Project Supervisor
Dr. Barbara Bonsall Wood

Principal Editor and Format Supervisor
Gwyn Rowland Rozzelle

Copy Editing
Steve Harding, Lily Auliff, Barb Gigar, Beth Bohac

Graphic Design and Layout
O'Conner Group
Pam Cullen, Page Productions

Contributing Ideas and Field Testing for New and Revised Activities

"Bottleneck Genes," ©1999 Smithsonian Institution, Conservation and Research Center, Education Outreach. Adapted with permission from the *Black-Footed Ferret Ambassador Program* by Shannon Dodge and Susan Peachy.

"Career Critters," U.S. Department of Agriculture. Adapted with permission from *Ecosystem Matters*.

"Changing the Land," Wisconsin Department of Natural Resources. Adapted with permission from "Changing the Land" by Al Stenstrup.

"Dropping in on Deer," Colorado Division of Wildlife. Adapted with permission from "Dropping in on Deer" by Winston Dines.

"From Bison to Bread," adapted with permission from the Kansas Department of Wildlife and Parks by Lisa Anderson, Connie Elpers, Bruce Palmer, and Roland Stein.

"Move Over Rover," Colorado Division of Wildlife. Adapted with permission from "Wonders in Nature—Wonders in Neighborhoods" (W.I.N.–W.I.N.), Unit 5 curriculum Guide, Colorado Division of Wildlife and Denver Zoological Foundation.

"A Picture Is Worth a Thousand Words," Colorado Division of Wildlife. Adapted with permission from "Then and Now: Wildlife Photo Analysis" by Chris Elnicki and Jeff Rucks.

"World Travelers," Wisconsin Department of Natural Resources. Adapted with permission from "Charting Exotics" by Jen Richards, Kelly Kearns, and Al Stenstrup.

Additional developing, testing, or adapting by the following educators:

Theresa Alberici, Lisa Anderson, Donna Asbury, Edna Barnes, Andrea Bleck Smith, Venita Bright, Jennifer Coggins, Dave Davis, Una Davoren, Gail De Marco, Winston Dines, Miriam Dunne, Bernice Early, Connie Elpers, Louis Erlich, Rachel Fields, Eugene Flanagan, Tisha Frederick, Josephine Freer, Deborah Frescura, Donald Garwood, John Gahl, Suzie Gilley, Sylvia Gude, Wendy Hanopy, Dave Harlan, Roderick Haynes, Jeannine Hendricks, Sonja Hipple, Bradley Howard, Jim Jenkins, Stan Johnson, Mary Ellen Kauffman, Mary Kots, Chuck Kowaleski, Stacey Lackey, Brian Lancaster, Belinda Lane, Laura Lang, John Loeffert, Debbie Lokay, Bates Mendel, Pat Miller, Mary Nowicki, Bruce Palmer, Julie Parquette, T. Dudley Parr, Elizabeth Petri, Jennifer Pilarski, Anthony Pipkin, Karen Raybuck, Marie Regina, Gwyn Rowland Rozzelle, Jeffrey Rucks, Kelly Schaefer, Kenneth Schamberg, Constance Schulte, David Schulte, Jr., Yvonne Schultz, Christian Shane, Art Shomo, Greg Smith, Nancy States, Rita E. Stevens, Shirley Sypolt, Vicki Tidwell, Vicki Tidwell, Molly Tkacik, Jackie Urband, Robert Van Newkirk, Kevin Weaver, Bobbie Winn, Barbara Bonsall Wood, Kari Young, Dell Young

Draft Reviewers

Theresa Alberici, Lisa Anderson, Bill Andrews, Sarah Armstrong, Donna Asbury, Lily Auliff, Steve Bates, Pat Berson, Karina Blizzard, Mendy Boyles, Venita Bright, Yaeko Bryner, Shannon Caldwell, Laura Carey, Jane Casimir, Orena Cassidy, Robin Dublin, Miriam Dunne, Dan DuPre, Bob Ellis, Connie Elpers, Dale Elshoff, Susan Eschbach, Lisa Evans, Bill Futrell, Rusty Garrison, Warren Gartner, Barbara Gigar, Suzie Gilley, Sylvia Gude, Maggie Hachmeister, Carrie Hamby, Josetta Hawthorne, Cheryl Hayes, Jake Hohl, Kevin Holliday, Dave Jensen, Georgia Jeppesen, Kelly Kearns, Rowena Kemp, Burnie Kessner, Frank Knight, Pat Knighten, Matt Knox, Chuck Kowaleski, Pam Landry, Jessica Leep, David Ode, Bruce Palmer, Sandy Reith, Jen Richards, Anna Rille, Christina Rolka, Nancy Rolli, Gwyn Rowland Rozzelle, Jeff Rucks, Kelly Schaefer, Rudy Schafer, Chuck Schatti, Elsie Sellars, Bob Sepanik, Art Shomo, Judy Silverberg, Greg Smith, Lyle Soniat, Georgia Spencer, Roland Stein, Al Stenstrup, Bryan Thompson, Vicki Tidwell, Laurie Usher, Fred von Mechow, Gail Von Mosch, Diana Vos, Audrey Walker, Sharon Walker, Jay Webb, Colleen Welch, Bobbie Winn, Barbara Bonsall Wood, Carolyn Zaugg

continued

Appendices

Acknowledgements

Artwork courtesy of

- Cindi Bruner: line drawings of animals and plants on pp. 146–150 (# 3, 4, 7, 8, 10, 11, 13, 14, 15, 16, 18, 19, 20, 21, 25, 33, 35, 36, 41, 42, 43), p. 375 (bat and ladybug), p. 376 (falcon and woodpecker), and p. 378 (badger).
- Brian Lancaster, Colorado Division of Wildlife: line drawings on p. 375 (bullsnake), p. 377 (gambusia fish, squirrel, and meadow lark), and p. 384.
- Jim McVoy: line drawing on p. 169 (toad).
- New Hampshire Fish and Game: line drawings on p. 169 (grasshopper and garter snake).
- Pat Oldham, New Mexico Fish and Game Department: line drawing on p. 19.
- Doug Pifer for the Virginia Cooperative Extension publication *A Landowner's Guide to Wildlife Abundance through Forestry*: original for the Forest Diagram on p. 168.
- Bob Samples: diagrams pp. 17, 18, 32, 33, 51, 52, 54, 71, 91, 92, 94, 113, 119, 130, 132, 242, 390.
- Ned Smith for the Pennsylvania Game Commission publication *50 Birds and Mammals of Pennsylvania*: line drawings of animals on pp. 146–150 (#1, 2, 5, 9, 17, 22, 23, 27, 29, 32, 37, 39, 40, 45), p. 169 (songbird, squirrel, turkey, mouse, owl, bear, deer, rabbit, sparrow, fox), and p. 376 (beaver).
- Ginger Wilson, V.P.W. Ink.: modifications to diagrams on pp. 162, 163, 168, 233, 354, 355, 356, 284, 422.

Photographs courtesy of

- Colorado Division of Wildlife: photograph on p. 389 and photographs (# 4, 5, 8, 9, 10, 11, 12, 13, 14, 16, 17, 18, 19) on pp. 414–417.
- Denver Public Library, Western History Department: photographs (# 1, 2, 3) on p. 414.
- John Hart: photograph (# 7) on p. 415.
- Peasley Middle School, Gloucester County Public Schools, Virginia: photograph on p. 449.
- Art Shomo, West Virginia Department of Natural Resources: three photographs on p. 63.
- U.S. Fish and Wildlife Service: photograph (# 6) on p. 414 and photograph (#15) on p. 416.

Second Edition: 1992 Update

Editorial Staff

Cheryl Charles, Judy Dawson, Janet Rasmussen, Dan Shaw, Mary Stuever

Small Group Reviews

Dr. Hans Anderson, Louise Ashman, Richard Baumfalk, Susan Beck, Mark Bennett, Nancy Brown, Becky Brown, Nancy Caldwell, Sam Carmen, Amy Chandler, Laurie Christie, Barbara Church, Jane Cleaves, Rodger Coombs, Phil Cooper, Randy Cotten, Clif Daniels, Shelly Davis, Jerry deBin, Elizabeth DelVerne, Alvin Diamond, Jo Dodds, Ed Donovan, Carolyn Dunmore, Miriam Dunne, Linda Eastwood, Mary Beth Eberwein, Jim Edwards, Kathy Farr, Beth Fasnacht, Jack Finger, Carl Finstad, TC Floy, Susan Foote-Martin, Terri Franklin, Nancy Franz, Connie Gahl, John Gahl, Warren Gartner, Rick Gilchrist, Susan Gilchrist, Alan Gray, Robert Griffin, Corey Hall, Lynn Haralson, Kerry Harkins, Bonnie Helzer, Mel Hickman, Earl Hodil, Carol Holden, Jean Holland, Douglas Housskeeper, Susan Ilgner, Elizabeth Javrin, Jan Jose, Twila Kadel, Michael Kamen, Marti Kane, Michael Karmen, Jeff Kiefer, Julie King, Judy Klippel, Sherry Klosiewski, Bill Koehler, Jackie Lane, Tim Lemon, Chris Martin, Jim McCollough, Jack McNeel, Cathy Meyer, Brenda Miller, Carrie Morgan, Tim Morgan, Margha Mulling, Stu Murrell, Jim Nelson, Deb Neuenschwander, Rod Nichols, Mike Overton, Rod Parker, Deborah Patton, Barbara Pietrucha, Mark Pochon, Polly Powell, Teresa Prather, Christine Raabe, Anna Radue, Barbara Reed, Marian Rendall, Ken Riddleberger, John Russell, Dave Sanger, Nancy Schneider, Ann Seppenfield, M. Sharp, Art Shomo, James Slater, Theresa Stabo, Caroline Sweigart, Jean Terry, Tracey Thompson, Mary Todd, Barbara Tucker, Kenneth Uhlhorn, Al Van Hoey, Karen Van Norman,

Appendices
Acknowledgements

Linda Walbruch, Bob Waller, Dave Wanisko, Jennifer Warwick, Luann Waters, Linda Watters, Brenda Weiser, Donna White, Frank Williams, Don Winslow, Shirley Wright, Julie Yamamoto, Dr. Dennis Yockers, Kathie Zager, Dean Zimmerman, Darci Zolman

Draft Reviewers
Miriam Dunne, John Gahl, Barbara Gigar, Suzie Gilley, Maggie Hachmeister, Ellie Horwitz, Dr. Cliff Knapp, Don MacCarter, Chris Martin, Colleen Matt, Cheryl Mollohan, Ken Riddleberger, Larry Sarner, Nancy Schneider, Daphne Sewing, Art Shomo, Dr. Cindi Smith-Walters, Heidi Solper, Jo Temte, Brenda Weiser, Carl Wolfe, Dr. Dennis Yockers

Independent Comments
Elaine Almeida, Bette Anderson, Paul Beckwith, Carol Beyna, Judy Binger, Sue Bogacz, Evelyn Bologna, Evelyn Boring, Gail Bouslog, Gerry Bryan, Sandra Buck, Sara Campbell, Susan Chambers, Rick Chase, Dorothy Chavez, James Colman, Michael Countess, Kelly Countouris, Ellen Cunningham, Jan Davis, Patrick DeSantis, Barbara Dunbar, LuAnne Folks, Janene Fowler, J. Frey, Sharon Giza, Jim Goodwin, Andy Greif, Karen Grimes Cooper, Linda Gruberski, Karen Hangrove, Linda Harris, Jean Harris, Bob Hernbrode, Earl Hodil, Kathie Holden, Mary Jane Holmes, Bonielee Hooper, Karen Hostetter, Mary Hurst, Jodi Jenkins, Laura Jodice, Jeffrey Keidel, Janice Kesler, Pat Knighten, Pat Lang, Mickey Larkins, Gretchen Leuenberger, Haile Macurdy, Barbara Marshall, Roy Martin, Dale Mason, Beth McCanley, Shalon McCart, Jim McCullough, Terry McLaughlin, Mary Melican, Justine Menci, Patricia Mercker, Cathy Meyer, Debra Miller, Suzanne Miller, Susan Miller, Matt Miller, Sterling Miller, Gerald Mohr, Marie Monfredo, Fran Morris, Jane Moynihan, Kim Mumper, Tom Nelson, Dorcas Newkirk, Connie O'Brien, Helen Panagiotopoulos, Lynette Parkhurst, Deborah Poti, Earl Richardson, Dolores Ringdahl, Wanda Rowland, Linda Sand, Larry Sarner, Rachel Schneider, Mary Shapiro, Art Shomo, Lisa Silverman-Gent, Rick Sinnott, Lucy Slinger, Marlies Smith, Cecil Buckey Smith, Dean Smith, Jacquelyn Sparrow, David St. Clair, Paula St. Clair, Catherine Stefanides, Michael Stephan, Regina Stovall, Jack Turner, Dennis Unkenholz, Larry Vanderlinden, Jane Vollmer, Mary Frances Wagner, Dave Walters, Arthur Washburn, Kenneth Watkins, Elizabeth White, Ellen Wilken, Debbi Wilkinson, Tim Williams, Laurie Woodall, Jill Yeager, Eileen Yost, Janice Young, Cathy Zazanis, Judy Zeider, Sue Zimmerman, Nancy Zuschlag

First Edition

Reviewers of Project WILD Curriculum Framework
The Project WILD Curriculum Framework was reviewed by hundreds of individuals, representing a range of organizations including conservation groups, natural resource agencies, private industry, public education, and private education. We regret not being able to list the many individuals and organizations by name, but appreciate their substantial contributions to the overall accuracy and quality of the framework that formed the basis for the development of the Project WILD instructional materials. We would like to especially acknowledge Cliff Hamilton for his exceptional effort and skill in serving as general editor of the final framework.

Project WILD Writing Conference Participants
Alaska: Dolores Moulton, Edward Eschler, Lew Nelson, Kris Kantola, Sue Matthews, Paul Arneson, Eric Morris, Wendell Shiffler, Nancy Murphy, Peter Buck, Sue Quinlan, Walter Suomela, Hal Neace, Sister Bridget M. Connor, Judy Hauck, Cheryl Charles. *Arizona:* Rosemary Elkins, Jean Fields, Patty Horn, Cleo Scheyli, Eloise Babcock, Valerie Davison, Ann Motley, Peggy Griego, Judith Enz, Kitty Fischer, Mary Howell, Dean Holland, Bob Hernbrode, Kerry Baldwin, Joanna Lackey, Jerry Tucker, Wendy Greenberg, Cheryl Charles, Gerry Hernbrode, Jim Hudnall, Tanna Baldwin. *California:* Rudy Schafer, Augie Scornaienchi, Larry Rose, Anne Manolis, Evelyn Cormier, Phyllis Shuck, Molly Whiteley, Carolie Sly, Marlynn Kaake, Jan Rensel, Bob Flasher, Steve Wilkes, Martin Abrams, Otis McCain, John Mackenzie, Juanita Gex, Olina Gilbert, Mary Rodgers, Susan de

continued

Treville, Dolores Moulton, Cheryl Charles, Rocky Rohwedder. *Colorado:* Russell Skillings, Glenn McGlathery, Paul Bauman, Jeff Brigham, Sue Miller, Evaline Olson, Carol Bergevin, Kathy Williams, James Jackson, Cheryl Charles, Kerry Baldwin, Bud Smith, Gene Carroll, Jack Anderson, Helen Davis, Cliff Hamilton, Roxy Pestello, William Turner, Stu Murrell, John Ernst, Kris Gabrielson, Robin Hernbrode, Joanna Lackey, George Ek, Sandy Sanborn, Dave Perry, Bill Huntley, Dr. Norma Livo, Kathy Kelley, Bill Haggerty. *Idaho:* Marjorie Reinecker, Nancy Christensen, Royce Williams, Glendon Jones, Bob Humphries, Mary Lynn Popplewell, Begie Hatmaker, Joanna Lackey, Bob Hernbrode, Cheryl Charles, Jerry Tucker, Lewis Nelson, Cliff Hamilton, Edward Eschler, Richard Kay, Ray Remund, Stu Murrell, Ben Peyton, Harry Mills, Bob Nisbitt, Lea Williford, Shelley Davis, Creed Noah, Dennis Cartwright, Cindy Teipner, Joe Vogler, Connie Gilman, Lyn Fleming.

Field Test Teachers and Administrators
Teachers, administrators, and students in school districts in the states of Colorado, Virginia, and Washington assisted in the formal field testing of the Project WILD materials. The confidentiality of the testing process requires that we not identify the participating personnel and districts. We ex-tend our grateful thanks to all of those involved for their assistance.

Pilot Teachers, Students, and Administrators
Teachers, administrators, and students in school districts in the states of Washington and Arizona assisted in the formal pilot testing of the Project WILD materials. We thank each of those people for their dedicated and generous assistance. In particular, we would like to acknowledge the coordination and support provided by Lynn Olson, Principal, La Center, Washington; and Dick Clark, Science Supervisor, Washington Public Schools, Phoenix, Arizona. In addition, we would like to thank the following individual teachers for providing a wealth of valuable information that was used to improve and revise the Project WILD materials: Becky Staley, Jacque Sniffen, E. Helledy, Nancy Schmidt, M. Little, Virginia Barton, Bonnie Lock, M. Bruder, Robert Ryan, Sandy Mraz, Kitty Whitlaw, Gary Wallace, Karen Atkins, M. Balkenbush, M. Dollar, Mr. Gissell, Brenda Pierce, Charri Strong, Albert L. Pitzer, Tom Lutz, J. Gallagher, M. Kelbourn, M. Mitchell, Mary Anne French, Mr. Allison, Mr. Schoenborn, Mary Cowan, Diana Smiley, Tom Kennedy, Lea Hamlet, M. Russell, M. Christofanelli, K. Klaas, M. Bergmann, W. Hart, M. Pruitt, Doris Rankin, Mary Flanders, T. Kreuser, Shirley Corn, B. Charles Dorsey, Lydia Whitey, Sandy Stanley, M. Schmidli, Linda Lee Tatro. If we have inadvertently omitted anyone who assisted, please let us know, and we will make the appropriate corrections in the next printing of these materials.

Special Personnel and Materials Assistance
Alameda County Office of Education (California), Alaska Department of Fish and Game, American Humane Association, Arizona Department of Game and Fish, Boulder Valley Public Schools (Colorado), California Department of Game and Fish, Colorado Department of Education, Colorado Division of Wildlife, Defenders of Wildlife, Hawksong Associates, Idaho Department of Game and Fish, Montana Office of the Superintendent of Public Instruction, National Audubon Society, National Wildlife Federation, New Mexico Department of Game and Fish, Ohio Depart-ment of Natural Resources, Oregon Department of Fish and Wildlife, Pennsylvania Game Commission, U.S. Forest Service, U.S. Fish and Wildlife Service, Utah Department of Natural Resources, Virginia Department of Education, Washington Department of Game, Washington Office of the Superintendent of Public Instruction, Wyoming Department of Game and Fish

Principal Editors, Contributing Editors, and Authors, plus Writing Conference Participants
Kerry Baldwin, Liz Caile, Dr. Cheryl Charles, Judy Dawson, Dr. Lyn Fleming, John Gahl, Dr. Gary Hall, Cliff Hamilton, Bob Hernbrode, Dr. Richard Konicek, Dr. Ben Peyton, Joanna Prukop Lackey, Dr. Don Lundstrom, Ernie McDonald, Dolores Moulton, Dr. Lew Nelson, Jan Rensel, Bob Samples, Rudy Schafer

Appendices

Acknowledgements

Evaluation
Pilot Testing: Dr. Ben Peyton, Principal Investigator; Dr. Lyn Fleming, Associate. *Field Testing:* Dr. Lyn Fleming, Director; Dr. Rick Kroc, Dr. Ben Peyton, Dr. Norris Harms, Contributing Consultants; Dr. Gene Glass, Dr. Mary Lee Smith, Dr. Kenneth Hopkins, Technical Assistance

Additional Special Assistance
Tom Charles, Harry Mills, Tony Angell, Donna Szuhy, Dale Crider, Linda Crider, Dick Draney, Bob Flasher, Marlynn Kaake, Jim Gladson, Jim Graban, Bill Hammond, Tex Hawkins, John Herrington, Dick Hess, Larry Littlebird, June McSwain, Dr. Jake Nice, Jim Phillips, Augie Scornaienchi, Jan Rensel, Bob Samples, Robin Hernbrode, Chris Wille, Irene Shelver, Bill Shelver, Stician Samples, Dr. Tom Fitzgerald, Perl Charles, Mattie Charles, Teresa Auldridge, George Ek, Dave Boynton, Dr. Judith Enz, Dr. Jon Hooper, David A. Kennedy, Craig Thompson

Reviewers of Pilot Materials
Carlton Owen, June McSwain, Lester DeCoster, Rocky Rohwedder, Bob Flasher, Dore Zwingman, Janet Sheldon, Bev Wu, Larry Malone, Linda DeLucchi, Bill Bolar, Kerri Lubin, Joy Crupper, Dr. Jim Armitage, Phyllis Clarke, Tina Yeager, Wanda Headrick, David Yeager, Tiajuana Cochnauer, Shirley J. Wright, Dana Bowyer, Dean Williams, Ron Hamilton, Nancy Christensen, Pam Aikins, Jim Carlson, Ernie McDonald, Bob Samples, Dr. Gary Hall, Cliff Hamilton, Bob Hernbrode, Dr. Lew Nelson, Dr. Ben Peyton, Vince Vandre

Copy Editing Assistance and Additional Technical Review, First Edition
Dick Hess; Former Chief, Information and Education, Colorado Division of Wildlife

Project WILD
Council for Environmental Education
5555 Morningside Drive, Suite 212
Houston, TX 77005
Phone: (713) 520-1936
Fax: (713) 520-8008
E-mail: info@projectwild.org
Web: www.projectwild.org

Council for Environmental Education (CEE) Staff

Josetta Hawthorne
Executive Director

Suzy Sanders
Manager, Project WILD

Elisa Lewis
Manager, Education Programs

Heidi Massin
Project Assistant

Project WILD Supplementary Resources

The following resources may be purchased from the Project WILD National Office. An order form may be obtained by accessing the Project WILD web site, www.projectwild.org, or by contacting the National Office at 5555 Morningside Drive, Suite 212, Houston, TX 77005, (713) 520-1936, or by fax at (713) 520-8008.

Taking Action: An Educator's Guide to Involving Students in Environmental Action Projects, 74 pages, 1995.

Developed in cooperation with the World Wildlife Fund, *Taking Action* inspires ideas and provides models for conducting effective environmental projects. From adopting species to protecting habitats to saving energy, this guide will help educators plan, implement, and evaluate environmental action projects. Samples of more than 30 projects from around the country provide a glimpse of how groups of students have recognized a need in their community and successfully worked together to implement change.

WILD School Sites: A Guide to Preparing for Habitat Improvement Projects on School Grounds, 56 pages, 1993.

This guide helps students and teachers learn about the importance of biodiversity, understand the basic steps of creating a wildlife habitat, develop a plan for action, and gain community support. The purpose of this guide is to assist educators and their students in taking responsible action to improve their communities for people and wildlife, beginning on their school grounds.

"Exploring School Nature Areas," Video, 1994.

Produced in cooperation with St. Olaf College's "School Nature Area Project," this video is designed to demonstrate the value of school sites and school nature areas. The video, targeted for teachers and administrators, provides examples of outdoor classrooms around the country and shows students in action at school sites. The purpose of the video is to motivate educators and students to initiate environmental action projects that will improve habitats for wildlife and people.

WILD About Elk: An Educator's Guide, 80 pages, 1994.

This guide is a product of the Rocky Mountain Elk Foundation and CEE. *WILD About Elk* provides a summary of the biology and ecology of elk. Topics addressed include elk's physical characteristics and adaptations, habitat and historical range, behavior, life cycles, social structure, migratory patterns, and the present and historical relationships between elk and humans. A primary message woven throughout the guide is the importance of habitat to the elk's survival. Activities in the guide assist educators in helping their students learn about elk and their habitat.

Correlations to the National Science Education Standards, 36 pages, 1999.

To meet the demands of education reform, Project WILD has developed a correlation of the *Project WILD K–12 Curriculum and Activity Guide* (2nd Edition) and *Project WILD Aquatic K–12 Curriculum and Activity Guide* (2nd Edition) to the *National Science Education Standards* (the *Standards*). This document is divided into three sections: K–4, 5–8, and 9–12. Each of the activities has been correlated to an assessment rubric that indicates the fundamental concept taught in each activity. Using this document, educators can easily fit Project WILD activities into their lesson plans by following the user-friendly format for each section of the *Standards*.

NOTE: These correlations are to the 2nd Edition of *Project WILD* and *Project WILD Aquatic K–12 Activity and Curriculum Guides*. New activities that have not been correlated to national standards have been added to more recent editions of the guides.

Project WILD Spanish Supplement, 240 pages, 1998.

This guide contains 34 translated activities taken from *Project WILD K–12 Curriculum and Activity Guide* and *Project WILD Aquatic K–12 Curriculum and Activity Guide*. The Spanish supplement introduces Project WILD to new audiences—teachers; scout leaders; school volunteers; parks and recreation staff members; and nature center, zoo, and museum staff members—who live and work in primarily Spanish-speaking communities. Project WILD hopes that these materials will open the outdoors to a new generation of students and volunteers.

The Changing Face of Project WILD, 16 pages, 1998.

This document highlights the success stories and lessons learned through Project WILD's participation in WILD in the City and Environmental Education and Training Partnership (EETAP) projects from 1995–1997. Success stories include working with diverse audiences; building partnerships, education reform, and innovative resources; and increasing participation in Project WILD programs across the country.

Science and Civics: Sustaining Wildlife, 300 pages, 2000.

Supported by the National Environmental Education and Training Foundation (NEETF), Environmental Protection Agency, and Phillips Petroleum Company, this guide is designed to meet the expressed need of secondary educators and administrators for materials that will prepare students to select and implement environmentally focused service learning projects. The program will also help teachers and students meet state course requirements by using the environment as a means to apply science, social studies, and other disciplines to real-world situations. This curriculum guides students in the investigation of wildlife concerns and encourages them to collaborate their findings in responsible action projects that benefit wildlife, people, and the environment.

Alphabetical Listing

A Picture Is Worth a Thousand Words	409
Adaptation Artistry	128
And the Wolf Wore Shoes	180
Animal Charades	280
Animal Poetry	282
Ants on a Twig	88
Arctic Survival	234
Back from the Brink	355
Bearly Born (new title: Bearly Growing)	19
Bearly Growing	19
Beautiful Basics	58
Bird Song Survey	406
Birds of Prey	111
Bottleneck Genes	172
Cabin Conflict	353
Can Do!	446
Career Critters	371
Carrying Capacity	46
Cartoons and Bumper Stickers	192
Changing Attitudes	255
Changing Societies	258
Changing the Land	345
Checks and Balances	387
Classroom Carrying Capacity	9
Color Crazy	2
Deadly Links (new title: Hazardous Links, Possible Solutions)	326
Deer Crossing	392
Deer Dilemma	426
Does Wildlife Sell?	213
Drawing on Nature	285
Dropping in on Deer	420
Eco-Enrichers	102
Ecosystem Facelift	166
Energy Pipeline	105
Enviro-Ethics	443
Environmental Barometer	77
Ethi-Reasoning	203
Ethi-Thinking	303
Everybody Needs a Home	59
Fire Ecologies	140
First Impressions	178
Flip the Switch for Wildlife	319
For Your Eyes Only	197
Forest in a Jar	137
From Bison to Bread: The American Prairie	395
Good Buddies	91
Graphananimal	49
Grasshopper Gravity	4
Habitat Lap Sit	61
Habitat Rummy	14
Habitracks	53
Habitrekking	79
Hazardous Links, Possible Solutions	326
Here Today, Gone Tomorrow	154
History of Wildlife Management	267
How Many Bears Can Live in This Forest?	23
I'm Thirsty	134

Improving Wildlife Habitat in the Community	440
Interview a Spider	12
Know Your Legislation: What's in It for Wildlife?	272
Learning to Look, Looking to See	278
Let's Talk Turkey	248
Litter We Know	434
Lobster in Your Lunch Box	245
Make a Coat!	243
Microtrek Treasure Hunt	82
Migration Barriers	308
Move Over Rover	144
Museum Search for Wildlife	182
Muskox Maneuvers	130
My Kingdom for a Shelter	28
No Water Off a Duck's Back	305
Noisy Neighbors	317
Oh Deer!	36
Owl Pellets	100
Pay to Play	216
Philosophical Differences	364
Planning for People and Wildlife	436
Planting Animals	152
Playing Lightly on the Earth	432
Polar Bears in Phoenix?	125
Power of a Song	194
Prairie Memoirs	188
Pro and Con: Consumptive and Nonconsumptive Uses of Wildlife	338
Quick-Frozen Critters	122
Rainfall and the Forest	73
Rare Bird Eggs for Sale	335
Riparian Zone	341
Saturday Morning Wildlife Watching	184
Seed Need	98
Seeing Is Believing!	116
Shrinking Habitat	310
Smokey Bear Said What?	314
Spider Web Geometry	34
Stormy Weather	85
Surprise Terrarium	120
Sustainability: Then, Now, Later	449
The Hunter	287
Thicket Game	114
Time Lapse	158
To Zone or Not to Zone	321
Too Close for Comfort	300
Tracks!	30
Turkey Trouble	367
Urban Nature Search	70
We're in This Together	44
What Bear Goes Where?	118
What Did Your Lunch Cost Wildlife?	68
What You Wear Is What They Were	210
What's for Dinner?	96
What's That, Habitat?	56
What's Wild?	7
Which Niche?	66
Who Fits Here?	64
Wild Bill's Fate	270
Wild Words	41
Wildlife on Coins and Stamps	208
Wildlife Bibliography	253
Wildlife in National Symbols	186
Wildlife Is Everywhere!	51
Wildlife Issues: Community Attitude Survey	297
Wildlife Research	418
Wildwork	385
World Travelers	330

Notes

Notes

Notes